The Hague School

DUTCH MASTERS OF THE 19TH CENTURY

This exhibition has been organized by the Haags Gemeentemuseum
and the Dienst Verspreide Rijkskollekties, The Hague
in collaboration with the Royal Academy of Arts, London
and the Musée du Louvre, Paris.

The exhibition is sponsored by Unilever, with financial assistance
from the Arts Council of Great Britain.

The Hague School

DUTCH MASTERS OF THE 19TH CENTURY

Edited by
Ronald de Leeuw, John Sillevis, Charles Dumas

GRAND PALAIS, PARIS
ROYAL ACADEMY OF ARTS, LONDON
HAAGS GEMEENTEMUSEUM, THE HAGUE
1983
Catalogue published in association with
WEIDENFELD AND NICOLSON, LONDON

N
2482
H3

COVER ILLUSTRATIONS
Front: Jozef Israëls *The Cottage Madonna* (The Detroit Institute of Arts)
Back: Jacob Maris *Fishing Boat* (Haags Gemeentemuseum)

House editor Vicky Hayward
Designed by Allison Waterhouse
for George Weidenfeld and Nicolson Limited
91 Clapham High Street, London SW4 7TA

ISBN 0 297 78069 7 (casebound)
      0 297 78219 3 (paperback)

Set in Monophoto Bembo and printed by
BAS Printers Limited, Over Wallop, Hampshire
Colour separations by Newsele Litho Ltd., Italy

Contents

Organizing Committee

Theo van Velzen
John Sillevis
    Haags Gemeentemuseum, The Hague

Robert de Haas
Ronald de Leeuw
    Dienst Verspreide Rijkskollekties, The Hague

Hubert Landais
Irène Bizot
    Réunion des musées nationaux, Paris

Jacques Foucart
    Musée du Louvre, Paris

Piers Rodgers
Norman Rosenthal
    Royal Academy of Arts, London

Simon Levie
    Rijksmuseum, Amsterdam

Hans Hoetink
    Rijksmuseum H. W. Mesdag, The Hague

Charles Moffett
    The Metropolitan Museum of Art, New York

Executive Committee

Ronald de Leeuw
    Dienst Verspreide Rijkskollekties, The Hague

John Sillevis
    Haags Gemeentemuseum, The Hague

Charles Dumas
    Gemeentearchief, The Hague

Acknowledgements

The executive committee would particularly like to thank the following people for their advice and help:

Russell Ash	Gerlof Janzen
Irène Bizot	Hans Kraan
H. Bordewijk	Charles Moffett
Joop Breeschoten	Micheline Moisan
Tineke Breeschoten	Dewey Mosby
Janet Brooke	J. Nieuwstraten
Christopher Brown	Janine Perryck
Martha op de Coul	Sir John Pope-Hennessy
Lily Couvée-Jampoller	Willem Rappard
Antonia Demetriadi	Joseph Rishel
Jacques Foucart	Norman Rosenthal
Ursula de Goede	Koos Salomons
Janine Gosschalk	Enno Thedinga
M. D. Haga	John Walsh Jr
Vicky Hayward	Patricia Wardle
Nel Heldoorn	Allison Waterhouse
Richard Hussey	L. W. F. Wijsenbeek

Index of Lenders

Photographic Acknowledgements

The following kindly made photographs available. All other photographs were provided by the owners of the paintings or drawings.

A.C.L., Brussels: Cats. 31, 114; figs. 70, 71, 72
Annan Photographers, Glasgow: figs. 50, 53, 54
Archief Pulchri Studio, The Hague: fig. 57
A. Dingjan, The Hague: Cats. 23, 42, 75, 90, 120, 121, 141; figs. 9, 38, 44, 75, 85, 130
Documentation photographique de la Réunion des musées nationaux, Paris: Cats. 63, 91, 110
M. Dommisse, The Hague: fig. 60
Duplan, Mairie, Lille: fig. 33
Foto-buro Meyer B.V., The Hague: fig. 65
Fotobureau Scholte, Oss: Cat. 78
Foto-Commissie Rijksmuseum, Amsterdam: Cats. 1, 2, 7, 8, 16, 40, 51, 53, 55, 73, 89, 98, 104, 107, 142; figs. 6, 7, 15, 18, 27, 28, 46, 55, 87, 125, 138; colour Cats. 43, 89
Foto Stijns, Dordrecht: Cat. 84, 145
B. Frequin, Voorburg: Cats. 69, 158; figs. 63, 93

Frequin Photos, Voorburg: Cats. 33, 46, 48, 99, 106, 109, 123, 132; figs. 12, 45
Gemeentearchief, Arnhem: Cat. 5
Gemeentearchief, The Hague: figs. 58, 59, 133, 135, 136, 142, 144, 145
Salomon R. Guggenheim Museum, New York: Cat. 157
Tom Haartsen, Ouderkerk a.d. Amstel: Cat. 146; colour Cats. 19, 24, 25, 26, 72, 79, 84, 90, 101, 122, 137, 145, 151, 153
R. Kampman, Almelo: fig. 121
Kunsthistorisch Instituut der Rijksuniversiteit, Utrecht: Cat. 124
Eric E. Mitchel, Philadelphia: colour Cat. 100
Marco de Nood, Dordrecht: Cats. 19, 39
Rijksbureau voor Kunsthistorische Documentatie, The Hague: figs. 49, 101, 143
P.A. Scheen B.V., The Hague: Cats. 3, 10, 15, 26, 49, 82, 83, 87, 137, 138; fig. 52; colour Cats. 119, 127, 129, 136, 143
Tom Scott, Edinburgh: Cat. 21
Stichting Johan Maurits van Nassau, The Hague: Cats. 23, 42, 75, 108; figs. 2, 5, 96; colour Cat. 23

Foreword

Four years ago Mr J. A. van Alphen, Cultural Counsellor at the Dutch Embassy, suggested to us that it was an appropriate time to mount, with the help of the Gemeentemuseum and the Dienst Verspreide Rijkskollekties (State-owned Art Collections Department) in The Hague, a definitive exhibition of Dutch nineteenth-century painting, including works by such artists as Jozef Israëls, Willem Roelofs and the Maris brothers, who, like Constable and the painters of the Norwich School, had drawn inspiration from their seventeenth-century predecessors.

We welcomed this proposal not only because of the quiet appeal and authority of the works themselves, once so popular among Victorian collectors in this country, but also because of the influence they were to exert, through Vincent Van Gogh and Piet Mondriaan, on the subsequent development of European art.

The exhibition has been made possible through the generous support of Unilever. We are most grateful in particular to Mr K. Durham (Chairman of Unilever PLC), Mr H. F. van den Hoven (Chairman of Unilever N. V.) and to Mr Tony Fisher, who is in charge of Arts Sponsorship at Unilever, for their direct personal interest in the project.

Thanks are due also to the Arts Council for their substantial contribution to our costs, to Her Majesty's Government which, recognizing the importance of the exhibition, has provided us with an indemnity, and to the staff of the Dutch Embassy for their efficient, patient and continuous help.

Finally we must thank Mr Theo van Velzen, Director of the Hague Gemeentemuseum and Mr Robert de Haas, Director of the Dienst Verspreide Rijkskollekties, and their staffs to whose knowledge and energies this exhibition owes its fine quality and interest.

Sir Hugh Casson
President of the Royal Academy

A Note from the Sponser

UNILEVER is delighted to be associated with this unique exhibition of paintings of the Hague School. This is the second exhibition Unilever has sponsored at the Royal Academy. In 1980 – Unilever's Golden Jubilee year – we sponsored the Lord Leverhulme Exhibition. William Hesketh Lever, the first Lord Leverhulme, was the founder of the British side of our company and it was, therefore, particularly appropriate that we should support an exhibition of some of the paintings and other objects he had collected during his lifetime and which are now housed at the Lady Lever Gallery at Port Sunlight.

It is equally appropriate for Unilever to be associated with this exhibition of the Hague School. Unilever is an Anglo-Dutch company and we are particularly pleased to be able to help bring what has been called 'the last great undiscovered School of European Painting' to the Royal Academy. In the lovely setting of the Private Rooms of the Royal Academy a whole new audience will be given an opportunity of seeing many of these pictures for the first time and we hope that the exhibition will give a great deal of pleasure to very many people.

K. Durham
Chairman, Unilever PLC

H. F. van den Hoven
Chairman, Unilever NV

Preface

This exhibition of the work of the Hague School painters is the culmination of many years planning. A reappraisal of their work has been long overdue, particularly in the light of recent research on the subject; the last major exhibition, entitled 'Masters of the Hague School', was held in the Gemeentemuseum, The Hague, in 1965. It was assembled by Dr Johannes de Gruyter, whose book about the School is still a standard work of reference for anyone interested in the subject. This is perhaps the most appropriate place to pay tribute, alas posthumously, to his enthusiasm and research, the results and benefits of which are still being reaped today.

De Gruyter concentrated primarily on the individual achievements of the Hague School artists: this is reflected in both the catalogue of the 1965 exhibition and his book, which is, in effect, a series of monographs. In the present exhibition, the emphasis has been on the Hague School as an artistic movement and the catalogue follows the history of the group from its inception in the 1860s until the First World War, by which time nearly all its members had died.

Two internationally famous artists have been added to this exhibition: Vincent van Gogh and Piet Mondriaan. Recent research has shown that their links with the Hague School were of far greater importance for their artistic development than had previously been assumed. Earlier exhibitions, such as 'Vincent van Gogh in his Dutch Years' (Rijksmuseum Vincent van Gogh, Amsterdam 1980) and 'Mondriaan and the Hague School' (Manchester, Florence, Milan and Paris 1980–82) have convincingly demonstrated the existence of links which are examined here in the context of the Hague School.

The international background to the Hague School is also considered in some detail. It is of importance in two ways. Firstly, the influence of Dutch seventeenth-century landscape painting on English painters such as Constable, Turner and the artists of the Norwich School, and on the French painters of the Barbizon School, played an important role in the genesis of the Hague School. Secondly, the Hague School had its first critical and commercial success outside the Netherlands: ironically, recognition came much more slowly at home. It is not really possible to speak of a general appreciation of the work of the Hague School artists in their home country until the last two decades of the nineteenth century, although by 1900 the School had come to dominate artistic life there.

In recent years there has been an international reappraisal of nineteenth-century art, particularly of German and English Romanticism, European Realism and Symbolism. A reassessement of the Hague School is particularly appropriate now, and this exhibition and catalogue have been prepared with that in mind: previously unused records have been sifted and the copious literature on the subject has been ordered and classified.

Such an enormous undertaking could not have been realized without the help of many people, and we are particularly indebted to those thanked in the Acknowledgements and to all those who have generously lent to the exhibition. We would also like to thank Professor A. Bachrach and Professor J.N. van Wessem for their help in initiating discussion and establishing contacts in England, and the Department of International Relations of the Ministry for Cultural Affairs, Recreation and Social Welfare for their very real support. Messrs. J.C. van Praag, J.A.F.S. van Alphen, C.F. Stork and A.D.H. Simonsz of the Dutch embassies in Paris and London have also given us very valuable help and advice.

The importance of this exhibition in the eyes of the Haags Gemeentemuseum (Municipal Museum, The Hague) and the Dienst Verspreide Rijkskollekties (State-owned Art Collections Department) may be measured by the time and energy Ronald de Leeuw and John Sillevis have devoted to it. They made the selection of works and edited the catalogue with Charles Dumas, who also took on the considerable task of assembling a comprehensive bibliography. This triumvirate has not merely worked with great dedication, but also brought their own impeccably high standards to the exhibition and catalogue, and we consider ourselves fortunate that they were able to undertake this work. We offer them our thanks.

We are delighted that the project has now safely reached its conclusion and that it has proved possible for the exhibition to be shown in England and France, the two countries which so inspired the Hague School artists. It is therefore with great pleasure that we now present this exhibition.

Drs. T. van Velzen
Director, Haags Gemeentemuseum

Drs. R.R. de Haas
Director, Dienst Verspreide Rijkskollekties

Introduction

RONALD DE LEEUW

During the 1870s the work of a group of artists in the Netherlands known as the Hague School began to be seen as a renaissance of the achievements of the 'Golden Age' of Dutch painting. Like their seventeenth-century predecessors, they drew their inspiration from the flat polder landscape and the everyday lives of the peasant and fishing communities of their native country, extracting from these ordinary and unpretentious subjects a poetry which for two centuries had been virtually ignored. But the achievements of the Hague School were not recognized in the Netherlands for several years; it was only when the evident approbation of connoisseurs and collectors elsewhere in Europe and in the United States filtered back to the artists' homeland, that they received their due recognition and came to occupy a leading position in artistic circles there. Even then the masters of the Hague School encountered some opposition and, for a time, there were conflicting opinions about their work, but gradually they became firmly established and, despite the advent of other artistic movements in the 1880s and 1890s, dominated artistic life in the Netherlands until after the turn of the century. It was only after the First World War that the reputation of the Hague School declined and the names of such artists as Israëls, Maris and Mauve were relegated to the footnotes of art history. Outside the Netherlands, their names meant something only to those who delved into the origins of Vincent van Gogh or Piet Mondriaan, who were, from then on, the sole representatives of nineteenth and early twentieth-century Dutch art, as far as most people were concerned.

In the Netherlands itself, the Hague School was never completely forgotten, although its renown was undoubtedly at a very low ebb in the inter-war years. It was still accorded a certain recognition as the principal Dutch equivalent of the realist and impressionist movements of the second half of the nineteenth century, but often only as a background against which the movements that followed stood out more clearly. It is only recently that there has been a genuine reappraisal of the Hague School; in 1965 Dr Jos de Gruyter organized a large retrospective exhibition in the Haags Gemeentemuseum (Municipal Museum in The Hague) and this was followed by the publication of his standard work on the School in 1968–69. In this he presented a balanced portrait of each of the leading artists, making the best possible use of the extensive but generally not very inspiring literature on the subject. The reputation of the School is now once more in the ascendant and the interested visitor to Boston or New York, to Glasgow or Edinburgh, to London or Munich, once again has the opportunity to see the work of The Hague masters in museums where their work seemed until recently to have been banished for ever to the stores or even, in one or two instances, to have been sold. The role of the art market in this renewal of interest in the Hague School, traditionally a determining factor in its reputation, should not be underestimated.

With the growing appreciation of these nineteenth-century artistic movements that aimed at a realistic interpretation of their subject, and a greater awareness of a specifically northern contribution to the European tradition of art, the moment for an international revaluation of the Dutch contribution to this seems to have arrived. In this perspective, it is not insignificant that the work of Jongkind and Van Gogh, which was originally to be included in the French section of the catalogue at the Louvre, has now been returned to the Dutch section.[1] The work of the Hague School artists stands out among the rediscoveries made through recent critical reassessment, not so much for its themes, which are notable more for their ordinariness, but for its great pictorial beauty. Whereas much realist art, when judged from a painterly point of view, cannot stand the test of critical scrutiny, most artists of the Hague School can boast a matchless command of their medium. The quality of their work does not, on the whole, stem from their virtuosity, but rather from their integrity, in conjunction with a technique derived from the best Dutch traditions, which caused them to find a great admirer and follower in Vincent van Gogh. Even if one agrees with Rudi Fuchs when, in his history of Dutch art, he states that as an embodiment of the principle 'art for art's sake', their work could eventually lead on to nothing further, it is still justifiable to conclude that the art of the Hague School will always be more than a mere historical record.[2]

The Hague

In art history the term 'school' is used to denote a group of artists who are linked together by a certain relationship between their ideas or styles. Sometimes they have banded together deliberately and constitute a specific movement. In other cases it is only later that art historians have recognized similar tendencies in the work of a number of artists and grouped them together, either around a given master, Rembrandt for example, or on a geographical basis, as with the schools of Delft, Haarlem, Leiden and Utrecht of the seventeenth century. The second type of school can extend over several generations, and the artists in it do not necessarily have identical aims. The grouping of the Hague School incorporates something of all these elements and its name, first used by the critic Van Santen Kolff in 1875, perhaps places too strong an emphasis on the geographical factor.3

The principal members of the group had certainly come together in The Hague shortly after 1870 and the remaining members of the group were also to settle there eventually. Johannes Bosboom, Jan Hendrik Weissenbruch, the three Maris brothers and Bernard Blommers had lived there since childhood, and Gerard Bilders and Willem Roelofs did part of their training there. But other towns are no less important in the early history of the School, which may be traced back to the 1850s. Jozef Israëls, one of the leading members of the School, made his name and attracted his first followers in Amsterdam; he established a considerable reputation there for his pictures of life in the fishing villages, well before 1871 when, almost symbolically, he moved into the house of Andreas Schelfhout, the leader of the established painting tradition in The Hague. Anton Mauve and Paul Gabriël had originally come from Haarlem, then worked for a time in Amsterdam where Gerard Bilders's parents also lived. The marine painter Hendrik Mesdag who, like Israëls, was born in Groningen, came to The Hague after studying in Brussels. Before him Willem Roelofs and Paul Gabriël had also moved to Brussels, in 1847 and 1866 respectively, although every summer they would leave the city, and return to the Netherlands to paint out on the polders. Vincent van Gogh, who as a rule was well informed, thought in 1873 that Gabriël was a Belgian painter, a confusion of nationality that one regularly encounters in exhibition reviews. Roelofs even found it necessary to inform Christiaan Kramm, the compiler of a well-known dictionary of artists, that he had never taken Belgian nationality. Jacob and Matthijs Maris too received an important part of their training in Antwerp and Paris, Jacob in particular being exposed to a variety of influences since he stayed in Paris for six years.

It is, in fact, quite astonishing that such a mixed collection of artists, who, furthermore, were of very different ages and spanned two generations, should have become prominent in the 1870s as a relatively homogenous group. This can be explained partly by the fact that they were principally practitioners of the same two genres, landscape painting and the lives of fishing people, and partly by the fact that most of them already knew each other to at least some extent. Many of the younger painters had met at Oosterbeek, on Veluwezoom in the province of Gelderland, where they had gone to study landscape in very much the same way that a number of French painters had gone to Barbizon and the time they spent there had been fruitful on a personal as well as an artistic level.

That it was specifically The Hague that became the centre of the new school of painting need cause no surprise. In marked contrast to Amsterdam and Rotterdam, cities which had grown rapidly as centres of trade and industry, The Hague maintained its semi-rural character until well into the nineteenth century. It was surrounded by meadows, polders with picturesque waterways, woods and dunes. The shrewder landscape painters were careful to select houses near a railway or tram station so that they could set off on painting excursions as soon as the weather was suitable. The nearby seaside town of Scheveningen was an inexhaustible source of material for painters who drew their inspiration from the coast and everyday life of the fishing people. The painter Eugène Fromentin described in his *Masters of Former Times* how virtually nothing had changed there for two centuries.

One has only to remember one or two of the artless paintings of the Dutch School and one knows Scheveningen; it has remained what it was. Modern life has altered the details; each period brings new characters on to the stage and furnishes it with its own modes and customs. But what does that signify? The change of a few details that are barely observable in the outlines of the view. The burghers of the past, the tourists of today are never more than small, picturesque, moving, changing touches, fleeting dots that succeed each other century after century between the huge sky, the great honeycomb of the immeasurable dunes and the yellow sands.4

By making a minor shift in perspective, in other words by confining themselves to the depiction of the fishing people, the painters of the Hague School kept even their compositions unsullied.

Curiously, Fromentin did not consider The Hague to be a typical Dutch city. In contrast to his English-speaking colleagues, who invariably described the Hague School as the 'New Dutch School' or the 'Modern Dutch School', Fromentin characterized The Hague as 'definitely one of the least Dutch cities in Holland'. (Perhaps he was implying that The Hague, unlike either Delft or Haarlem, had never had its own distinctive school of painting in the seventeenth century.) However, he not only remarked upon a certain elegant cosmopolitanism that he sensed there, he also acknowledged that it was 'a place of residence that I would recommend to all those who have taken a dislike to big cities on account of their ugliness, their commonness, their bustle, their small-mindedness or their empty luxury, but not to cities in general'. If he had to choose a place 'to work in, a place for relaxation, where one feels at ease, breathes a delicious air, sees beautiful things and dreams of others still more beautiful', then he would opt for The Hague.5

If in the seventeenth century painting in The Hague had had no distinct character or school of its own, apart from the painters who worked for the Court of the House of Orange, the situation was very different by the beginning of the nineteenth century. The political and social *milieu* was obviously more favourable for art, for it was painters from The Hague who determined the development of Dutch Romanticism in the first half of that century, particularly in the genre of landscape. Bart van Hove, Andreas Schelfhout, Wijnand Nuyen, Sam Verveer, Hendrik van de Sande Bakhuyzen and Simon van den Berg were regarded as outstanding masters and no less excellent teachers of their genres, and it was their pupils who laid the foundations for a genuine Hague School.

The masters

The image of a school is primarily determined by its 'masters', a group selected principally on grounds of quality, whose works epitomize the character of its styles and subjects. There is, on the whole, a general consensus between present-day opinion and that of the last century when it comes to selecting the masters of the Hague School. Nowadays Gerard Bilders is

fig. 1 J. Maris *Collecting Shellfish c.* 1878–79
(William Rockhill Nelson Gallery of Art,
    Atkins Museum of Fine Arts, Kansas City)

seen more clearly as the forerunner of the Hague School and the qualities of Paul Gabriël and Jan Hendrik Weissenbruch, whose reputations were not established until quite late in the nineteenth century, are more fully recognized; the reputation of these three artists is now equal to that of Bosboom, Israëls, the Marises, Mauve, Mesdag and Roelofs. In fact, this re-assessment has led many critics to regard Weissenbruch as the greatest of them all.[6]

Together, these artists form a varied group, but they are not entirely representative of the Hague School as a whole and the attention given to them in the past has overemphasized the image of the School as a group of landscape painters. For example, Jozef Israëls has often erroneously been characterized as an exception among the Hague School artists in his choice of subject matter, but, in fact, life in the fishing villages was from the start one of the most important themes of the Hague School artists. In order to restore the balance a little, works by Adolphe Artz, Bernard Blommers and Albert Neuhuys, who are generally dismissed as 'minor masters', have been included in the exhibition. The great international fame enjoyed by Blommers and Neuhuys in their own time, a fame far exceeding that of Roelofs, Gabriël or Weissenbruch, for example, is a further justification for including examples of their work in the exhibition.

At least four generations of artists, born between roughly 1820 and 1880, can be included in the Hague School in its widest sense. Bosboom, Israëls and Weissenbruch belonged to the first generation, while the second generation, those born around 1840, comprised Artz, Bilders, Blommers, Gabriël, the

Marises, Mauve, Mesdag (who was actually rather older) and Neuhuys. Of these Bilders played a part only in the early years of the School, while Gabriël's ideas are in many ways more in accordance with those of the first generation.

The exhibition is confined to the work of these first two generations, who came to public attention as a relatively recognizable entity around 1870 and whose paintings from the following 15 years, known as the grey period, are now regarded by some people as the finest work produced by the School. Others, however, disagree and consider that 1890 was its peak period.[7] There are two aspects of this question which have not yet been brought out clearly enough. If one disregards the early history of the School up to 1870 – its realist phase – then its history falls into two parts: the so-called grey period, which can be dated between roughly 1870 and 1885 (chapter IV) and the period in which the artists' reputation was at its height, from the 1880s to the early twentieth century (chapter V). In the grey period the Hague School emerged for the first time as an identifiable group, whose art was manifest in its purest form in the work of Mauve and Jacob Maris. At that point the School was the most important innovatory movement in Dutch painting, a position it was forced to abdicate by the Amsterdam Impressionists and the Symbolists in the second half of the 1880s. From a purely artistic point of view, however, the work produced after that time cannot merely be dismissed as a 'late flowering' for many of the painters, including, strangely enough, one or two of the older generation such as Weissenbruch and Israëls, created their finest work at this late period when the School's fame was at its height at home and abroad.

Although one or two artists of the third generation, such as Théophile de Bock, Willem Bastiaan Tholen and Willem de Zwart, made a contribution that was certainly not un-important, and although their work, especially that of Tholen, can sometimes hold its own with that of the earlier genera-tions, their art is none the less little more than a harmonious epilogue, in which traces of influence from other artistic movements can be detected. Thus the third generation eventually came to be seen as standing somewhat outside the mainstream of Dutch art history, in particular those among them who must be written off simply as epigones. These artists, who link up with yet a fourth generation, prolonged the life of the Hague School up to the Second World War and did a great deal of damage to its reputation.

In the 1850s the emergence of new artistic principles can be discerned in the work of all the future masters of the Hague School. This period (up to c. 1870) can be regarded as that of the School's gestation, during which the romantic vision evolved, sometimes with irritating slowness, into a new approach, in which romanticism remained as an undercurrent, but with realist and impressionist elements now playing a more important role. The joint appearance of two generations explains why there were so many differences in emphasis in the artists' paintings and why the work of the School lacks homogeneity.

Roelofs and Gabriël, for instance, at various points dis-sociated themselves, both verbally and stylistically, from the latest developments within the School – the excessive neglect of form and the loss of colour. However, this is no more a reason to exclude them from the School than is their residence in Brussels.[8] Essentially, they did subscribe to the principles of the Hague School, which they had themselves helped to mould some years earlier, and the fact that they both decided to settle there in the 1880s confirms their identification with the city.

Like Gabriël and Roelofs, Bosboom seems on occasion to have been scornful of the Hague School of painters among whom he was beginning to be counted by his contemporaries. One can understand why this older artist, who had behind him a considerable career as a painter of church interiors, had reservations about being associated with a group whose ideas he only partly shared and in which the tone was set by younger men. But that he was not unsympathetic to their aims was already apparent from his drawings and watercolours of the early 1860s and becomes clearer still in the 1870s when he also tackled Scheveningen subjects. Even before this he could be recognized as one of the painters who had deliberately thrown off the mantle of romanticism in order to try and achieve austerity combined with a more deeply-felt look at reality. He had taken the first step in this direction with his *Communion Service in St Gertrude's Church, Utrecht* (Cat. 11) of 1852.[9] If we discard the traditional narrow definition of the School as landscape painters, then there is nothing to prevent us from recognizing in Bosboom's church interiors the very amalgamation of nostalgia and realism that constitutes the keynote of the Hague School.

Matthijs Maris is perhaps the most controversial member of the Hague School. His eccentric work, eventually produced in total isolation, seems far removed from that quintessentially Dutch art which is in turn dubbed realist and impressionist. But the fact that Maris's work is rooted in Romanticism and in many respects heralds late nineteenth-century Symbolism does not disqualify him from membership of the Hague School, for his work has an undeniable stylistic affinity with that of other painters of the School. And if one further accepts that the essential character of the Hague School is an atmospheric impressionism with subjective overtones, then the only true criterion by which to judge whether or not Thijs Maris belonged to the movement is the degree to which his work was related to the real world around him.

For his contemporaries the question did not apply; they automatically identified him with the School of which his brothers were also members. He was the outsider who nevertheless belonged, and the collectors who bought the work of Jacob and Willem were no less eager to buy the paintings of Matthijs. As a result, he also became associated with the early years of the School and when the Hague and Rotterdam art societies organized a Maris exhibition in 1893, all three brothers were represented in it alongside one another. In the view of the organizers of this exhibition Matthijs Maris stylistically, and thereby essentially, belongs only to the early history of the Hague School; the fact that his late paintings eventually faded away into an all-enveloping grey mist is not a valid reason for including him in the Grey School. Until his departure for Paris in 1869, however, he had numerous links with the embryonic Hague School and exercised an influence on his brothers and a number of young painters, which should not be overlooked and certainly did not escape the notice of contemporary critics.[10] A clearly demonstrable realist element is still evident in his work half-way through his Paris period; even in an avowedly fairy-tale painting like *The Butterflies* of 1874 (Cat. 77) the boundary between reality and dream has still not irrevocably been crossed.[11]

Matthijs Maris later dismissed his early works as potboilers in numerous letters. A deep-rooted hatred of the practices of the art trade, of which he felt he was a victim, was often the prime motive behind this. In fact his denial of his early work says more about his later ideas than about the background against which the early work originally came into being. However, when he finally abandoned his subjective experience of the outside world for the interpretation of dream images, his work no longer represented the principles of the Hague School taken to an extreme, and a late work like *The Enchanted Castle* (Cat. 78) makes it clear how far he had travelled since his outdoor study of tree roots in Oosterbeek (Cat. 66). If the Hague School possessed its Emanuel de Witte in Bosboom, its Rembrandt in Israëls and its Ruisdael in Jacob Maris, it found first its Johannes Vermeer and then its Hercules Segers in Matthijs Maris.

The seventeenth century

The idea that 'Dutch art, which seemed to have slumbered for a while, was awakened to a new life', thanks to the Hague School, has already come up several times.[12] It has gradually become a commonplace that the eyes of the Hague masters were opened to the true significance of their own Golden Age only via a roundabout route, the intervention of foreign artists. It is argued that the rediscovery of the art of Ruisdael, Hobbema and Cuyp in England by Constable and the Norwich School painters permeated through to the romantic generation in France, and that the Barbizon School eventually passed on these new impulses derived from seventeenth-century Dutch art to the young painters of the land where they originated. This interpretation of the origin of The Hague's landscape realism was already current in the nineteenth century and does provide a broad outline of the train of events, but it is also undoubtedly an over-simplification. It is necessary to emphasize that the Hague School did not come into being as the result of a chain of events in a closed circle. If one analyses the points of the Barbizon School's demonstrable influence, direct or indirect, they turn out to be a series of confrontations (around 1850, when Roelofs settled in Brussels and visited Barbizon; around 1860, when Bilders was confronted by the Barbizon School in Brussels; the end of the 1860s, when Jacob Maris was working in Paris) through which young Dutch artists were encouraged by their French colleagues to go further in a direction that they themselves had already taken. It was not until the 1870s and 1880s that the fashion for the Barbizon School was established among Dutch artists, boosted considerably by Mesdag's activities as a collector. How decisive the influence of Barbizon was before that – through the contacts made at Oosterbeek, for example – is something that is impossible to establish precisely until the relationship between the Netherlands and Belgium, hitherto badly neglected in the study of the Hague School, has been more thoroughly examined.[13] For the time being the opinion of De Boer, that 'the influence of the haughty Barbizon painters on The Hague was purely spiritual and on the Marises in particular it had the character more of an awakening than of a formative power', still seems valid.[14]

One of the leaders of the Barbizon School, Théodore Rousseau, is known to have been annoyed by the critic Thoré-Bürger's habit of noting the extent to which every modern painter he saw was indebted to Ruisdael, Hobbema or Cuyp. This happened even more frequently in the Netherlands where no painter, whether he made townscapes, landscapes, still lifes

fig. 2 VAN RUISDAEL *View of Haarlem from the Dunes at Overveen c.* 1660 (Mauritshuis, The Hague)

fig. 3 SCHELFHOUT *Summer Landscape c.* 1840 (Dienst Verspreide Rijkskollekties, The Hague)

fig. 4 J. MARIS *Allotments near The Hague c.* 1878 (Haags Gemeentemuseum, The Hague)

or portraits, could set brush to canvas without one of the masters of the Golden Age looking over his shoulder. Virtually all the painters of the Hague School spent their apprenticeships copying the old masters, so that it is almost impossible to make out in which cases they drew their inspiration directly from the seventeenth-century artists and in which it came indirectly through the painters at Barbizon. Gerard Bilders wrote to his patron Johannes Kneppelhout,

That the last interpret the first is nevertheless true, for they say of the work of the new masters: it's like Rembrandt, or it's inspired by Potter, Cuyp or Ruisdael. . . . But added to this is their own conception of nature; they combine their memory of the beauties of the old masters with their individual feeling and study. But what is not clear is why a beautiful modern landscape should spur me on to work and study more than an old painting. It is perhaps too strong a sympathy with my own time and what is done in it, but the cause may lie outside as well as within myself in excercises, training, conversations and opinions that are now generally held and are influential; in directions one sees taken by others; in everything that is going on around us and that permeates the atmosphere we breathe, that thus exerts its influence.[15]

Bilders was not the only artist to find himself enmeshed in the heritage of his nation's rich artistic past. Strangely, the artist least affected by it was Jozef Israëls, despite his later affinity with Rembrandt. He, after all, had enjoyed an almost classical international training, so that when he turned to painting fishermen he could adopt a freer approach to it than those artists who had been schooled in it from the start. This total specialization in and lifelong fidelity to a single genre, or even a subsidiary genre, is one of the most typically Dutch traits that the Hague painters acquired from their predecessors. Once he had trained under a painter of architecture and begun his career as a painter of church interiors, Bosboom was never able to break away from this. Only in drawings and watercolours did he occasionally venture outside his genre. And however emphatically Willem Maris, like Gerard Bilders before him, claimed that he did not paint cows for their own sake, but for the light, he nevertheless painted cows from the moment he began his studies under the animal painter Pieter Stortenbeker (1828–98). The same pattern applied to Mauve for even though there is some variety in his œuvre, its character is determined by the horses, cows and sheep that his teachers Pieter Frederick van Os and Wouter Verschuur taught him how to paint. The conventions passed on from generation to generation were abandoned only if an artist was certain that he had established a new base. The Hague School did eventually develop new expressive forms of its own, but the link with tradition remained strong and on close inspection it becomes clear that the number of new formulas was limited.

In landscape painting a number of established subsidiary genres were inherited from the seventeenth century, of which the woodland scene, the panoramic landscape and animals in a landscape attracted the most followers. Among the romantic

fig. 5 POTTER *The Young Bull* 1647
(Mauritshuis, The Hague)

fig. 6 W. MARIS *Cow Reflected in the Water*
(Rijksmuseum, Amsterdam)

artists, the woodland scene, dominated by ancient oaks with mighty crowns, had been the preserve of Barend Cornelis Koekkoek (1803–62) and his pupils. As a result, it re-appears in the early work of Paul Gabriël, who for a time studied under Koekkoek in Cleves (fig. 44). Roelofs too was attracted by the woodland scene, especially in the 1850s and 1860s. Some of his etchings of trees are reminiscent of Ruisdael, but he drew most inspiration from Théodore Rousseau (fig. 33). In his later work, however, Roelofs preferred to paint the open countryside. In a letter to P. VerLoren van Themaat dated April 1868 he mentioned that he had undertaken 'quite a large painting with trees (beeches in autumn)', adding that he had repeatedly been accused of neglecting the genre.

The later phases of the Hague School clearly revealed its painters' predilection for wide, flat landscape. In this period, the tradition of the panoramic landscape, perfected by Ruisdael and Koninck in the seventeenth century and partly re-established by Andreas Schelfhout at the beginning of the nineteenth century (figs. 2, 3), was more important than the woodland scene. Jan Hendrik Weissenbruch and his friend J.J. Destree (1827–88) were the most faithful advocates of this genre. Roelofs's panoramas are mainly to be found among his

fig. 7 GABRIËL *A Watercourse near Abcoude* 1878
(Rijksmuseum, Amsterdam)

early drawings, while Jacob Maris's *Allotments near The Hague* (fig. 4) must have been inspired by Ruisdael's '*Haarlempjes*'. Maris also liked the upright format that had been favoured by Ruisdael.

But there is no doubt that the most important genre was the animal painting. Most early Hague School paintings of cattle in a landscape were nothing but paraphrases of Paulus Potter's *The Young Bull* (fig. 5) and his no less popular *Cow Reflected in the Water*, both in the Mauritshuis. Anton Mauve and Willem Maris in particular laboured under Potter's yoke, but they gradually abandoned a traditional *coulisse*-like composition based on receding planes of different colours for a freer conception, ostensibly more fragmentary, in which the landscape was no longer presented as a rounded whole. This kind of approach, for which Mario Praz has coined the phrase 'the photoscopic vision of realism', is clear in a work like Willem Maris's *Cow Reflected in the Water* (fig. 6), in which traces of Potter's influence can nevertheless be recognized.[16]

One striking characteristic of the painters of the Hague School was their preference for placing their motifs in the centre of their pictures, which, despite the liveliness of the increasingly free brushwork and the sparkling atmospheric painting, gave their pictures a certain static quality. They reduced subsidiary details to a minimum in their attempt to achieve an even starker simplicity so that their subjects – a windmill, an animal or a ship – at one and the same time perfectly merge with the surrounding landscape, but appear to have been isolated from the rest of the world. A painting like Jacob Maris's *Collecting Shellfish* (fig. 1) strikes us at first as an acutely observed atmospheric moment, but what started as a loving analysis of a particular instant in nature has become in the hands of the artist so separated from its surrounding reality that it has turned into an autonomous object of contemplation, a sort of *Andachtsbild* (devotional painting). The grey palette of the School also contributes a great deal to this aesthetic alienation. The sentiment of grey of which Gerard Bilders wrote, should not simply be equated with a preference for that colour, although Jacob Maris and Mauve did go a long way in that direction. What it really meant was a preference for tonal painting, in which bright, contrasting colours were replaced

fig. 8 J. Maris *Amsterdam* (The Burrell Collection, Glasgow Art Gallery and Museum, Glasgow)

by a range of subtly ranging tones that would create an impression of total harmony. Bilders spoke of his ideal as a 'fragrant, warm grey' and certainly not 'a conglomeration of cardboard with a bit of colour here and there', as Gabriël scornfully remarked on one occasion.

The Hague School painters' restrained use of colour and the simplicity of their subject-matter led them to recognize the full potential of the beauty of the Dutch polder landscape (fig. 7), and in these paintings they achieved a perfect fusion between the panoramic landscape and the animal painting. The Hague School's ability to paint the cloudy skies of the Netherlands was equalled only by their predecessors in the seventeenth century, and the inter-relation between earth and sky became their principal theme. This determined everything in their paintings. For Weissenbruch, 'sky and light are the great magicians. The sky determines a painting. We must get it from the top. We live on rain and sunshine and go through the dry patches [*sic*] with our palettes'.[17] Similar pronouncements were made by Roelofs and Jacob Maris. Indeed, Maris was so confident of his ability to paint skies that when an acquaintance once remarked to him, 'What a beautiful sky, eh', he shrugged his shoulders and replied, 'Oh, it's all right, but I'll paint it better'.[18]

The painters of the Hague School were seldom interested in painting recognizable scenes or views. This time-honoured function of the topographical artist, which had a long and respectable tradition in the Netherlands and had been very popular in the preceding century, had been rejected by the early nineteenth-century painters of townscapes who pieced together charming pseudo-seventeenth-century towns from picturesque brick houses with scant regard for authenticity. Indeed, this had not been unusual in the work of the creators of the genre, Jan van der Heyden and Gerrit Berckheyde. Seen in this light, Jacob Maris's townscapes, compiled from various elements of existing towns, conform with Dutch tradition.

The townscape found few practitioners in the Hague School. Gerard Bilders had recognized 'that Amsterdam is an outstandingly picturesque city, as regards both forms and colours'. He also saw

that our townscape painters, the best of them not excluded, can certainly frame or fabricate a nice façade or gateway in their paintings, but they entirely lack all those lush, luxuriant tones and colours, those fanciful and fantastic forms and lines that strike every foreign artist and every foreigner in general, most particularly in Amsterdam, and which actually give it its local colour.[19]

It was not Bilders but Jacob Maris who succeeded in capturing that beauty a few years later (fig. 8). Maris had seized on the early seventeenth-century tradition of Salomon van Ruysdael and Esaias van de Velde when looking for a new landscape formula in his series of ferries and he now likewise borrowed from this early phase of seventeenth-century realism for his townscapes (Esaias van de Velde's *View of Zierikzee* in the Staatliche Museen, Berlin-Dahlem, or some of Van Goyen's townscapes are examples of this tradition). Only sporadically does one find in the paintings of the Hague School an intimate townscape, a rendering of a small corner or street à la Jacobus Vrel or Vermeer's *The Little Street* in the Rijksmuseum. Only Weissenbruch and the Marises occasionally painted such subjects.

Strangely, marine painting is almost entirely absent from the early years of the School, although Jacob and Matthijs Maris worked for a time as assistants to the marine painter Louis Meijer (1809–66). Around 1870, however, Jacob Maris (still in Paris), Jan Hendrik Weissenbruch and Hendrik Mesdag began to paint seascapes and beach scenes; Mesdag continued to paint them for the remainder of his career. Here again the variations within the genre are minimal, although the style of the painters is unmistakably their own. No extraneous drama is imposed on the scene and again the subjects can be counted

fig. 9 J. ISRAËLS *Alone in the World* (Rijksmuseum H. W. Mesdag, The Hague)

on the fingers of one hand: fishing-boats and smacks beached on the shore or anchored off the coast, in calm or windy weather (the Hague School painters liked to paint nature in a boisterous mood), often painted with the light behind them. Mesdag, like the Dutch seventeenth-century masters, had a predilection for moonlight effects.

There is a fluid transition from marine painting to figure and genre painting in the depictions of shellfish gatherers and their carts, women mending nets, fishermen's wives gazing out to sea and, in a rather more lighthearted vein, the courtships of seafaring men and women and scenes of children playing at the edge of the sea. In contrast, the painters deliberately ignored the more fashionable life of a seaside resort, which was certainly present in Scheveningen.

The second main genre of the Hague School, an extremely popular one, was the interior scene. These were set mostly in the picturesque dwellings of peasants or fishermen; the quaint details like Delftware tiles and gleaming copper pots and pans, in which the romantic generation so delighted, were gradually replaced by the play of light and shadow rendered by variations of tone and texture. Often a bright window is the only source of light. A favourite subject is a family at their frugal meal, with a steaming dish in the centre of the table, as in Van Gogh's *The Potato Eaters* (fig. 115). Other motifs that constantly recur are a pensive figure by a window, an expectant mother beside a wicker cradle, an old man or woman playing with a child. Only Israëls occasionally strikes a rather more dramatic note. His series of scenes from life in the fishing villages in the 1850s and 1860s begins with a group in which death is the central theme. His later work is more joyful, but the deathbed returns now and then, in particular in the sombre *Alone in the World* (fig. 9). Of the success of such

fig. 10 GABRIËL *Pansies*
(Stedelijk Museum, Amsterdam)

canvases he once remarked, '*On aime à être amusé, mais on préfère à être ému*'.[20]

The exuberance and gaiety that Dutch genre painting had known in the work of Jan Steen and Adriaen Brouwer, and that had contributed so much to making 'vulgar' Dutch realism so unpopular with lofty souls like John Ruskin does not recur in the work of the Hague School, with the exception of one or two early drawings by the Marises. When they did not paint the life of fishing people or peasants, the Hague artists confined

fig. 11 J. ISRAËLS *Old Age*
(The Art Institute of Chicago, Chicago)

fig. 12 BILDERS *Trees along a Brook* (drawing)
(Museum Boymans-van Beuningen, Rotterdam)

fig. 13 GABRIËL *Polder Landscape* (drawing)
(Haags Gemeentemuseum, The Hague)

themselves to a simple interior of a kitchen or their own studio (Cat. 20, 46, 136).

Genres that the painters of the Hague School practised surprisingly seldom were portraiture and still life, although it has occasionally been remarked that the qualities of still life painting sometimes characterize their landscapes. Jacob Maris arranged the elements in his townscapes as Cézanne did in his still lifes. Gabriël occasionally painted a flowerpiece (fig. 10), a genre that Roelofs also recommended to his pupils for study. Flowerpieces were depicted professionally mainly by the women painters related to the Hague School, such as Geraldine van de Sande Bakhuyzen (1826–95), Margaretha Roosenboom (1843–96) and Sina Mesdag-van Houten (1834–1909).

Although all the Hague School artists, particularly Israëls,

did execute successful portraits, this genre was not their forte. Their strength lay in the painting of types, not of specific characters; the old man whom Israëls painted in fig. 11 has no name and, significantly, the title of the picture, *Old Age*, is generic.

Watercolours, drawings and prints

The Hague masters should not only be reassessed as oil painters, for they also showed original qualities as draughtsmen and printmakers. Most of them had had a sound training in drawing in their youth and retained a remarkable eagerness to learn until late in their lives. Some of them regularly attended the evening drawing classes at Pulchri Studio and the foundation of the Hollandsche Teeken-Maatschappij (Dutch Drawing Society) in 1876 can be counted as one of the milestones in the history of the Hague School.

The Hague School encompassed most of the styles and methods of drawing current in the nineteenth century, from academic drawing in the classicist style (figs. 24, 25, 26), through the early sepia drawings of Roelofs, Weissenbruch and Bosboom and the detailed studies in pen and pencil of Bilders, Gabriël, Mauve and the Marises, to the chalk and charcoal drawings so popular in the realist period (Gabriël, Roelofs and Jozef Israëls). The charcoal drawings of Israëls and Roelofs in particular are equal to their oil paintings in expressive power, as Van Gogh's enthusiastic descriptions of them testify.

Nor were the Hague School artists unrepresented as printmakers. One or two of them experimented with lithography, but it was primarily in etching – a somewhat neglected medium at that time – that they excelled. Nevertheless, printmaking was for most of them only a by-product of their painting. Thus their most important contribution to the history of graphic art in the Netherlands was that, in the period between the demise of the Haagsche Etsclub (Hague Etching Club) in 1860 and the foundation of the Nederlandsche Etsclub (Netherlands Etching Club) in 1885, they were the only painters of any calibre who held any regard for the art and thus kept it alive. One or two of the artists who are included in the Hague School even owe their reputations primarily to their graphic work: Carel Nicolaas Storm van 's Gravesande (1841–1924) and Philippe Zilcken (1857–1930). Zilcken's reproduction prints contributed a great deal to the dissemination of the work of the Hague School.

The one medium other than oil in which the Hague School artists excelled was that of the watercolour, in which some of them reached a standard equalling that of the most famous practitioners of the genre, Jongkind and the English watercolourists of the early nineteenth century.

The watercolour had come to the fore as an independent art-form in England at the end of the eighteenth century and in the first decades of the nineteenth its popularity extended to France, mainly due to the work of Richard Parkes Bonington. There it had a particular appeal for some of the Romantics, including Delacroix, Huet and Isabey, although it met with surprisingly little response from the Barbizon painters, possibly because its translucent character was not suited to the earthy colours and heavy paint of their landscape painting. Only Corot had a command of the technique, but he kept his creations in this medium strictly to himself, so that they became known only long after his death.

In order to understand fully the Hague School artists' love of

fig. 14 BOSBOOM *Courtyard in the Palace of the Prince-Bishops at Liège* (watercolour)
(Musée des Beaux-Arts de Montréal, Montréal)

fig. 15 BOSBOOM *Figure Studies after Emanuel de Witte* (watercolour)
(Rijksmuseum, Amsterdam)

fig. 16 MAUVE *Figure Studies* (charcoal drawing)
(The Toledo Museum of Art, Toledo)

the watercolour one must take a brief backward glance at the history of the medium in the Netherlands. Drawings coloured in with watercolour were not uncommon at the end of the eighteenth century, but there is a world of difference between the tame, conventional watercolours of poultry-yards and flowers from that period and the broadly conceived creations of the Hague School, which seem to have grown out of the materials and the medium itself. An important link between the two traditions is again provided by Andreas Schelfhout, whose watercolours had a great influence on Weissenbruch, Roelofs and Jongkind. Like the younger Wijnand Nuyen (1813–39), he was thoroughly familiar with the watercolours of English artists like Harding and Prout, whose influence is unmistakable in the early work of Bosboom (fig. 14); Isabey, who taught both Nuyen and Jongkind, also helped to disseminate their work. Schelfhout advocated the watercolour drawing as a medium for studies made out of doors, thus paving the way for two of the greatest watercolourists of the century, Jongkind and Weissenbruch.

The watercolour was widely used for figure studies as well as landscape sketches, although it was eventually superseded by the rapid pencil or chalk sketch and the oil study (figs. 15, 16).

As early as 1847 Roelofs stated on his arrival in Brussels that 'coloured drawings' found a ready market. Gerard Bilders at one point also decided to start making watercolours for commercial reasons: 'It is quite a source of income at present; people really buy a lot of drawings, but not a single paint-ing'.[21] The Marises too made a living for a time by copying romantic landscapes in watercolour (fig. 18) and it was in this very medium that they scored their first successes at exhibi-tions in the 1860s. Israëls, who was not lacking in commercial acumen, was in the habit of making watercolour versions of his most successful oil paintings for the benefit of collectors of more modest means, while watercolours were also very popular with the English-speaking patrons. It is striking how perfectly Israëls managed to translate his intentions from the one medium to the other, despite the adverse comments of his critics who used to accuse him of a 'fumbling' and 'sloppy' technique. Israëls's watercolours were, in contrast to those of most of his colleagues, sometimes dark and heavy and he also made use of bodycolour, but in his old age he surprised the

world with a series of watercolours full of light and air that were very advanced in their conception.[22]

However, not all the Hague masters were equally proficient in the technique. Bilders got no further than a few water-colours that he himself called 'horrors'. Gabriël has one or two fine watercolours to his name (Cat. 26), but they constitute

fig. 17 MAUVE *Wood-cutters in the Forest* (watercolour; Museum of Fine Arts, Boston)

fig. 18 M. MARIS *Landscape after B. C. Koekkoek* (watercolour)
(Rijksmuseum, Amsterdam)

only a small part of his total output. He was more at home with chalk or charcoal, as was Roelofs. Yet Mesdag described Roelofs as 'actually the first who began to make watercolours of any significance'[23] and, as the founder of the Société Belge des Aquarellistes, he acted for many years on behalf of his colleagues living in the Netherlands. Jacob and Matthijs Maris, for example, were made honorary members of the society in 1862. Roelofs himself continually doubted his own abilities as a watercolourist, once writing, 'My drawings generally come off in one day or two at the most or they prove difficult and are then mostly *not* good'.[24]

The critic Josephus Alberdingk Thijm disliked the water-colours of the Hague masters as much as their paintings:

The painters avoid the term watercolour drawing, preferring just to speak of watercolours, probably because they feel that there is often no drawing to be found in them. But if you none the less ask for drawing, then they say that what you want is literature and that art aims only at colour effects and that the intention is to express only moods with those colours. The great men of today declare that the subject is nothing more than a vehicle and that those who attach value to it confuse illustrators with artists.[25]

For these reasons Thijm would have found little fault with Bosboom's watercolours, which were always very draughts-manlike in character, even though he used impressionistic effects now and then. In 1881 Bosboom himself uttered a warning against the tendency of some of his colleagues

to want to raise watercolours to the power of paintings. Fortun-ately most of our Dutch Artists have managed to steer clear of that pitfall and to preserve in their Drawings that characteristic spareness that has made our Drawings increasingly renowned – and sold – for their special cachet in recent years – even in England![26]

The Marises, Mauve, Israëls and Weissenbruch are among the undisputed masters of the painterly watercolour. The watercolour technique even seems to have influenced Weis-senbruch's oil painting technique. The medium reached an almost improbable transparency in his work long before the advent of synthetic paints and the use of the airbrush. It was under Mauve's guidance that Van Gogh mastered the water-colour technique, having admired the achievements of the Hague School painters for years at the exhibitions of the

14 BOSBOOM *Interior of Trier Cathedral*

15 BOSBOOM *Limekiln in the Quarry at Chaudfontaine*

20 BOSBOOM *The Artist's Studio*

19 BOSBOOM *Interior of the German Synagogue, The Hague*

7 BILDERS *Pond in the Woods at Sunset*

3 BILDERS *Landscape with Cattle in the Betuwe at the Approach of a Storm*

32 J. ISRAËLS *The Cottage Madonna*

34 J. Israëls *Girl in the Dunes*

33 J. Israëls *Baby in a High Chair*

35 J. ISRAËLS *Growing Old*

43 J. Israëls *Meditation*

fig. 19 M. MARIS *Carpenter* (drawing)
(Haags Gemeentemuseum, The Hague)

fig. 20 J. ISRAËLS *The Shepherd's Prayer* 1864
(The Toledo Museum of Art, Toledo)

Hollandsche Teeken-Maatschappij (Dutch Drawing Society). The early work of Mondriaan, too, includes splendid landscape watercolours, which are hardly conceivable without the work of Hague School.

Realism

Just as in the most ordinary life there are motives that ennoble the manner of acting, so one also feels in this art, which has the reputation of being so down-to-earth, in these famous painters, who were generally regarded as shortsighted imitators, a grandeur and goodness of character, an affection for the truth and a warm love of reality that lend their work a value that the things themselves do not seem to possess. That is the origin of their ideal....[27]

Whether Eugène Fromentin, who wrote these words, also saw works by the Hague School during his visits to the Netherlands is not known, but his remarks could perfectly well apply to them, for his vision of the Dutch seventeenth century, to which the quotation actually refers, was strongly coloured by French nineteenth-century ideas about realism. His compatriots Hippolyte Taine and Théophile Thoré before him had already linked the realism of the Dutch burgher of the Golden Age with that of their own epoch, and French painters, led by Courbet and Millet, had consulted the old Dutch masters because they found in their work a ready-made formula for their own new and often more radical realism. Courbet even spent some time in Amsterdam for the purpose, living in a studio that was later used by Mauve.

The early history of the Hague School is often equated with a Dutch version of Realism as it was known in France, but it is often overlooked that, insofar as this comparison is valid, the pre-Hague School painters were not the only artists in the Netherlands to show realistic tendencies in their work. In genre painting and portraiture in particular there were several artists working in Amsterdam, August Allebé (1838–1927) and Johann Georg Schwartze (1814–74) for example, whose work was pronouncedly realistic but who never became part of the Hague School. Moreover, the Hague version of Realism always retained strong romantic characteristics. 'Even though one represents nature literally, one is still not certain of having represented one's emotion, but that is the main thing: one must try above all to reflect oneself in one's work'.[28] These words of Bilders are poles apart from the programmatic aims of French Realism, imbued with its powerful dose of social sentiment.

In contrast to France the focus in the Netherlands was on the depiction not of man, but of the landscape.[29] Only Israëls's position is to some extent comparable with that of his French counterparts. He had, after all, enjoyed a typically French academic training from his teachers François Picot and Jan Adam Kruseman, who had studied under David, and his decision in 1855 to turn his back on history painting in order to depict the life of fishermen is a milestone in the early history of Realism in the Netherlands, comparable to that of Courbet's *Stone Breakers*. What is lacking, however, is the fierceness, the commitment that the French brought to their portrayal of the life of the lower classes. At first Israëls's figures are still conceived in a romantic idiom and later this is transmuted into resignation. Mario Praz associates this kind of passive attitude towards fate with the new absence of prospects within a class that lived not only without any purpose, but also without God.[30] In the work of the Dutch genre painters one does not find any close involvement with the fate of the victims of a harsh social system. Their attention is focused on poverty as a source of the picturesque, 'the beauty of workmen's hands', not unlike the way their colleagues who painted townscapes rendered the play of light over a crumbling brick wall. Only Philip Sadée (1837–1904) displays something of a greater social commitment in about 1870 in works like *Outdoor Relief Day* and *The Poor of the Village*. However, he probably derived this from his period in Düsseldorf or from the paintings of the French Realist Lhermitte, with which his own work has much in common.

A great deal has been written about the influence of Millet on the Dutch Realists, but little systematic research has yet been done into it. That there are striking similarities between his work and that of Israëls cannot be denied (fig. 20), but much of this can be traced back to a common source: the old Dutch masters. In the 1870s, however, Millet's influence becomes clearer, first on Mauve, who held him in high esteem, and later on many young Amsterdam painters.

In landscape painting, the Realist evolution took place almost silently. An increase in the degree of reality in the rendering of a meadow with cows or a canal with ducks is at first a question of more subtle observation and more convincing presentation. What strikes us first is the much greater differentiation between the various seasons of the year and moods of nature.

fig. 21 VAN ALBADA *Shell Gatherer c.* 1900 (photograph)
(Rijksuniversiteit, Leyden)

Whereas most Romantic landscapes had drawn their strength from the simple contrasts between summer and winter, day and night (which explains also why landscapes were often painted as pendants), the seasonal changes were now more carefully observed. This is most evident in the winter scenes, for which only a small number of types had been developed in the seventeenth century when the genre had been brought to maturity. Jacob Maris, Mauve and Israëls discovered completely new possibilities in the genre, which the numerous specialists in winter scenes of the previous generation, such as Schelfhout and Leickert, had left untouched (Cat. 64, 96, 108). Fuchs has pointed out the surprising limitations in the way a cloudy sky was represented in the seventeenth century, when cloud formations were depicted according to a limited number of standard formulas.[31] Perhaps it was because the rendering of atmosphere, where the sky determined everything, was so central to their painting that the Hague School painters had such a low opinion of Schelfhout, who nonchalantly whistled while he painted his skies.

A striking characteristic of Hague Realism is the selective way in which the artists chose their motifs. Admittedly, like Courbet, they rejected everything that could not be perceived by the eye and abandoned the embellishments of Romanticism, but they cannot truthfully be called *peintres de la vie moderne*. They completely ignored city life, particularly any modern aspects of it. Van Gogh and his colleague Breitner were exploring new ground when they painted the recent urban expansion of The Hague, while Gabriël, who had a reputation for being prosaic, painted the newly-built Kurhaus in Scheveningen (Haags Gemeentemuseum, The Hague) more as a vision of Matthijs Maris than as a rendering of a contemporary palace of entertainment. The one train that Gabriël painted (Cat. 25) is a great exception, just as unusual as the presence of a steamship in Mesdag's seascapes. For an impression of the Netherlands as it really was at the end of the nineteenth century, it is necessary to turn to photography, the illustrators of the periodicals and the odd genuinely realistic painter such as J. C. Greive (1837–91). With the growth of industrialization and the building of new residential areas even The Hague did not remain untouched, and the painters were eventually compelled to seek their artistic paradise elsewhere. In doing so they kept the unspoilt places they discovered a closely guarded secret. Jacob Maris increasingly created towns of his own and Courbet would never have discovered a fellow-realist in Bosboom, who was until the end incapable of doing away with the seventeenth-century costumes for the figures in his church interiors. Even photographers in the Netherlands allowed their vision to be governed more by the Hague School than by reality (fig. 21).

It should be mentioned that a number of canvases painted by Mesdag during his time studying in Brussels are a noteworthy exception to this and surprisingly photographic in conception. In his absolute obedience to Roelofs's injunction to look at the world through his own eyes, the young artist painted a series of fragmentary street scenes which are striking for the dry handling of paint and the unorthodox way in which they are cut off. His contemporaries were dumbfounded by these ultra-realistic slices of life, which they might perhaps have imagined as small oil studies, but not as such large paintings, least of all for exhibition to the public. Mesdag's later seascapes are by comparison extremely traditional in every respect.

Hague Realism may have been less rigorous than its French counterpart and more limited in its choice of subject-matter, but it does meet some of the criteria that Thoré-Bürger had posited for Realism. Nowhere does his conviction that 'the smallest piece of farmland offers a prospect of heaven and forms part of the infinite' apply so strongly, while the Hague School also avoided the, in his eyes, 'absurd separation of realism and idealism. The ideal resides in the manner of painting and not in the subject'. Moreover, the School compensates for what it lacks in fighting spirit by complying fully with Thoré's idea of 'a naturalism blended with humanity'.[32]

Impressionism

Many of the current vague ideas about the Hague School can be attributed to the lack of a 'manifesto', a short, succinct statement of its objectives. The School never was a movement in the strict sense of the word and most of those who spelled out its ideals – Jan Veth, Max Eisler, Albert Plasschaert – belonged to a later generation. Most of its artists never put pen to paper and there is little interesting correspondence. That of Bilders and that of Roelofs are the most informative, but they essentially state the position of the School before 1870 and the same is true of the letters of Mauve to Willem Maris, which paint a detailed picture only of the Oosterbeek period. Otherwise historians have only anecdotes and apocryphal stories about the painters from which to draw their conclusions and these have been the basis for all the literature on the Hague School. Very little material written by the artists themselves has survived from the 1870s and 1880s and only the articles in

De Banier by J. van Santen Kolff seem to have been written by somebody who shared the painters' milieu. Perhaps Van Gogh's letters are still the best sources for those studying the ideas that were current in the Netherlands in the 1870s and 1880s, although it will always remain difficult to distinguish his personal vision from that of his contemporaries. And, of course, he himself belonged to a younger generation.

The consequence of the School's lack of a strong theoretical basis was the artists' uncritical acceptance of many of the ideas that came from France in the criticism of Thoré and the biographies of Millet and the painters of the Barbizon School. This was also the case with the concept of Impressionism, which from the 1880s was applied to the painting of the Hague masters, although few people in the Netherlands were familiar with Impressionism itself. Later writers have introduced a distinction, arguing that the Hague School adopted the landscape side of Impressionism while the so-called Amsterdam Impressionists, such as Breitner and Isaac Israëls, represented its urban variant.

It is, however, highly debatable whether the Netherlands ever really understood Impressionism's celebration of colour and light before Leo Gestel and Jan Sluyters practised the technique *en passant* shortly after 1900. Remarkably enough, the Neo-Impressionism of Seurat and others was taken up in the Netherlands shortly after it was created through Jan Toorop, who had belonged to *Les Vingt*, the *avant-garde* group of artists in Brussels; he practised Neo-Impressionism himself and invited his French and Belgian friends to exhibit at the Haagsche Kunstkring (Hague Art Circle). Manet was the main contemporary French influence on the Amsterdam artists mentioned above, but so far no one had adopted Monet's rendering of light. Vincent van Gogh, who was extremely well-informed about developments in the art world, had to go to Paris in order to come into contact with Impressionism, for in the Netherlands the high reputation of the Barbizon School had prevented it from gaining any hold in artistic circles. As late as 1888 the Hague branch of Goupil, the art dealers which had played a decisive role in establishing the reputation of the Hague School, had to send work by Sisley, Degas, Monet and Pissarro back to France after several months because they were unable to sell it. The lack of acceptance of their work in the Netherlands at that time is still reflected in the scarcity of Impressionist art in Dutch museums today.

Insofar as we know anything of the Hague masters' opinion of Impressionism, they do not appear to have cared for it. As late as the beginning of this century Blommers was highly critical of the French painters.[33] Yet the Hague School was tacitly incorporated in Impressionism by later historians, along the lines sketched by Bernard Dorival in his *Histoire de l'art*:

There is undoubtedly no more prestigious name in art history today than that of Impressionism. This movement is even so highly regarded that its label is stuck on to artists who do not actually have much to do with it, while others, who are said to be its precursors [Jongkind's reputation may be recalled here!] or to have prolonged its fame, are lauded for this, although the greatness of these artists lies in a completely different direction. Thus a name that was once a jibe has suddenly acquired the brilliant effect of a halo.[34]

Obviously the comparison is not devoid of all significance. There are points of similarity in the aims of the two groups of artists where the position of the Hague School within Dutch art is analogous with that of French Impressionism. The Hague School was the leading movement of renewal in the country and it helped 'to purge art of traditional influences and make it independent and thus to lead it into new paths' (Theo van Doesburg). But there were far fewer clashes with established opinion in the Netherlands than in France, even though the School for many years had a fierce opponent in Josephus Alberdingk Thijm, who even accused Israëls, whom he had at first admired, of having declined 'into the excess of Impressionism'. His tirades are typical of the reactionary opinions voiced by some critics in the early 1880s.

Outlines are no longer thought about; lines are regarded as horrible and the aversion to the costumes of civilized society is so great that no virtue is seen any more in anything but evil-smelling interiors, people with grimy hands and scenes that begin to suffer from a miserable triviality.[35]

Artistic life in the Netherlands as a whole differed markedly from that in France. The Tentoonstellingen van Levende Meesters (Exhibitions of Living Masters) can be compared only in a very general way with the Paris Salons, and in the Netherlands state prizes and commissions carried scarcely any of the weight that was accorded to them in Paris. Although not insensitive to official recognition, the Hague School painters knew that they could support themselves through the art market from the early 1870s. On the rare occasions when the members of the Hague School did act as a group in protest against the all too critical opinions of an exhibition jury or purchasing committee, practical considerations usually weighed more heavily than ideals. Although it is certainly possible to give examples of serious opposition, it is an exaggeration to speak of a struggle for recognition comparable to that of French Impressionism.

The artistic inspiration of the Hague School was seldom the same as that of the Impressionists. Their French models remained Corot, Troyon, Rousseau, Dupré, Daubigny and Millet, while Breton and Bastien-Lepage also had some influence on the younger artists. But Hague Impressionism never became a hymn to colour, a glorification of light or the encapsulation of a split-second of nature. The Hague artists sought to convey the enchantment of subtle tones, the hazy atmosphere of their own polders and the peace of a single moment. The aura that the name of Impressionism may perhaps have conferred at first eventually worked more to their disadvantage, for by confusing their intentions with those of the French painters, people failed to appreciate their individual vision. They were considered to have fallen short judged by French standards and although it was recognized that the nature recorded by these artists of the misty north was less brilliant than the Impressionists' landscapes drenched in southern sunlight, the balance nevertheless remained tipped against them.

NOTES

1. In the supplement to the *Catalogue sommaire illustré des peintures du musée du Louvre*, II. *Italie, Espagne, Allemagne, Grande-Bretagne et divers*, Paris 1961, p. 372, the compilers write: 'Cases to be noted are those of Van Gogh and Jongkind, who were originally allotted to the French School because their principal and most famous activities took place in France. But if one adheres strictly to the legal concept of nationality dating from the 19th century and if one notes that these artists, Van Gogh in particular, still remain largely indebted to the north in their formation and their aesthetic, then they ought to be classed in the Flemish and Dutch School, as is correctly done in the catalogues of the museums in the Netherlands.' See further in this connection exh. cat. *The Realist Tradition, French Painting and Drawing 1830–1900*, The Cleveland Museum of Art, Cleveland 1981; Robert Rosenblum, *Modern Painting and the Northern Romantic Tradition, Friedrich to Rothko*, London 1975, chapters II–3 and IV–7. However, in the exh. cat. *Post-Impressionism*, Royal Academy of Arts, London 1979–80, Van Gogh's work is still included under France.

2. R.H. Fuchs, *Dutch Painting*, London 1978, p. 167.

3. See chapter IV, p. 83.

4. E. Fromentin, *De meesters van weleer, vertaald, ingeleid en van aantekeningen voorzien door Dr. H. van de Waal*, Rotterdam 1976, p. 95.

5. *ibid.*, p. 92.

6. For instance, B. Dorival who, in his *Histoire de l'art*, IV. *De Réalisme à nos jours*, Encyclopédie de la Pléiade, Paris 1969, p. 70, calls Weissenbruch 'the best artist of the group', and his watercolours 'not unworthy of Jongkind'. As regards his assessment of the other artists, Gerard Bilders (confused with his father Johannes Warnardus in the index) is strangely transmogrified on p. 323 from a precursor to an epigone together with 'Poggenbeck (*sic*), Tholen, Van der Maurel (*sic*)'.

7. V. Hefting suggests 'around 1870' in her introduction to J. de Gruyter, *De Haagse School*, Rotterdam 1968–69, p. 9, while G. Colmjon (*The Hague School*, Rijswijk 1951), dates it *c.* 1890.

8. Gabriël expressed his irritation over the 'grey school' to the critic Loffelt: 'a conglomeration of cardboard with a bit of colour here and there and that's called poetry'. In his view the Dutch landscape was 'colourful, lush, fat'. See De Gruyter, *op cit.*, p. 77.

9. See J. Bosboom, 'Een en ander betrekkelijk mijn loopbaan als schilder' in exh. cat. *Johannes Bosboom*, Pulchri Studio, The Hague 1917, p. 11.

10. See J. Knoef, *Een Eeuw Nederlandse Schilderkunst*, Amsterdam 1948, pp. 109–10.

11. It was probably the element of reality in the scene that gave rise to the irritation of Bernard Canter, the critic, who accused the painter as late as 1917 of having depicted a child in an 'improper' pose in *The Butterflies*. See *Holland Express*, 12 Sept. 1917, p. 443.

12. See A. Bredius, *De Schilderkunst, Amsterdam in de 17de eeuw*, III (*Kunst*), The Hague 1901–04.

13. See exh. cat. *Het landschap in de Belgische kunst 1830–1914*, Museum voor Schone Kunsten, Ghent 1980, in which there is no mention at all of contacts between the Netherlands and Belgium and one looks in vain for the names of Roelofs and Gabriël. For Mesdag's contacts and life in Belgium see S. de Bodt, 'Hendrik Willem Mesdag en Brussel', *Oud Holland* 95 (1981), pp. 59–84.

14. H. de Boer, *Willem Maris*, The Hague 1905, p. 30.

15. A.G. Bilders, *Brieven en dagboek*, Leiden 1876, p. 274.

16. M. Praz, *Mnemosyne, the parallel between literature and the visual arts*, Princeton 1970, pp. 153–89.

17. See exh. cat. *Schilderijen en aquarellen door J.H. Weissenbruch*, Kunsthandel F. Buffa & Zonen, Amsterdam 1899.

18. De Boer, *op. cit.*, p. 17.

19. Bilders, *op. cit.*, p. 293.

20. Cat. *Museum Mesdag*, The Hague 1979^2, p. 82.

21. Bilders, *op. cit.*, pp. 314–15 (letters of 2 and 17 April 1863).

22. See illustrations to cat. nos. 65a, 65e and 65m in exh. cat. *Jozef Israëls*, Groningen Museum, Groningen 1961.

23. See H.F.W. Jeltes, *Willem Roelofs, Bizonderheden betreffende zijn leven en werk*, Amsterdam 1911, p. 93.

24. Letter to P. VerLoren van Themaat, 30 March 1867.

25. *De Amsterdammer*, 22 April 1888.

26. Bosboom, *op. cit.*, p. 15.

27. Fromentin, *op. cit.*, p. 107.

28. Bilders, *op. cit.*, p. 96.

29. G. Weisberg pays only very limited attention to landscape painting in his catalogue *The Realist Tradition* (see note 1).

30. Praz. *op. cit.*, p. 176.

31. Fuchs, *op. cit.*, p. 163.

32. Thoré-Bürger, cited by L. Venturi, *Histoire de la critique d'art*, series *Images et Idées*, Paris 1969, pp. 143–45.

33. For example, Blommers said of Monet, 'Impressionism. . . . Just look at Monet. . . . They want to express light . . . even if they do it with their toes'. See T. van Veer, 'Van een schildersleven', *Elsevier's Geïllustreerd Maandschrift*, Sept. 1906, pp. 146–63.

34. Dorival, *op. cit.*, p. 257. See also pp. 71, 422.

35. *De Amsterdammer*, 7 Sept. 1884.

Romanticism and Realism

JOHN SILLEVIS

Teachers and pupils

Art historians writing about the nineteenth century have now come to realize that the period cannot be characterized solely as one of contrast and conflict between academism and successive representatives of the *avant-garde*.[1] That is not to say that this contrast and conflict did not exist, but recent research has shown that the situation was too complex for our picture of nineteenth-century art to be based on it alone.

Academism was for a long time seen as a movement of stubborn reactionaries who were entrenched in the rules established by the Academy training and who defended their ossified views at all costs against a series of rebellious innovators, who have thus invariably been cast as the heroes of the piece. According to this view, which is still to be found in numerous handbooks and general surveys of art history, academism was characterized by an imperative to join forces with the cultural and political establishment and, as a corollary, its adherents are said to have occupied key appointments, from which they were able to block artistic progress. The academic conspiracy could be broken only by a heroic struggle on the part of the *avant-garde*, a struggle that did not simply concern artistic differences, but also involved making a stand against a government that militated against artistic change.

It has, however, emerged that artistic movements, groups of artists and individual artists cannot be divided into two opposing camps so easily. This model has traditionally been used mainly for nineteenth-century French art, taking Ingres and Delacroix as the representatives of the opposing camps for the first half of the century and Salon art and Impressionism for the second half of the century. But, as had been said, this simplification has proved untenable and, moreover, quite useless as a model for the historiography of nineteenth-century art in other countries in Europe. For instance, attempts to equate the Hague School with French Impressionism and thus to allot it a revolutionary, heroic role, take on a somewhat unlikely air when one scrutinizes the lack of opposition experienced by these artists in their lifetime.

If we want to gain a clear idea of the renewal in Dutch art that was undoubtedly brought about by the Hague School as a movement, it is necessary to look at the meaning of academism in the Netherlands, which itself involves understanding the character of Dutch Romanticism and Realism. Furthermore,

since only a few of the painters of the Hague School were self-taught, it is also necessary to know something more about artistic training in the period that preceded that of the Hague School to be able to trace their artistic origins.

The Haagse Academie van Beeldende Kunsten (Hague Art Academy) was the oldest in the country, having been founded as early as 1682 on the instigation of painters like Augustinus Terwesten and Willem Doudijns.[2] It grew up around the circle of the Confrèrie Pictura, a painters' society that had broken away from the St Lucasgilde (Guild of St Luke) in 1656 because its members no longer felt at home among the craftsmen who belonged to the same guild. Painters were expected in those days to have considerable erudition and a wide knowledge of classical literature and mythology. These were essential for an artist who wanted to compete for the monumental commissions that were from time to time conferred by the nearby court of the princes of Orange, who held the office of 'Stadholder' for the larger part of the seventeenth and eighteenth centuries, claiming the royal title only after the defeat of Napoleon in 1813. The Academy was originally accommodated in the Boterhuis, also known as the Boterwaag (weigh-house for butter) on Prinsegracht. A short time later it moved to the Korenhuis, also on Prinsegracht, where it had four rooms at its disposal: one for sales, one for meetings, one for drawing and one for the servant. Drawing was limited to working from plaster casts and nude models. On Saturdays the committee met in order 'to discuss the affairs of the Academy and painting and to regale one another with a glass of wine', the first instance, perhaps, of the social element that we shall find again in the nineteenth century in Pulchri Studio, the artists' society in The Hague to which most of the Hague School painters belonged. The Academy in The Hague certainly had some formative importance for its members, but, in contrast to the Académie in Paris, it was not a didactic institution and it had no formal course of training.[3] Studying plaster casts and life drawing were things that proficient artists continually practised in order to maintain their skill.

In Leiden too, and later in Amsterdam, societies were established that served mainly as meeting-places for artists and connoisseurs: the academy in Leiden dates from 1694, but it was not until 1777 that the Felix Meritis was established in Amsterdam. In 1778 the Teyler Foundation in Haarlem began holding lectures on art and competitions for the writing of theoretical treatises on the subject. In addition, drawing schools with avowedly didactic programmes were set up during the eighteenth century (Utrecht 1717, Amsterdam 1718, Middelburg 1778).

In 1780 the Haagse Academie was transformed into an art school where drawing was taught free of charge and some remuneration was given in the form of prizes for the best pupils. In fact, the city authorities had put in a request to the Stadholder as early as 1779 to be allowed to reform the Academy, arguing that the promotion of drawing would contribute 'to the prosperity of factories and industry and the general welfare of the citizenry'. It was evidently felt that education would have a salutary effect on society.

A strongly anti-academic attitude had also developed in other countries. In Germany, it had grown up within the ideas of the Sturm und Drang movement and out of opposition to the regulation of art and the formulation of rules for artists. According to Goethe, good art was '*mehr gefühlt als gemessen*'. In France all academies had been abolished after the Revolution, the Convention decreeing on 8 August 1793, '*Toutes les académies et sociétés littéraires patentées ou dotées par la Nation sont supprimées*'. This measure was prompted by the hatred of all the institutions associated with the rule of the absolute monarchy and by the aversion to the old French Academy system, against which David in particular fulminated. Yet a new institution had to be put in its place. In 1795 the Institut National was founded, which was '*chargé de recueillir les découvertes, de perfectionner les arts et les sciences*'. The Institut was divided into three departments: *sciences physiques et mathématiques*, *sciences morales et politiques* and *littérature et beaux-arts*. Napoleon changed its composition, introducing four departments: *classe des sciences physiques et mathématiques*, *classe de la langue et de la littérature françaises*, *classe d'histoire et de littérature ancienne* and *classe des beaux-arts*.

This development was to be of great importance for the Netherlands, for during the French occupation (1806–13) the Koninklijk Instituut van Wetenschappen, Letterkunde en Schoone Kunsten (Royal Institute of Sciences, Literature and the Fine Arts) was set up in Amsterdam by King Louis Napoleon, on the model of the French Institut, with the aim of 'perfecting the sciences and arts'. Louis Napoleon had already appointed a Director General of the Fine Arts whose task was to establish an Academy of Art where painting, engraving, sculpture and architecture would be taught. He was further charged with awarding prizes to talented students, which would enable them to complete their training in Paris and Rome, while it was also stipulated that a collection of plaster casts must be acquired to serve as study material.

The artists who benefited from the travel grants were Kleijn, Knip, Teerlinck and Sminck Pitloo. Both Teerlinck and Sminck Pitloo continued to live in Italy and played an important part in the revival of interest in landscape painting in nineteenth-century Italian art; Sminck Pitloo became a teacher at the Academy in Naples and a central figure in the Scuola di Posilippo. They had little influence on their Dutch contemporaries.

There is no doubt that art in the Netherlands had reached a very low ebb, despite the government's considerable efforts; it was even suggested that teachers should be brought in from abroad.

It is with sorrow that we say it; the arts in a noble manner and such

fig. 22 The Hague Academy, Princessegracht

as our forefathers practised have fallen to such depths in your Kingdom that unless foreign artists are invited to settle here and become members of your Academy, we despair of Holland ever achieving its former fame or of it being able to boast anew of having a School of its own, which will make other nations long for its products, so that they will become an article of export and consequently of trade and at the same time an object of honour.[4]

This last aim was not to be realized until the heyday of the Hague School.

Once the Koninklijk Instituut had been established, the fourth department, the *classe des beaux-arts*, was responsible for the direction of the new academy of art within it. But the further development of these plans was interrupted by the abrupt end of Louis Napoleon's kingship and the incorporation of the Netherlands into France in 1810. However, when a prince of the House of Orange was placed on the Dutch throne after the fall of Napoleon in 1813, the plans were taken up again and gradually put into action.

On 31 January 1814 King William I agreed to become the patron of the Hague Academy and authorized the holding of the first public exhibition in The Hague of paintings, drawings, engravings and sculpture. Among the students at that time were Andreas Schelfhout, Bart van Hove and Hendrik van de Sande Bakhuyzen, figures who were later to be of significance, each in their own way, for the development of the Hague School. In 1817 the Koninklijke Academie van Beeldende Kunsten (Royal Academy of Art) was founded in Amsterdam, but not until 1820 were the first students enrolled. In 1821 the School voor Burgerlijke Bouwkunde (School for Civil Architecture) in The Hague was amalgamated with the Academy, which now became known as the Stads Teeken Academie (City Drawing Academy); two teachers were responsible for teaching drawing from models and plaster casts and the number of students steadily increased.

The Hague Academy reflected the new national self-assurance. In 1839 a proud building in the Ionic style, designed by the city architect Reijers and with enough room for training 400 students (figs. 22, 23), was built on Princessegracht. This symbol of the revival of art after the turbulent period of the Napoleonic Wars also represented an improvement in the training facilities for young artists, but the public

fig. 23 The Hague Academy, The Cast Room

still had to be won over.

The limits of public interest in the value of painting are brilliantly caricatured in Hildebrand's *Camera Obscura*, one of the finest portraits of Dutch society in the Biedermeier period. The description of the updating of the painted wall-hangings in the chapters on the house party at the Stastok family's home is very revealing.

The splendid wall-hangings above a high grey wainscot with gilt-edged mouldings, painted with a not unattractive mountainous landscape with sunrises and sunsets, sandy roads with deep ruts and pools of water with reeds and swans; further peopled with women carrying baskets on their backs, out of which bundles of straw are protruding; men by the waterside pulling up fish on long rods; children with bare heads and bare feet lying beside a goat in the grass; travellers on brown horses with their backs to you, so as to show you their portmanteaus, or on white horses holding slender riding-crops very upright; walkers with enormous walking-sticks and three-cornered. . . . But what am I saying? Yes, they did have three-cornered hats on once, but that time was over; the room had been 'done up' a few years before and in this Petrus Stastokius Sr, however old-fashioned he might be in many respects, had decided he must give proof of having moved with the times. He had had all the costumes modernized. On his instructions a smart painter had changed all the hats to the latest fashion of the day, got from a hatter, and all the walkers had been given brown, yellow or striped strapped pantaloons of the newest cut. All wigs had been banished. The ladies, who had hitherto given open evidence of our grandmothers having been much more *decolletées* on their perambulations than our sisters at their balls, had acquired high-necked gowns with tuckers, wide sleeves and long bodices, and even the hair of the half-naked children had been cut in the name of civilization. It is true that this modernization still left a great deal to be desired in many respects, especially as regards the canes, umbrellas and parasols, which had kept their old forms; but the fans had all been changed into nosegays, so that there was no longer the slightest anachronism there.5

Camera Obscura appeared in 1838. Its satire reveals the extent to which the life of the Dutch petty bourgeoisie remained undisturbed by outside influences. The Dutchman's home appeared to be one of the safest hiding-places from the storms of history. The passage of time was marked only by the regularity with which the mailcoach went by at set intervals

and no one concerned themselves with the state of the fine arts as long as their own homes looked neat and smart. Indeed, the role of easel painting had in the eighteenth century become very restricted and landscape painting in particular had become confined to the making of wall decorations. Foreign portrait painters were more sought after than their Dutch counterparts, while painters of townscapes were virtually ignored. The talented La Fargue family of artists in The Hague, who specialized in making topographical drawings and paintings, had to be regularly admonished by the Confrèrie Pictura over arrears in the payment of their sub-scriptions;6 all that awaited them was a life of debts and an end in the poorhouse.

Louis Napoleon had made a genuine effort to cure the malaise in the Dutch art world, not only by reforming art education, but also by stimulating exhibitions and drawing up plans for a national museum. Furthermore, he understood that it was the job of the government to buy work by contem-porary artists. In 1808 he arranged the organization of the first exhibition in the Palace on Dam Square in Amsterdam, which was advertised as a 'public exposition of the products of National Art', to include not only the art of the past, but also works by 'living masters'. About 40 artists took part in this exhibition which was of a kind completely new to the Netherlands. Nor were the public slow in responding: an artist noted on the third day after the opening, 'People are trampling over one another for the love of art'.7 Among the exhibitors were Van der Koo, De Lelie, Jelgerhuis, Kleijn, Linthorst, Dupré and Van Os.

King Louis Napoleon showed enthusiasm and had pur-chased a number of works by the above-mentioned and other artists, but others were less enchanted by the works on display. A German traveller remarked that the Dutch crowded into the exhibition and praised it highly, but foreigners could discover little to attract them.

The aspiring young artists have followed the lead of the unjustly renowned French School, painting large history pieces with figures twelve to twenty inches high frozen in theatrical attitudes, and the light in their pictures is just like that in an ordinary room on a dull day. Outside the exhibition room we came upon a salon where a few old paintings were installed, a bitter humiliation for the present day.8

It is quite true that history painting, which took pride of place in the hierarchy posited by the theories of French academism, had sunk to a lamentable level in the Netherlands. Proficiency in the painting of landscapes, townscapes, portraits and even genre pieces had been maintained since the seven-teenth century, but the grand flourish and the monumental conception required for a convincing history piece had been lost in the eighteenth century, passing beyond the ken of the Dutch artist. Thus, even though history painting was still attempted, the results were often dire. The Teyler Society in Haarlem even held a competition in 1807 for a treatise on history painting, and in 1809 an anthology of the entries was published under the title 'Treatises . . . setting out the reasons for the small number of Dutch history painters and the means of making good this lack'.9 But whatever the means suggested, they were of little use and for the remainder of the nineteenth century history painting continued to play only a minor role in contemporary Dutch art.

The initiative behind the Amsterdam exhibition of 1808 had important results: after 1814 exhibitions of the work of

'Levende Meesters' (Living Masters) were held every two, and later every three years, each time in a different place, and so the public and art critics, who were beginning to take an interest could now follow developments in Dutch art. King William I maintained government involvement in the arts, pictures being bought regularly from contemporary artists. In 1838 the national collection of modern art was installed in 'Het Paviljoen', a country house at Haarlem. It eventually passed to the Rijksmuseum in Amsterdam in 1884.

The Rijksmuseum as we now know it was the final stage of a plan that had first been started upon in the reign of Louis Napoleon, who had a collection of old paintings put on exhibition in the Palace on Dam Square in Amsterdam in 1808. In 1815 the collection was transferred to the Trippenhuis, where it remained until the present Rijksmuseum was completed in 1885. The collection there of works by Dutch and Flemish masters served, among other things, as an education for the artists of the day, who had to copy their great predecessors in order to acquire the skills that were so sadly lacking in contemporary art.

Meanwhile, most of the collection of the Stadholder William V, which had been carried off to the Louvre by the French troops in 1795 as the spoils of war, was returned to The Hague in 1815. One of the most famous works in it was Potter's *The Young Bull* (fig. 5). It was not until 1828, however, that this collection, which had passed into the hands of the State, was installed in the Mauritshuis.[10] There, too, there was an opportunity for artists to make copies of illustrious models. For the painters of The Hague School this collection of seventeenth-century masters in the Mauritshuis was to be of incalculable value, Dutch landscape painting constituting a lasting source of study and inspiration for them. At the age of 17 Gerard Bilders wrote to his benefactor, the writer Kneppelhout,

Mr S. van den Berg [his teacher] is also entitled to my thanks, since he has been kind enough to secure permission for me to copy in the Museum immediately. Thus I have already settled in there, since last Friday, in front of Potter's great bull. I have begun to copy the sheep with the lamb, which will be no easy task, despite their great simplicity. The longer I look at that painting, the more beauties are revealed to me in it and if I did not know for a certain fact that I was sitting in front of my easel in the Mauritshuis in The Hague, I would imagine that the creatures were alive and were staring at me with their innocent faces, just as they do in the meadow at Oosterbeek, and asking, 'What on earth are you doing?'. On Monday evening (8 December) I shall be going to the Academy for the first time and starting with the Gladiator. . . .[11]

Bilders's letter makes clear the components of a prospective painter's training, copying old masters in a museum in the daytime and drawing plaster casts or living models at the academy in the evening (figs. 24–26). The role of the teacher and the lessons in the studio, which did not follow a formal pattern, are often much more difficult to trace. The Simon van den Berg (1812–91), to whom Bilders refers and to whom Kneppelhout had entrusted his protégé, specialized in painting animals, so that it is obvious why he directed his pupil to Potter's *The Young Bull*. He himself had been a pupil of the animal painter Pieter Gerardus van Os.

Jan Hendrik Weissenbruch is also known to have copied the *Bull* in 1849 at the age of 25. He later wrote concerning this,

fig. 24 BOSBOOM *Apollo* 1833
(Haags Gemeentemuseum, The Hague)

fig. 25 M. MARIS *Academic drawing after the antique* 1854–55
(Haags Gemeentemuseum, The Hague)

fig. 26 BLOMMERS *Academic drawing of an Italian Model* 1867–68 (Haags Gemeentemuseum, The Hague)

A Dutch painter who cannot draw flawlessly is no good. This principle applies also to Paulus Potter, whose genius consists in the taking of correct measurements, in the curves of a line. . . . I remember that in my youth the paintings of those old Dutchmen in our museums took my breath away by the way they made nature speak to you. If anyone taught me how to look at nature, it was our old masters.[12]

It is perhaps not superfluous to point out that the teaching of art at the academy was limited to drawing lessons. No instruction was given in painting, which still had to be learned in the old way, in the studio of a painter who was willing to take pupils. The romantic Hague artist Wijnand Nuyen, for example, was enrolled as a student at the Haagse Tekenacademie (Hague Drawing Academy) from 1825 to 1829, but at the same time he took painting lessons from Andreas Schelfhout. His drawing teacher was Bart van Hove, who was later also to teach Johannes Bosboom and Jan Hendrik Weissenbruch and who was the head teacher at the Tekenacademie.

After receiving elementary drawing lessons from Van Wicheren and Buys in Groningen, the young Jozef Israëls went to Amsterdam, where he became the pupil of Jan Adam Kruseman. During the day he took painting lessons in Kruseman's studio on the Amstelveld together with some ten other pupils, and in the evenings he drew at the Amsterdam Academie also under Kruseman's instruction. David van der Kellen Jr, one of Israëls's fellow pupils, later recorded the method employed by the pupils.

As studious followers of the prevailing method of the day, we wasted half an hour every morning in mixing flesh tones before the arrival of the model. The tones were set on the palette in four or five rows. The first row consisted of white with the addition of yellow ochre, a very little at first and then more and more; in the second row a little vermilion was added; part of the first row was given an addition of vine black and formed the third row, while the same addition to part of the second occupied the fourth row. So we continued and, thus armed, awaited the model. We took care to use a separate brush for each tone as prescribed and in this way the studies of the same model all resembled one another.[13]

On Kruseman's advice, Israëls also traced prints by Pinelli and Flaxman in order to gain a command of classical profiles, while in the Trippenhuis he copied the heads of Rembrandt's *Syndics* and Gerard Dou's *Hermit*.

In Paris some painters had extensive studios where pupils could train under the eye of the master. One of the best known was David's *école particulière*, which was later continued by Gros; the same system was also adopted by Delacroix, Delaroche, Coignet, Gleyre and Couture. After his apprenticeship in Groningen and Amsterdam, Jozef Israëls worked and studied in this way in the studio of Picot in Paris, as did Jacob Maris in that of Hébert. The main advantage of this system of tuition was that the pupil was guided by a single master, so that the instruction had a personal character, although if there was a large number of pupils, the individual attention that the teacher could give them was limited. This training system was copied by some academies in other countries. The German painter Von Schadow, for example, introduced what was known as the *Meisterklasse* into the academy at Düsseldorf in 1831 as the final stage of a course that consisted of an elementary class, a preparatory class and a '*Klasse der ausübenden Eleven*'. In 1846 this idea of the *Meisterklasse* was also introduced at the academy in Antwerp,[14] which may be the reason why Antwerp acquired a special reputation among young Dutch artists and why promising pupils were even given grants to complete their training there. Both Jacob and Matthijs Maris, for example, who had started by taking drawing lessons at the Hague Tekenacademie, spent a number of years in Antwerp (Jacob from 1854 to 1856, Matthijs from 1854 to 1858).

Gabriël studied at the Amsterdam Academie and worked for some time in the studio of the romantic landscape painter Barend Cornelis Koekkoek in Cleves and later under the guidance of the Haarlem artist Cornelis Lieste, who often worked in association with Hendrik van de Sande Bakhuyzen and the Belgian artist Eugène Verboeckhoven. Willem Roelofs was in his turn a pupil of Van de Sande Bakhuyzen, while Anton Mauve was trained in the tried and tested tradition of painting animals and livestock by Pieter Frederik van Os and Wouterus Verschuur in Haarlem (fig. 27). With Gabriël he was later to discover the landscape of Gelderland, in particular that around Wolfheze and Oosterbeek, and to establish contacts with the Maris brothers and the elder and the younger Bilders. We shall come back to the significance of Oosterbeek later. At this point it is worth noting that the painters whom we now regard as the masters of the Hague School in many cases knew each other by the middle of the century, either as a result of having teachers in common or for other reasons.

Points of contact with Romanticism; the role of Barbizon
However varied the Dutch teachers of the Hague School painters were, they all had one factor in common: landscape.

fig. 27 MAUVE *The Studio of Pieter Frederik van Os (1808–1892)* 1855–56 (Rijksmuseum, Amsterdam)

Andreas Schelfhout, Barend Cornelis Koekkoek and Hendrik van de Sande Bakhuyzen (fig. 28) were painters who seldom produced anything but landscapes; Simon van den Berg, Pieter Frederik van Os and Wouterus Verschuur were primarily animal painters, while Bart van Hove is still known for his townscapes. Significantly, in those cases where Hague School painters did not confine themselves purely to landscapes in their later work, there is often already some indication of that future development to be found in the persons from whom they received their training. Jozef Israëls had worked at the Amsterdam Academie under Jan Adam Kruseman and Jan Willem Pieneman, both of whom had won names for themselves as painters of portraits and historical scenes in which the depiction of the human figure played an important part. Jacob and Matthijs Maris, too, had not been trained exclusively by landscape painters and the work of both their early and late periods gives proof of their proficiency in the rendering of the human figure. On the other hand, it is clear that those Hague School painters who lacked such a specialized background often had difficulty in the representation of human figures, even as details in a landscape.

It is difficult to explain the preoccupation with landscape in Dutch art of the early nineteenth century. Some indication has already been given. The eighteenth century had not been very inspiring; artists had endeavoured with varying success to force themselves into the straitjacket of French taste and the elegance they had acquired in doing so was difficult to shake off. The period of the Napoleonic Wars was a time of great uncertainty and highly unfavourable material circumstances, so that there could be no question of a resurgence, despite all the good intentions of Louis Napoleon. The new kingdom under William I offered numerous stimuli, but hardly any new genres came into being. History painting remained a misfit; it was well known that it was regarded internationally as the highest genre, but it had never had a strong tradition in the Netherlands and existed only as forced and, alas, all too obvious efforts. In addition, there was a growing realization that international interest in Dutch seventeenth-century landscape was actually increasing, and this must certainly have constituted an element of confirmation for those who had trained in the genre at the beginning of the century. The romantic movement, which crept very gradually into the artistic world in the Netherlands, also undoubtedly contributed to the reappraisal of landscape as a theme.

Of the landscape painters in The Hague the most authoritative was Andreas Schelfhout. His winter and summer landscapes (fig. 3) enjoyed universal esteem, both in the Netherlands and abroad. He maintained contacts with French and German contemporaries and also put his pupils in touch with them; the most influential in this respect were Théodore

fig. 28 Van de Sande Bakhuyzen *Self Portrait: the Artist Painting a Cow in a Meadow Landscape* 1850 (Rijksmuseum, Amsterdam)

Gudin (fig. 30), Eugène Isabey, Charles Hoguet, Pierre Duval-Le Camus and Hippolyte Garnerey in France, and Andreas Achenbach, Rudolf Jordan and the Düsseldorf School in Germany. Their influence is clearer in the paintings of Schelfhout's pupils, such as Wijnand Nuyen and Jongkind, than it is in the work of their teacher, not just in terms of style, but also subject-matter.

In particular the predilection for coastal landscapes, scenes from the life of fisherfolk and the atmosphere surrounding harbours came to play an increasingly important role in their work. Wijnand Nuyen went to France, to Rouen and to the Normandy coast which was so dear to painters like Eugène Isabey, Paul Huet and Bonington in search of these subjects. He studied the lithographs of Samuel Prout, James Harding and Isabey and even copied Isabey's seascapes,[15] but after his return to the Netherlands the new influences from abroad proved to have little appeal for the art critics. The *Algemene Konst- en Letterbode* waxed indignant in its review of the landscape section of the Hague Exhibition of 1833.

We also saw that in this field [landscape painting], which must be firmly rooted in a faithful study of nature, some artists are increasingly beginning to depart from that golden path that our old masters trod with such renown, to the detriment of their own work and of art in general. This was principally to be seen in the paintings of

a young and very promising artist [Nuyen], who is more and more beginning to incline towards the faulty Romantic taste and who, swept along by the fashion of the times, seems to be aiming at a facile effect without truth or naturalness rather than a lively and powerful rendering of things.[16]

Andreas Schelfhout did not share this opinion, however, and he himself also went to Normandy, returning with a fresher palette. Romanticism nevertheless remained for many a suspect fashion which, it was believed, artists would do better to avoid. Not only Nuyen, but also Koekkoek, who later won considerable renown, were reproached by their contemporaries for having inclined too much towards the romantic taste in their work.

Wijnand Nuyen died young at the age of 26 in 1839. The painters of his generation were shocked. They had seen him as an example of a painter with an international perspective and appeal that reached beyond Dutch drawing-rooms, where only strictly representational art was praised. Antonie Waldorp, Huib van Hove, Sam Verveer and Johannes Bosboom were among his friends. Bosboom wrote of Nuyen in retrospect, 'The Romantic Movement under the leadership of the brilliant Nuyen also attracted me as a follower. And although by taking that path one did fall into colourfulness and showiness, often degenerating into chic, there later arose from

fig. 29 BOSBOOM *View of Rouen* (watercolour; Haags Gemeentemuseum, The Hague)

fig. 30 GUDIN *On the Scheveningen Coast* 1844
(Location unknown)

painting *Quai de Paris, Rouen* of 1839, an unashamedly romantic
townscape with strong contrasts of light and shade and with
the accent on the medieval, Gothic aspect of the city (fig. 29).

After Nuyen's death the musician Johannes Verhulst wrote
to Bosboom, 'The death of the unforgettable Nuyen has moved
me deeply. Hopes for the budding school of painting now rest
on you, Jan. After Nuyen you are certainly the only one who
can fulfil them.'[18] But Bosboom was not able to fulfil these
expectations. In both the early period and the heyday of the
Hague School, he was a respected master and his judgement
was highly valued, but he never assumed the position of a *chef
d'école*. Nevertheless, the following account of Bosboom
giving advice to Weissenbruch, based on the latter artist's own
recollections, is characteristic.

Years and years ago as a very young man, I had some watercolour
drawings after nature, including this one . . . ; I showed this drawing
and some other daubs to Schelfhout, the pre-eminent painter of his
day. He liked them and saw a lot of good in them. 'Really, my boy,
it's very nice. You must come to my place. I'd like to see you', said
Schelfhout. [Weissenbruch showed Schelfhout some more and was
invited to go and work in his studio. He talked to Bosboom about it,
but Bosboom dissuaded him from becoming a pupil of Schelfhout,
who was rather lukewarm about painting out of doors, as such a lot of
paint was wasted that way.] 'You mustn't do it, Weiss,' said Bosboom,
'You must learn to stand on your own feet. Don't go to Schelfhout.'

it a more intelligent quest for the enlivening of colour and
heightening of effect – increasing relief'.[17] This judgement,
dating from 1881, represented a somewhat different stance
from that of Bosboom's early period, at which time his
admiration for Nuyen was clearly detectable, especially in the

'But I can't refuse Mr Schelfhout, can I?' 'Do so, all the same, Weiss! You must keep on looking through your own lens.'[19]

Some of the painters of the Hague School had to work very hard to break away from the instructions of their teachers and the requirements imposed on them by their artistic training. After studying under Jan Adam Kruseman in Amsterdam, Jozef Israëls still felt that he did not have a complete command of the painter's craft. When he saw Ary Scheffer's *Gretchen at the Window* at the Amsterdam Exhibition of 1845, however, he thought that he had found his ideal. Scheffer was in the eyes of many *the* painter when it came to rendering themes from *Faust* and was even praised by Goethe himself for his depiction of Gretchen, but was reviled by others as a typical representative of the painters of the *juste milieu*, not too progressive and not too conservative; for Israëls, however, Scheffer could do no wrong. Without troubling too much about the financial consequences, Israëls decided to continue his education and formation as a painter in Paris where Scheffer had built up his reputation. There he was referred to Picot, who ran a large training studio where 60 to 70 pupils worked every day under his supervision. Israëls was made to start all over again, drawing plaster casts first and only later going on to life drawing. Once, Picot caught him working prematurely from a nude model and warned his pupil that he would not correct his work any longer.

Picot was the prototype of the neo-classical artist, taking his subjects, such as *The Meeting between Venus and Aeneas* (fig. 31), from Greek and Roman mythology. But it did not escape the young Israëls that the neo-classical tradition was nearing its end and that completely different themes and styles of painting were coming to the fore. Nonetheless he continued to study in Paris from 1845 to 1847: he worked in Picot's studio from half-past six to eleven every morning, then in the evenings at the École des Beaux-Arts, where he studied drawing under the very strict tuition of Horace Vernet, Pradier and Delaroche. In his free afternoons he wandered around the Louvre looking at the great seventeenth-century Spanish and Dutch masters.

Yet the fame of Barbizon also reached him. Israëls was aware that a number of painters had taken up residence in Ganne's inn and curiosity led him to make drawings of the farmhouses and the humble interiors in the surrounding area. Although there was probably no question of Israëls having direct contact with the painters of the Barbizon School, this was nonetheless the first time that an artist of the Hague School had been to Barbizon and the Forest of Fontainebleau.

There was, as yet, little of this to be seen in his paintings. After his return to Amsterdam, he exhibited two works, *Aaron with his Younger Sons* and a *Portrait of Madame Taigny*, in which his ideals were still the works of Ary Scheffer and the Belgian Gallait, and the quasi-oriental genre pieces of Decamps. His painting *Day-dreaming* (1850) was also entirely in keeping with that romantic line. The writer and patron of the arts J. Kneppelhout wrote a favourable review of this representation of a pensive girl beside rippling waters and it was sold for a large sum which enabled Israëls to embark on a visit to Düsseldorf, where Andreas Achenbach and the Düsseldorf School had acquired a great reputation. On his way back Israëls called at Oosterbeek, where he met the painter Johannes Warnardus Bilders, father of Gerard Bilders.

In 1853 Israëls returned to Paris, this time on a personal visit to see Ary Scheffer. During his second stay in France he again

fig. 31 PICOT *The Meeting between Venus and Aeneas*
(Musées Royaux des Beaux-Arts de Belgique, Brussels)

fig. 32 J. ISRAËLS *Margaret of Parma and William the Silent*
(Stedelijk Museum, Amsterdam)

spent a week in Barbizon and Fontainebleau, drawing and sketching. Jan Veth even says that he bought peasant garments in order to be able to work from them at home in his studio. Subjects from Dutch history such as *Margaret of Parma and William the Silent* (fig. 32) and the *Last Letter of Oldenbarnevelt* were among his last forays into history painting, which were soon to make way for scenes from the daily life of fisherfolk and peasants with their own heroism and tragedy.

Brussels

The young Willem Roelofs, too, decided after a short period in The Hague not to remain in the Netherlands. In 1847 he opted to settle in Brussels. This decision has been interpreted by some art historians as a longing to share in the dynamic artistic life of the Belgian capital – his biographer Jeltes gives no reason for it – but a letter to Jan Weissenbruch, one of his friends in The Hague, would appear to reveal quite different reasons. Brussels certainly did develop into an effervescent artistic centre in the second half of the nineteenth century, but in the 1840s it was still in the last throes of Romanticism. The preoccupation then was with arguments between the professors of the academies in Antwerp and Brussels, who either championed a colourism inspired by Rubens or else clung to

fig. 33 ROELOFS *Wooded Landscape* 1854 (Musée des Beaux-Arts, Lille)

the classicist precepts of the school of David and Navez. Roelofs was unenthusiastic – at first at any rate – about the artistic milieu in which he found himself. He wrote to Jan Weissenbruch on 18 December 1847:

In general I have been well received here and I've made some very good acquaintances – Ortmans, among others, seems a nice fellow and he has a very good judgement of paintings, *something that is pretty rare here in my opinion*. I am not very taken with what I have seen here in the way of landscapes etc., especially as regards colour, and much better things are being produced in The Hague. They are all, without exception, great spinach-lovers. Khune has improved a lot since I saw some of his work a few years ago, but it is still pretty green nonetheless. Bodeman's work you know, Devigne – another landscape painter – Bovie, etc., do not appeal to me very much . . . . As far as the way of life is concerned I find it quite pleasant here, but it's a pity the painters look each other up and visit one another so rarely. There is a certain penchant for meeting in *estaminets*, which seems to be preferred to seeing each other at home; there they gamble and drink beer, but otherwise they don't trouble much about each other. However, for daily companionship I have some other acquaintances, including Van de Kolk, who, as you know, has a print shop here and whom I see every day. As far as my work is concerned, I was not very happy at first and, perhaps because of the new room and

so on, I couldn't get into my stride, I was even a bit surprised that you thought the little picture of Mieling quite good. It seems to be quite liked here as far as the [lacuna] . . . is concerned – *here much is made of Dutch paintings in general*. People speak of Schelfhout, Waldorp, etc. with even more respect than we do and they make a great deal of Nuyen in particular . . . . Coloured drawings seem to be preferred and I have not yet seen many by artists working here. With the exception of Louters. He makes very beautiful watercolours and there are various pastels by him that I like too. These last seem to be coming into fashion here again. . . .[20]

The letter is too long to quote in full, but there follows a passage 'à propos the perils of love', from which sections are missing, but from which it could be concluded that Roelofs left The Hague for personal reasons and that artistic motives were not his main consideration. Again, in 1860, he wrote to C. Kramm, the compiler of a dictionary of Dutch and Flemish artists (*De levens en werken der Hollandsche en Vlaamsche kunstschilders . . . van den vroegsten tot op onzen tijd*, Amsterdam 1857–64, a sequel to the work by Immerzeel) in answer to a request for biographical details, 'I am not able to say in which newspaper in Belgium it was said that I was Belgian, or in which it was refuted, but this much is true, that I am a Dutchman and do not intend to change'.[21]

Nevertheless, Roelofs continued to live in Belgium until 1887, although he went to the Netherlands each year in search of the beautiful Dutch motifs that proved so popular with collectors, and he was of prime importance for the relationship between Dutch and Belgian art in the nineteenth century. Later he was often to function as a contact and to give assistance and instruction to fellow-artists of the Hague School, such as Gabriël and Mesdag. He himself can certainly be counted as a full member of the School by reason of his manifold contacts with his friends in The Hague and his regular participation in exhibitions in the Netherlands, although at the same time he participated fully in Belgian artistic life. From as early as 1848 he took part annually in the Brussels Salon, the *Exposition générale*, his entries scoring an immediate success.[22] He won the gold medal with his *Landscape in Guelders* and the King of the Belgians bought his *Landscape on the River Drenthe*. This established his renown in Brussels where, from that moment, he was regarded as a new spirit in landscape painting (fig. 33).

We cannot be sure how Roelofs first learnt about the innovations of the Barbizon School, who did not begin to exhibit regularly at the Brussels exhibitions until after 1855. Of the Dutch who did exhibit regularly in Brussels, Johannes Warnardus Bilders stands out with a number of Gelderland landscapes. In 1851, Roelofs himself went to Barbizon, but as in the case of Israëls, a few years earlier, it is not known whether he had any personal contact there with the French painters who worked in the Forest of Fontainebleau.

Gerard Bilders's training, which, as we have seen, had begun under the guidance of Simon van den Berg in The Hague, was also continued abroad. Bilders cherished a strong desire to go to Paris, but his benefactor Kneppelhout, the man of letters, was of the opinion that he would only go astray there. He did, however, make it possible for his protégé to undertake a journey to Switzerland to receive lessons from the artist Charles Humbert in Geneva.[23] Humbert's work had at first showed strong romantic traits, as in a dramatic scene of animals surprised by a thunderstorm in the Alps, but by the time he acquired Bilders as a pupil, he had gone over to a type of landscape closer to the *genre intime* and to the making of animal paintings of an almost Dutch inspiration (fig. 34); Arnold Neuweiler even says in his *La peinture a Genève de 1700 à 1900* that, after training under Hornung in Geneva and Ingres in Paris, Humbert made a study trip to the Netherlands. His animal paintings are most reminiscent of those of Potter, while his later works tally in mood with those of Rosa Bonheur.

At the end of 1858 he wrote to Kneppelhout about his pupil's progress.

Our mutual friend, Bilders, has asked me to inform you and to write a few words about the progress that he has made during his stay in Switzerland. . . . There is little cause for comment as regards his drawing, for which he very definitely has a good feeling; in addition, he makes tasteful compositions and he has a very lively feeling for colour. Nature in all her aspects invariably makes a strong impression on him and, as far as I am concerned, I am certain that with his intelligence and by working hard, just as we all have to, Bilders will not shame his family, his friends or himself. . . . You will see, Sir, that his main advance, a real and tangible one, is in his understanding of light, something he did not often bring out before. I attribute this advance to his stay in the countryside at a time of year at which light is abundantly present and the sun bathes the whole landscape in colour.[24]

Despite the inspiration afforded by the Swiss scene, Gerard Bilders had a longing to be back in the Dutch – or rather Gelderland – landscape which was a favourite subject for the paintings of his father, Johannes Warnardus Bilders. Bilders 'the Elder', as he is generally called, had not only succeeded in the Netherlands with these pictures, but also attracted the attention of Belgian art lovers. From 1848 onwards he had regularly taken part in the *Exposition nationale des Beaux-Arts* at Brussels with works with such titles as *Landscape near Nymegen* (1848), *Landscape in Guelders* (1851), *Forest Interior* (1857) and *Mist, a view near Wolpheren* [Wolfheze] *in Guelders* (1860).

In 1860, father and son went to Brussels to see the exhibition. For Gerard it was to be a revelation, for here he saw for the first time works by Corot, Courbet, Diaz de la Peña, Dupré, Millet, Robert-Fleury, Rousseau and Troyon. There he found what he had long been searching for. As he had written earlier that year, 'I am looking for a tone that we call 'coloured grey', that is, all colours, however strong, unified in such a way that they give the impression of a warm, fragrant grey. But the only thing that I strike at the moment is the grey of a kitchenmaid's dress, white and black, pepper and salt or at best a washy milk-chocolate colour. To preserve the *sentiment* of grey, even in the most intense green, is surprisingly difficult and he who discovers how to do it is a lucky fellow. I abhor bright coloured paintings, but with grey you run the risk of becoming heavy, dense, dull or tame if you don't hit on the right tone'.[25] On 25 September 1860 he wrote to Kneppelhout:

In Utrecht I drew some landscape studies and also painted. After I had been there for eight to ten days, my father suddenly appeared out of the blue one evening and asked me if I'd like to go with him to Brussels, where he wanted to go for the big exhibition. Since I was very curious both about Brussels and about the big exhibition, I abandoned the landscape studies and went with him. It was a stupid thing to do financially, but otherwise I am very glad I went, for I saw paintings there such as I'd never dreamed of, in which I found all that my heart could desire. . . . Solitude, peace, gravity and, above all, an inexplicable intimacy with nature struck me in these paintings.[26]

The characteristic aspects of the Barbizon School were present in only a few works, namely Diaz's *The Serpents' Pool: The Forest of Fontainebleau* (fig. 35), Dupré's *Group of Oaks*, Rousseau's *In the Forest of Fontainebleau*, and Troyon's *View from the Slopes of Suresnes*, but for Bilders that was enough. He recognized his own aspirations in their work, he saw the common source of inspiration, namely seventeenth-century Dutch landscapes, and this confirmed him in his conviction that he was on the right path. But he was not destined to have a long career. Neither his father nor Kneppelhout gave him the support that he needed. According to Gabriël the elder Bilders was a peevish man who often adopted the pose of the 'injured artist' and who was also 'consumed with jealousy'.[27] Kneppelhout wanted to 'educate' his protégé according to his own principles, but the young artist was not docile enough to suit him, even though he certainly looked up to the rich and erudite Kneppelhout and took his sometimes bewildering pronouncements greatly to heart.[28] He was uncertain of his own capacities and he was no businessman. Moreover, his health was undermined by tuberculosis and, despite all his bravura and zest for life, he died on 8 March 1865 at the age of 27.

The critics failed to share his enthusiasm for the 'coloured

fig. 34 HUMBERT *Landscape with Cattle* 1876 (Location unknown)

grey' palette. In 1860 Bilders wrote to Kneppelhout, 'some said that my paintings in Rotterdam appeared too grey'.[29] Matthijs Maris also incurred the same reproach, being told he simply must take off his 'grey spectacles', while Willem Maris and the young Anton Mauve, who had made friends at Oosterbeek, were likewise denounced by the art critics for their predilection for grey. One critic wrote of Mauve in the *Algemeen Handelsblad*,

A few months ago he seemed to be going his own way, but he now evidently sees things entirely through the spectacles of the painter Maris. Dangerous! . . . Mauve used to see nature as warm and strong in colour, but now everything that meets his eye appears to be shrouded in crêpe.[30]

It was not only Matthijs and Willem Maris who influenced Mauve's interpretation of nature, but also, in all probability, the ideas of Gerard Bilders. Mauve was one of the pall-bearers at Bilders's funeral in 1865.

Despite this loss, the achievements of the Barbizon School began to be felt more strongly in the Dutch art world. If the theoretical premises of French Realism and of Courbet in particular were at best dubbed 'courageous' by Bilders and kindred spirits, his works, particularly those of the period of the *Pavillon du realisme* were described by the Dutch critics as tasteless and shocking. Van Westrheene, the critic of the *Algemeene Konst- en Letterbode* wrote of the International Exhibition of 1855 in Paris:

fig. 35 AFTER N. DIAZ DE LA PEÑA
The Forest of Fontainebleau (print)

I cannot close without saying something about *Courbet*, the most eccentric of the so-called realists in the French School. He has eleven paintings in this exhibition and about the same number were rejected, probably because it was felt that the realistic element was a good deal too dominant in those pictures. But Courbet has not let that put him off. A few days ago he opened an exhibition of his own, showing 40 of his paintings right next-door to the Palais des Beaux-Arts. Large posters, on which the watchword *Réalisme* is to be read in gigantic letters, invite one to visit it, particularly in the city. I naturally complied and, as far as is possible on beholding those ultra-realistic paintings, I have come to the conclusion that Courbet is an artist of great talent, but that, either because he is guided by bad taste or in order to make himself noticed, he tries to render most truthfully precisely those elements in nature which are repugnant to us and from which the artist otherwise averts his gaze. On top of that a certain pretension, something that tends towards a deliberate violation of the rules of beauty and health, cannot be overlooked. Meanwhile, he has achieved his aim: he is certainly talked about.[31]

However true this was of France, Dutch attention and discussion remained focused on the masters of Barbizon, with whom a greater affinity was clearly felt. This was, indeed, also already apparent in Van Westrheene's own review.

Rosa Bonheur and Troyon compete for the honours in their genre. For my part, I would award it to Troyon; there is more depth, air and harmony in his largest painting than in that of Rosa Bonheur. Yet her oxen, on the other hand, are admirably painted, and it is a pity that the melancholy tone of the sky detracts from this. Gudin maintains his

fame as a poetic, romantic colourist with . . . earlier paintings that have already been exhibited, which are also already a bit old-fashioned. People here want at least a little more truth nowadays and the search for this comes out quite clearly in the pictures of the best French landscape-painters. Rousseau stands pre-eminent; I will gladly allow that he has good intentions and that he is concerned with arriving at the plain truth, but the route he has chosen to reach it does not strike me as the best, and is certainly not the shortest. . . . It is a shame that Rousseau himself cannot resolve to introduce rather more form and drawing into his foregrounds; the middle distance and the background are generally glorious.[32]

This was to remain the tone of Dutch criticism in the 1860s. It was realized that the romanticism of Gudin's shipwrecks and coastal scenes was finished, but the innovations, both in subject-matter and style, met with only cautious praise. The skies could not be too dark and too grey, good drawing could not be abandoned in favour of a freer, more painterly style and, above all, form was not be be lost. The 'truth' of a painting was praised, but painters were none the less expected to view and reproduce reality with an artist's eye.

NOTES

1. See R. Zeitler, *Die Kunst des 19.Jahrhunderts*, Berlin 1966; cf. T.J. Clark, *Image of the People*, London 1973, pp. 18, 19. See also T. Zeldin, *France 1848–1945*, Oxford 1973, p. 471.

2. See J.H. Plantenga, *De academie van 's-Gravenhage, en haar plaats in de kunst van ons land*, The Hague 1938.

3. For the history of art education in the Netherlands see N. Pevsner, *The Academies of Art, Past and Present*, Cambridge 1940; J. Gram, *De Schilders-confrerie Pictura en hare academie 1682–1882*, Rotterdam 1882; W. Moll, 'Het archief van de confrerie Pictura en van de academie voor beeldende kunsten', *M.D.K.W.I.* (1919–1925); P.A. Haaxman, 'De Academie van beeldende kunsten te 's-Gravenhage in de vijfde halve eeuw van haar bestaan' (1882–1932), *Jaarboek Die Haghe* (1932); L. Brummel, 'De zorg voor kunsten en wetenschappen onder Lodewijk Napoleon', *Publicaties van het genootschap voor Napoleontische Studiën* I (1951), pp. 11–26; R. van Luttervelt, 'Herinneringen aan de Bonapartes in het Rijksmuseum IV. De kwekelingen van Koning Lodewijk', *Publicaties van het genootschap voor Napoleontische Studiën* XIII (1961), pp. 561–72; J. Huizinga, 'Van Instituut tot Akademie', *Verz. Werken*, vol. 8, Haarlem 1951, pp. 426–49; R.E.O. Ekkart and others, *Leids kunstlegaat, kunst en historie rondom 'Ars Aemula Naturae'*, Leiden 1974; *Kunstonderwijs in Nederland Nederlands Kunsthistorisch Jaarboek* (1979) vol. 30, Haarlem 1980 (with contributions from P. Knolle, J. Offerhaus, A. Martis, M. Trappeniers, L. Frey, J. Hofkamp, E. van Uitert).

4. Report of 1806 of a committee consisting of Messrs. Meerman, Van Styrum, Flament and Thibault, with recommendations for the foundation of a Royal Academy (National Archives; Home Office Archives, Portfolio 896); cited in Brummel, *op. cit.*

5. Hildebrand [Nicolaas Beets], *Camera Obscura, De familie Stastok*, Haarlem 1914, p. 57. The first edition was published in 1839.

6. See J.J.Th. Sillevis, *Door Holland met de trekschuit, een tocht langs Hollandse steden en dorpen met de 18de eeuwse kunstenaarsfamilie La Fargue*, Alphen aan den Rijn 1976; see also *idem* & M. van der Mast in exh. cat. *Den Haag in de pruikentijd, gezien door de familie La Fargue*, Haags Gemeentemuseum, The Hague 1973–74.

7. See J. Knoef, 'De kunsttentoonstelling van 1808' in *Tusschen Rococo en Romantiek*, The Hague 1948, p. 147.

8. From B.G. Niebuhr, *Nachgelassenen Schriften Nicht philologischen Inhalts*, Hamburg 1842, p. 291, quoted in Knoef, *op. cit.* p. 151.

9. *Verhandelingen . . . opgevende de redenen van het klein getal der Nederlandsche historieschilders, en de middelen om in dit gebrek te voorzien.* See exh. cat. *Het Vaderlandsch Gevoel*, Rijksmuseum, Amsterdam 1978. Cf. exh. cat. *Gods, Saints and Heroes [God en de Goden]*, National Gallery of Art, Washington/ The Detroit Institute of Arts/Rijksmuseum, Amsterdam 1981.

10. See E.W. Moes & E. van Biema, *De Nationale Konst-Gallery en het Koninklijk Museum*, Amsterdam 1909; W. Martin, 'Notice historique' in *Catalogue raisonné des tableaux et des sculptures, Musée royal de la Haye* (Mauritshuis), The Hague 1914; C. Blok, *Doolhof of museum*, Bussum 1965.

11. Letter of 7 December from Gerard Bilders to Johannes Kneppelhout, The Hague, in *A.G. Bilders, Brieven en dagboek*, Leiden 1876, published by Kneppelhout (see p. 2). When Bilders wrote the letter, he had been in The

Hague for a week.

12. See exh. cat. *Schilderijen en aquarellen door J.H. Weissenbruch*, Kunsthandel Frans Buffa & Zonen, Amsterdam 1899 (foreword by J.H. Rössing).

13. See J. Veth, *Portretstudies en silhouetten*, Amsterdam [1908], pp. 94, 95.

14. There was a *Meisterklasse* in Dresden and Frankfurt by 1840, in Munich by 1843, in Vienna by 1852, in Cassel by 1867 and in Berlin by 1875. Information taken from Pevsner, *op. cit.*

15. See exh. cat. *Wijnand Nuyen, Romantische werken*, Haags Gemeentemuseum, The Hague 1977, p. 23.

16. See 'Gedachten over den tegenwoordigen toestand der Beeldende Kunsten in ons Vaderland, bij het zien der Haagsche tentoonstelling van Kunstwerken in 1833', *Algemene Konst- en Letterbode* II (1833), p. 229.

17. See J. Bosboom, 'Een en ander betrekkelijk mijn loopbaan als schilder', 1881, in exh. cat. *Eere-tentoonstelling ter herdenking van Johannes Bosboom*, Pulchri Studio, The Hague 1917, p. 11.

18. See J. Knoef, *Van Romantiek tot Realisme*, The Hague 1947, p. 59; see also 'Brieven van en aan Joh. J.H. Verhulst', *Caecilia* XLVIII (1891), p. 222.

19. See introduction to exh. cat. Kunsthandel Frans Buffa & Zonen, Amsterdam 1899 (foreword by J.H. Rössing), *op. cit.*

20. Letter of 18 December 1847 from Willem Roelofs to Jan Weissenbruch, Municipal Archives, The Hague.

21. Letter of 16 December 1860 from Willem Roelofs to C. Kramm, Rijksprentenkabinet, Rijksmuseum, Amsterdam, wrongly dated *c.* 1864 in H.F.W. Jeltes, *Willem Roelofs. Bizonderheden betreffende zijn leven en werk*, Amsterdam 1911, pp. 168–70. The date is clearly legible on the original.

22. In 1848 Roelofs exhibited in Brussels:
cat. nos. 807. *Paysage, site pris dans la Gueldre*; 808. *Paysage, vue prise sur la Drenthe*; 809. *Paysage*, aquarelle.
The catalogue gives his address as Rue Potagère 31 à Saint-Josse-ten-Noode, lez-Bruxelles.

23. The painter in question here is Jean Charles Ferdinand Humbert (Geneva 1813–81), not David Pierre Giottin Humbert de Superville (1770–1849), as Victorine Hefting wrongly states in *Schilders in Oosterbeek 1840–1870*, Zutphen 1981. Gerard Bilders did not arrive in Geneva until 1858, by which time Humbert de Superville had been dead for nine years. See A. Neuweiler, *La peinture à Genève de 1700 à 1900*, Geneva 1945.

24. Letter dated 31 October 1858 from C. Humbert to Johannes Kneppelhout written at Plainpalais near Geneva. Bilders, *op. cit.*, pp. 62–83.

25. Letter dated 10 July 1860 from Gerard Bilders to Johannes Kneppelhout in *ibid.* p. 153.

26. *Ibid*, p. 164.
Among the paintings Bilders saw were the following:
cat. nos. 167 Corot *Paysage, soleil couchant*; 174 Courbet *Les demoiselles des bords de la Seine (été)*; 175 Courbet *Paysage; hiver*; 176 Courbet *Le femme au miror*; 177 Courbet *Les falaises d'Honfleur*; 330 Diaz de la Peña *La charité*; 331 Diaz de la Peña *Le reveil de Jésus*; 332 Diaz de la Peña *Venus et Adonis*; 333 Diaz de la Peña *La mare au serpents, forêt de Fontainebleau*; 361 Jules Dupré *Paysage*; 362 Jules Dupré *Groupe de chênes*; 694 J.F. Millet *La tondeuse de moutons*; 695 J.F. Millet *La mort et le bûcheron*; 813 J.N. Robert-Fleury *Entrevue de Jules 11 e de*

Michel-Ange à Bologne; 814 J.N. Robert-Fleury *Lecture, sous Clément* VII, *de fameux formulaire provoqué par le livre de Jansénius*; 838 T. Rousseau *Intérieur de la forêt de Fontainebleau*; 952 C. Troyon *Vue prise des hauteurs de Suresne*; 953 C. Troyon *Chien en arrêt*.

Taken from exh. cat. *Exposition des Beaux-Arts 1860, Bruxelles 1860*. Dutch participants included Gabriël, Jozef Israëls, Willem Roelofs and, as already mentioned, Bilders 'the Elder'.

27. Letter of 8 September 1893 from Gabriël to A.C. Loffelt, Scheveningen; Municipal Archives, The Hague.

28. See the correspondence already mentioned above (notes 24–26).
29. Bilders, *op. cit.*, p. 153.
30. See 'Tentoonstelling van Schilder – en andere Kunstwerken van Levende Meesters in Arti et Amicitiae', *Algemeen Handelsblad* (15 Oct. 1863), p. 1.
31. T. van Westrheene Wz., 'Tentoonstelling te Parijs', *Algemeene Konst- en Letterbode* no. 26 (1855), reprinted in *Tentoonstelling te Parijs, overgenomen uit den Alg. Konst- en Letterbode* (n.d.) p. 7.
32. *Ibid,* p. 6.

Towards a New Landscape Art
RONALD DE LEEUW

'A painting by Mauve or Maris or Israëls says more, and says it more clearly, than nature itself.'

Vincent van Gogh

The Exposition Universelle of 1855 in Paris caused the art journal *Kunstkronijk* to reflect on the character of Dutch painting at that time. It declared with some satisfaction that Dutch painters were, in comparison to those of other countries, producing work that was 'certainly not brilliant or surprising, but none the less sound and encouraging'. The article continued, with reference to the Dutch school of painting:

As far as simplicity and soundness are concerned, it compares favourably with many another movement, even with many that number geniuses or outstanding talents among their adherents. An eye open to the beauty and harmony of nature; a lively sense of the poetry and sublimity of which her [nature's] appearance is merely a reflection; faithfulness, sensitivity and truth in the rendering of that outward appearance; these are the things in which it excels, in which it still invariably proves to be imbued with the spirit and principles of our forefathers. Not that it has remained entirely estranged from the spirit of our own time . . . on the contrary, it has shared in general developments . . . but it none the less stands on its own through having preserved that which constitutes its originality.[1]

The writer went on to admit that Dutch genre and history painting lagged behind those of other countries, but considered that landscapes, townscapes and 'our only church painter' – a reference to Bosboom – could easily hold their own against 'so many pretentious and wearisome paintings of other schools'. Apart from their technical perfection the Dutch painters' strong point was their 'diligent study of the old masters and above all the oldest mistress of all, Nature'.

The unmistakable self-satisfaction of the *Kunstkronijk* was not shared by the foreign press. Théophile Thoré-Bürger declared in 1859, 'The Dutch School of the present day possesses hardly any character. It lives off imitations of half a dozen of its old masters'.[2] Obviously unaware of Bosboom's and Israëls's attempts in this direction, he added with relief that the Dutch had omitted Rembrandt from their imitations, which was fortunate since this would not have led them anywhere! He laid the blame for the low standard not only on the Dutch painters' lack of talent, but also on the unfavourable artistic climate throughout Europe: 'We are between two schools, one that has ended, the other which is perhaps beginning. We find ourselves in a state of confusion, if not in an impasse'.

In retrospect, the years 1855–70 can be seen as the gestation period of the Hague School. Numerous developments of which contemporaries knew very little were taking place away fom the public eye. Certainly no hint of them was to be seen in the work shown at international exhibitions. At the 1867 Exposition Universelle for instance, Dutch landscape painting was represented posthumously by Koekkoek, which caused one critic to conclude, 'It is not in the genre of landscape that the modern Dutch school of painting excels.'[3] But at the same time the *Kunstkronijk* evidently cherished the expectation that an Amsterdam genre school would spring up at any moment.

We look in vain for a transition between the works of Israëls and those of his confrères. Years ago we thought that he would form a school in Amsterdam, but since then those who we counted almost as members have gone their own way. Whether this has proved advantageous or disadvantageous to them and to the art of this country is something on which we dare not pronounce.[4]

The birth of the Hague School in the 1870s came as a great surprise to contemporary observers of the art world. Yet the first signs of new ideas in landscape painting, as well as in genre painting, actually appeared in about 1855. Jozef Israëls's conversion to 'great genre' was immediately appreciated by his contemporaries, but the formation of a colony of young landscape painters on the Veluwezoom near Oosterbeek escaped notice, because it took time to mature. The critics certainly recognized a general endeavour to achieve 'naturalness' and 'truth' (terms that now became more frequently and more emphatically bandied about than ever), but they found it hard to work out exactly where the younger artists were heading. Whereas the example of Dutch seventeenth-century art helped the French artists in their search for more realistic expression, the Golden Age was not just a source of inspiration to the young Dutch painters, it was also an oppressive burden for them: on the one hand they sometimes imitated them too closely, on the other it was impossible for them to avoid comparison with the achievements of their illustrious predecessors.

fig. 36 J. W. BILDERS *Houses near a Brook* 1852 (Dienst Verspreide Rijkskollekties, The Hague)

The revival of the landscape tradition

In the last century the Netherlands was the 'Land of Rembrandt' to a greater extent than it had been in the seventeenth century, if such a thing was possible.[5] The nationalism that held sway throughout Europe was as strong in the Netherlands as elsewhere and no sentiment was more highly rated than patriotism.[6] In painting this applied to the practitioners of landscape and genre as much as to the history painters. It was the intervention of the Barbizon School (see page 41) that revived landscape painting, and gave new life to a tradition that had been stagnating.

To speak of a landscape tradition, however, is to suggest that this had been unbroken. In fact the brilliance of Dutch landscape painting had faded in the early eighteenth century. This has never been satisfactorily explained, but the fact remains that only a handful of Italianate painters struggled on beyond the end of the seventeenth century, after which decorative wall hangings were the only remaining form of landscape painting. It was only at the end of the eighteenth century that the Dutch came to reassess their cultural heritage, and the revival of Dutch art began. In an address delivered at the Tekenacademie (Drawing Academy) in Amsterdam in 1781, Cornelis Ploos van Amstel suggested the following course of action to his fellow artists 'If a Practitioner of Art contemplates and studies the works of art of these great men

with diligence, taste and judgement and compares them with Nature, he will be seized by a desire to be able, where possible, to produce similar works of art himself.' He continued that if the painter saw

in Nature a picturesque Aspect of some landscape or building, let him remember how faithfully, how nobly and precisely Adriaen van de Velde, Ruisdael or Van der Heyden would have rendered it. If his talent inclines towards the painting of Animals, let him picture to himself how happily a Berchem, Potter and Van der Does succeeded; or if he would rather become a Marine Painter, let him see with what art Willem van de Velde and Bakhuyzen have managed to imitate the turbulence of the waves or the calm waters, before he devotes himself to copying from life in that branch of Painting.[7]

Few theoreticians can have seen their ideas so widely practised. Ploos van Amstel's advice was followed, more or less literally, for nearly half a century. Andreas Schelfhout, Barend Cornelis Koekkoek, Pieter Gerardus van Os, Wouterus Verschuur, Cornelis Springer and the elder and younger Schotel all sincerely believed themselves to be worthy upholders of the seventeenth-century tradition, although unknowingly at an inadequate level. There were very few artists who could truthfully have said, as did the neo-classicist Italianate painter Knip, 'I admired the old masters, but I had my own way of working'.[8] This is not necessarily to denigrate

fig. 37 JAN WEISSENBRUCH *Near Elshout*
(Teylers Museum, Haarlem)

fig. 38 ROCHUSSEN *Fishing Vessels on the Beach at Scheveningen* 1872
(Private collection)

fig. 39 VAN DER MAATEN *Landscape with Cattle*
(lithograph reproduced in *Kunstkronijk* 1865)

the specific character and quality of these artists' work, but they failed to perceive that, despite the many elements they had borrowed from their predecessors, it emanated an unmistakable Biedermeier atmosphere. Foreigners were sharper in their judgement: 'The Dutch landscape has certainly retained very little of its former greatness.'9 Only two artists who died young, Wouter Johannes van Troostwijk (1782–1810) and Wijnand Nuyen (1813–39), broke out of the mould, but they had little real impact on the long term development of Dutch landscape painting.10

With the advantage of hindsight, the route by which the later masters of the Hague School made the transition from Romanticism to Realism appears logical and natural, but a closer analysis reveals that for many of the artists this course was not clearly charted. Only Jan Hendrik Weissenbruch's development seems to have followed such a pattern, reaching its natural conclusion by a gradual process.11 Moreover, the role played by painters who have now been forgotten in these developments has been obscured by selective research. Among those who died young only the reputation of Gerard Bilders has been preserved intact and it is questionable whether, without the publication of his letters and diaries, we would have known him any better than painters like Johan Daniël Koelman (1831–57) or Alexander Mollinger (1836–67). It is only shortly before the Second World War that Bilders came to be recognized as the harbinger of the Hague School.12 When Bilders's letters were published in 1876, Vincent van Gogh was among those who were not convinced that Bilders was an asset to the Hague camp. This negative assessment was perhaps the projection of Van Gogh's own fears as a promising young artist in a similar position to that of Bilders; Van Gogh was looking not for the doubts expressed by Bilders, whom he regarded as morbid and romantic, but for certainty. He wrote: 'When you read Sensier's book on Millet, you are encouraged, but that by Bilders makes you miserable.'13 He wanted to discover in Bilders a *Heldenleben* for the Hague School, but instead he found a painter who, while admittedly describing the 'warm grey' as no one else had, had progressed no further than 'always ... the grey of a kitchenmaid's dress.'14

Failed masters

Among the painters of whom great things were expected in their own day were Martinus Kuytenbrouwer (1821–97) and Louwrens Hanedoes (1822–1905). They had discovered the Forest of Fontainebleau even before Roelofs and had conceived some attractive and original works there. Kuytenbrouwer eventually remained in France and neither his work nor that of Hanedoes ever made a complete break with the romantic manner. However, Hanedoes was not insensitive to the newer movements; he was one of the first to purchase works by the Marises, his collection included Matthijs Maris's controversial *Village Street* and in the early 1870s Jacob added figures to several of his Auvergne landscapes.

In the 1850s, at a time when Jan Hendrik Weissenbruch was still displaying 'too much of the pupil in his work',15 his slightly older cousin Jan Weissenbruch (1822–80) was highly regarded both at home and abroad. Jan Weissenbruch's work is, like that of his friend Johannes Bosboom with whom he is often linked, notable for a natural peace and serenity, although it is quite different in its decidedly sunny character. It is this absence of a more subtle rendering of atmosphere, which his etchings and the occasional oil sketch show he was capable of achieving, that makes his townscapes appear to lack the deeper contact with their subjects that is so characteristic of the Hague School. Very occasionally he appears to have attained this. The critic Leclercq found it, almost against his will, in Weissenbruch's *St Lawrence's Church, Rotterdam* which is 'enveloped in a fine haze that robs it of its solidity; the sun is weak; but (*sic*)

fig. 40   W. MARIS *Shepherd with Cattle and Sheep* (watercolour; Haags Gemeentemuseum, The Hague)

his talent has a dreamy charm which at once evokes one's sympathy'.[16] Mesdag possessed a small sketch of this work. In the splendid *Near Elshout* (fig. 37), which his cousin Jan Hendrik revered until the end of his life, Weissenbruch perfectly heralded the new ideal that was to come to the fore a decade or so later.

The same can be said of Johannes Warnardus Bilders (1811–90), although he specialized in Ruisdael-like woodland scenes. However, the critics noted very early on that his work could be spoilt by mannerisms, so that he too should be considered as one of the painters who remained only on the threshold of the new era.

Charles Rochussen (1814–94) was a more versatile painter; trained by Nuyen and one of Jongkind's earliest friends, he developed into a fluent painter and illustrator, who could turn his hand to any genre. 'Sketch-like and sparkling in spirit as the canvases of this artist are, his work is impossible to compare with that of others. It bears the mark of genius. Where others fall victim to some fashionable process or other, or study nature through the eyes of others, Rochussen continues to maintain his originality.'[17] But despite its verve and dash, his work always had an air of decorative refinement which muffled the impact of direct observation. Although he was a friend of Gerard Bilders (he spoke at his funeral), he later took sides against the Hague School and in 1882 he even joined with Herman ten Kate and Cornelis Springer in organizing a protest exhibition against the Hollandsche Teeken-Maatschappij (Dutch Drawing Society).

During the 1850s and 1860s J.J. van der Maaten (1820–79) was also considered to be one of 'the most faithful depicters of the Dutch landscape'.[18] Nowadays his work appears dry – Knoef called him 'the unimaginative Van der Maaten' – but the critics recognized in him a striving for the truth and 'a really moving genuineness'. His work was technically honest 'like a painting of the Gothic era; no artful play of brush-strokes, no brio: the technique fades away before the expressions of sincere feeling'.[19] Such an approach accorded with Israëls's ideas; as he wrote, 'I would rather have the capturing of a moment of emotion than all that talk about "beautiful effects of tone", "devilishly cleverly done" or "what daring".'[20] Van der Maaten's masterpiece was *Burial in the Corn*, which was the success of the 1863 Brussels exhibition and was shown afterwards in Paris in 1867. Van Gogh so admired it that he pinned a reproduction of it on the wall among those of works by Bosboom, Israëls and Matthijs Maris.[21]

Johan Daniël Koelman, now completely forgotten, was equally famous in his own day. He was singled out by the *Kunstkronijk* in 1851, together with Pieter Stortenbeker (1828–98), as the most promising painter in the genre of animal painting. Koelman, who died young and was the younger brother of a better known Italianate painter of the same name, played a highly formative role in the early work of Willem Maris according to Knoef, although Stortenbeker was his 'official' teacher. Koelman attracted attention in 1851 with a landscape painted near Wolfheze and shortly afterwards he exhibited animal paintings that seem indebted to Rosa Bonheur and Troyon. These influences, as well as some compositional elements and the misty lighting of Koelman, are also found in the work of the young Willem Maris. (see fig. 40).[22]

fig. 41 SADÉE *Scheveningen Women Gleaning Potatoes* 1874 (Rijksmuseum, Amsterdam; on loan to Dienst Verspreide Rijkskollekties, The Hague)

The last in the series of failed masters to be considered here is Alexander Mollinger (1836–67). He was a pupil of Willem Roelofs and enjoyed a shortlived international fame in 1861, when the English press praised his entry to the exhibition in London even more highly than that of his teacher. Bilders's mentor Kneppelhout considered buying work from him at that time and Roelofs, who was very fond of Mollinger, wrote to his friend VerLoren van Themaat that he saw 'in this painter a very great talent, in precisely those parts of his work that are generally considered unsuccessful', but added that he was afraid Mollinger would not be able 'to score a success in Holland with his manner unless he makes a name elsewhere'.[23] Israëls, who was also a friend of Mollinger's, spoke of the interesting intermediate position Mollinger's art had occupied at the time of his death in 1867: 'He was not actually a landscape painter, nor a figure painter, but he can be said to have found a genre of his own.'[24] His specific contribution lay in the prominence he gave to the figures in his landscapes, a development that was already evident in the work of Courbet, Breton and Millet in France, but which in the 1860s was still to be found only in Israëls's work in the Netherlands. Somewhat later Philip Sadée (1837–1904) painted his scenes of fishermen's wives on the beach or in the dunes in the same intermediate genre. In the 1880s this kind of landscape was taken up only in the work of Mauve and young Amsterdam realists like Willem Witsen and Ernest Witkamp.

The grey palette

One characteristic of the new painting perceived by the art critics with consternation was the loss of colour, which they interpreted as a preference for grey. Long before Gerard Bilders started philosophizing about warm greys, the Rotterdam artist Petrus Marius Molijn was criticized on this count in a piece that appeared in the periodical *Kunstkronijk* under the pseudonym Curor Veritatis. 'Are objects in the open air really as dun and grey as they are painted by this painter? Leaves are greenish, after all, and the ground one sits on out of doors has

fig. 42 F. H. WEISSENBRUCH AFTER MOLLINGER (lithograph reproduced in *Kunstkronijk*)

too many nuances of colours for one to be able to give it this ashen tone.'[25] Elsewhere the same journal asked, 'Why does Mr Hartogensis see grey in nature?', and the animal painter Bombled was likewise advised to avoid grey. Matthijs Maris was also castigated by the critics in 1863 (see page 48) and even Willem, who was generally accorded a more positive reception, could not venture very far without incurring a reprimand.

I am quite prepared to believe that W. Maris thinks he is doing the right thing by leaving well-trodden paths and looking for a new direction for his unmistakable *savoir-faire*, but when this leads him to paint the *Rhine* in a grey mist and the *Mountains* in cloud of grey dust, so that the contours of asses or oxen are lost in them – what help is his skill to me then? The far-fetched is never beautiful, yet the search is to be commended.[26]

Sketches

The critics also disliked the increasing sketchiness of works that the artists themselves regarded as finished. As late as 1869 the *Kunstkronijk* still considered that Gabriël and Mauve had gone too far in this respect.

Berghem, Both or Potter ought just to have come up with a canvas as unfinished as that *Early Morning* by Gabriël and the *Flock of Sheep* by Mauve that hangs below it. They are nothing but sketches and, in addition, that by Gabriël is an unpleasant subject, although it does also promise to be good in colour.

The writer appears to have expected that the painter would go on to finish his 'sketch'.[27]

Greater sketchiness and looseness of touch were, apart from a question of stylistic preference, closely bound up with painting in the open air, where the struggle with the constantly changing light in the landscape compelled the painter to adopt a more rapid and thus less precise style of painting. It is difficult to make out now how common the *plein air* oil sketch was in early nineteenth-century Holland, owing to the relative scarcity of source material and, above all, the limited research on this subject. In art theory at that period the study of nature on the spot and life drawing in the studio were considered of equal importance, so in that respect there were no obstacles to intensive study out of doors. All that can be said at present is that most Dutch artists before the Hague School were in the habit of making their studies out of doors in pencil, chalk or charcoal. Schelfhout advocated the watercolour drawing for this purpose, a method to which we owe the works of two of the greatest watercolourists of the century: Jongkind and Jan Hendrik Weissenbruch. However, Jeltes's remark that Roelofs was the first Dutch painter to take his paintbox with him *en plein air* in emulation of the French is certainly incorrect.[28] It is well known that Koekkoek and painters of his circle, as well as a number of Belgian painters, were making oil sketches in the open air as early as the end of the 1830s.[29]

For the time being, however, there was still an unbridgeable gap between the oil sketch and the finished painting; this was as true of the romantic artists as the new realists. One would be tempted to put Johannes Tavenraat (1809–81), for example, among the modernists on the basis of his sketches, but in fact he is generally reckoned to be one of the few 'genuine' Dutch romantics. Even he complained about the 'minute detail' forced upon him by the demands of his patrons, which neither he nor his colleagues cared for.[30] Jacob Maris may once have said that as far as he was concerned a painting was 'done' as soon as one could see what it showed, but most of the Hague School artists still clung to the idea that the sketch was distinct from the painting. Gerard Bilders considered that the sketch had its merits, 'but the finished work is superior to it all the same' and Roelofs too believed that in the long run the studio painting was more satisfying than a brilliant improvisation;[31] Gabriël also acknowledged this when he advised his pupil Tholen to return quickly to his studio whenever he had made a study in the open air and work up the sketch as soon as possible, so that the freshness of his impression would be retained in the finished work.[32] His advice seems to confirm that the sketch was mainly a model for the Hague School artists.

One of Mesdag's earliest paintings from his Brussels period was far from sketchy, being rather pedantically precise and dry, yet this too was the result of following the advice to look at nature with one's own eyes, without taking account of the work of the other artists (the advice had been given by Roelofs in this instance). When this ultra-realistic and unpicturesque Brussels street scene was exhibited, the critic writing for the *Kunstkronijk* was completely dumbfounded, writing, 'There is probably some aspiration behind it that I have failed to see.'[33]

fig. 43 DE HAAS *Oil Study of a Cow Facing Left* (Dienst Verspreide Rijkskollekties, The Hague)

Oosterbeek

There was no area in which working *en plein air* was practised with more enthusiasm in the period 1855–70 than the country-side around Oosterbeek in the Veluwezoom. It has been called the Barbizon of Holland; but it had been a favourite spot for an earlier generation long before the time of Gabriël, Bilders, Mauve and the Maris brothers. The pleasing alternation of heathland and parklike wooded landscape around Oosterbeek, coupled with its proximity to the Rhine, had caused many a Romantic artist to pause there on the way to Cleves, which has been dubbed the Barbizon of the Romantics. In her book *Schilders at Oosterbeek* Victorine Hefting has described the strategically-placed inns where artists could share their experiences and enthuse over their new discoveries in convivial surroundings. Rarely well-off, they found lodgings with farmers in the area or in Oosterbeek itself. The centre of this community was De Parre, the house of Johannes Warnardus Bilders, who can be credited with the discovery of Oosterbeek. He lived there from 1841 to 1845, but his second visit in the 1850s, when Gerard Bilders also went there regularly, was more important.

The elder Bilders does not seem to have been equally popular with everyone in the artists' colony. Gabriël recounted Bilders's initial reluctance to share any beauty spots he discovered with other artists.[34] However, he seems to have come to terms with the loss of his monopolies and even to have acted as high priest at the 'baptism' of newly arrived artists which took place in the brook near the trees known as Wotan's Oaks at Wolfheze. On these occasions the artists 'set out with music at their head (all manner of instruments) and a great barrow of provisions decked out all over with greenery and flowers'.[35]

Oosterbeek was not only an artists' paradise, but also a favourite haunt of numerous wealthy Amsterdammers, who had their country houses there. Thus a number of prominent literati, such as P. A. de Genestet, Jacob van Lennep and Gerard Keller, used to visit the writer Johannes Kneppelhout at his property on the *De Hemelsche Berg* estate. Here Kneppelhout met the 17-year-old Gerard Bilders in 1856 and decided to civilize this 'uncultivated, but also completely unspoilt child of nature'. The correspondence between them, in which we learn of Gerard's development as a man and a painter and Kneppelhout's good intentions and censoriousness, rank with

fig. 44 GABRIËL and MAUVE *Wooded Landscape with Cattle* (Private collection)

the letters of Van Gogh as some of the most remarkable human documents of Dutch painting. Gerard's letters and diary make it plain to us why Kneppelhout was for a long time convinced that there was a writer rather than a painter concealed in the young man and give us insight into Bilders's struggles as an artist and his conception of landscape, but contain surprisingly little general information about the artistic milieu in Oosterbeek. The little that Bilders did write about other artists, like Hanedoes, Mauve and the Marises sounds as if it was observed from a distance; thus he appears to have learnt of the 'brilliant efforts' of Willem Maris only by hearsay. Of the painters who worked in Oosterbeek in the early 1860s, Mauve and De Haas seem to have been the ones he knew best.

It was mainly the younger generation of those painters we now regard as members of the Hague School who worked in Oosterbeek. Roelofs certainly went there, but the area held no special fascination for him since he had already been to the real Barbizon and anyway preferred the polder landscape. Jan Hendrik Weissenbruch went to Oosterbeek only sporadically (cf. Cat. 124) and Jozef Israëls did so only in 1851 on his way back from Düsseldorf. Israëls's Groningen friend Mesdag spent the summer of 1866 there in preparation for his apprenticeship under such diverse mentors as Willem Roelofs and Laurens Alma Tadema.

Among the younger generation the list of visitors was headed by four Haarlem artists, H. D. Kruseman van Elten, Paul Gabriël, Johannes de Haas and Anton Mauve.

The first two were pupils of Cornelis Lieste (1817–61), who had a good name as a teacher, but about whom Gerard Bilders wrote, 'To me his evening scenes are pale reflections of feeble impressions. He hasn't the power to express either the grave peace of the glowing passion of the evening, or that mood that improves one's spirit and devotion and . . . arouses inexplicable longings' (letter to Kneppelhout, 6 June 1862). Gabriël later said that in his time with Lieste he produced only 'trash' and that he preferred to regard himself as 'a pupil of my own experience and the open air'. De Gruyter described Gabriël's early work as that of a 'more rugged Koekkoek, painted with dutiful strength but little refinement'.[36] For him the Oosterbeek period was one of very hard work, but it was also the happiest time of his life. Kruseman van Elten (1829–1904) followed in the wake of the new developments rather than contributing very much to them himself.

A number of pictures painted around 1860 bear the joint signatures of Gabriël and Johannes de Haas (1832–1908). De Haas had trained at the evening classes of the Koninklijke Academie (Royal Academy) in Amsterdam, and subsequently worked – as Mauve's predecessor – in the studio of the Haarlem animal painter Pieter Frederik van Os (1802–92). His forte was the painting of cattle, which are placed solidly and squarely in the picture and show great skill in the rendering of texture. Roelofs, too, was glad to make use of De Haas's services as a painter of animals. But his own landscapes were seldom more than a background for his cattle and he failed to achieve the complete fusion of animal and setting that is the characteristic of the later Hague School.

De Haas's Oosterbeek period lasted from 1853 to 1857, after which, like Roelofs a few years before him and Gabriël a

fig. 45 MAUVE *The Young Shepherdess*
(Private collection)

decade later, he went to live in Brussels. In contrast to Gabriël and Mauve, he did not have to wait long for success. At the Exposition Universelle of 1855 in Paris he won the praise of the critic Gustave Planche, who would however have liked '*plus de solidité dans les terrains*'.37 Théophile Thoré-Bürger was no less admiring in 1860, while in 1864 J. J. Guiffrey expressed his appreciation of De Haas's attempts to make his paintings more dramatically interesting and imbue them with 'a certain feeling of melancholy', while at the same time preserving 'a certain nobility of line that is praiseworthy in these days of the banal imitation of nature'.38 In 1867, however, P. Mantz considered his work at the Exposition Universelle 'facile, superficial and a bit banal'.39

The collection of oil sketches De Haas built up over the years affords an interesting insight into his method. This series of details from landscapes and animal studies grew into an impressive repertoire of over 300 canvases, from which the artist drew 'infinitely diverse inspiration' for his work. They were sought after by academies as far afield as Berlin and Madrid as teaching material for prospective painters and 167 of them were bequeathed to the Rijksacademie (National Academy) in Amsterdam in 1908.40

After 1888 De Haas acted for many years as commissioner for the Dutch entries to the exhibtions at Munich. He did not always endear himself to the younger generation in this capacity, since neither his own style nor his taste had changed significantly in the years since Oosterbeek. Israëls does not seem to have liked him much either.41

In his dissertation on Mauve, Engel took a more positive view of De Haas's role in the 1850s. He pointed out that his contact with Roelofs in Brussels enabled him to pass on to the younger artists who he met on his visits to Oosterbeek the innovations inspired by the Barbizon School.42

The cattle in one large woodland scene by Gabriël, in which the figures were painted by Mauve, are instantly recognizable as the hefty cattle at which De Haas excelled (fig. 43). Mauve, who had just finished an apprenticeship in Van Os's stuffy studio, was taken to Oosterbeek by Gabriël in 1858 and it was here that his heart was 'opened to the beauties of nature', as the Hague School artists liked to describe it. In the years that followed nature was to be his 'best and only counsellor'.43 Although his financial position only allowed him to leave

'dreary' Haarlem occasionally, he did his utmost to paint on the Veluwezoom as often and as long as possible. He never actually lived there, but the years 1858–68 can none the less be called his Oosterbeek period. The Bilders family were among his friends there, especially the daughter Elisabeth who was 'so very sweet and cordial to him'. Of the artists working at Oosterbeek, he admired the qualities of Nakken, the painter of horses, but thought that those of the painter C.H. Meiners were 'nothing so very special'.44

A far more significant meeting was that between Mauve and Willem Maris, which took place in 1862. The story of Mauve's introduction to Maris, who was then a mere boy of 18 but already a more daring draughtsman than Mauve was after years of toil, has an apocryphal ring to it, but the lifelong friendship that resulted from the meeting testifies to its importance for both artists. Sadly, only Mauve's letters have survived from their correspondence, but these reveal the sometimes almost passionate affection he felt for Maris. If Willem stayed away too long, Mauve would try to entice him to Oosterbeek by enthusiastic descriptions. He wrote from Haarlem on 30 August 1863, 'Who knows what beautiful days are still to come. Just imagine us turning homewards again over the heath towards evening under a fine autumn sky with our jottings and paintboxes. This is something we must enjoy together again', and later that year, after his arrival in Oosterbeek, he enthused, 'Oh, my dear chap, you ought to have been here in the last few days. I've walked a great deal, been everywhere, just to see it and because I want to imprint it and stamp it on my mind. The Divine glory and beauty of that Wolfheze countryside with its brooks and pine trees!'45

For Willem Maris, working *en plein air* was nothing new.

As far as I can remember, before I was twelve I was already out in the meadows drawing cows both in the morning before school and in the evening, and since my brothers were four and six years older than me, I naturally got my first instruction in drawing and later in painting from them.46

In summer Willem worked in the fields, in winter in the stables. Thus when Mauve visited him occasionally so that they could work together in Scheveningen, it was not the beach and the dunes that they drew (as Mauve did several years later), but the interiors of stables. Since Mauve had been a pupil of the horse painter Verschuur for a time shortly before his first visit to Oosterbeek, horses and stables constituted an important part of his repertoire and it was themes of this kind that he first exhibited.

The other friends with whom Mauve painted at Scheveningen included Frederik Hendrik Kaemmerer, Ferdinand Sierich and Bernard Blommers. Blommers said that he met Mauve in Oosterbeek, but he also visited him in Amsterdam, where Mauve lived in a studio on Vijzelstraat that had previously been rented by Courbet.

Jacob and Matthijs Maris had visited Oosterbeek before their younger brother Willem, in 1859 and 1860, although opinions differ as to the precise number and dates of their visits. The painter Sadée mentions having been there with Matthijs in the autumn of 1859 and Matthijs himself said that he only made one visit.47 However, from a letter written by Mauve to Willem Maris and dated 10 November 1864, it can be deduced that Jacob at least, accompanied by Kaemmerer, spent more time there that year.48

Relatively little is known about the landscape work of the

fig. 46 M. MARIS *Brook in the Woods* c. 1860 (Rijksmuseum, Amsterdam)

two elder Marises before they went to Oosterbeek. They seem to have drawn out of doors a good deal in their Antwerp period and a number of watercolours after Koekkoek, Klombeck and Schotel in the Rijksprentenkabinet show that they were familiar with the traditions of landscape, although they had until that time been seen mainly as figure and genre painters.

Jacob had begun as a pupil of Johannes Stroebel (1821–1905) and Huib van Hove (1814–1864), both painters of interiors in the manner of Pieter de Hooch. When Van Hove was forced to flee to Antwerp on account of his debts, he was followed by his pupil. He seems to have been a very demanding teacher, who left Maris little room for self-development. Thus Matthijs's arrival in Antwerp in 1855, with a grant to pursue his studies, benefited Jacob as well since it gave both the brothers more financial freedom. At this time they were sharing a house with Laurens Alma Tadema, who was training in Antwerp as a figure and genre painter under Henri Leys. Ironically, the divergence of the three friends' careers later in the century gave rise to unfavourable comparisons between their work, which were governed almost entirely by the personal preferences of the critic concerned.49

In 1857 Jacob returned to The Hague, Matthijs following a year later. A commission to copy a series of portraits of members of the House of Orange for Princess Marianne ensured them a reasonable income for several years, from which they were able to pay not only for visits to Oosterbeek but also for a trip down the Rhine. Although Jacob and Matthijs visited Fontainebleau on the return journey, their only early landscapes known to us are those associated with Oosterbeek. Their work is so similar at this period that some of the sketches are difficult to attribute; this applies also to work by their friends.50 The picturesque bridges, fences meandering through the meadows, babbling brooks, gnarled tree roots and tumbledown sheep-pens that the Marises painted at Oosterbeek are among the most attractive works that are known to us from their early period. In one instance, Jacob added a group of bathers to one of his landscapes in order to make some money out of it!

The Marises' Oosterbeek period was particularly fruitful for Anton Mauve. One critic wrote in the *Algemeen Handelsblad* of 11 June 1863 that it would be fitting 'to move him up a peg, for that lovely painting next to Mollinger's little jewel is broad and vigorous in conception. . . . The general aspect is truly powerful and sunny'. However, this was again followed by the advice that he should aim for more 'finish. That is the one stumbling-block that young Bilders should also avoid . . .'. Later that same year Mauve was more seriously admonished not to let himself be deviated by the 'brilliant, but untenable conception of a very promising artist', meaning Matthijs Maris.51 In retrospect it is easy to see that these worries about Matthijs Maris's apparently strong influence during his Oosterbeek period were unfounded. The path taken by Matthijs was far too personal for painters like Becker, Blommers, Jozef Neuhuys, Sierich and Vrolijk to be able to follow him for long. Oosterbeek was for him merely an interlude.52

His journey down the Rhine, with the visit to Lausanne as its climax, was much more influential. In the nineteenth century this was a customary journey for artists, just as the visit to Italy had been in the seventeenth century; Willem Maris made the same trip in 1865 with Blommers. But the journey had important artistic consequences only for Matthijs Maris. The impressions he gained there can be recognized in the *Back Street* that caused such a furore in the Dutch press in 1863. The landscapes he painted later (Cat. 74, 78) have nothing at all in common with the Oosterbeek work. By then he had in mind something he could not find in nature: 'so I tried to imitate nature, but I had no heart for it'.53 To an increasing extent he had to contend with an aggressive lack of understanding of his work. On the few occasions that it was thoroughly naturalistic, people complained of not having known 'that the soberest truth can be so disagreeable',54 while, conversely, the *Handelsblad* considered that a townscape exhibited by Matthijs 'defames the beauty of nature in such a way that he ought to have been kicked out of the door for high treason'.55 Willem Roelofs too, who did not know the Marises personally, but had proposed them for membership of the Société Belge des Aquarellistes, showed himself perplexed by Matthijs's work a few years later when he described one of his drawings, *Les deux mères*, as 'curious'. He recognized the talent, 'but the subject is an enigma and could be called a dream or vision'.56

In 1869 the *Kunstkronijk* referred to Matthijs as an example of how 'an unmistakable talent can be submerged in the most capricious excesses of an unbridled imagination'.57 Discouraged, Matthijs once more looked to Jacob, who had then been living in Paris for some years, for support. During the first years of his stay in Paris, Matthijs produced little work, but during the turbulent period of the Commune when Jacob and his family were keeping a low profile, Matthijs gave full rein to his resentment against the Philistines and acted out a remarkably flamboyant and much romanticized role (fighting with the Communards) that has recently been reduced to reasonable proportions in an article by Heijbroek.58 Both brothers emerged unscathed from the ending of the Commune and Jacob returned to the Netherlands at the earliest opportunity. Matthijs, however, remained behind, probably in the belief that his brother would return. Although he later tried to dismiss most of the works he painted in Paris after 1871 as 'potboilers', his paintings of that period are now regarded as amongst his most successful. *Souvenir d'Amsterdam* (Cat. 73), *Four Windmills*, *Kitchenmaid* (Cat. 75) and *The Christening* (Cat. 76) each in their own way hark back to realist moments of Maris's career, but recognizable reality is clearly rendered in a transcendent manner, despite the ostensible concession to public demands. It is this added quality that later caused the critics to compare Matthijs Maris with Johannes Vermeer rather than Pieter de Hooch.

Scheveningen

What Oosterbeek was to the landscape painters of the embryonic Hague School, Katwijk and Zandvoort were to the genre painters who drew their themes from the life of the fishing people. Since their work has also been important in determining the image of the Hague School, it will be appropriate to spend a little time here on the artists who initiated this new development.

The small fishing villages on the North Sea coast had, of course, been popular with painters long before the advent of the Hague School. Andreas Schelfhout, Sam Verveer and the young Jongkind had already painted beach scenes and villages in the dunes enlivened by colourful seafaring figures in emulation of Adriaen van de Velde. Thus the idea that Jozef

Israëls discovered the life of the fishing communities as a subject for painting, and the suggestion that his visits to Katwijk and Zandvoort led him in a radically new direction are not accurate. Israëls's decision to abandon history painting in order to devote himself to the depiction of the poverty and struggle in the fishing villages was certainly significant. Nor can it be denied that the picture generally regarded as his first in the genre, *Passing Mother's Grave* (Cat. 28), which he exhibited in 1856, made a great impression on his contemporaries and may be regarded as a milestone in the growth of Realism in the Netherlands. But, if considered critically, Israëls's stay in Zandvoort marks a turning-point in a direction already hesitantly essayed, rather than an instant revelation. He had already painted *The Little Fisherman* in 1849, we know of drawings of boats and bargemen in Amsterdam of 1851 and two years later he sketched peasant interiors on a short visit to Barbizon. He also began to collect peasant costumes at that time. It is difficult to determine whether it was the example of Millet or Israëls's association with the artists of the Düsseldorf School with their ethnographical interests that was decisive here, but we do know that it was Johann Georg Schwartze who first suggested Zandvoort as a mine of picturesque subjects and that he had first heard of it from a Düsseldorf painter of the group around Rudolf Jordan. Two art historians were recently simultaneously struck by the great influence that Jordan's scenes from the life of fishing people on the island of Helgoland must have had on Israëls.[59]

Where Israëls did clearly break with his predecessors and contemporaries was in the less arbitrary form in which he presented his subjects. He showed a striking preference for sombre themes and moments 'bubbling over with emotion', such as had also characterized his history pieces. In about 1860 he painted a series of works with a leitmotiv of death. They are theatrical in conception and could not have failed to move their audience. Later he preferred more winsome subjects like the 'knitters' and 'children of the sea', but there are always more serious undertones beneath the surface charm of these works since he invariably endeavoured to evoke a certain emotion in his spectators. Although he saw himself as a realist, he would certainly have concurred with Roelofs's words of 1886.

> Nature is the *material* on which we must draw. But do not let the modern theories make you believe that the imitation, the copying of nature is *everything*. The goal, the aim of Art is, like that of music, to move and cause sensations to arise in our souls which are not, because they cannot be put into words, felt any the less by those who have a true feeling for art.[60]

Thus for Israëls, who was continually persecuted by criticism of his 'slovenly' technique, a work was succesful if 'the spectator forgets the whole business of colour and handling, fine execution and whatnot and is brought by the artist to the point of being drawn into the private circle of his thoughts, so that he succeeds in feeling and enjoying his emotions'. It did not matter to him whether 'angry artists or critics scream at it, "One of those subjects again" or "Oh, that sentimentality, that petty anecdote."' His real concern was that 'thought is not entirely excluded'.[61]

Knoef has demonstrated how fundamental elements in Israëls's early pictures of the fishing people – the dark rooms, the brightly-lit figures looming up at us, and the neo-classical compositions and many of the themes – are also found in the

fig. 47 AFTER ELCHANON VERVEER *A Fisherman's Family* (lithograph reproduced in *Kunstkronijk*)

work of the Rotterdam painter Petrus Marius Molijn and a number of artists of the Antwerp circle in which he moved.[62] Molijn began by working in the light-hearted manner of the genre pieces by Ferdinand de Braeckeleer and later became friendly with Eugène de Block, whose studio at that point formed the centre of a small Dutch colony.[63] A striking similarity between De Block's etching *What a Mother Can Suffer* and Molijn's *Deathbed* on the one hand, and works of Israëls like *The Day of the Parting* on the other, elicited from Knoef the all too cautious conclusion that the young Israëls 'only needed to link up with what already existed; he discovered that the foundations had been laid'.[64] Such characteristic Israëls subjects as the good-natured communication between young and old, the young woman gazing out of a window and the frugal midday-meal appear in various phases of Molijn's work.[65]

Thoré-Bürger once metaphorically described the Antwerp school of painting as a tugboat that towed Dutch painting along for the considerable period after 1830 when there was no-one to steer it.[66] Jacobus Josephus Eeckhout (1793–1861), who for many years occupied the post of director at the Haagse Tekenacademie (Hague Drawing Academy), also came from that artistic milieu. His paintings of the life of fishing people, which are not devoid of sentiment, preceded those of Israëls; in one such work entitled *Scheveningen*, published as a lithograph in the *Kunstkronijk*, a mother comforts her offspring while a ship appears in distress in the background.[67]

The same emotions find expression in the work of Elchanon Verveer (1826–1900). At the Hague exhibition of 1849 he exhibited *A Fisherman's Wife Waiting for her Husband at the Approach of a Storm* and in 1853 the *Kunstkronijk* reproduced his *Netmender* depicted against the background of the sea. The theme of children playing on the beach, which later became a

fig. 48 KAEMMERER *Beach at Scheveningen* (Haags Gemeentemuseum, The Hague)

favourite of Israëls, as in *Children of the Sea*, is also found in Verveer's work in 1848. Thus it may be concluded that it is simplistic to describe him merely as a follower of Israëls. He was probably also the first to tackle the subject of the *Donkey Ride*, which he exhibited in The Hague in 1862 and which appeared some years later in the work of Willem Maris and Anton Mauve (Cat. 81). Verveer became best known for his light-hearted scenes of old seadogs recounting their re-miniscences; these *Invalids of the Sea* (formerly in the Haags Gemeentemuseum) are the genial predecessors of JanToorop's sombre *Watchers on the Threshold of the Sea* (Boymans-van Beuningen Museum, Rotterdam). However, the wood engravings he made for books about peasant costume probably constituted his most important contribution to the growing popularity of peasant types. In France similar publications were the most important source for realistic figure painters.[68]

Jacob and Matthijs Maris also painted themes from peasant life in Scheveningen for a number of years, although these pictures have tended to be eclipsed by their later work. Most notably, Jacob exhibited Scheveningen interiors, painted in the manner of his teachers Stroebel and Van Hove with little vistas in the style of Pieter de Hooch, as early as 1854 and 1856.[69] Jan Veth has pointed out that Maris may have been influenced here by Christoffel Bisschop (1828–1904), a painter he had known as a youth in Van Hove's studio where Bisschop was then a pupil. The contact between the two artists may well have been renewed in the 1860s, when Maris's friend Blommers was working in Bisschop's studio. After 1860 Bisschop specialized in Hindeloopen interiors, which in their

fig. 49 KAEMMERER *Women Doing Laundry in the Garden* 1864
(Location unknown)

emotional restraint reminded Joris-Karl Huysmans of the work of Vermeer, a comparison he drew in a review of the Salon.[70] Bisschop's technique, *fini en diable* (highly finished), excludes him from ever being included in the Hague School, but there seem to be traces of his distinctive clarity and simplicity, as well as his restrained elegance, in the work of Bernard Blommers and the Maris brothers. The influence of Bisschop can also be detected in the work of Albert Neuhuys, although this artist only began painting peasant interiors in the early 1870s.

Bernard Blommers and Adolphe Artz are considered as two of Israëls's best-known followers. Yet Blommers in particular initially owed more to his association with the Marises than to the influence of Israëls, who was still living in Amsterdam at that point. The two artists do not appear to have met each other until 1865; Blommers had, however, already visited Artz in Amsterdam with Willem Maris, thus forging the first direct link between the Hague artists who painted fishing people and the circle around Israëls.

Adolphe Artz had met Jozef Israëls during evening classes at the academy in Amsterdam; although Israëls was already famous he was not too proud to go to the classes occasionally to do a little more life drawing. The great spiritual ascendancy of the older artist made an unmistakable mark on Artz's work. Thus Willem Roelofs was hardly accurate when he stated in 1868 that Artz was 'entirely devoid of imitation of Israëls', although one would never confuse Artz's dryer, more academic style of painting with that of Israëls.[71] Artz's paintings are also quieter in expression, which explains Huysmans's recommendation of his work in one of his Salon reviews as a sober alternative for anyone who found Israëls's art too sentimental.[72]

Artz lived in Paris from 1866 to 1874; he caused quite a stir on his arrival by unpacking a sizeable collection of Scheveningen peasant costumes. Artz, like Gerard Bilders, was a protégé of Johannes Kneppelhout, from whose work he borrowed several subjects for paintings.[73] Both Kneppelhout and Israëls had provided him with numerous letters of recommendation, to Thoré-Bürger among others; the famous critic advised him to consult Gustave Courbet, but the latter's counsel was confined to the words, '*Louez un atelier, prenez un modèle et fermez votre porte.*'[74]

Kneppelhout consigned his pupil Jan de Graan to Artz's care from 1869–70 and 1871–72. Artz painted several portraits of this violin-playing infant prodigy, who was hailed by contemporaries as a new Mendelssohn; the mood of the portraits is strongly reminiscent of the work of Henri Fantin-Latour.[75] Artz's closest friends included the painter Kaemmerer, who had been living in Jacob Maris's house before Artz moved in there, Alexander Mollinger and, from 1870, Philip Zilcken (1857–1930).[76] At this period he was also very close to Matthijs Maris, who loved talking to him; their friendship is commemorated by one of Matthijs's most successful portraits (fig. 132).[77]

Jacob Maris in Paris

With the astonishing *Ferryboat . . .* he established himself as a pure painter of Dutch ancestry; powerful and delicate, distinguished and intimate, his work inaccessible to the multitude, expansive to anyone who understands and loves it; a master around whom the young respectfully flocked, he was from the beginning to the end the great master of the Hague School, the absolute leader.[78]

It was in these terms, the words almost tumbling over each other, although their meaning is quite clear, that Marius described her teacher Jacob Maris and the place she felt should be reserved for him in the pantheon of Dutch masters. She seems to have believed that Maris emerged almost overnight in the 1870s as a fully developed artist – rather like Athene springing fully armed from the forehead of Zeus – and claimed his rightful position as *chef d'école*. But in fact his period in Paris, which preceded these years of eminence and followed so illogically up his time in Oosterbeek, saw his career take a most unpredicted course. That a painter who had once made a faithful study of nature should then have persisted for years in

fig. 50 J. MARIS *Outside a Café*
(National Gallery of Scotland, Edinburgh)

painting *Italiennes* (Italian girls) was something that many of his fellow-artists and biographers found hard to stomach. Jozef Israëls, who met Maris once in Paris during a visit to his friend Artz, could not believe his eyes when he later recognized 'the man of the Italian dollies' as the bold landscape painter.

Italiennes were a favourite genre in the nineteenth century. It was not only French and German painters (the Nazarenes in particular) who immortalized the beauty of the Italian peasant girls in their picturesque costumes; in the Netherlands too they were introduced early in the century by Cornelis Kruseman (1797–1857). He was speedily followed by J.H. Koelman (1820–87) and C.F. Philippeau (1823–97), who made them their speciality. *Italiennes* and their male counterparts, *Savoyards*, posed at the drawing evenings of Pulchri Studio, and Jacob and Matthijs Maris sketched them there before they went to Paris. The subject was not automatically doomed to degenerate into a pretty picture, as is shown by a robust rendering of an Italian girl painted by Edouard Manet.

It is by no means inconceivable that Jacob Maris might have continued to develop in this completely different direction, as happened in the case of his friend F.H. Kaemmerer (1839–1902).[79] Kaemmerer, a member of the group to which Blommers, Mauve, Sierich, the Marises and others belonged, initially worked as a landscape painter, also at Oosterbeek. The *Woodcutters* he exhibited in 1863 brings Mauve's contemporary description of such a motif to mind: 'There I encountered a timber wagon with four horses yoked to it engaged in carrying its great logs away. I followed the party and came in the end to see a whole painting.'[80] If elsewhere Mauve linked Kaemmerer's name with that of Jacob Maris, the

fig. 51 Van Ruysdael *Ferryboat with Cattle* 1649 (Dienst Verspreide Rijkskollekties, The Hague)

fig. 52 J. Maris *The Ferry* 1871
(Private collection)

Kunstkronijk detected the influence of Matthijs in his work, and paintings like *Washday* and *Women doing Laundry in the Garden* (fig. 49), both known only from reproductions, bear out the latter assessment.

In February 1865 Kaemmerer went to Paris where he concluded a contract with the art dealer Goupil and began to study under Gérôme, another of Goupil's artists and a celebrated master, who in Emile Zola's sarcastic judgement supplied 'something for everyone'. Kaemmerer's work quickly underwent a radical metamorphosis, inspired by the example of Mariano Fortuny (1838–74) who was the most versatile artist in Goupil's stable, nicknamed the 'acrobat' by his contemporaries. He turned to frivolous genre pieces, set in the days of powder and patches, which Goupil also marketed in large numbers as photographs, and from that time forth he remained tied to Paris by a successful career. His work was to be seen in the Netherlands only in the form of airy illustrations for *Elsevier's Geïllustreerd Maandschrift*.[81] His *Beach at Scheveningen* in the Haags Gemeentemuseum can be seen as an unsentimental adieu to his Hague period (fig. 48).

It was undoubtedly on the instigation of Kaemmerer, who would have given him an introduction to Goupil's, that Jacob Maris settled in Paris in the spring of 1865, choosing Ernest Hébert as his teacher. He left the latter's *atelier d'élèves* after only six months, but continued to paint *Italiennes* because that was what Goupil expected of him. He was, however, open to the most diverse influences during those years. A *Woman Nursing a Baby* (National Gallery, London) is reminiscent of Fantin-Latour,[82] while two remarkable paintings, a shepherdess struggling along in a squall and a beggarmaid with a staff, possess a monumentality borrowed from Millet. We even find him experimenting with the orientalist style in vogue at that time (fig. 50).[83]

Jacob turned to landscape painting again towards the end of the 1860s during the painting excursions he made in the immediate vicinity of Paris. He was obviously in a perfect position to gain a thorough knowledge of the modern French artists, although he seems to have done so primarily through

48 J. MARIS *View of Montigny-sur-Loing*

52 J. MARIS *Dutch Canal, Rijswijk*

65

54 J. MARIS *View of Old Dordrecht*

56 J. MARIS *Fishing Boat*

57 J. MARIS *Allotments near The Hague*

59 J. Maris *Girl Asleep on a Sofa*

71 M. Maris *Townscape*

72 M. MARIS *Woman with Child and Kid (The Introduction)*

77 M. MARIS *The Butterflies*

76 M. MARIS *The Christening*

79 W. MARIS *Cows beside a Pool*

84 W. MARIS *Summer*

fig. 53 DAUBIGNY *Sunset* (National Gallery of Scotland, Edinburgh)

fig. 54 J. MARIS *Watermill at Bougival* (National Gallery of Scotland, Edinburgh)

fig. 55 J. MARIS *The Arrival of the Boats* 1884
(Rijksmuseum, Amsterdam)

to name a host of Dutch artists who painted the subject, from an early Dordrecht master like Leendert de Koningh (1777–1849) up to and including Paul Gabriël (with his *Driel-Ferry*). Nor is it correct that Maris took up the subject for the first time in Paris;[86] in the collection of H. van Leeuwen there is a small panel dated 1864, on which a ferry is depicted, though small in relation to the composition as a whole.[87]

If Veyrassat's contribution to Maris's slow evolution as a landscape painter is thus somewhat unclear – Knoef also ascribes to him the origin of the towpath motif that later became so important in Maris's work – the importance of Charles Daubigny's role can, on the other hand, be regarded as firmly established. It was again Knoef who saw in Daubigny's *Sunset* (fig. 53) a convincing parallel to Maris's much-admired *View of Montigny-sur-Loing* (Cat. 48). In the small sketch *Watermill at Bougival* (fig. 54) it can be seen clearly how Maris's style had been transformed by that of the French master; he was never again to lose hold of that broad touch and elaborate pictorial structure. Jacob Maris's development as a landscape painter now began to quicken. In 1869 he delivered five landscapes to Goupil and these were followed in 1870–71 by the series of ferries.[88] Yet at the same time he can still surprise us with a portrait of his wife in a Watteau costume and, in 1871, with a *Moorish Lady*.[89]

Some people have deplored the loss of Maris as a figure painter in his development as a landscape painter, but although figure painting certainly did recede into the background in his *oeuvre*, he never made a complete break with it. He painted a few more figure studies derived from the life of fishing people (fig. 55) immediately after his return to The Hague, as well as watercolours of his children. In the *Nederlandse Spectator* of 17 August 1878 the critic Van Santen Kolff reported how Maris's watercolour *Towards Evening*, which depicted a witch-like fishwife in the dunes was 'for most painters ... *the* drawing' in the exhibition of the Hollandsche Teeken-Maatschappij (Dutch Drawing Society), 'roughly comparable with the Gospel of St John for the orthodox admirer of the Bible' in terms of importance.

Finally, one must conclude by noting, somewhat ironically given Marius's view that Jacob Maris was the 'great master' and 'absolute leader' of an ostensibly realist school, that in a sense he moved back towards the work of his exceptional brother Matthijs, for his townscapes increasingly became the products of his imagination. Miss Marius made this plain in 1891 with reference to one such work in the Rijksmuseum: 'Jacob Maris did not paint this townscape from reality. He stopped doing that years ago.'[90]

their work and not through personal contacts. The influence of Corot, a preference that Maris was to pass on to his pupils Théophile de Bock (1851–1904) and Philip Zilcken (1857–1930), is unmistakable in his early work of this period.[84]

In an article on the French influences on Jacob Maris's work, Knoef suggested that it was the painter Jules-Jacques Veyrassat (1828–93) who inspired Maris to paint his series of ferries, which were interpreted by Marius and others as the revival of a peculiarly Dutch theme in the tradition of Jan van Goyen and Salomon van Ruysdael (figs. 51, 52).[85] Although Knoef weighed his arguments carefully, some additional observations should be made here. For example, his supposition that the ferry theme scarcely appeared in the Netherlands in the early nineteenth century and that Maris's inspiration was thus probably of French origin has proved incorrect; it is possible

NOTES

1. *Kunstkronijk* XVII (1856), p. 16.
2. W. Burger, 'Exposition à la Haye', *Gazette des Beaux-Arts* III (1859), pp. 104–05.
3. P. Mantz, 'Les Beaux-Arts à l'Exposition Universelle', *Gazette des Beaux-Arts* XXIII (1867), p. 21.
4. *Kunstkronijk* N.S. VIII (1867), p.59.
5. *Land van Rembrandt* was the title of a book by C. Busken Huet, published in 1882–84.
6. See. exh. cat. *Het Vaderlandsch Gevoel*, Rijksmuseum, Amsterdam 1978, which deals with Dutch history painting in the nineteenth century.
7. Address on 'The Nature and Practice of the Poetry of the Art of Painting' delivered on 30 May 1781 in Cornelis Ploos van Amstel, *Redenvoeringen gedaan in de Teken-Academie te Amsterdam*, Amsterdam 1785, pp. 249–50.
8. Cited in exh. cat. *J.A. Knip 1777–1847*, Noordbrabants Museum, Bois-le-duc 1977, p. 36.

9. E. Chesneau, *Les nations rivales dans l'art*, Paris 1868.
10. J. Knoef notes that the sale of Van Troostwijk's estate, which did not take place until 1875, passed virtually unnoticed. See further J. Knoef, 'W.J. van Troostwijk' in *Tusschen rococo en romantiek*, The Hague 1943, pp. 111–34. For Nuyen see exh. cat. *Wijnand Nuyen Romantische werken*, Haags Gemeente-museum, The Hague 1977.
11. On the occasion of Weissenbruch's 75th birthday Jozef Israëls wrote in the *Nederlandse Spectator* of 24 June 1899: 'He showed us everything, what he had made during the past forty years and what he had been working on just yesterday. In subject-matter and conception they did not differ much, but the difference in execution was unusually great. What had previously been meagre, slight and neat was now broad and firm.'
12. The exhibition devoted to Gerard Bilders in 1938 took place as part of a series on forgotten masters (Fodor Museum, Amsterdam).
13. Vincent van Gogh, *The Complete Letters of Vincent van Gogh*, New York

1958, vol. I, p. 444, letter 227. Théophile de Bock, who was elsewhere compared by Van Gogh with Bilders Sr, spoke in his book on Jacob Maris of 'the relative infertility of his [Bilders'] talent for painting' (p. 23). Johannes Bosboom, on the other hand, was laudatory. He wrote to J. Gram on 22 May 1891; 'But the *majority* are so close to the ground and Bilders flew so high above them' (cited in H.F.W. Jeltes, *Uit het Leven van een kunstenaarspaar. Brieven van Johannes Bosboom*, Amsterdam 1910).

14. Letter dated 10 July 1860 from Gerard Bilders to Johannes Kneppelhout.

15. *Kunstkronijk* III (1851), p. 65.

16. E. Leclercq, 'Exposition de Bruxelles', *Gazette des Beaux-Arts*, XV (1863), p. 390.

17. *Algemeen Handelsblad* (1860), cited in exh. cat. *Ary Scheffer, Sir Lawrence Alma-Tadema, Charles Rochussen of De Vergankelijkheid van de Roem*, Lijnbaancentrum, Rotterdam 1974, p. 28.

18. *Kunstkronijk* III (1851), p. 63.

19. Leclercq, *op. cit.*, p. 386.

20. J. Israëls, *Uit mijn dagboek*, 12 December 1903, cited in cat. Museum Mesdag 1975, p. 189.

21. Van Gogh, *op. cit.* (note 13), pp. 33, 34, 116, 125.

22. 'J.D. Koelman en de jeugd van Willem Maris' in J. Knoef, *Van romantiek tot realisme*, The Hague 1947, pp. 223–32.

23. Letter from Willem Roelofs to P. VerLoren van Themaat, 12 June 1864.

24. *Nederlandse Spectator* (1867), p. 321.

25. *Kunstkronijk* XII (1851), p. 69.

26. *Kunstkronijk* N.S. VI (1865), p. 80.

27. *Kunstkronijk* N.S. X (1869), p. 6.

28. H.F.W. Jeltes, *Willem Roelofs Bizonderheden betreffende zijn leven en werk*, Amsterdam 1911, pp. 29–30. 'But none of this in any way prevents Roelofs from continuing to keep his indisputable and imperishable fame in the history of our modern painting as the first to place himself directly in front of the rich landscape in the open air, on the model of the French.'

29. See R. de Leeuw, in exh. cat. *Johannes Tavenraat 1809–1881*, Cleves / Dordrecht / The Hague 1981, pp. 9–10.

30. See his letter of 9 January 1861 to C. Kramm (Rijksprentenkabinet, Amsterdam), published in *ibid.*, pp. 120–21. Gerard Bilders wrote in his diary on 6 March 1860. 'Oh, how sweet art is! What a glow of sweet dreams and golden hope one lives in! Honour, reputation, renown, they stand in the distance smiling upon you. But the art dealer? – Not enough detail'.

31. See *A.G. Bilders. Brieven en dagboek*, vol. 2, Leiden 1876, p. 50 (diary, 23 March 1860).

32. Letter from P.J.C Gabriël to W.B. Tholen dated 14 October 1879, published in *Oud Holland* XLIII (1926).

33. *Kunstkronijk* N.S. X (1869), p. 92. For Mesdag's Brussels period see S. de Bodt, 'Hendrik Willem Mesdag en Brussel', *Oud Holland* LXXXV (1981), pp. 59–84.

34. J. de Gruyter, *De Haagse School*, Rotterdam 1969, vol. 2, p. 12.

35. See note 34.

36. De Gruyter, *op. cit.*, vol 1, p. 79.

37. 'More solidity in his landscapes', *Revue des Deux Mondes*, (1855), cited in A.G.C. van Duyl, 'J.H.L. de Haas', *Elsevier's Geïllustreerd Maandschrift*, II (1892), vol. IV, p. 24.

38. J.J. Guiffrey, 'Exposition des Beaux-Arts à Anvers', *Gazette des Beaux-Arts* XVIII (1864), p. 372.

39. P. Mantz, *art. cit.* in *Gazette des Beaux-Arts* XIII (1867).

40. J. Six, *Rijks-academie van Beeldende Kunsten te Amsterdam, Het legaat Johannes Hubertus Leonardus de Haas*, Amsterdam 1909 (with a foreword by A.J. Derkinderen). De Haas's oil sketches are now in the possession of the State-owned Art Collections Department, The Hague.

41. This emerged in 1894 when Israëls wanted to borrow a portrait in De Haas' possession for an exhibition. He asked P. Haverkorn van Rijsewijk to leave out the usual personal greetings from him when requesting the loan, as he was 'not too keen' on including them in De Haas' case (letter dated 12 August 1894 in Rijksprentenkabinet, Amsterdam).

42. E.P. Engel, *Anton Mauve*, Utrecht 1907, p. 29.

43. V. Hefting (*Schilders in Oosterbeek 1840–70*, Zutphen 1981, p. 32) mentions a brief visit to Oosterbeek in 1856, but gives no evidence for this statement. Most authors give 1858 as the year of Mauve's first visit to Oosterbeek.

44. Letter of 1863 (October?) from A. Mauve to W. Maris, Netherlands Institute for Art History, The Hague.

45. *Ibid.*

46. Letter of Willem Maris of 1901, cited in exh. cat. *De Haagse School, aquarellen en tekeningen uit de collectie van het Haags Gemeentemuseum*, The Hague 1979, p. 34.

47. See A. Wagner, in exh. cat. *Matthijs Maris*, Haags Gemeentemuseum, The Hague 1974, p. 13.

48. Mauve had already been in Oosterbeek for several months at the time. He wrote to Willem, having asked first about Matthijs, 'Kaemmerer and your brother made a lot of studies here again, despite the rainy weather, don't you agree?' Somewhat earlier, on 16 September 1864, Bilders had likewise written to Kneppelhout about the bad weather, mentioning that in addition to Hanedoes and Mauve he had also met 'a Maris'. Thus he must have meant

Jacob and not Willem, as Engel mistakenly thought (*op. cit.* p. 26). S.H. Levie has already referred to Jacob Maris's stay in Oosterbeek in 1864 on an earlier occasion in an article for *Openbaar Kunstbezit*. This also gives us a plausible date for Jacob's oil sketch of *Kaemmerer at Work* (Haags Gemeentemuseum, The Hague).

49. The comparison between Matthijs Maris and Alma Tadema dominates the whole of Lodewijk van Deyssel's article 'Matthijs Maris' of 1895. He visited both artists in London in 1894, but declared he would give all the Alma Tademas in exchange for 'that single painting of the Butterflies by Thijs Maris'.

50. Blommers related in 1906 how at the sale of Théophile de Bock's estate the year before he had found a study by him of the Oosterbeek heath, which was being offered as a Matthijs Maris. The study in question was probably no. 81 (18 × 29 cm) at the De Bock Sale, Amsterdam (F. Muller & Co.), 7–10 March 1905. See Theo de Veer, 'B.J. Blommers', *Elsevier's Geïllustreerd Maandschrift* XVI (1906), vol. XXXIII, pp. 146–63.

51. *Algemeen Handelsblad*, 15 October 1863. 'A few months ago he seemed to be going on his way, but now he is evidently seeing things entirely through the spectacles of the painter Maris. Dangerous! How easy it is to lose one's sight in that way. Mauve used to see nature as warm and strong in colour, but now everything that meets his eye appears to be shrouded in crêpe.'

52. Anna Wagner, *op. cit.*, p. 14. Wagner writes that Matthijs certainly made 'some sketches' in Oosterbeek and that the area 'did at all events provide him with inspiration for a number of works', but the way she puts this reveals her doubts as to the importance of the stay for the course he ultimately took.

53. Letter from M. Maris to A. Plasschaert dated 9 March 1909, published in cat. Museum Mesdag 1975, p. 194.

54. *Kunstkronijk* N.S. VI (1865), p. 78.

55. *Algemeen Handelsblad* (1865) cited in P. Haverkorn van Rijsewijk, 'Matthijs Maris te Wolfheze en Lausanne', *Onze Kunst* XXII (1912), vol. 4, p. 134.

56. Letter dated 7 April 1866 from Roelofs to P. VerLoren van Themaat.

57. *Kunstkronijk* N.S. X (1869), p. 92.

58. J.F. Heijbroek, 'Matthijs Maris in Paris 1869–1877', *Oud Holland* LXXXIX (1975), pp. 266–89. This also gives further information on the Marises' time in Paris.

59. D. Dekkers in an unpublished degree essay on the early years of Jozef Israëls (Utrecht University); H. Kraan in the chapter 'The Vogue for Holland' in this catalogue. Work by Jordan was to be seen in exhibitions in the Netherlands and in 1849 a painting by him was reproduced in the *Kunstkronijk* (facing p. 50).

60. Letter dated 8 June 1886 from Roelofs to Jhr. F.A.E.L. Smissaert, published in Jeltes, *op. cit.*, p. 153.

61. J. Israëls, *art. cit.*, is cited in cat. Museum Mesdag 1975.

62. See J. Knoef, 'Een voorloper van Jozef Israëls, P.M. Molijn' in Knoef, *op. cit.*, pp. 115–34.

63. See De Leeuw, *art. cit.* in exh. cat. *Johannes Tavenraat 1809–1881*, Cleves/Dordrecht / The Hague 1981, pp. 22–26, 111.

64. Knoef, *op. cit.*, p. 134.

65. *Ibid.*, pp. 124 and 131. Molijn exhibited his *Frugal Midday-meal* at the *Tentoonstelling van de Levende Meesters* (Exhibition of Living Masters) in The Hague in 1843.

66. Guiffrey, *op. cit.*, p. 373.

67. *Kunstkronijk* I (1840), II (1841).

68. A lithograph by E. Verveer in the *Hollandsch Schilder- en Letterkundig Album* of 1849, showing a girl seated in a landscape with a child reaching out towards a butterfly, is strikingly similar to work of the 1860s by Matthijs Maris, both in subject-matter and overall conception. Cf. H.E.M. Braakhuis & J. van der Vliet, 'Patterns in the life and work of Matthijs Maris', *Simiolus* X (1978–79), pp. 159–70. See also Cat. 77.

69. G.P. Weisberg, *The Realist Tradition, French Painting and Drawing 1830–1900*, Bloomington 1980, pp. 6–8.

70 'Le Salon Officiel en 1880' in J.K. Huysmans, *L'Art Moderne/Certains* (Série Fin de Siècle), Paris 1976, p. 159. Thoré-Bürger had confined himself to a comparison with Pieter de Hoogh in 1867.

71. Letter dated 15 April 1868 from Roelofs to P. VerLoren van Themaat.

72. Huysmans, *op. cit.*, p. 158.

73. e.g. *Mad Truken*, which he exhibited at the *Tentoonstelling van de Levende Meesters* (Exhibition of Living Masters) in The Hague and the Exposition Générale des Beaux-Arts in Brussels, both in 1866.

74. 'Rent a studio, take a model and shut your door!'. R. Heath states in 'Adolphe Artz', *The Magazine of Art* [1896–97], p. 81 that it was Israëls who gave Artz a letter for Courbet.

75. Kneppelhout became interested in De Graan's fortunes at the end of 1864 and after the latter's death wrote a memoir of him. This was published in 1875, a year before a similar work on Gerard Bilders. See J. Kneppelhout, *Een beroemde knaap* (edited by M. Stapert-Eggen), The Hague 1981. Artz painted several versions of the portrait of De Graan, one of which was turned down by Kneppelhout for personal reasons. At the sale of Artz's estate in 1891 a sketch for this portrait was acquired for D.F. Scheurleer's music collection (sale Pulchri Studio, The Hague, 27–28 Jan. 1891, no. 45). Another version now hangs in the Concertgebouw, Amsterdam. The influence of Fantin-Latour at

this period can be explained by the fact that Artz's friend Otto Scholderer (1834–1902), the German painter and another of Kneppelhout's protégés, belonged to Fantin-Latour's circle of friends. He is portrayed in the latter's well-known painting *A Studio in the Quartier des Batignolles*.

Unfortunately, of the extensive correspondence that must have been conducted by Artz and Kneppelhout on De Graan's stay in Paris, only Kneppelhout's letters have survived (there are 95 letters in the Dutch Literature Museum, The Hague), so that a great deal of information about the Marises' Paris contacts has probably been lost. De Bock says in his book on Jacob Maris that the latter eschewed any direct contacts with the artistic world there and quotes his statement, 'They [the French artists] give us the best of what they have in their work. It is in that that they make themselves known at their finest' (De Bock, *op. cit.*, p. 42).

76. Evidence of these friendships is provided by the presence of five works by Kaemmerer and four by Mollinger, among other things, in the sale of Artz's estate (see note 75). Zilcken wrote the introduction to the catalogue for the sale.

77. The artist later wrote in a note on a photograph of this portrait in the Netherlands Institute for Art History: 'Poor Artz, I didn't in the least want to make it. He wanted it for his intended. He hated sitting for it and couldn't stand the light in his eyes and I hated doing it.' However, P. A. Haaxman Jr. assures us in 'David Adolphe Constant Artz', *Elsevier's Geïllustreerd Maandschrift* VIII [1898], vol. XV, p. 308 that Artz himself held 'this portrait in high esteem'. On the occasion of Artz's second marriage in 1880 Matthijs Maris gave him his *Fairy Tale* (Rijksmuseum, Amsterdam).

78. G.H. Marius, *De Hollandsche Schilderkunst in de negentiende eeuw*, 1920[2], p. 134.

79. See the article on Kaemmerer in Knoef, *op. cit.*, pp. 247–60.

80. Letter of 1863 (October?) from A. Mauve to W. Maris, Netherlands Institute for Art History, The Hague.

81. See Knoef, *op. cit.*, p. 252.

82. Marius, *op. cit.*, p. 142. Marius found the painting in Jacob Maris's estate and likewise thought it 'painted with something of the French manner in a grey-brown tone'. See also note 75.

83. We know of a study of an Arab by Maris from as early as 1864, before his Paris period (drawing no. 128 at the Maris exhibition, Arti et Amicitiae, Amsterdam 1899). Orientalism never made such an impact in the Netherlands as in the rest of Europe. C.J. Fodor (1801–60), whose collection included some prime pieces by Decamps among other things, was the leading Dutch collector of this genre. In a letter of 5 May 1863 to Kneppelhout Gerard Bilders gives an enthusiastic description of an Algerian landscape by Marilhat in the Fodor Museum. The most important orientalist painter in the Netherlands at this time was Willem de Famars Testas (1834–96). Among the Hague artists who specialized in oriental subjects Philippe Zilcken, H.J. Haverman and, in particular, Marius Bauer deserve special mention. Bauer's etchings were much admired by Jozef Israëls, who also painted oriental subjects himself from time to time. In 1844 he exhibited a *Turk in Repose*, while a watercolour of a *Musician Seated on a Wall in front of an Oriental City*, done during his visit to Spain and North Africa in 1894, is surprisingly close to Bauer's work stylistically. For an illustration of the watercolour see sale Amsterdam (De Zon), 19 November 1978, no. 4031.

84. At the end of 1980 there appeared on the art market in New York a landscape by Zilcken, which appeared to fall into two separate halves, one painted by Maris and the other by Corot.

85. J. Knoef, 'Fransche invloeden op Jacob Maris'. *Oud Holland* LXI (1946), pp. 204–12.

86. Knoef *op. cit.*. Knoef suggested that Jacob Maris, in contrast to Matthijs, was not in the habit of painting from memory, a point of view which seems untenable. Moreover, thanks to the assistance of W. Rappard and M. op de Coul of the Netherlands Institute for Art History, it has proved possible to trace a great many versions of the ferry motif, all of which were painted before Maris's Paris period. These include countless examples by artists with whom he had associated. In addition to the names cited in this essay and Apol, Gerard Bilders and Stortenbeker, who are mentioned by Knoef, we know of ferryboats by a follower of Abels, Hendriks, Hilverdink, Van Hove (1842), De Koningh, Kimmel, Nuyen (1838), Pelgrom, Rochussen (1841), Schelfhout, Verveer (1850), J.A. Vrolijk (1867), J.M. Vrolijk (1863) and Jan Weissenbruch (1846). P. Haverkorn van Rijsewijk (*op. cit.*) mentions a sketchbook with studies of Scheveningen and Gelderland landscapes, which he attributes to Matthijs Maris and which certainly date from the early 1860s. In it there are two sketches of ferries, the authorship of which was expressly denied by Matthijs in a letter of 21 September 1912 to W.J.G. van Meurs, in which he says they are 'by Jaap'.

87. According to Knoef's own criteria, this must point to a Dutch inspiration for the motif. The painting is still notably romantic in character, although much sketchier in its handling.

88. The five landscapes were *On the Seine*, *Beach*, *Landscape with Boat* (all in upright format) and *Beach at Sunset*, *Fishing Boat on Beach* and *Morning*.

89. This work was sold in New York on 3 February 1915 (illustration at the Netherlands Institute for Art History).

90. G.H. Marius, 'Jacob Maris', *Elsevier's Geïllustreerd Maandschrift* I (1891), vol. II, pp. 1–13. Maris's conception of the construction of a landscape probably owed a lot to his association with Sam Verveer in his first period in The Hague. Matthijs Maris quotes a remark of Verveer's that is interesting in this connection: 'I remember how old Verveer would always get angry when they asked him . . . "Where is that?" "Well, damn it, if you're a painter, then you make a town yourself!"' (letter dated 27 February 1892 from Matthijs Maris to Ph. Zilcken, Rijksprentenkabinet, Amsterdam).

The Heyday of the Hague School (1870-1885)

JOHN SILLEVIS

It is sometimes difficult to find a satisfactory explanation for certain historical phenomena. The formation of the Hague School is one such phenomenon: why should a number of artists have settled in The Hague around the year 1870, in such a way that it has become possible to speak of a Hague School? Why did they settle in The Hague in particular and why at that precise period? In fact, the question does not apply to all the artists whom we now number among the Hague School. Paul Gabriël and Willem Roelofs lived in Brussels and, although they spent some months in the Netherlands every year and took part in exhibitions there, they continued to live in Belgium until well into the 1880s. Others, such as Bosboom, Jan Hendrik Weissenbruch and Willem Maris, never left The Hague, at least not for any length of time. The group of artists with whom we are principally concerned are those who flocked to The Hague at the beginning of the 1870s: Hendrik Mesdag, Anton Mauve, Jozef Israëls and Jacob Maris, who were to form the nucleus of the Hague School.

There are certain parallels between the formation of the Hague School and the coming together of the Macchiaioli around 1855, when artists from all over Italy went to Florence, giving rise to an artistic movement with an unmistakable common denominator. The art historian Corrado Maltese has called this 'Il momento unitario'[1] and it could be said that the Netherlands experienced a comparable moment of unity when the Hague School artists began to establish themselves in that city at the beginning of the 1870s. It would be simplistic to try and ascribe this development to chance alone. On the other hand, personal, non-artistic considerations also played a part in the artists' individual decisions to settle in The Hague.

Hendrik Willem Mesdag had decided in 1869 that he wanted to become a marine painter – a decision that he had reached while he was living in Brussels. He could easily have gone to work at the Belgian coast every now and then, like the Belgian marine painters Verwee and Artan who continued to live in Brussels. But not Mesdag.

In the same year he moved to The Hague, choosing to live at the nearest possible point to the road to Scheveningen. He later gave the following explanation for his decision to move.

I had sat at home [in Brussels] all winter fidgeting with a piece of work; it was a coastal scene, but so naively painted. Then I said: you must see the sea in front of you, every day, you must live with it,

otherwise you'll get nowhere. And then we went to The Hague.[2]

Jacob Maris had been living in Paris, where he had a lucrative agreement with Goupil the art dealer for making *Italiennes* (genre pieces with girls in Italian costume), since 1865. His decision to move back to The Hague may have been influenced by concern for his family during the serious food shortages in Paris during the Franco-Prussian War and the fighting on the barricades during the Paris Commune. There is said to have been heavy fighting in Rue Marcadet where he was living at that time. It is also possible that Maris felt he had reached a turning-point in his artistic development. His *Shepherd Boys by a River*, for instance, which he painted in 1868, was much closer to landscape painting than his usual work; it was rejected by Goupil, but immediately snapped up at the Salon exhibition by Wallis, an English dealer. In The Hague, where Maris was intending originally to stay for only a short while according to his brother Matthijs, he found new motifs literally just outside his front door. His well-known painting *The Truncated Windmill* (Cat. 51) shows the white bridge on North West Buitensingel, where he and his family had taken up residence in 1871.[3]

No firm reason has been discovered for Jozef Israëls's move to The Hague in 1871. It can be argued that he felt attracted by the flourishing artistic life of the city, or that Mesdag, his childhood friend from Groningen, persuaded him to go there, or, yet again, that he was drawn by the beauty of The Hague and its environs in the days before its great expansion and growing industrialization. But all these theories remain merely hypotheses and none are completely satisfactory explanations. During the course of the 1860s Jozef Israëls had become a widely appreciated artist and had already scored his first international successes, both in England and in France. Amsterdam, too, had its flourishing artists' societies, such as Felix Meritis and Arti et Amicitiae; the latter in particular regularly organized exhibitions and other artistic events.

Anton Mauve, with his nervy, depressive disposition, often moved from place to place. He was a great friend of Willem Maris, with whom he had painted *en plein air* in Oosterbeek years before, and his decision to go and live in The Hague in the spring of 1871, at more or less the same time as Jozef Israëls, may be explained simply by his friendship with Maris, although, if this was the reason, one wonders why he did not

fig. 56 J. MARIS *Dutch Landscape (View of the Mill and Bridge on the Noord-West Buitensingel, The Hague)* 1873 (Private collection, New Jersey)

decide to move any earlier. Mauve married in 1874 and this brought a certain peace and regularity into his life, while the growing appreciation of his work to some extent counterbalanced his uncertainty about the scope of his artistic powers.

To these explanations of the development of the Hague School, based on biographical detail, conjecture, the social and political milieu and contemporary descriptions of The Hague, must be added the role of the Hague artists' society Pulchri Studio, which was a significant binding force. It is striking that all the artists mentioned above became members of Pulchri Studio immediately after their arrival in The Hague, Mesdag in 1869 and Mauve, Israëls and Maris in 1871. Jacob Maris had already become a member some time earlier, but he had probably let his membership lapse during his years in Paris. Bosboom, Roelofs and Jan Hendrik Weissenbruch had been founder members in 1847, Bilders had been proposed as an active member in 1857 when he was a pupil of Simon van den Berg and Willem Maris had become a member in 1860; only Gabriël joined as late as 1884.

The foundation meeting of Pulchri Studio had taken place on 13 January 1847 at the house of the painter Lambertus Hardenberg in the presence of Jan and Jan Hendrik Weissenbruch, Willem Roelofs, Jan Frederik and Willem Anthonie van Deventer, Jacob van der Maaten and Hendrik Michaël, with the aim of setting up an artists' society where members could make drawings after clothed models and discussions on art could be organized. The first general meeting was held ten days later in the Korenhuis on Prinsegracht; the first committee consisted of Bart van Hove (chairman), Michaël (secretary) and Johannes Bosboom (treasurer). Huib van Hove and Reinier Craeyvanger were responsible for the drawing evenings, Hardenberg and Jan Weissenbruch for the discussions. Then, as now, the society comprised both artists and art-lovers (the latter are now classed as society members).

Numerous Hague School artists were to hold one or more positions on the committee of Pulchri Studio over the years.[4]

The name Pulchri Studio was suggested by the classicist Dr Benyen, who appended the translation 'In the pursuit of the beautiful'. A Latin motto was evidently an indispensable attribute; a society of shorter duration with roughly the same founder members as the later Pulchri Studio had existed under the name Assiduitas, while in Amsterdam there was Arti et Amicitiae and in Leiden Ars Aemula Naturae, known respectively as 'Arti' and 'Ars'. In the same way, Pulchri Studio came to be known familiarly as 'Pulchri'.

At the end of 1847, the year of its foundation, the society, which was growing rapidly in membership, established itself in the large hall of the Boterhuis on Grote Markt, the room in which the Confrèrie Pictura had met in the seventeenth century (see p. 37). In 1861 Pulchri Studio moved to the Hofje van Nieuwkoop (fig. 58) also on Prinsegracht but a little further from the centre, and in 1886 it acquired 57 Prinsegracht, where there were also facilities for holding exhibitions of the work of such artists as Daubigny, Millet, Mancini, Walter Crane and, of course, the society's own members. Finally, in 1901, the society used the proceeds of a public sale of works by members, plus a substantial contribution from the then chairman, Mesdag, to buy its present premises on Lange Voorhout in the historic heart of The Hague.

Some of the most important Pulchri meetings were the discussion sessions, which were devoted to getting to know each other's work and ideas. From 1847 onwards they took place every month – this was later reduced to five times a year – and became the subject of increasing interest.[5] At first the meetings took the form of what were known as seated discussions, in which the members sat at a horseshoe-shaped table and showed each other their drawings, giving a commentary on them. In later years, when the interest in these meetings had grown, the committee decided to change them into viewing sessions with the members walking about. From 1877 onwards these took place in the foyer of the Arts and Sciences Building on Zwarte Weg and with this move the meetings underwent a change in character from a general discussion in the atmosphere of a meeting to a social event combined with an exhibition. It is important to note that Pulchri Studio did not hold regular exhibitions until the period after the move to 57 Prinsegracht and that only in the building on Lange Voorhout did it have really spacious exhibition rooms at its disposal (fig. 59).

The discussion sessions were also attended by the Court, in particular by Queen Sophie, the wife of William III, who was a regular visitor. In later years Queen Wilhelmina, who herself painted, was also to become a member of Pulchri Studio. This interest on the part of the Court stimulated the art-lovers – as opposed to active members – not only to attend meetings regularly but also to buy works in emulation of the royal example. Thus, in this sense, these gatherings represented a potential source of income, both for the artists and for the society, which according to the regulations had a right to five per cent of the sale price.

Apart from the opportunities for study and discussions, Pulchri Studio offered an avowedly social side. The artists' parties were renowned and a great deal of time and trouble was expended on the *tableaux vivants* that formed part of them (see page 90). The artist members were expected to contribute a great deal in this respect, but it is clear from their reports and reminiscences that they did not in the least mind doing so. Vosmaer's comment on Jacob Maris is illustrative in this respect: 'He did not concern himself, so to speak, with the outside world, his home and his art being everything to him. Only if he could do something for a fellow artist or to further Pulchri's interests, did he willingly offer his time and assistance'.[6] Jozef Israëls and Hendrik Mesdag (fig. 60), who lived far less isolated lives, contributed an enormous amount to the prosperity of the society during their time as chairmen. This period of prosperity was indissolubly linked with the heyday of the Hague School, even though Pulchri's members did not all work in the manner of the School.

The critics

The artists' feelings of unity and solidarity were further strengthened by participation in exhibitions abroad. Painters like Roelofs, Israëls and Jacob Maris had already taken part in exhibitions in Brussels, London and Paris in the 1850s and 1860s. They had certainly not gone unnoticed, but it was only after 1870 that art critics abroad began to comment on a certain cohesion in the Dutch entries, usually those by the artists from The Hague. Up to that point contemporary Dutch art had found little favour, particularly with French critics. This state of affairs was in itself understandable enough since the critics, especially the more conservative ones, had invariably focused on history painting as the highest genre in art and even the Dutch had to admit that they certainly did not excel in that field. But gradually, as a result of the Barbizon School's success in France after 1855 and the growing appreciation of Corot's and Courbet's work, the critics too began to change their criteria and landscape painting received much more attention in exhibition reviews. This brought with it a new appreciation of the Hague School painters from a quarter from which they themselves had perhaps not immediately expected it.

fig. 57 Members of Pulchri Studio, photographed on the occasion of the eightieth birthday of the artist Bart van Hove, the first chairman of the society
(Gemeentearchief, The Hague)

fig. 58 Bosboom *Hofje van Nieuwkoop*
Pulchri Studio's meeting place and home 1861–86
(Location unknown)

Mention must also be made of the increasing admiration for Dutch seventeenth-century painting in France. If one leafs through the early volumes of the *Gazette des Beaux-Arts*, one finds, time and again, articles about paintings, prints and the decorative arts of 'Holland's Golden Century'; readers were even urged to go and visit exhibitions of the Dutch Masters in Amsterdam. Some of the critics themselves made the journey to the Netherlands, where they were forcibly struck by the parallels between Dutch seventeenth and nineteenth-century art. One of the first to do so was the well-known French critic Thoré-Bürger, who had written two series of articles entitled *Musées de la Hollande* and *Études sur les peintres hollandais et flamands* as early as around 1860. He wrote in connection with the Tentoonstelling van Levende Meesters (Exhibition of Living Masters) in the Hague in 1859 that it was a bad time for painting: '*Nous sommes entre deux écoles, l'une qui finit, l'autre qui commencera peut-être*'.[7]

In connection with the Paris *Salon* of 1866, however he wrote,

Jozef Israëls, from Amsterdam: *Interior of the Orphanage at Katwijk, Holland*: three girls sewing in a room that is softly lit by the light

fig. 59 Pulchri Studio; the Exhibition Hall.
On the far wall are a number of paintings by Breitner.
(Gemeentearchief, The Hague)

fig. 60 PRINS *Hendrik Willem Mesdag and Jozef Israëls at an Exhibition*
Mesdag is standing in the centre foreground with Israëls on his right.

from a window. Again an allegory! Yes, those three, those orphan girls represent Simplicity, Chastity and Work, but they nonetheless wear grey gowns, caps and kerchiefs. Ah! How surprising it is to find the idea of human qualities conveyed successfully without recourse to the charlatanism of symbols. This painting by Israëls is certainly one of the freshest works at the Salon and it gives outstanding expression to the customs of everyday life with that naive touch that is characteristic of the Dutch masters of the seventeenth century like Pieter de Hooch, Jan Steen, Van Ostade, Terborgh.[8]

In his review of the Dutch pavilion at the Exposition Universelle of 1867 in Paris, Thoré-Bürger also wrote about the other Dutch painters as a group.

Even if they no longer have the great seventeenth-century tradition of civic painting, they have at least retained the feeling for family life and the love of nature. They restrict themselves almost entirely to scenes of everyday life, landscapes, animal paintings, seascapes, townscapes, rendering them all with great sincerity. Their entry, although small in size – only one hundred and seventy numbers – is highly meritorious. Israëls takes the lead among his compatriots and even, in my opinion, among his foreign rivals. If I were allowed to select a painting from the Dutch pavilion, I would choose his *Orphanage at Katwijk*, which already made a great impression at the Salon of 1866. . . . The poses and the facial expressions are so natural that one does not want to imagine them as being in any way different. The colour is precisely captured and very harmonious in its neutral half-tones. No fireworks, but the truth, pure and simple. The *Children of the Sea* has also already been seen at a previous exhibition. The *Rabbi David*, a portrait study in the style of Rembrandt, belongs to Mr J. de Clercq of Amsterdam. *The Last Breath* shows a deathbed scene in the interior of a Dutch farmhouse. A sentimental drama, but rendered in

a quiet manner, with that calm, resigned grief that is peculiar to people in the country. Israëls, whom the jury has honoured greatly by awarding him a third medal, has just been made a *chevalier* of the *Légion d'Honneur*. I recommend that he ties the medal firmly on to its ribbon and hangs up this trophy in his studio.[9]

It is not surprising that Israëls was grateful for such a good review. He even invited Thoré-Bürger to visit his studio the next time he came to Holland.[10] And the visit did take place, for in his review of the Salon of 1868 Thoré-Bürger wrote,

Israëls paints what he sees and he paints it very well. Recently, while still in Amsterdam, he showed us his sketches with studies after nature; they are sketchbooks that evince a background knowledge which is far more fruitful for an artist than old texts in dead languages.[11]

This last remark was meant as a hit at Alma Tadema, whose pretentious Roman fantasies were not at all to Thoré-Bürger's taste. He also wrote enthusiastically about the work of Willem Roelofs and Willem and Jacob Maris, but this was still only a foretaste of what was to come.

The critic René Ménard also had a keen eye for the new developments in Dutch landscape painting. In connection with the International Exhibition of 1873 in Vienna he wrote,

We have no hesitation in placing at the head of the Dutch painters Mr Israëls who, while he lacks nothing in the field of official recognition, is in high favour among all those who are concerned with art in France. Israëls draws with shadow and light and he sees in nature a succession of tints that flow into or emerge out of each other, without his ever discerning in them a sharply outlined form or a firmly established contour. Although he does not draw with precision, he does so with expressive power and suppleness and his figures, which always have a definite meaning, say precisely what they have to say. . . .
Landscape painting stands on the eve of a change. The Dutch painters have gradually and without much fuss returned to their original sources. They are now busy on their dunes and along their canals, observing minutely and relating what they have seen with a rare feeling for local atmosphere and a compelling detachment. Maris is a very fine colourist. The tones he finds on his palette are all his own and in no way derived from Rue Lafitte. . .Mesdag has already shown himself to be a landscape painter who deserves the very closest

fig. 61 MESDAG *Breakers in the North Sea* (Location unknown). In 1870 this work won a gold medal at the Paris Salon.

attention. Having had it constantly dinned into us for twenty years that landscape painters exist only in France, we have finally come to believe that we have a monopoly on them. We have had, and we still do have some admirable landscape painters, but we must not let ourselves be blinded by success and become like the fakirs in India who do nothing but contemplate their own navels. It would not be a bad idea at all to have a look at other countries every now and then to see what is happening there. Among that small group of painters that is growing up on the coast of Holland we find a certain sincerity that ought to set us thinking.[12]

In his review of the Salon of 1873 Paul Leroi reported in similar terms that Maris and Mesdag had begun to display a highly personal style of painting (see fig. 61).

They have made a resolute break, as Israëls had already done before them, with the dull and impotent Dutch School of 1830, which had such long-lasting and disastrous consequences in that free and virile country, the fatherland of Rembrandt and Frans Hals, of the Ruysdaels and of Hobbema, of Jan Steen and of the Ostades. They have stalwartly tried, like a number of their compatriots, to return to the tradition of that immortal group of masters of the seventeenth century, the most independent of all artists and the most painterly painters who have ever existed.[13]

The tide had turned. Leroi wrote of the Salon at Antwerp that three-quarters of what was on display would not that year have been accepted by the Salon des Refusés in Paris. In contrast, he picked out painters like Israëls, Mesdag and Max Liebermann as examples who were worthy of attention.

In 1878 the prominent critic Duranty wrote of the Dutch entry to the Exposition Universelle in Paris,

The Hague and Brussels are the two cities where Dutch painters are formed and one would not be mistaken in attributing this to Israëls. Thirty years ago there were no painters in Holland. Now it is once again a land of painters, where they are not as deft as they are in Belgium, but where there are certain persons who, by applying a few colours to a canvas without noticeable difficulty, succeed in expressing deep feelings, strong impressions and lively and subtle perceptions. . . . Not all Dutch art has reached that point, obviously, and it is not enough to have been born in Holland and to paint in order to possess all these virtues, but I am speaking here of a dozen or perhaps fifteen artists.

In Duranty's eyes, as in those of his colleagues, Israëls was the leading Dutch artist. He praised *The Pancake Maker* and *Alone in the World*, describing the latter in lyrical terms: '*Ce tableau est peint d'ombre et de douleur.*[14] Charles Blanc, another eminent critic, wrote of the same painting, 'Figure painters are rare in Holland. Mr van Haanen studies his figures in Venice, but a man with his heart in the right place, a moved and moving artist, Israëls, the painter of *Children of the Sea* (fig. 62), of *The Pancake Maker* and of *Alone in the World*, adds to the genius of the old Dutch School something that, among the old masters, is to be found only in the great spirit of Rembrandt';[15] and this although he had still been able to write in 1866 that Dutch subjects were best executed by French artists, because they could, after all, offer 'their unmistakable contribution of good taste and *esprit*'.[16] Even Joris-Karl Huysmans, who crushed artists more often than he praised them in his early reviews, had a good word to say for *The Return of the Fishing Boat* by Mesdag at the Salon of 1879,[17] although Israëls was too sentimental for his taste.

Finally, the Dutch art critics, who were on the whole slow to praise the work produced in their own country, followed suit with favourable reviews of the Hague painters. In 1875 the critic Jan van Santen Kolff wrote a long article in the periodical *De Banier*, in which he used the term Hague School for the first time, introducing the painters as an identifiable group in the context of the Triennial Exhibition at the Hague Academy. The article is somewhat diffuse, but it is nonetheless interesting for the criteria of judgement used by the author.

Our attention is captured immediately by the so-called 'realist' school, a newly discovered and most recent invention. I say 'so-called' because the use of terms such as 'romantic', 'classical' or 'realist', does

fig. 62 J. ISRAËLS *Children of the Sea* 1863 (Stedelijk Museum, Amsterdam)

not, when one looks at the matter properly, help in the slightest and appears in most cases merely to prove the truth of the well-known saying '*Denn eben wo Begriffe fehlen, Da stellt ein Wort zur rechten Zeit sich ein*' [For just when ideas fail, a word comes in to save the situation]. But if one understands by 'realist' solely *inspired by reality, recognizing only the truth*, without attaching any secondary ideas to the term, then our landscape movement – which I have in mind here – is definitely not a so-called school but a truly realist, indeed a healthily realist school – for there also exists unhealthy and false realism – and it follows from this that the term 'realist' cannot but be regarded by all artists, whoever they may be, as anything but an honorific title, a diploma for *those who are true artists*. For it is the endeavour of our day, and in the main a very wholesome one, that *truth* (reality) and *art* (that is, *poetry*) should no longer be regarded as opposite poles or antipodes, but more and more as being indivisibly bound up together, unified as one. But now to business. The school in question has its seat and headquarters, its commanders and general staff in The Hague, but it also has believers and diligent disciples here and there in other cities (among others, Jozef Neuhuys in Amsterdam). It is a singular quirk of fate that it should be in this city, which is in the musical field distinguished by a strong conservatism, . . .that it should be in this royal seat, which is likewise one of the bastions of theological orthodoxy, *that the new ultra-radical movement in painting has sprung up, so that we can speak with confidence of a Hague School*, just as one speaks of a Düsseldorf, Weimar or Munich School, of the School of Tervueren etc. On account of the warm sympathy which it so fully merits, I shall give its best products precedence here over some works by our most outstanding '*Altmeister*', which I shall save for later.

A not inconsiderable list of well-known names unrolls before our eyes here, not dissimilar in length to Leporello's famous catalogue. Mesdag, J. Maris, Louis Apol, Jozef Neuhuys, Jan Vrolijk, Théophile de Bock, Fred. Du Chattel, Boks, Ter Meulen – I am limiting myself in this nomenclature to our exhibition, here at The Hague, otherwise I would certainly have included the name of the excellent Mauve near the beginning, if not placed at the head of the list – these are the names of the pioneering masters or those who are, to a greater or lesser extent, promising disciples of this movement. . . . Can anyone but a Dutchman see nature so, conceive of it and render it so, embody such a wealth of poetry in the most unembellished, sober representation of the simplest reality? I doubt it. As regards the Dutch landscape, at any rate, the leading masters of our landscape school – take Mesdag or Mauve, Apol or Maris, for example – are unsurpassable specialists. . . . This new way of seeing and rendering is a veritable *iconoclasm* in the field of painting. What, for instance, is to become of the fine, finished brushwork and the beautiful colours of a Gudin and a Meyer, or of the Indian ink waves of a Schotel, when we have learned to find beautiful the broad touch, the impressive truth and power of tone of Mesdag?. . .

Yet another characteristic peculiarity of this movement strikes one immediately. The artists try, by preference, to render *mood*; and they give precedence to *tone* above *colour*. Hence their almost exclusive rights over the depiction of what is known as 'dirty weather'. . . . They treat telling effects of light with neglect, or preferably disdain them altogether, while on the other hand they have revealed the poetry of *grey* in a hitherto unprecedented manner. In that grey atmosphere they find the ideal gradations of tone that they are looking for and we must recognize with admiration that they succeed in rendering what people had no idea of before with a fine sensitivity. Mauve, Sadée, Israëls, Artz . . . all of them patrons of grey painting! With them the reign of grey has begun . . . . If we look more deeply into Mesdag's *On the Dutch Coast*, it makes us feel as if the salt sea air has penetrated our nostrils and lungs, as if we have felt the fresh sea breeze blowing through our hair, as if we have heard the breakers hissing and roaring. Mesdag here stretches out his hand to Anton Rubinstein, who produces the same illusion in the first two movements of his *Océan* symphony . . . . Here we have before us realism at its most true and healthy and I am deeply convinced that our landscape and marine painters must all follow this path sooner or later, if they want to keep on creating in accordance with the spirit of our time.[18]

The Dutch Drawing Society

The international reputation of the painters of the Hague School was, however, not heightened only by the phenomenon of very large exhibitions in Europe and the United States. It was also boosted by initiatives from within the School's own circle. The Hague School was not organized as such, as has been said, but its members could make their mark via the painters' society, Pulchri Studio. The discussion sessions offered artists an opportunity for showing drawings and watercolours to amateurs and collectors. But these meetings were still rather closed in character and apart from the Exhibitions of Living Masters there were not really many openings for Pulchri members to show their work in The Hague itself.

In Brussels, however, the Société Belge des Aquarellistes had already been founded in 1855 with Willem Roelofs as one of its founder members. This was one of the first societies of watercolourists on the continent; a Watercolour Society had, in fact, been set up in England as early as 1804, but this had had little effect on artists outside the British Isles. Three years after the foundation of the Belgian society, the committee of Pulchri Studio got in touch with Roelofs in order to find out whether the two societies could not work together. Roelofs wrote from Brussels in reply to the approach from Pulchri, made by Hardenberg, who was at that time a committee member,

As regards our plans for uniting the Société des aquarellistes Belges and your society, I have thought about this again and discussed it with some of my fellow-members. The acceptance and exhibiting of drawings from Pulchri here seems to us to be somewhat fraught with difficulties, for you know that what we have is an exhibition and not a discussion, so that the drawings have to be *framed*. Our space is rather limited and up until now we have had no permanent premises, so that we are afraid of having too large a number of drawings. But since we still have to have another meeting, the matter will certainly be discussed and considered again.[19]

Despite this somewhat reserved reply, which clearly reveals the difference between Brussels and The Hague in the appreciation of the watercolour as an autonomous work of art, members of Pulchri Studio, such as the Maris brothers, were individually invited to become members of the Belgian society over the years. In 1863 Matthijs Maris exhibited his *Christening* in Brussels, after which he was offered an honorary membership, in 1866 Jan Hendrik Weissenbruch exhibited his watercolours in Brussels for the first time while in 1870 the participants in an exhibition of the society in Brussels included Bosboom, Roelofs, Gabriël, Mauve, Jongkind, Blommers and Alma Tadema.

Possibly as a result of the example set by the Belgian society, it was decided to set up a comparable body in The Hague under the name of Hollandsche Teeken-Maatschappij (Dutch

fig. 63 Jozef Israëls in his Studio c. 1903

Drawing Society). The Society was founded on 31 January 1876 and the first committee consisted of Hendrik Willem Mesdag, Jacob Maris and Anton Mauve. Jan Hendrik Weissenbruch, Adolphe Artz, Albert Neuhuys, Pieter Stortenbeker and Elchanon Verveer were among the first artists to be proposed for membership. The society was from the start international in scope, with honorary members, who did not live in The Hague, as well as ordinary members. They included Clays, Hermans, Huberti and Madou in Belgium, Herkomer in London, Mosè Bianchi in Milan and Vincenzo Cabianca in Rome. Max Liebermann, Lhermitte and Millet later became members as well.

It is perhaps not superfluous to point out that the name Hollandsche Teeken-Maatschappij alluded primarily to water-colours, which were at that time mostly referred to in Dutch as drawings, or sometimes as coloured drawings. The society was primarily one of watercolourists and its very foundation was important in underlining the significance of the watercolour as a work of art that merited exhibition on its own. It is in this context that one should see the watercolours by the artists of the Hague School.

The most talented watercolourists, in the true meaning of the word, were Jan Hendrik Weissenbruch, Anton Mauve, Jozef Israëls and Jacob Maris. Weissenbruch is particularly famous for his townscapes and beach scenes, and the atmosphere and play of light is exceptionally fine in some of his interiors as well. Tradition has it that Weissenbruch used to leave his watercolours lying around on the floor of his studio and would unconcernedly walk over them, and that he would wash them off time after time and begin again, but in fact, after studying his watercolours, one must consign most of these tales to the mythology of art history, for the care, skill and confidence with which they were generally executed allows no possibility of such nonchalance. The use of areas of white paper left in reserve is sometimes superb, as is the translucency that Weissenbruch managed to achieve, whereas the continual washing off of watercolours would inevitably have produced the opposite result of muddiness and opacity. Nonetheless it is perfectly possible that it was Weissenbruch himself who put the story around. He had no time for adulation and the empty talk that surrounded the art world in his day. He disliked official occasions and would not allow himself to be fêted in grand style on every conceivable anniversary, as did Jozef

Israëls or Hendrik Mesdag. 'The cheerful Weiss', as he was known, also had a sharp tongue on occasions, and he knew that people also called him 'the merciless sword'. His professed guilelessness with regard to his watercolours could equally well have been a façade. Be that as it may, they soon became popular with English, Scots and Canadian collectors.

Mauve, too, was a loved and admired watercolourist. His watercolours differ little from his paintings in subject matter, but the execution, even in his early years, is often freer and more daring. His interiors of stables and his landscapes tinged with melancholy are particularly attractive.

A photograph of Jozef Israëls's studio makes it clear that it had one corner for painting in oil and one for painting watercolours (fig. 63). A paint cupboard with drawers and a flap top, in which the artist could keep paint and brushes, stood beside his canvases. For making watercolours he had a small antique Dutch table equipped with a tray for brushes and a beaker for water. Israëls's watercolours scarcely differ from his paintings in subject-matter and style and they are sometimes even quite large in size.

Jacob Maris's watercolours diverge more markedly from his oil paintings. His large, finished works painted in the 1870s and until fairly late in his career, such as *The Fishing Boat* (Cat. 56) and *View of Old Dordrecht* (Cat. 54) were very draughtsmanlike and precise in their detailing, despite the perfect feel for colour, but his watercolours of the same subjects are much looser and more sketchy. It is not impossible that the freedom he allowed himself in his watercolours had a decisive influence on the style of his later oil paintings, in which he abandoned the draughtsmanlike quality and sharp outlining of his earlier work in favour of broad, robust brushwork.

Prints

Graphic art was not of great importance to the masters of the Hague School, but it did play a role in their work. Vosmaer wrote of Jozef Israëls: 'In 1874, greatly admiring Rembrandt's and Ostade's prints, he was seized by a desire to make etchings. The fruits of this are: some 15 sheets the little child in the high-chair, the girl in the dunes, the children on the beach and the invalids are among the most successful of them.'[20] Roelofs had already turned to etching in the 1850s. Jacob Maris's etching *The Bridge by the Loosduinse Weg* was reproduced in the *Kunstkronijk* of 1875. Mauve made a limited number of etchings, and Matthijs Maris too was an accomplished and highly individual printmaker (fig. 64).

The lithograph performed only a subservient function in those years before it became possible to reproduce photo-graphic illustrations. Paintings and drawings by members of the Hague School were often reproduced in lithographic form in art periodicals, but lithography was rarely practised as an autonomous art form by the painters themselves. Its upsurge in the Netherlands came only in the final decade of the century under the influence of artists like Toorop, Thorn Prikker and Theo van Hoijtema.

It will be clear from this account of the development of the Hague School between 1870 and 1885 that the future held great possibilities: circumstances were exceptionally favour-able, internationally people were keen to follow artistic developments in and around The Hague and, finally, the understanding that existed between the artists themselves considerably strengthened their sense of cohesion and shared

fig. 64 M. Maris *Wooded Scene with Kid* (etching; Haags Gemeentemuseum, The Hague)

objectives. These years, the quintessential period of the Hague School, saw the creation of a number of paintings, such as Jan Hendrik Weissenbruch's *View of the Trekvliet* (1870), Matthijs Maris's *Christening* (1873), Willem Roelofs's *Rainbow* (1875), Jacob Maris's *Fishing Boat* (1878) and Jozef Israëls's *Growing Old* (1878), that must be reckoned among its greatest masterpieces. But at the same time it should perhaps be mentioned that a number of Hague School artists reached new peaks in the following period.

The Mesdag Panorama

One of the most remarkable products of this period of the Hague School was undoubtedly Mesdag's *Panorama Maritime*, a marine view painted in the round (fig. 65). The growing reputation of the School abroad gave a number of Belgian entrepreneurs the idea of setting up a Société Anonyme du Panorama de La Haye, and they asked Mesdag to carry out the project.

Panoramas have become a rarity in our day, but in the nineteenth century most large European cities had at least one, sometimes more (they had become particularly popular in Paris and London), while travelling panoramas were also made in order to reach the public in smaller places. These travelling panoramas, which were of very variable quality, had given the panorama in general the reputation of a fairground attraction –

in other words, a genre from which a great deal of money could no doubt be made, but in which no serious artist should involve himself. Thus, when Mesdag was approached by the Belgian Society in 1880, the reactions of his fellow artists in The Hague were generally unfavourable.

Mesdag, however, was undeterred. He informed the gentlemen of the Société that he would accept their offer, but only on a number of conditions. He set his fee at 100,000 Belgian francs – no small sum – and he himself was to be allowed to choose the subject of the panorama and to appoint his assistants. It was to be a painting in the round, 'with no boundaries' as it was so picturesquely described, covering some 1,600 square metres. Mesdag picked as his subject the view from the Seinpostduin at Scheveningen, the highest dune near the fishing village, a spot he knew very well and chose for its wide view of the beach, seaside resort and sea, with The Hague on the horizon on the other side. But the view was not the only consideration in Mesdag's choice of subject; it was also intended as a monumental protest against the plans of the Hague Municipality to partially level the Seinpostduin and build a café-restaurant there that would contribute to Scheveningen's further development as a fashionable resort. Hotels and bathing-establishments had already been built there in the years before 1880, but they were situated further away from the village. Other artists protested about the proposed development too, but all in vain. Thus Mesdag was recording in his panorama a piece of old Scheveningen that was doomed to disappear. This attitude towards the rapidly increasing urbanization of their own surroundings was later to prove significant for the painters of the Hague School. New buildings and industrialization were no subjects for their paintings and it was precisely because they continued to depict the more rustic and touching aspects of life in peasants and fishing communities that they offered solace to a public that wanted to escape from the increasing ugliness of modern life.

Remarkably, a second panorama was installed in The Hague in 1880, just when Mesdag was beginning work on his panorama. The architect Wesstra had designed the pompous Panorama Building – which had a strong stylistic resemblance to Seinpost, the establishment he was later to build on the levelled dune of that name – on Bezuidenhout. The businessmen financing the project had originally asked the Dutch artists Rochussen and Ten Kate to paint a panorama, but they refused and so the financiers went, again in vain, to the famous French specialists Detaille and Philippoteaux. They finally had to content themselves with *The Battle of the Pyramids* by Charles Langlois, the French painter-cum-army colonel. This did not prove a commercial success, however, and in 1887 the canvas was sold and the building demolished.

Despite all this, Mesdag began the panorama in 1880 in good spirits. He knew that he could not count on a great deal of co-operation from other Hague School painters, so he got in touch with George Hendrik Breitner, then aged 24, who he knew would appreciate a handsome commission. Théophile de Bock, who was 29 and had given up a career with the railway company in order to be able to paint, was also called in, as was the more established painter, Bernard Blommers. But Mesdag himself remained firmly in charge with the practical assistance of his wife Sientje.

Blommers evidently did not much care for working to instructions from others, so he made no further contribution to the panorama after he had painted a fisherman's wife and children. De Bock worked mainly on the dune landscape, but the most difficult part, the old village of Scheveningen, which presented problems of perspective if a perfect optical illusion were to be achieved, was in Breitner's hands. Squared drawings by Breitner, in which the roofs of the houses in Scheveningen were rendered in such a way that they could then be transferred on to the canvas in the correct proportions, are still preserved in the Kröller-Müller Museum. There are also some photographs of the view taken from the Seinpost-duin, taken in 1880 and now in the Panorama archives, which agree very closely with the final painted result.[21] Whether or not these photographs were used during the actual execution of the panorama cannot be said, but we do know of other cases where lantern slides and projectors were used to try to get as close as possible to reality and that Mesdag was assisted by Nijberck, the Belgian panorama specialist. However, the precise nature of his contribution is difficult to ascertain. The foreground, or *faux-terrain* of the panorama, an indispensable adjunct to the illusionistic whole, was constructed by C.J. Laarman, an architectural draughtsman from The Hague, with the aid of real dune sand, planted marram grass and fishermen's gear.[22]

Painting began on 28 March 1881, each participant indulging in his own specialist areas. Mesdag, of course, painted the sea and the beach with the fishing boats (Scheveningen still had no harbour at that time and the boats had to be hauled up on to the beach by horses). Breitner painted a cavalry detachment trotting along the sands, a theme that was to occur often in his later work, as well as the village of Scheveningen. If the *Panorama Maritime* was indeed done with aid of photographs, then this could well have been the first occasion on which Breitner made use of photography in his painting, a practice which was later to play a very important part in the painting of his Amsterdam period, as Paul Hefting has shown.[23]

The *Panorama Maritime* was opened amid wide public interest on 1 August 1881, four months after it had been started. The doubts initially felt by other artists evidently completely melted away. Bosboom wrote,

A massive, shining leaf has been added to the laurels of the Dutch school of painting and it is your true and powerful talent that we have to thank for this, Hendrik Willem Mesdag. You have brilliantly maintained the traditional renown of Holland's school of painting with your great panorama.

Vincent van Gogh too hastened to see the panorama and his comment, made in allusion to a well-known judgement of one of Rembrandt's works, was that 'This picture's only fault is that it has no faults'.[24] The critic Vosmaer also waxed enthusiastic and praised Mesdag's effort and the artistic power of the panorama.

But, for all that, the *Panorama Maritime* was not the commercial success that the Belgian investors in the Société had hoped it would be; and the company was put into liquidation as early as 1885. Mesdag, who wanted to prevent the disfigurement of his finest achievement at all costs, saw no alternative but to buy the Panorama, building and all, and exploit it himself. We read in a newspaper cutting of 1887,

In the building of the Mesdag Panorama people are busily engaged in taking down the gigantic canvas and carefully rolling it up and packing it under the direction of the author of the panorama, after which it will be sent to Munich some day in order to be exhibited in the Panorama Building there. . . . A singular detail that should be added here is that the so-called *faux terrain* is also being moved to Munich, not only the anchors, ropes and other material, but also the golden North Sea sand from the dunes of Holland, from which the panorama of Scheveningen derives its local colour. The red sand of Bavaria would, of course, utterly destroy the effect of the canvas. . . .[25]

From 1889 to 1891 the canvas was shown in Amsterdam and after that it returned to The Hague for good. In 1910 the Mesdag Panorama became a limited family company and it has remained so up until the present day. Now, over a century later, the Panorama enjoys very wide public interest. The canvas has recently been cleaned, restoring it to its former glory, and its effect is still just as surprising and convincing as it was for our forebears.

Mesdag himself regarded it as his most important work, 'because it gives such a great impression of nature'.[26] The Hague School painters' image of nature had begun to become an *idée fixe*; the changing landscape, expanding cities and the demands of an industrialized society did not fit into their conceptions of it. Mesdag deplored the construction of the harbour at Scheveningen because it robbed him of a motif for his paintings of fishing boats on the beach. The painters of the Hague School were trying to escape the prosaicness of the

fig. 65 The Mesdag Panorama, The Hague

modern age and they now began privately to search for places where nature could still be found untainted. Somehow they kept the places they found secret from each other. Roelofs went to Noorden, Weissenbruch to the Nieuwkoop lakes, Israëls and Mauve made regular visits to Laren; the beauty of Drente and Brabant was also discovered. Some of them decided to continue living in the city in order to experience a shock each time they went to work in the countryside; others, like Mauve, fled from the city for good, opting for a studio surrounded by heathland and sheep folds.

NOTES

1. See C. Maltese, *Storia dell'arte in Italia 1785–1943*, Turin 1960, chapter v: '*Il momento unitario dell'arte italiana dell'Ottocento*', pp 168ff.. Cf. A. Wagner, J. Sillevis in exh. cat. *I. Macchiaioli, Italiaanse tijdgenoten van de Haagse School*, Haags Gemeentemuseum, The Hague 1972–73.
2. See interview in *De Nieuwste Courant* (9 March 1901).
3. Miss Marius gives the year wrongly as 1869. The family was registered at the Registrars' office in The Hague on 25 April 1871. Cf. G.H. Marius, *De Hollandsche Schilderkunst in de negentiende eeuw*, The Hague 1920,² p. 119, and H.E. van Gelder, *Jozef Israëls*, Amsterdam (1947), p. 23.
4. Survey of membership of Pulchri Studio:
J. Bosboom, member 1847–91; founder 1847; Treasurer 10/2/1847–1/10/1848; Secretary 1/10/1848–15/1/1851; Chairman 15/1/1852–1/10/1853; honorary member 1887–91.
P.J.C. Gabriël, member 1884–1903.
J. Maris, member 1871–99; Drawing Studio Committee 1/10/1863–1/10/1869; Social Gatherings Committee 1/10/1875–1/10/1878; Exhibitions Committee 1893–97.
W. Maris, member 1860–1910; Discussions Committee 1/10/68–1/10/1872 and 1/10/1881–1/10/1884; Exhibitions Committee 1898–1903 and 1906; Chairman of Art Gallery Committee 1900–10.
A. Mauve, member 1871–86; Discussions Committee 1/10/1876–1/10/1879; Treasurer 1/10/1879–1/10/1883; outside member 1886.
H.W. Mesdag, member 1869–1915; Chairman 1/10/1889–1907; honorary member 1908–15; Honorary Chairman 1908–15.
J. Israëls, member 1871–1911; Chairman 1/10/1875–1/10/1878; honorary member 1894–1911.
W. Roelofs, member 1847–97; founder 1847; honorary member 1859–97; Exhibitions Committee 1893.
J.H. Weissenbruch, member 1847–1903; founder 1847; Drawing Studio Committee 1/10/1857–1/10/1861.
G. Bilders, member 1857.
5. For futher details see M. van Delft 'Kunstbeschouwingen bij Pulchri Studio 1847–1917', *Jaarboek Geschiedkundige Vereniging Die Haghe* (1980), pp. 147ff.
6. C. Vosmaer, *Onze hedendaagsche schilders*, vol. 2, Amsterdam 1883, p. 5.
7. 'We are between two schools, one that has ended, the other which is perhaps beginning'. W. Bürger, 'Exposition à la Haye', *Gazette des Beaux-Arts* III (1859), p. 104.
8. See *Salons de W. Bürger, 1861 à 1865 avec une préface par T. Thoré*, vol. 2, Paris 1870, p. 301.
9. *Ibidem*, pp. 392, 393.
10. See letter from Jozef Israëls to Thoré-Bürger, Amsterdam, 25 April 1867, Institut Néerlandais, Paris, Fondation Custodia no. 1. 6760; cf. exh. cat. *Mondrian et l'École de la Haye*, Institut Néerlandais, Paris 1982.
11. Bürger, *op. cit*, p. 513.
12. R. Ménard, 'Exposition de Vienne', *Gazette des Beaux-Arts* VIII (1873), pp. 203–06.
13. P. Leroi, 'La gravure au Salon', *Gazette des Beaux-Arts* VIII (1873), p. 141.
14. 'This picture is painted in shadow and grief'. Duranty, 'Exposition universelle, Les écoles étrangères de peinture', *Gazette des Beaux-Arts* XVIII (1878), pp. 166, 167.

15. C. Blanc, *Les Beaux-Arts à l'exposition universelle de 1878*, Paris 1978, p. 341.

16. C. Blanc, 'Salon de 1866', *Gazette des Beaux-Arts* xx (1866).

17. 'The sea, seen from above as in Manet's battle of the *Alabama*, wets the gilt of the frame with its sea-green waves. In the centre dances a boat, while others are silhouetted in the distance. His view of the Market Place at Groningen, with its houses with step gables and shutters in pear-green, is amusing, but also a bit lean and a bit dry'. See J.K. Huysmans, *Le Salon de 1879*, in *L'art moderne/Certains*, préf. *Hubert Juin*, Paris 1975, p. 23.

18. See J. van Santen Kolff, 'Een blik in de Hollandsche schilderschool onzer dagen, dl. iv', *De Banier, tijdschrift van 'Het Jonge Holland'* 1 (1875), pp. 158, 159, 160, 161, 166, 170, 187.

19. Letter dated 13 November 1858 from Willem Roelofs to L. Hardenberg, Brussels; see H.F.W. Jeltes, *Willem Roelofs*, Amsterdam 1911, pp. 134, 135.

20. C. Vosmaer, *Onze Hedendaagsche Schilders*, The Hague 1885, p. 5.

21. See J.J.T. Sillevis, 'Een schilderij zonder grenzen', *Openbaar Kunstbezit* xxiv (Oct.–Nov. 1980), pp. 170–74.

22. See L.M. Rolling Couquerque, *Het Panorama Mesdag te 's-Gravenhage*, The Hague 1947, and E.J. Fruitema, P.A. Zoetmulder, in exh. cat. *Het Panorama Fenomeen*, Panorama Mesdag, The Hague, 1981.

23. See P.H. Hefting & C.C.G. Quarles van Ufford, *Breitner als fotograaf*, Rotterdam 1966; A. B. Osterholt, *Breitner en zijn foto's*, Amsterdam 1974 and P.H. Hefting, *G.H. Breitner in zijn Haagse tijd*, Utrecht 1970.

24. Letter of 1881 (?August) from Vincent van Gogh to Theo, Nr. 149.

25. Documentation Dept., R.K.D., The Hague. The cutting is undated.

26. See interview in the *Nieuwe Rotterdamsche Courant* (11 March 1906), cited in J. Poort, *Hendrik Willem Mesdag, artiste peintre à la Haye*, The Hague 1981, p. 46.

The Years of Fame (1885-1910)

JOHN SILLEVIS

A question of generations

The painters who are generally grouped together as the Hague School were not all of the same generation; half of its founding fathers – including Bosboom, Israëls, Roelofs and Weissenbruch – were in their early, or even late, fifties when the school emerged more or less as an entity in the 1870s, while the other half – for instance the Maris brothers and Mauve – were then in their mid-thirties. Mesdag held a kind of middle position, since he had been a painter for only a short time when he came to live in The Hague, but was a member of the elder generation in terms of age. Since in the 1880s a new group of painters made their debut, they properly constitute a third generation, but in terms of artistic development and of the history of the Hague School itself, they are perhaps better characterized as the school's own *second* generation. They were attracted by the example of painters who by then belonged to an established school, but whose ideas were still regarded as modern and pioneering. For these younger artists, joining the Hague School was a deliberate decision to break with tradition.

The great figures of the Hague School taught a number of these young artists and gave them advice, but however great their personal success, none of them ever held a permanent teaching post at an Academy. The ideas and practice current in these institutions had clearly not been kept pace with theirs, as was made clear to George Hendrik Breitner (1857–1923; fig. 67) when as a student of the Hague Academy, he visited the Driejaarlijkse Tentoonstelling (Triennial Exhibition) with his teacher Koelman. Jan Veth takes up the tale:

When The Hague put on its exhibitions, Koelman went with the young people into the rooms set aside for them in the Academy and pointed out the faults in the paintings by Israëls, the Marises, Neuhuys and Blommers. In fact he did not think any of the Dutch painters were any good. And once, when Breitner had been to look at fine French paintings at old Mr van Wisselingh's, Koelman said to him, 'Have you been to see all that realistic filth as well?'.[1]

Koelman, who was the director of the Hague Academy, was known as a fervent supporter of classicist ideals which he had imbibed during a long stay in Italy. Breitner had enrolled at the Academy for the academic year 1875–76, Willem de Zwart and Philippe Zilcken followed a year later and Willem Bastiaan Tholen, Isaac Israëls (Jozef's son) and Floris Verster

fig. 66 THOLEN *Skaters on a Pond in The Hague Wood* 1891 (Haags Gemeentemuseum, The Hague)

signed on for the year 1877–78. The teaching methods had remained virtually unchanged since the beginning of the century and as long as Koelman remained director, he was at pains to see that this continued to be the case.

Willem Maris, who gave the young Breitner instruction in landscape painting, could still, many years later, remember the atmosphere of controversy in The Hague: on one side were the teachers at the Academy aligned with the 'official' members of Pulchri Studio and on the other were the 'artists' such as Jozef Israëls, the Marises, Mauve and Mesdag. Maris recalled:

The venerable old men, Schmidt Crans, Koelman and others, frequented Heyser's (a Hague café). They were the bigwigs, you see. We were the revolutionaries. And how they obstructed us! A pamphlet was strewn about in the Kurhaus during our first exhibition. We were berated as 'mud painters'. Old Vogel fulminated at a Pulchri meeting, 'They must be exterminated'. But later on he imitated us![2]

In a manuscript entitled *Reminiscences of a Dutch Painter of the Nineteenth Century*[3] Zilcken described his dislike of the established academic teaching methods and the formative significance of his association with the Hague painters.

As a result, the studies we did on our own had more influence on our artistic development. Later on Mauve would come to my studio

fig. 67 BREITNER *Academic Drawing of a Nude Man* 1877–78
(Haags Gemeentemuseum, The Hague)

made heavy by an annual layer of thick distemper, exhibited a rare richness of colour. Those painters' festivities, the like of which have never been seen again, made an unforgettable impression on those who took part in them because of the splendour of the tableaux and the exceptional picturesqueness of the spectacles, all this being achieved by extremely simple means such as people fail to understand in general, for normally when *tableaux vivants* of that sort are put on, carefully made and completely finished costumes are used, whereas the Marises achieved a much more intense and striking effect by the lighting of the figures and by touching up their sackcloth costumes with distemper. Thus, for some official occasion or other in the building, Jacob Maris put on Rembrandt's *Nightwatch* in a tableau that reproduced the lighting and life of the original to perfection. As a pupil of Mauve, I was singled out in one or other pantomime in which I played a small part and was ironically dubbed 'the child of the Grey School' because that name was given – how wrongly! – to the group of Mauve, Jacob and Willem Maris and Mesdag. These painters, the great pioneers in the field of art, were positively detested by influential, conventional *arriviste* painters, who did not want any power taken out of their own hands and who did everything possible to injure or ridicule them.

Thus, there undoubtedly was very real resistance to the Hague School, but in the eighties the painters witnessed a gradual growth in their ranks. The steadily increasing interest in their work abroad, among both art critics and collectors, gave the School an important boost and this unmistakably percolated through to, and had an effect on, the opinions of the artists' compatriots. Zilcken recalled that Théophile de Bock used to say, 'If you're successful abroad, then they say here that you must have talent'.[4]

Not all the younger artists who went to the masters of the Hague School for instruction can be counted as members of the School. Breitner, van Gogh and Isaac Israëls, for instance, all had clear links with it, but at a certain moment in their careers they opted for a different path. However, alongside these artists there is a fairly extensive group of followers of the Hague School, as well as a group generally denoted by the French term *petits-maîtres*, who are certainly of no minor importance for the picture of the Hague School as a whole. Some of them enjoyed great fame in their own day and took part in international exhibitions, but they damaged their own reputations by the facile repitition of certain themes to the point where some subjects, while invariably continuing to impress in the work of greater artists despite their familiarity, in the hands of these *petits-maîtres* degenerated into worn-out clichés. Louis Apol, Nicolaas Bastert, Pieter ter Meulen, Geo Poggenbeek and Willem Rip all belonged to this group. Johannes Akkeringa, Adolphe Artz, Floris Arntzenius, Bernard Blommers, Théophile de Bock, Gerrit van Houten, Alexander Mollinger, Sientje Mesdag-van Houten, Taco Mesdag and Frits Mondriaan were more talented, while the works of Willem Bastiaan Tholen and Willem de Zwart are of a high standard.[5]

It is possible to see, from a very brief survey of the 'second generation', just how comprehensive the term Hague School had become and, in consequence, how difficult it is to define. Some painters continued to paint in the style of the School until late in life, up to the beginning of the Second World War. Their constant repetitions of peasant interiors and landscapes with cows and windmills, which had become so far removed from twentieth-century reality, were undoubtedly responsible

now and then to look at my work. He sometimes took me with him on his walks, when he went out of town to get ideas for his paintings or watercolours. At that time he was living on Alexanderveld in the row of houses that bordered the parade ground, so that clear light fell unimpeded into his studio.

We often walked in the near part of the Woods [Boschjes], but even more frequently in the vicinity of the Laan van Meerdervoort, as it was in those days. Near Bronovo there used to be a wooden bridge and further on innumerable vegetable gardens, separated by canals and bordered by pollard willows, among which the funny, old-fashioned, high footbridges that reminded one of Ostade's etchings stood out most picturesquely. This extensive area, which began near the Van de Spiegelstraat, was a rich source of inspiration for the Hague painters. Jacob Maris did his *Vegetable Gardens* [now known as *Allotments near the Hague*; Cat. 57], among other things, there when the old Hague windmills still stood up on the horizon. Duchattel often came there too and in the mornings there was generally a meeting of young and old artists, who in those happy times thought of nothing but their work.

At that time I was put up by Mauve as a working member of Pulchri and was accepted. This club, which was accommodated in the boardroom of the Hofje van Nieuwkoop, held all its meetings on Saturday evenings. People played billiards and every now and then uncommon artistic evenings took place, with *tableaux vivants* or short pantomimes, of which Dr Jan ten Brink was the explicator and for which the backdrops were painted by none other than Jacob and Willem Maris, assisted by the most gifted young members. These masters devoted a great many evenings to painting the drops, which,

g. 68 THOLEN *Fishing Boats on the Beach at Scheveningen c. 1889* (Groninger Museum, Veendorp Collection, Groningen)

g. 69 DE ZWART *The Wagenbrug, The Hague* (Stedelijk Museum, Amsterdam)

for much of the discredit into which the Hague School later fell, although other factors were also involved (see chapter x). What had begun as a realistic movement ended in romanticized cliché.

Foreign contacts

In the last quarter of the nineteenth century the Hague School enjoyed steadily growing interest, particularly internationally. It became synonymous with modern Dutch art and its support was in demand wherever efforts were being made in the name of modern art. Many of these international contacts were made by Jozef Israëls and Hendrik Willem Mesdag, both of whom had travelled a great deal, knew the art world and had sufficient powers of discrimination to establish precisely those contacts that would open up new avenues for the painters of the Hague School. Neither of them ever forgot their own interests, but they always allowed their confrères to benefit from any entrées they made abroad.

The role of Brussels as the meeting-place for a number of the Hague School artists, such as Roelofs, Gabriël and Mesdag, has already been discussed, but it is important to point out that his contact with Brussels continued and was not just confined to the early years. The similarities between some Belgian painters and the Hague School are too striking to be passed over. Hippolite Boulenger's *The Rainbow* (fig. 73) offers an obvious comparison with Willem Roelofs's work of the same title, Gabriël is unmistakably related to De Knyff and Edouard Huberti (fig. 70) in his approach to landscape painting and Mesdag's career as a marine painter is indissolubly bound up with the models provided by Louis Artan (fig. 71) and Clays and the advice of his friend Alfred Verwee (fig. 72). The Belgian artist Courtens even bought a house in the neighbourhood of Haarlem and at exhibitions in Amsterdam successfully showed landscapes that are sometimes strongly reminiscent of Mauve. These contacts were continued in the exhibition of the Brussels Groupe des Vingt, to which Jozef Israëls, Jacob Maris and Anton Mauve were invited in 1884, Mesdag and Toorop in 1885 and Willem and Matthjis Maris in 1887, while Toorop invited Les Vingt to an exhibition organized at the Hague Art Society in 1892.

Germany

Germany was another very important area of contact. Jozef Israëls had exhibited successfully in Munich from as early as 1869 and works by Hague School painters were from that time on to be seen in Berlin and Dresden as well. It cannot be said for certain in exactly which year Max Liebermann saw work by the Hague School for the first time. He made his first visit to the Netherlands in 1871, but at that time his interest was primarily focused on the masters of the seventeenth century, with a special preference for Frans Hals. In 1876 he came back again, mainly to make copies after Frans Hals's military pieces and group portraits, but he also looked for subjects in Scheveningen, Amsterdam and the environs of Leiden. The art dealer Buffa placed a studio at his disposal in Amsterdam, not far from the City Orphanage in Kalverstraat, one of Liebermann's favourite and most successful subjects. In the summer of 1880 he painted the garden of the Catholic Old Men's Home near Rembrandtplein. What fascinated him there was the peculiar quality of the light falling through the canopy of foliage in the garden and casting bright spots in the

fig. 70 HUBERTI *Landscape in the Kempen* (Location unknown)

fig. 71 ARTAN *Marine* (Koninklijk Museum voor Schone Kunsten, Antwerp)

fig. 72 VERWEE *Foals in a Meadow* (Koninklijk Museum voor Schone Kunsten, Antwerp)

shady corner where the old men used to sit and enjoy the summer weather. The beautiful rendering of this play of light did not escape the critics at the Paris Salon the following year, where the painting scored a great success and the jury awarded Liebermann an honourable mention.

Nor had he remained unnoticed in the Netherlands. When Liebermann visited a Dutch Drawing Society exhibition in the same year, 1881, Jozef Israëls came up to him and said, '*Comment, c'est vous qui a fait ces bonhommes?*' This was the

fig. 73 BOULENGER *The Rainbow* (Location unknown)

beginning of not only a personal friendship between Israëls and Liebermann, but also a series of exhibition exchanges and thus a very real contribution to the development of German art by the Hague School. On 26 July 1892 the committee of the Dutch Drawing Society under the chairmanship of Jozef Israëls decided to admit Liebermann as a member and from 1892 to 1907 he regularly took part in their exhibitions.[6]

He had, meanwhile, become one of the leading figures in German modern art, which had met opposition here from the conservative artists and academicians just as it had done in the Netherlands. In Munich he formed part of the Vereinigung der XI in 1892 and he was also closely involved in the Münchener Sezession, a movement which departed from traditional conceptions of art and which was led by Slevogt, Von Stuck, Trübner and Uhde. It was supported by Jacob and Willem Maris, Breitner, De Bock, Gabriël, Mesdag, Tholen, Weissenbruch and De Zwart, who participated in its exhibitions, and Jozef Israëls was awarded an honorary membership for his services.

Liebermann had also always been in favour of a federation in Berlin that would link up with the movement in Munich, as is clear from a letter to Jan Veth (18 January 1893).

Perhaps you have read that we Germans are going to break away from the older generation, now at this very moment. Piglhein of Munich is in Berlin to set up a federation of all the young, progressive elements among the German artists. Let us hope it will succeed, but

fundamentally I believe that only talent can herald a new era in art. It has nothing to do with societies. However, struggle is obviously preferable to stagnation. . . .[7]

A month later he wrote,

My best friend, you must certainly know that a *Sezession* took place among the German artists last year, comparable with that in Paris. All the foreign artists – you just as much as Israëls, Mesdag, etc. – form part of our *Sezession* and everything would be fine if only the Bavarian government in Munich, which is in the hands of the clerics, wasn't against us. We don't care a fig for the government, but what is very important is that the palace in Munich where the exhibitions are held (the *Glaspalast*) has been given to the opposition. They . . . are putting on their usual exhibition and they'll be sending a certain Bartels to invite you to take part [Hans von Bartels was a professor at the *Akademie der bildenden Künste* in Munich]. Piglhein, the president of the *Sezession*, has just asked me to make sure that you come in with us . . . and I hope the Hollanders won't join in with those old fogies.[8]

The Dutch artists gave their support, as Liebermann hoped, but that was not the end of the story. A group was not immediately set up in Berlin in association with that in Munich, despite pressure from a number of sources, but the hostility between the old guard, supported by the court and the Emperor himself (who had pretensions to being an art-lover), and the moderns nevertheless steadily increased. The breaking-point came in 1898 when Leistikov's painting

fig. 74 LIEBERMANN *Woman with Kids* 1890
(Bayerische Staatsgemäldesammlungen, Neue Pinakothek, Munich)

Grunewaldsee was rejected by the jury of the Grosse Berliner Kunstausstellung. In protest, a group of modern artists set up the Berliner Sezession, electing Liebermann as their president. But the most remarkable part of the story was Jozef Israëls's purchase and presentation of Leistikov's painting to the National Gallery in Berlin as a gesture of support for the protest.9 Tschudi, the director of the Gallery, who was on the side of the moderns and a friend of Liebermann's, welcomed the gift with open arms. By 1901, just three years later, the Berlin Sezession consisted of 62 ordinary members and 96 corresponding members, including Breitner, Jozef Israëls, Toorop and Veth. In his foreword to the 1901 catalogue Liebermann wrote,

In addition to the entries of our members, we are grateful for the willing assistance of the owners of some of the most beautiful works of Dutch art and also of French Impressionism. The paintings of Israëls or Jacob Maris are acknowledged classics, but Pissarro, Renoir and Claude Monet, whose works were rejected in alarm on their first showing, also strike us as classics now – a generation after their creation.10

Bosboom, Vincent van Gogh, Isaac Israëls, Willem Maris, Neuhuys and Veth were also represented at this exhibition, Van Gogh by as many as five paintings.

In that same year Liebermann put his high admiration for Jozef Israëls on record in an essay, in which he defined the difference between the genre piece by Kraus, such as *The Wisdom of Solomon* and Israëls's *Son of the Chosen People*:

The German genre painters offer an illustration of their subject, looking more for the anecdotal, the characteristic chance occurrence. But Israëls abandons all detail, looking for the typical, the poetic synthesis instead of the reasoned analysis.11

Italy

The Hague School's contacts with Italy came about mainly through Vittore Grubicy de Dragon, a Milanese art dealer. Zilcken wrote of him in his memoirs:

Around 1880 a very unusual man, Vittore Grubicy de Dragon, an Italian of Hungarian extraction, came to The Hague – for what precise reason I do not know. He was the brother of an art dealer in

Milan, where he lived with his mother. He settled in The Hague for quite some time (several years all in all) and made the best modern Italian art known to selected collectors and a small group of Dutch painters. In this way we got to know the works of artists like Cremona, Segantini in his first period, Quadrelli the sculptor and others.

Grubicy soon became a friend of Jacob and Willem Maris, of Mauve and Mesdag and of young artists like Breitner, Van der Maarel, De Bock and myself. The force emanating from his unusual personality, his motivated enthusiasm, his deep knowledge and rare understanding of art made talking to him, which we did every day, not only pleasurable, but also very instructive. Indeed, after his death I met the highly talented sculptress Signorina Arpesani in Venice and she said to me of Grubicy, '*Ce n'était pas un homme, c'était un âme . . .*'. He even once asked Mauve to lend him a collection of a score of selected studies, which he sent to the young Segantini in order to acquaint him with the ideas of the best Dutch painters; Grubicy maintained that Mauve's work was a revelation to the Milanese painter and had had a great influence on his development before he went over to the division of colours.

Grubicy devoted himself to art later on. He exhibited in Venice and elsewhere in Italy, not without attracting attention. I was able to look him up on one occasion at that time in Milan, where he was then engaged with much patriotism in giving the works he owned by Italian and other modern masters to various museums and collections, with the aim of making them available as speedily as possible as models for the rising generation.12

Grubicy was, indeed, a good friend of Mauve, Jacob, Willem and Matthijs Maris, Jozef Israëls and Mesdag, all of whom presented him with paintings, watercolours and etchings, often bearing dedications;13 in the Mesdag Museum there is a painting *Selling Fish* by Mauve (fig. 75) with the inscription '*A. Mauve à son ami Grubici*'. In fact the friendship had far-reaching consequences, for it was Mauve who led Grubicy to develop into an artist (initially against his will). He received his first instruction in making watercolours and etching from Mauve, his first etching being a view of the Vijverberg in The Hague (fig. 76).14 Grubicy himself described his association with Mauve:

From 1882 to 1885 I maintained friendly and business relations in Holland with the great painters Israëls, the Maris brothers, Bosboom, De Bock, Blommers, Mesdag, Neuhuys and, above all, my best friend Mauve. His health was poor and every now and then he suffered from attacks of melancholy when he had too much on hand. I constantly went out walking with him and I bought from him those works he had executed in my presence on the basis of impressions gained during our perambulations in the countryside. It happened that he left the city (The Hague, where I was also living) and betook himself to the lonely heath of Laren, five or six hours away from The Hague, in order to paint an important picture for the Paris Salon. When I went round to ask his wife how he was getting on, I discovered that the dear fellow had already been sending despairing letters for two weeks, from which it appeared that he was on the point of collapse again. I took the train at once and hurried off to Laren. When he saw me coming, after the first happy surprise he was overcome by a burst of anger. He felt himself under attack! What have you come here for? I could see from his wild eyes that he was on the brink of an explosion, so I was obliged to conceal my intentions and I answered that I had come to see the beautiful landscape in order to do something myself. And I'd never yet set pencil to paper! . . . Without saying a word he let himself be taken to the station and set off

fig. 75 MAUVE *Selling Fish*, dedicated by the artist '*à son ami Grubici*' (Rijksmuseum H. W. Mesdag, The Hague)

for The Hague (it was a Saturday evening), leaving me on my own in a shabby inn (Hotel Hamdorff), where I could only make myself understood by gestures, since I did not know the dialect of the village. What was I to do? I had to justify my story to Mauve and so I forced myself with the greatest exertion honestly to work after nature. In this way I spent the Sunday, Monday and Tuesday alone. On Wednesday afternoon Mauve returned, embraced me effusively and complimented me for hours on end because my drawings were so spontaneous, fresh and genuine, and he was convinced that that was why I had come. And so I began to develop. . . .[15]

Vincent van Gogh also knew of Mauve's bouts of depression. He wrote to his brother Theo, 'Poor Mauve, he won't get better until his big painting is finished and then after that he'll be worn out', thus confirming the accuracy of Grubicy's character sketch of Mauve and also supplying a possible date for the episode in Laren (Van Gogh's letter dates from February 1882).[16] In any case, it is clear that the incident took place before Mauve settled in Laren for good. Not until 1885 did he move into 'Arietta', the house on Naarderweg, thus becoming a neighbour of Albert Neuhuys who had already been living there for two years. Other artists who regularly stayed and worked in Laren were Kever, Van Essen, Steelink, Valkenburg and Offermans. Jozef Israëls is credited with the

fig. 76 GRUBICY *The Vijverberg in The Hague* (etching)

'discovery' of the place.

Grubicy must have told Segantini a lot and in great detail about Mauve. When the latter died in 1888, Segantini wrote to Grubicy, 'Dear Vittore, I have read your heartfelt letter about the loss of Mauve with deep sorrow and it was, indeed, a heavy blow, because I regarded Mauve as a distant friend. May his soul rest in peace. Yours, G. Segantini.'[17]

The drawings by Mauve that Grubicy sent to Segantini had a detectable influence on his work, particularly on his

fig. 77 SEGANTINI *The Two Mothers*
(Rijksmuseum H. W. Mesdag, The Hague)

fig. 78 MANCINI *The Anniversary* 1885
(Rijksmuseum H. W. Mesdag, The Hague)

renderings of shepherdesses with sheep, a theme with which Mauve was also much occupied at that period, as for instance in his *Return to the Sheepfold* (1882), *Back from the Meadow* (1883–84), *Flock on the Move* and *Moonlight* (1883). Mesdag bought two drawings from Segantini and they are still to be seen in his collection: a black chalk drawing of *Moonlight* and a pastel entitled *The Two Mothers* (fig. 77). Charles Drucker, whose collection forms the basis of the Hague School collection in the Rijksmuseum in Amsterdam, gave his collection of Segantinis to the Segantini Museum at St. Moritz.

During the years that Grubicy lived in The Hague Segantini also began to exhibit in the Netherlands.[18] In 1882 he took part in an exhibition in Rotterdam for the first time and in 1883 he won the gold medal at the International Exhibition in Amsterdam with his *Ave Maria in trasbordo*. That same year he was admitted to membership of the Dutch Drawing Society, which organized an exhibition in his memory in 1900, the year of his death.

Other Italians, too, were members of the Society, including Mosè Bianchi, Biseo, Bucchi, Cipriani, Cabianca, Joris, Maccari and Quadrelli. There is still a watercolour by Bianchi in the Mesdag Museum, while Quadrelli is said to have been one of the artists introduced to The Hague by Grubicy. Bucchi was a fan painter; his fans are mentioned in Louis Couperus's Hague novel *Eline Vere*.[19]

A relationship of a quite different kind, in which the element of stylistic affinity was less important, existed between Mesdag and the Italian painter Antonio Mancini. Mesdag had evinced a predilection for Mancini's work around 1880, via contacts in Paris, and he already owned four of Mancini's paintings by the time the Italian artist first approached Mesdag for financial support. Mancini was a somewhat unstable character who was particularly bad at handling money, so that he was almost continuously on the verge of bankruptcy, despite successes in Italy and France. Mesdag took on the new role of patron without making too many bones about it, although he let it be known that he could not keep on buying endlessly and that he was gradually running out of space in his art gallery. But Mancini kept on appealing to him and Mesdag even managed to get other members of his family, including his brother Taco, to buy Mancini's work. The Mesdag Museum still has 15 works by this Italian master in its collection (fig. 78).

In 1882 Mancini's work formed part of the Barbizon School exhibition that was held in The Hague on the occasion of the bicentenary of the Hague Academy. Although this may seem strange it is not so surprising when one remembers that the loans in fact came from Mesdag's collection. Later, in 1897 and 1902, Mesdag organized one-man exhibitions of Mancini's work in the rooms of Pulchri Studio.[20] The Amsterdam artist Kees Maks, a friend of Breitner's, was a pupil of Mancini's for a while around 1902 in his studio on the Via Margutta in Rome; it is not certain whether this contact came about via an introduction from Mesdag or whether Maks knew Mancini's work from one of the exhibitions in The Hague. From the fact that one seldom comes across a Mancini in Dutch private collections, however, it can only be concluded that Mesdag's partiality for him was shared by few of his compatriots.

Collecting in the Netherlands never really developed to the extent that it did in other countries. Mesdag was exceptional among his fellow artists in The Hague, although they certainly did not lack the means to form their own collections, especially in the later years. As painters, they themselves enjoyed particular popularity among the great collectors in England, Scotland, the United States and Canada. The collector Forbes is known to have declared, 'I can't resist an Israëls', but collections like that of Alexander Young and the Drucker-Frasers also contained a series of Hague School masterpieces (cf. chapter VIII). As for Canada, around 1900,

Dutch pictures became a symbol of social position and wealth. It was also whispered that they were a sound investment. They collected them like cigaretcards [*sic*]. You had to complete your set. One would say to another. 'Oh, I see you have not a De Bock yet'. 'No – have you your Blommers?' The houses bulged with cows, old women peeling potatoes, and windmills . . . If you were poor and had only half a million, there were Dutchmen to cater to your humbler circumstances. Art in Canada meant a cow or a windmill.[21]

The Hague School became an obligatory part of international exhibitions. The Metropolitan Museum bought its first Hague School watercolours at an exhibition of the Dutch Drawing Society at Boussod and Valadon's on Fifth Avenue in New York in 1895.[22] The Hague art dealer Tersteeg acted as intermediary here. Zilcken wrote of him in his earlier cited memoirs:

Mr Tersteeg, manager of Goupil's in The Hague, with whom I have been associated since 1880, at which time he bought my best watercolours for the sum of fifty guilders (which I regarded as quite a lot at that time) because there was a vogue for Dutch art in England and America . . . English art-dealers also often came and bought 'Dutch watercolours' from us by the square centimetre. . . . Like everyone else, I made landscapes with windmills and views of the dunes; and a singular thing that sometimes happened was that when my work had been bought by Goupil's, Mr Tersteeg *asked Mauve to put a few figures in my Dutch landscapes* to make them saleable!'[23]

Such practices certainly give a very remarkable picture of the avidity of those dealing in the Hague School.

In London there was even a Holland Fine Art Gallery, at first in Regent Street, and later in Grafton Street. The Hague School exhibitions there always received admiring reviews in leading art magazines such as *The Studio*. Zilcken acted as correspondent for *The Studio* for a number of years, during which he unceasingly emphasized the significance of the Hague School in the section entitled 'Studio Talk': 'Still, The Hague, by the presence of the most celebrated Dutch painters, like Israëls, Jacob and Willem Maris, Mesdag, etc., and by the considerable number of artists living there (about one painter per 700 inhabitants!) may be considered the principal centre in the country.'[24] He generally signed these contributions with his initials only, so that he sometimes included his own activities in his articles:

At the Venice Exhibition a great attraction is the large collection of etchings, including all the best original work produced during the last few years in Holland, that forms a separate group of uncommon artistic value, brought together by Mr Ph. Zilcken, who was appointed as a special commissioner of the exhibition for this purpose.[25]

Zilcken made an important contribution to the publicization of the Hague School by producing etchings after work by the Maris brothers, Jozef Israëls and Weissenbruch. In 1885, he founded the Nederlandsche Etsclub (Etching Club of Holland) in association with Jan Veth, Willem Bastiaan Tholen, Willem Witsen and Antoon Derkinderen. He also made the etchings for the *Memorial Catalogue of the French and Dutch Loan Exhibition in Edinburgh* (1885) and maintained contacts with American collectors and museum directors such as Samuel Putnam Avery (New York), Howard Mansfield Freer (Detroit), William Rice (Williamstown) and Beatty (Pittsburgh). In Paris he attended the De Goncourt *jour*, where he spoke to the critic Philippe Burty and the Italian painter Giuseppe de Nittis, famous for his views of Paris. Later, he was to become a friend of Verlaine and Huysmans.

The late years

At the end of the nineteenth century the Hague School was no longer a movement, but an institution. The early pioneers were now men with established reputations which were seldom contested. But alongside the rave reviews, first obituaries also began to appear.

In 1888, on 5 February, Anton Mauve died suddenly at the age of 50. His death was generally felt as a shock. Van Gogh, who heard the news in Arles, dedicated the painting he was working on at that moment – a flowering tree – to Mauve, adding the inscription *Souvenir de Mauve* at the bottom, and gave it to Mauve's widow (fig. 112). Mauve's Italian friend

Vittore Grubicy de Dragon also gave vent to his emotion and his indignation at the lack of official recognition of Mauve's talents in an obituary in the Italian paper *La Riforma*, which was reprinted by Dutch newspapers:

At Laren [Mauve died in Arnhem] the death has suddenly occurred, through a cerebral haemorrhage and at the full flowering of his talent, of Anton Mauve, the greatest poet of gentle melancholy, the unsurpassed painter of the quiet dunes and the verdant meadows, the sweetest songster of nature, animals and silent, dreamy shepherds of the lonely Dutch heath. . . . His constant study of nature had given him such a mastery of the difficult technique of brush and palette that he wrote the poem that rippled through his heart and mind on the canvas with a swift, feverish nervosity and a precise characterization, even down to the smallest details, no differently than he would have set a thought on paper with a pen in his hand. Of a quiet and melancholy character, he had retired with his family to the wide heath in the neighbourhood of Laren, an unspoilt corner he had discovered where the style of the houses, the customs and the inhabitants have continued to exhibit up to our own day the poems, that are so great in their simplicity, of the major Dutch masters of the seventeenth century.

Highly regarded everywhere abroad, he remained unnoticed and even opposed by the official, academic circles in his own country, so that they left him alone to live and die in his fiftieth year without even giving him a knighthood. And that in a country where the most sterile artistic mediocrities are showered with decorations. The same thing happened with Faruffini and Cremona here and with Millet in France and . . . the whole world is a field for official academism. But the works remain and each of them – and they number in their hundreds – will make his memory shine more than any mere empty honour and will transmit to posterity the imperishable name, surrounded by a nimbus of devout veneration, of the poet-painter Anton Mauve. To the mourning of his grieving Dutch confrères and of true, cosmopolitan, sincere art is added the sorrow of the Italian fatherland, cradle of the arts.[26]

Arntzenius commemorated Mauve in *De Gids*: 'People have spoken of the grey school, but Mauve said, if my paintings are grey, then they are no good. If they had called it the silver school, that would have indicated my intentions better'.[27] Two years later there followed a memorial exhibition in Pulchri Studio.

Retrospective exhibitions and announcements of deaths in the years that followed indicated that the Hague School could no longer lay claim to the élan of youth, but it seemed almost rejuvenated nevertheless. Artists like Jacob Maris and Jozef Israëls succeeded in changing their styles yet again at the end of the nineteenth century, Maris to the use of brighter colour and a freer brush-stroke and Israëls to an even quieter and more atmospheric palette and to subjects almost completely devoid of anecdotal details or elements, such as *The Evening of Life* (1907, fig. 79) or the *Self Portrait* with the painting of David and Saul in the background (Cat. 45). Weissenbruch, too, developed a broader use of paint in the last decade of the century in impressions of nature that used large areas of monochrome – his paintings were saturated with colour, his watercolours ethereal and transparent. At this period his work at last began to enjoy the great admiration that had, in contrast with Israëls and Mesdag, been withheld from him for so long. For Gabriël, too, fame came late. Meanwhile, Willem Maris increasingly painted nothing but the light that he so loved to see sparkling over reeds, willow boughs and cattle by the

fig. 80 The Jozef Israëls Memorial Exhibition, Toledo Museum of Art, 1912; a contemporary photograph of some of the paintings in the exhibition

waterside. Matthijs Maris, who had settled in London, would scarcely part with any paintings any more. He worked on the same pictures over and over again, continuing to paint until it was almost impossible to make out the subject any longer. Mesdag had become the president of Pulchri Studio and under his inspiring leadership one exhibition followed another, both in The Hague and abroad.

There was no question of a decline in the Hague School; if any objections were raised to it, they were precisely against its apparent inviolability and its unshakeable position, based mainly on the unremitting support of foreign critics and collectors. Works by the Hague School were to be seen all over the world: Milan, Chicago, Barcelona, St. Louis, Buenos Aires, San Francisco. But the ranks were beginning to thin. Mauve's death was followed by those of Artz (1890), Bosboom (1891), Roelofs (1897) and Jacob Maris (1899), while Weissenbruch and Gabriël both died in 1903.

Israëls and Mesdag, however, were to find still further glories. They had held seats on the *Comitato di Patrocinio* of the Venice Biennale since its institution in 1895, while Zilcken was special commissioner for prints. Their counterparts were in France Gustave Moreau and Puvis de Chavannes, in Germany Max Liebermann and in Italy Giovanni Boldini. The 1895 catalogue described the careers of Israëls and Mesdag in detail from their earliest youth. At the Fifth Biennale in 1905 Mesdag and Grubicy were represented in the same room, Grubicy by, for example, *Echo of Holland* or *In Scheveningen* and Mesdag by *Winter in Scheveningen* and *The North Sea*; two years later Mesdag lent works from his own collection by masters of the Hague School who had already died. At the Biennale of 1910, a year before his death, Jozef Israëls was honoured by a *Mostra individuale* comprising 37 paintings and five drawings, an act of homage which quite overwhelmed the old painter.[28] In 1911 further honours followed, this time at the International Exhibition in Rome, where the entire Hague School was represented in the *Sezione retrospettiva*: Bosboom, the Maris brothers, Mauve, Mesdag and his wife, Gabriël and Tholen. But it was to Mesdag that the greatest honour fell: the purchase of a painting (*The Fisherman's Return*) for the collection of the new Galleria Nazionale d'Arte Moderna in Rome, where it is still preserved today.[29]

fig. 79 J. ISRAËLS *The Evening of Life*
(Haags Gemeentemuseum, The Hague)

The Hague novelist Louis Couperus, who was at that time living abroad and who wrote occasional impressionistic pieces for a Dutch journal, was asked by his editors to compile an article about the exhibition in Rome. The way in which he wrote about the Hague School reveals that for him it was bound up with the past, with his own youthful memories as an aspiring writer.

A sudden wave of emotion passed through me! I would see Dutch painters again. Modern Dutch painters! I had not seen them . . . since the last exhibition at . . . Venice! And now, they were exhibiting in Rome! I can assure you, dear reader, that I went to the Belli Arti next morning with a heart pounding in anticipation. It was so strange: it was as if I had returned to my own country. That far off, damp, cold country that was sometimes so uncordial to me, that country full of cold Dutchmen, so stiff and severe to me, who was so used to Southern sun and Southern cordiality. . . . For I felt around me the atmosphere of my country which, strangely, I love, although I do not live there, although I am seldom there: I felt around me the atmosphere that had woven itself round the years of my boyhood and youth. . . .

Here, in this room, are the jewels of our great contemporary masters and they must truly strike the foreigner as dazzling. . . . How those Bosboom churches move me. . . . How beautiful and sensitive they are, with that white light over their stout walls and that solitary sparkle in the brass chandeliers. . . . All of a sudden I see the painter himself before me again, as I used to encounter him in The Hague, on Veenlaan – isn't that its name? – grey, friendly and jovial, and he would catch hold of me by the lapel of my coat and he would talk and talk and then ask, 'Won't you come and have a cup of tea again . . .?'

Couperus then goes on to relate his reminiscences of Bosboom's wife, who was renowned for her historical novels and to whom he had given his own first novels to read. After that he returns to the exhibition again and in the following passage succeeds in creating a brilliant evocation of it for his readers in the Netherlands:

What a lot that is grand and beautiful we can proudly point out to the foreigner. Those wonderfully fine interior atmospheres of Israëls, that transparent tissue of light and air dissolving into an ethereal haze devoid of any fixed colour, both indoors and out; the greyness that is feeling, the melancholy that is mollification; the sombreness that is sometimes the wistful tenderness of the old, but never becomes disconsolate . . . who can be compared with him for so many gems, which do not sparkle with colour, but which are the dreams of the poet of our enveloping mists, the painter of the veiled light that scarcely breaks out but only filters, grey and musing, through the houses of care and sorrow or gleams in the staring eyes of weary toilers and drudges . . . ? Here is the self portrait of the Master, and yes, he it is . . . and behind his likeness broods Saul's dejection and trills David's harp, because he saw not only the grey beauty of the Present, but also the illuminating legends of the Past. . . .

I breathe the air of my country. . . . A little, fine dune piece by Mauve here and there an obsessively murky black sky, with against it the tragic gesture of a windmill by Weissenbruch; ever-changing is the atmosphere of my country around me: Gabriël gives me the wide Dutch lakes under a wide, cloudy sky; Van Assen the heath-pastures bounded by a tree-clad horizon, Van Soest the desolation of our winter; Breitner the quiet beauty of the canals in our cities, along which dejected horses trudge. . . .[30]

A splendid tribute to the talents of the Hague School painters, albeit a posthumous one for most of them, but with its gaze unmistakably turned on the past. The admiration of younger artists like Toorop and Mondriaan was mingled with doubts as to whether art actually would continue to go in the same direction, while the Futurists, Boccioni in particular, bracketed Jozef Israëls with Sargent, Franz Stuck and Zuloaga, and placed them all in the category of '*incarnazione negativa*', stripped of any real significance.[31] The painters of the Hague School themselves, however, had little or no awareness of the rise of this new generation, who were to explode the Hague School's artistic achievement and exalted position with their own dynamic art.

NOTES

1. See Jan Veth, *Portretstudies en silhouetten*, 'Breitners jeugd', Amsterdam 1908, p. 186.
2. See C. Hans Tiepen, *Willem Maris Herinneringen*, The Hague 1910.
3. P. Zilcken, *Herinneringen van een Hollandsche Schilder der negentiende eeuw 1877–1927*, ms. in the Netherlands Institute for Art History, The Hague, see pp. 14–18.
4. *Ibid.*, p. 20.
5. There is insufficient space here to consider in detail the significance of these artists. For more information see J. de Gruyter, *De Haagse School*, Rotterdam 1968 and P.A. Scheen, *Lexicon Nederlandse Beeldende Kunstenaars 1750–1880*, The Hague 1981.
6. See J.J. Th. Sillevis, exh. cat. *Max Liebermann en Holland,* Haags Gemeentemuseum, The Hague 1980, p. 25.
7. Letter dated 18 January 1893 from Max Liebermann to Jan Veth, Rijksprentenkabinet, Rijksmuseum, Amsterdam.
8. Letter dated 1893 from Max Liebermann to Jan Veth, Rijksprentenkabinet, Rijksmuseum, Amsterdam.
9. See P. Paret, *Die Berliner Sezession, Moderne Kunst und ihre Feinde im Kaiserlichen Deutschland*, Berlin 1981, p. 372.
10. See M. Liebermann, *Berliner Sezession*, Berlin 1901, pp. 12, 13. Bosboom was represented by *Church Interior*; Van Gogh by *Self Portrait in a Fur Hat, Park at Arles, Garden in Provence, Landscape at St Rémy* and *Flat Landscape*; Jozef Israëls by *Growing Old* and *Along the Fields*; Isaac Israëls by *Portrait of a Lady*; Jacob Maris by *Summer on the Beach, River Scene, Dordrecht, Weary* and *Portrait of my Sister*; Willem Maris by *Milking Time*.
11. See M. Liebermann. *Jozef Israëls*, Berlin 1901, reprinted in M. Liebermann, *Die Phantasie in der Malerei*, Herausgabe G. Busch, Frankfurt am Main 1978, p. 83.
12. See P. Zilcken, *op. cit.*, pp. 20a, 20b. Paul Hefting wrongly changed the date of Grubicy's arrival in The Hague to 1884–5 in his dissertation *G.H. Breitner in zijn Haagse tijd*, Utrecht 1970, p. 78 and note 37 (p. 114). According to Grubicy himself, he was in The Hague from 1882 until 1885; see letter dated 14 February 1910 from Grubicy to Benvenuto Benvenuti printed in *Archivi del Divisionismo*, ed. T. Fiori, Rome 1968, vol. I. pp. 106, 107, 108. Hefting based his statement on E.P. Engels's dissertation *Anton Mauve* (Utrecht 1967), which limits the contact between Mauve and Grubicy to a meeting in Hotel Hamdorff in Laren on the basis of Wally Moes's memoirs, *Heilig ongeduld*.
13. These works are now in an Italian private collection.
14. See L. Vitali, exh. cat. *Incisioni lombarde del secondo ottocento all'Ambrosiana*, Vicenza 1970, cat. no. 61, illustrated in *Archivi del Divisionismo*, vol. II, fig. 49.
15. Letter dated 14 February 1910 from Grubicy to Benvenuto Benvenuti printed in *Archivi del Divisionismo*, ed. T. Fiori, Rome 1968, vol. I, pp. 106, 107, 108.

16. See *The Complete Letters of Vincent van Gogh*, New York 1958, letter 175.
17. Copy of letter in archives of the Netherlands Institute for Art History, The Hague.
18. For a survey of his contributions to Dutch exhibitions between 1882 and 1900 see J.J.T. Sillevis in exh. cat. *Verso l'astrattismo, Mondrian e la Scuola dell'Aia*, Florence, Milan, 1981–2, p. 22.
19. 'She [Eline Vere] was delighted: she had seen fans by Bucchi, unmade up and opened out behind glass, at the exhibition of paintings at the Academy last summer and she suddenly remembered now that she had admired them very much and expressed the wish to possess one of them . . .'; cf. M. Klein and H. Ruijs, *Over Eline Vere van Louis Couperus*, Amsterdam 1981, pp. 58–61.
20. Exh. cats. *Tentoonstelling van Schilderijen en Teekeningen door den Italiaanschen Kunstschilder Antonio Mancini te Rome*, Pulchri Studio, The Hague Oct.-Nov. 1897 (30 paintings, 8 drawings); *Tentoonstelling van schilderijen en pastels*, Pulchri Studio, The Hague 1902 (47 entries).
21. P. Mellen, *The group of seven*, Toronto 1970, p. 5.
21. See exh. cat. *First annual exhibition in the United States of the Society of Painters in Watercolours of Holland*, opening February 1895 at the galleries of Boussod, Valadon & Co. successors to Goupil & Co., Paris, 303 Fifth Avenue Corner 31st Street, New York; cf. *Notulen van de Hollandsche Teeken-Maatschappij 1876–1901*, The Hague 1914, published by W.B. Tholen, p. 55. Here it says that the Metropolitan Museum acquired works by Christoffel Bisschop, Jacob Maris and Albert Neuhuys.
23. P. Zilcken, *op. cit.*, p. 58.
24. P. Zilcken, 'Studio Talk', *The Studio* vol. 9 (1896–7).
25. *Idem*, 'Studio Talk', *The Studio*, (1898) p. 130.
26. Vittore Grubicy de Dragon in *La Riforma*, 15 February 1888; printed in translation in Dutch newspaper. Cutting in Mauve archives, the Netherlands Institute for Art History (R.K.D.), The Hague.
27. See A.R. Arntzenius, 'Anton Mauve', *De Gids*, March 1888, pp. 564–70.
28. See exh. cat. *IX. Esposizione Internazionale d'Arte della città di Venezia*, Venice 1910, pp. 54–8.
29. See Gianna Piantoni, exh. cat. *Roma 1911*, Galleria Nazionale d'Arte Moderna, Rome 1980, pp. 134, 135 with illus. and bibliography; cf. *Esposizione Internazionale di Roma, Catalogo della Mostra di Belle Arti*, Rome 1911, pp. 40, 41.
30. Louis Couperus, 'De Hollandse schilders' in *Van en over Alles en Iedereen*, Rome II, Amsterdam, (n.d.), pp. 53–61.
31. See U. Boccioni, *Pittura scultura futuriste (Dinamismo plastico)*, Milan 1914, p. 30, cited in C. Maltese, *Storia dell'Arte in Italia 1785–1943*, Turin 1960, p. 289.

The Avant-Garde (1885-1910)

RONALD DE LEEUW

By the 1880s the artists of the Hague School had unobtrusively become part of the artistic establishment; once they had been awarded prizes and medals at the Paris Salon the public in their own country could no longer ignore them. Thus, although most of the artists' work went abroad in the early years of the School, this changed later in the century. In 1873, it was possible for Victor de Stuers to declare in his controversial article 'The Narrow-mindedness of the Dutch', that even established masters like Bosboom and Israëls were still not represented in the national collection,[1] but shortly afterwards the leading Dutch museums did hesitantly begin to acquire their first works by Mauve and the Maris brothers. Even so, the Boymans Museum's purchase of Jacob Maris's *The Baker* in 1889 caused Charles Rochussen, the doyen of painting in Rotterdam, to resign from the Supervisory Committee after 20 years' membership. In reality, this represented little more than a final protest by the conservatives; the Hague masters had finally won public acceptance and they were to enjoy their position as part of the artistic establishment for a long time to come.

The years in which a particular school of painting establishes its reputation are usually marked by the growth of a new movement, and the 1880s and 1890s were indeed a period of many new ideas in Dutch art. The unique work of Vincent van Gogh is discussed elsewhere, but there were a number of other painters born around 1860 who shaped the development of Dutch art during the final two decades of the century. We will concentrate here on five such artists: George Hendrik Breitner (1857–1923), Willem Witsen (1860–1923), Isaac Israëls (1865–1934), Jan Toorup (1858–1928) and Johan Thorn Prikker (1869–1932). This chapter will examine the extent to which the Hague School had a formative influence on them and where they themselves felt they stood in relation to the elder generation. The other artists of the day can be mentioned only in passing.

The aims of this new generation are generally seen as a direct reaction to the 'superficial' art of the Hague School, a Dutch form of Post-Impressionism, but this interpretation is not entirely correct. However successful the Hague artists may have been commercially, they had been very slow to receive official recognition and in consequence had retained their image as progressive innovators much longer than might otherwise have been expected. It says much about the nature of

their reputation that *De Nieuwe Gids*, an important mouthpiece of the younger generation of artists, would still take a serious stand in defence of Hague Impressionism.

One reason for the Hague masters' popularity with the younger generation was their reputation for being straightforward and approachable, with none of the airs and graces of the stiff academicians against whom the young French artists had to fight.

Nor could they be accused of resting on their laurels. Although the commercialism of Israëls, the Maris brothers and Mesdag did not go uncriticized, it was acknowleged that most of them still continued to develop within the bounds of the principle 'art for art's sake'. Weissenbruch's late paintings and watercolours were hailed as a high point in Dutch landscape painting. The lyricism evoked in some of the late canvases of the normally conventional Willem Maris was equally surprising: the powerful atmospheric effects in some of his late work can be compared only with the sensitive poetry of Herman Gorter.[2] And when Jacob Maris stopped painting towns under white cloud-covered skies, he too could astonish with his delicate dune landscapes that were often reminiscent of Ruisdael.

Even Bosboom had grown closer to the new Hague School artists in his final years, while Jozef Israëls, the other heir to the tradition of Rembrandt, was considered by many to have painted his finest work at an advanced age. It appears that the new ideas introduced by Symbolism and Post-Impressionism struck a long-neglected chord in him, making him eager to return to the themes of his early years as a history painter, which he had later dropped because they had not suited his role as a leading realist. Now, as the grand old man of the Hague School, he sometimes abandoned the world of the Scheveningen fishermen for that of the Old Testament. *Adam and Eve*, *Saul and David* (fig. 81), *The Jewish Scribe* and *The Jewish Wedding* were immediately recognized by contemporaries as challenges to Rembrandt. That Israëls painted his most important self portrait (Cat. 45) with the biblical figures of Saul and David in the background is indicative of the new role in which he saw himself. He had a high reputation as a counsellor and mentor of younger painters, although he does not seem to have appreciated the greatness of Van Gogh.[3]

Mauve, from whom much was expected, died at an unexpectedly early age in 1888. His last work had caused a

fig. 81 J. ISRAËLS *Saul and David*
(Stedelijk Museum, Amsterdam)

great controversy and he had even been accused of betraying the principles of the Hague School by settling in Laren. Although he was known primarily as a painter in silvery grey, around 1880 he had rediscovered colour and his work had gained in clarity. Thanks to him Laren became a centre for young artists, many of whom came from nearby Amsterdam.

Despite the reputation for progressiveness enjoyed by the Hague School masters, Jan Veth later declared that many of the younger generation regarded them as artists to admire rather than emulate. That his judgement was a personal opinion is apparent from the countless band of imitators that sprang up and continued until well into the present century, far beyond the limits of this exhibition. These artists often concentrated on a single aspect of one of the great masters and, despite their limitations, their work continued in demand on the art market for years to come. Breitner dubbed such painters 'real tradesmen, wretched hacks',4 and they can be held responsible for much of the adverse reaction to the Hague School among modern artists. In Dordrecht, a group of minor masters whose work was fairly attractive maintained the heritage of Jacob Maris until quite recently,5 but, of all Hague School masters, Mauve was the most imitated. An initially promising painter like Pieter ter Meulen (1843–1927), one of the few peripheral figures of the School to write a worthwhile article about landscape painting,6 ultimately progressed no further than echoing Mauve's sheep and timber carts. Breitner's friend H.J. van der Weele (1852–1930) was slightly better, but it is painful to see how a painter like J.F.C. Scherrewitz could be content year in and year out with the repetition of two or three motifs. No wonder the critic Vogelsang wrote in 1904 of a generation 'weakened by thousands of dilutions and adulterations of a good example'.7

Laren

The 'innovations' of the Laren School appear in retrospect to have been nothing more than a shift in emphasis. After Mauve's death there were no new impulses and the School's work became a quagmire of cloyingly sweet pictures. Nevertheless, a visit to Laren was important for several younger artists, most of whom had trained at the Rijksacademie (National Academy) in Amsterdam. In her autobiography *Holy Impatience* the painter Wally Moes (1856–1918) described the comings and goings of young artists, who included foreign artists like Vittore Grubicy (1851–1920) and

Max Liebermann (1847–1935); 'but Anton Mauve was the heart and soul of the party. Everyone felt the charm that he radiated.'8 In the middle of the 1880s Mauve encountered there 'a collection of people who are just right for me'.9 Here he was referring to Etha Fles, Jan Veth and Willem Witsen, artists who met regularly during those years at Ewijkshoeve near Baarn, the country-house of Witsen's parents.

The painter Jan Veth's (1864–1925) fondness for the Hague School was of great consequence for their later reputation. 'Rembrandt, Millet and Jaap [Maris], there you have the artistic trio that constitutes my holy trinity', he wrote in 1886.10 Although he himself was primarily a portraitist and worked in a completely different style (see figs. 137 and 138), he held dear the art of the Hague School. As a critic at the turn of the century, he was one of the School's most intelligent advocates and much of the information we have about the artists came from pieces he wrote. In addition, he left us a series of striking portraits of them.

However, the contact between Willem Witsen and Anton Mauve was more interesting in artistic terms. Between October 1884 and November 1888 Witsen made regular visits to Ewijkshoeve, often with two other painters, Willem Tholen (1860–1931) and Piet Meiners (1857–1903), who later died there. Witsen's style was then not yet sharply defined, and his association with Mauve left clear traces in his work. They shared a great admiration for Millet (Witsen visited the Millet exhibition in Paris in 1887 and devoted an article to it in *De Nieuwe Gids*) and for a long time worked alongside one another, taking as their subject-matter potato gatherers, shepherds and vegetable gardens. Engel has suggested in his book on Mauve that the contact with the young Amsterdammers was an important stimulus for Mauve, and that it may be seen in his increased interest in the figures in his landscapes.11

A series of canvases in the Witsenhuis clearly show Mauve's influence on Witsen. His friend, the painter and writer Jacob van Looy, even felt obliged to write to him from Rome, advising him not to fall too heavily under Mauve's spell. His themes and the style of his painting (the play of light on clods of earth) are also astonishingly similar to Mauve's (fig. 82). Witsen used many of these canvases as the basis for etchings. His first contributions to the portfolios of the Nederlandsche Etsclub (Dutch Etching Club) were a *Shepherd Beside a Ditch* (1886) and a *Woodland Road with Cart Tracks* (1887). These early etchings also include a number of snowy woodland scenes, which are much indebted to Mauve, as well as two portraits of that artist. Witsen also occasionally reproduced works by artists of the Hague School. There is a reference to an etching after a painting by Jan Hendrik Weissenbruch in a letter from the dealer Cornelis Marinus van Gogh to P. Haverkorn van Rijsewijk12 while a *Church at Dordrecht* after Jacob Maris was included in Jan Veth's *Annals of Dutch Painting*, which appeared from 1896 onwards. Witsen clearly did not regard these early etchings as in any way dated, since nearly all of them were published by Van Wisselingh in new states around 1906.13

De Nederlandse Etsclub (Dutch Etching Club)

In 1885 a Dutch Etching Club was founded on the initiative of Jan Veth, Willem Witsen and Antoon Derkinderen.14 Their attempt to breathe new life into the somewhat languishing art of etching had been prompted mainly by their admiration for the achievements of the Hague *peintres-graveurs*. Etching had

fig. 82 WITSEN *Woman Gathering Potatoes* (Witsenhuis, Amsterdam; on loan to Dienst Verspreide Rijkskollekties, The Hague)

largely been a prerogative of the artists in The Hague; the new society even had a distinguished precursor in the Hague Etching Club.[15] Jozef Israëls, Anton Mauve, Jacob and Matthijs Maris had all built up a modest *oeuvre* in this field, but the Hague School artists' image in graphic art had been determined mainly by Philip Zilcken's reproductions, which had ensured that their art was very widely disseminated.

Several Hague masters contributed to the albums published by the Etsclub between 1885 and 1896; Blommers, Israëls, Jacob Maris, Mauve and Neuhuys each supplied one or more etchings. Even Mesdag participated, although at first Veth had opposed this. Unfortunately, his contribution merely elicited the sarcastic comment that it would make a first-rate vignette for a menu. But the invitation to the Hague artists did not spring solely from admiration of their work. There was undoubtedly also a degree of opportunism in the minds of the organizers. Veth wrote to Zilcken in 1889, 'Why do we invite people? Because, it seems to me, we think their work is *beautiful* or *important*'. It was for these reasons that he gave preference to the work of Max Liebermann, *chef d'école* of the young Germans, over that of certain Hague masters, such as Weissenbruch, 'whose work can be seen at all Dutch exhibitions. No one can take it amiss that we invite the three

acknowledged greats as representatives of our own country. If we keep to that, then no-one else is passed over, but if we admit only one more in addition, then two others will naturally follow, and so on and so forth.'[16]

The exhibitions of the Etsclub, held alternately in The Hague and Amsterdam, were not limited to Dutch work. Prints by the leading graphic artists of other countries, such as Redon, Rops, Whistler, Seymour Haden and Klinger, were also shown there. When the Club was disbanded in 1896, it was noted with satisfaction that etching had flourished so much in the intervening period that special encouragement was no longer necessary.

Amsterdam

It has become a commonplace of Dutch art history that the Hague School was followed by an Amsterdam School; it is also often suggested that the Amsterdammers developed in a quite different direction from their predecessors. Their characteristics have been defined purely in antithesis to those of the Hague School as a preference for townscapes, colour and movement – as opposed to the landscapes, grey palette and static tranquillity of the Hague School. In reality, the relationship between the two schools was much less clearcut.

fig. 83 WITSEN *Warehouses on an Amsterdam Canal*
(Rijksmuseum, Amsterdam; on loan to the Amsterdam Historisch
Museum, Amsterdam)

fig. 84 KARSEN *In the Harz Mountains*
(Rijksmuseum, Amsterdam; on loan to Dienst Verspreide
Rijkskollekties, The Hague)

Some of these contrasts may be seen in the early Amsterdam
work of Breitner and Israëls, but it is impossible to apply them
to most of the other artists who are included in the group.

Thus Willem Witsen was eventually to become the painter
par excellence of the static Amsterdam townscape from which
he completely excluded dynamic figures (fig. 83). This has
been seen in part as an inheritance from The Hague, as has his
preference for monochrome. And it is impossible to see Geo
Poggenbeek (1853–1903) and Nicolaas Bastert (1854–1939),
both students of the National Academy, as anything but
Amsterdammers who became Hague artists by adoption. The
work of Edouard Karsen (fig. 84), enveloped in 'faery dreams
and sunny thoughts' (Albert Verwey), primarily evokes
associations with Matthijs Maris, while controversy still rages
over the school to which Willem de Zwart (1862–1931) really
belonged. Nor can the Amsterdam-trained river painter Jan
Voerman in any way be described as dynamic, urban or
colourful.[17] It is evident that the power of the work of
Breitner and Israëls had created the image of a school that
should not really be defined as such. Thus Hammacher wisely
speaks of the 'Amsterdam impressionists and their circle' in his
book.

The diversity of the Amsterdam painters was primarily the
result of their very divergent backgrounds. Moreover, they
had extremely close links with the literary groups of the 1880s
and 1890s, and followed developments abroad very closely.
Thus their ideas about art could change more rapidly in a single
month than those of the Hague School artists did in decades.

Most of the young Amsterdammers met each other at the
Rijksacademie (National Academy), the leading art school in
the country, which since 1879 had been under the direction of
August Allebé (1838–1927). This artist belonged to the same
generation as the Marises. As a genre and figure painter August
Allebé shared the realist's fresh approach to their subject
matter. His style of painting was not very different from that
of the young Jacob Maris, but he never abandoned the
perfected, finished form. For this reason he followed the
developments of the Hague School with some misgivings.
Although he was known as a tolerant master who allowed his
students wide scope, he remained emphatically opposed to the
formlessness and vagueness of some Hague School work,
upholding the tradition of structured, finished compositions,
so that the term 'an Allebé man' became synonymous with
'anti-Hague School'.

The chair of aesthetics and art history at the National
Academy had been occupied since 1876 by the influential
Josephus Alberdingk Thijm. A bastion of reactionary theory,
'daubing and splashing', as he called impressionistic art, were
anathema to him. Jan Veth, who was himself a student at the
Academy until 1885, called his former teacher 'a mass of
assumed professorial ignorance' in an article in *De Nieuwe Gids*
in 1887.

Despite this, there was certainly no shortage of new ideas at
the Academy for in 1884 the artist Anthon van Rappard, a
friend of Vincent van Gogh, informed the art-loving public in
Utrecht that a new movement had appeared at the Academy
and that it was 'making great advances and already entering
the lists with honour alongside the so-called Hague School'.
He outlined the aims of the movement by describing it as 'the
school of drawing, of form, whatever you like to call it'.[18]
Despite this obvious difference in their basic premises, the
Amsterdammers and the Hague School artists shared a
penchant for the 'pictorial' and the goal of 'pure painterly
sentiment'. Van Rappard defined this sentiment as 'the
language of an artist's heart', but stated that this should never
be imposed on a work of art, since it ought to be allowed to
emerge from the paint itself. He considered it to have been
perfectly captured in a beach scene by Jacob Maris: 'The
feeling is certainly expressed in that infinite colour, but the
sentiment itself – one feels it, one doesn't see it'.[19]

fig. 85 I. Israëls *Bugle Practice* 1881 (Rijksmuseum H. W. Mesdag, The Hague)

Hammacher's view that the young painters who came together in Amsterdam 'had not yet broken away from the Hague formula, but wanted to do so, which united them in opposition even though they could not be called a "school"', is surely apt.[20] As well as trying to achieve a greater firmness of form, these artists undoubtedly preferred more intense colour. We have seen elsewhere how some Hague artists had already abandoned grey in the 1880s. The fluid colours of Jacob Maris's late work are almost a match for those of Breitner. However, this was obviously a question of degree: for an artist as obsessed by colour as Johan Thorn Prikker was around 1895, there was little, if any, difference between the 'dirt-coloured Breitners, Marises, Tholens, jet-black Israëlses'.[21]

Given these tendencies in the work of the Hague School artists, it is not surprising that the final crystallization of so-called Amsterdam Impressionism was ultimately precipitated by two artists who were trained in the Hague taking up residence there. Breitner moved to Amsterdam in 1886, to be followed by Isaac Israëls the year after. Both enrolled at the National Academy, where Israëls soon realized that he could learn nothing more. Essentially, he was an infant prodigy and although he probably began by copying some of his father's work,[22] he quickly struck out on a path of his own. The journeys on which Israëls accompanied his father brought him into regular contact with the French art of the day, and the constant coming and going of foreigners in his parents' house gave him a cosmopolitan flair. His work won early success. As early as 1883, he won a first prize in Amsterdam for his *Bugle Practice* (fig. 85), a work which Mesdag had reserved for his collection before it was finished, and which was said by Jan Veth to have inspired Jozef Israëls to paint his great *Sewing School at Katwijk* (fig. 86).[23]

In 1885, Isaac followed the example of Bosboom and Van Gogh and spent some time in the Borinage, the Belgian mining district, and in 1887 he set up on his own in

fig. 86 J. Israëls *The Sewing School at Katwijk* (The Taft Museum, Cincinnati)

Amsterdam. There he worked in the same manner as Breitner, favouring scenes of street and night life. Unfortunately, the two fell out over a trifle, a quarrel over a model, and Isaac began to shift his attention, eventually to the fashionable aspects of big city life, in particular in Paris and London, which he preferred to Amsterdam. He also emerged as a figure painter, although on the visits that he made to Scheveningen he painted the visitors rather than the fishing people. This sunny side of Scheveningen had been assiduously avoided by the Hague School artists, with the odd exception among Mauve's works, but Isaac Israëls and the other young Hague painters like Akkeringa, Arntzenius and De Jonge found it very attractive as subject-matter.

Breitner's early years and development, which were influenced principally by magazine illustrations and the

fig. 87 BREITNER *The Damrak, Amsterdam* (Rijksmuseum, Amsterdam)

history painter Charles Rochussen, were far more difficult than those of the infant prodigy Israëls. His career began inauspiciously, when he was expelled from the Hague Academy in 1880 for misbehaviour. That same year he came into contact with Willem Maris and Mesdag through the artist Van der Maarel. Mesdag in particular recognized Breitner's qualities and lost no time in securing his assistance on his Panorama, for which Breitner undertook to paint not only the cavalry on the beach, but also the village of Scheveningen. At around this time Mesdag also purchased *Reconnoitring in the Dunes*, a picture of a mounted hussar Breitner painted in the garden of Willem Maris's house at Oud Rozenburg.[24]

From 1880 onwards Hague themes frequently appear in Breitner's work. A *Girl in the Grass* is close to the work of Jacob and Willem Maris, while subjects such as boats on the beach, a woman mending clothes in an interior, women gathering potatoes and woodcutters show his interest in Millet and Mauve. Like Vincent van Gogh he explored the working-class districts of The Hague for a time, looking for themes that the other Hague artists had not yet touched. In the summer of 1882 he sent work to the exhibition of the Haagse Teeken-Maatschappij (Hague Drawing Society), but it was turned down; Willem Maris later told him that its admission had been vetoed by Mauve and Israëls.[25]

In 1884 Breitner worked at Cormon's studio in Paris, where Henri Toulouse-Lautrec and Émile Bernard were among his fellow students. The street scenes that he painted in Montmartre were a prelude to his later work in Amsterdam. The following year he visited the heathlands of Drenthe with

Willem de Zwart, but the landscape subjects there evidently did not inspire him. He settled in Amsterdam in 1886 and, hoping to improve his technique, he enrolled at the Academy of Professor Alberdingk Thijm who two years earlier had spoken of the meaningless 'landscape daubs of Mr Breitner'.[26] That year, 1886, he first established a name for himself with *Horse Artillery*, a painting full of colour and movement which was not only enthusiastically received by the press, but also bought by the Rijksmuseum. The young Amsterdammers immediately recognized Breitner as their leader.

There is no room here to describe Breitner's fascinating paintings of Amsterdam life, but the changing relationship between these works and those of his Hague period should be noted. After 1884, his vision was greatly influenced by photography. His handling of chiaroscuro became ever more dramatic, his touch and tone heavier. In particular, his admiration for close-up photographic techniques led him to close in on his subjects, so that the sky, which had been the determining factor in Hague Impressionism, often completely disappeared from the picture.

It has been noted elsewhere that Breitner's work seemed to lose some of its energy at the end of the 1890s and that his dynamism completely vanished after 1901, the year of the successful retrospective exhibition. He returned to quieter themes which seem to hark back to the world of Jacob Maris. Views of snow-covered boats lying on the frozen canals (fig. 87) became a leitmotiv in this later work. Like Maris, who had discovered the beauty of the Dutch canal towns, Breitner began to see the city more as a landscape, and the figures which had so enlivened his street scenes disappeared from his paintings. It is certainly no coincidence that it was Breitner who was the active organizer of the two Maris exhibitions at Arti et Amicitiae in 1892 and in 1899.

The Hague

In 1891, the Haagsche Kunstkring (Hague Art Society) was founded and Pulchri Studio ceased to be the only meeting place for artists and art-lovers in The Hague. This confirmed the advent of a new generation of artists who felt unable to find a place within the Hague School, of which Pulchri had become the symbol. The Society formulated broader objectives than those of Pulchri Studio, which was purely a painters' society. It distinguished itself from the very start by speaking in its rules of 'the furtherance of: painting, sculpture, *belles lettres*, music and the applied arts, and the linking up and working together of the practitioners of these different arts', thus clearly basing itself on the theory of cross-fertilization of the arts as propagated by Wagner in his *Gesamtkunstwerk*, which became an important manifesto in the Netherlands during the 1880s.[27]

The first general president of the Society, Théophile de Bock (1851–1904), himself a minor master of the Hague School and an acquaintance of Breitner and Van Gogh, had belonged in the 1870s to another progressive group of Hague artists, who met at the Café 't Vlondertje and later found a mouthpiece in the periodical *De Banier*. Marcellus Emants, the first chairman of the literary section of the Kunstkring, and Jan van Santen Kolff had both written many articles for *De Banier*, in which Van Santen Kolff championed Zola's novels, Wagner's operas and the realistic painting of the Hague, which for him embodied the same artistic philosophy. Thus he would compare the painting *Burial on the Island of Marken* with the funeral march from *Götterdämmerung,* while recognizing the same qualities in Israëls's *Sewing School* and Wagner's spinning chorus in the *Flying Dutchman*.

The Brussels artists' society Les Vingt was one of the inspirations for the foundation of the Haagsche Kunstkring, but it is not entirely clear why it was found necessary to set up a new body at all. Simon Moulijn, for instance, a founder member of the Kunstkring, remarked that there was little evidence of new objectives in the young artists' work at their first exhibition. One possible reason was that the younger artists were no longer finding it so easy to make a name at the now moribund Pulchri Studio; in particular they were put off by Mesdag's heavy hand.[28] But the choice of De Bock as the Kunstkring's first president indicates that no abrupt break was made with the style of the Hague School. On the contrary, one of the first things that the Society did was to exhibit the sketchbooks of Johannes Bosboom, who had just died. In 1892 it organized the first exhibition devoted entirely to the three Maris brothers, and this was followed by similar acts of homage to Mauve and Weissenbruch. The masters of the grey palette were also represented at the Internationale Invitatie-Tentoonstelling (International Invitation Exhibition) organized by the Kunstkring in 1895 alongside artists like Redon, Degouve de Nuncques and Segantini. In 1899 Jozef Israëls was invited to speak to the Society about his visit to Spain and was apparently very well received.

The Kunstkring owed its image as a successful *avant-garde* artists' society almost entirely to Jan Toorop, who as chairman of the painting section helped to organize numerous events soon after its foundation. Thus he introduced members to

Neo-Impressionism – the work of Seurat, Signac and some of his Belgian friends – and gave them their first contact with the work of Odilon Redon, Vincent van Gogh and Toulouse-Lautrec through various exhibitions he organized. Lugne-Poë's Théâtre de l'Oeuvre performed Ibsen and Maeterlinck there, and Chausson and Vincent d'Indy played their own music at informal recitals. Toorop also invited lecturers such as Henry van de Velde, Sâr Péladan and Paul Verlaine. Many younger artists of the symbolist movement found the meetings and events at the Kunstkring stimulating and attended regularly. Here we follow two, Jan Toorop and Thorn Prikker, more closely in their relation to the Hague School.

Jan Toorop

Toorop's work in the 1890s is an intriguing instance of stylistic confrontation between the experiments of the moderns and the tried and tested manner of the Hague School. There are particularly striking resemblances between his work and that of Jozef Israëls. When Toorop returned to the Netherlands in 1891 after a long stay in Belgium, he chose to live not in The Hague, but in the isolation of Katwijk. Later he did go to The Hague because his work for the Art Society was so time-consuming but initially he devoted himself entirely to an almost obsessional study of life in the fishing villages. Jozef Israëls had, after his early dramatic pictures, been interested mainly in the charming and homely aspects of fishing people's lives, the women knitting and children at play (Cat. 31 and 33), but for Toorop the fascination lay primarily in man's struggle against the elements, 'the fanaticism of those people who as ever are harried and pursued by dark death'.[29] Sometimes it was the contrast between this old world and the modern age that engrossed him, as in the *Venus of the Sea* or *Hetaere*, which shows a father and mother 'bewailing the loss of their child, who is leaving the simple fishing village for more worldly affluence'.[30]

Toorop's formative influences were quite different from those of most of his compatriots, even though he spent a short time at the Amsterdam academy. Only his very earliest work of 1879–80 shows any stylistic similarity to that of the Hague school; *The Windmill*,[31] for example, is strongly reminiscent of Gabriël's *In the Month of July*, although Gabriël did not paint that picture until years later.[32] Toorop's association with Ensor and his membership of Les Vingt had brought him into contact with the *avant-garde* in France and Belgium, as a result of which he became the first Dutchman to practise the new pointillism. Thus his pictures of life in the fishing villages, painted around 1890, are notable not so much for a similarity of style as for one of subject-matter.

A description of Toorop's watercolour *Melancholy* (fig. 88), written in the 1890s by the artist Bremmer, evokes reminiscences of Israël's famous *Ida, the Fisherman's Daughter* (Cat. 31). 'At the entrance to a fisherman's cottage stands a fisherman's daughter, silhouetted against a very soft grey and purple background.' Then the picture starts to differ in detail.

> She stands there with her face that has purposely been made too long, the upper part of her body leaning against the doorpost as if dislocated from the lower part, her arms beside that heavy body, holding in one hand a stocking she has been knitting, which hangs down as if forgotten. . . .

But the emotional charge that Bremmer then ascribes to the

fig. 88 TOOROP *Melancholy* (watercolour and pencil)
(Rijksmuseum Kröller-Müller, Otterlo)

fig. 89 TOOROP *Fishing Boat at Katwijk c.* 1891
(Stedelijk Museum, Amsterdam)

fig. 90 TOOROP *Motherhood* 1891 (pastel)
(Rijksmuseum Kröller-Müller, Otterlo)

work again seems applicable to Israëls': the woman stands 'staring and musing over things from the past or the future, entirely withdrawn and alone with her thoughts hovering in spheres other than that in which her physical body is living'.33

As early as 1889 Toorop painted several scenes with fishing boats on the beach, which are interesting viewed in relation to the work of the Hague School since he achieved a completely individual interpretation of one of their favourite themes. He appears to have used the work of the Hague School, with which he was thoroughly familiar, as a springboard for his first versions of the subject, but clearly quickly developed his own entirely individual vision. In his *Fishing Boat* (fig. 89) of 1889 he seems to have broken radically with the world of Maris or Mauve. In Maris's work a fishing boat is a 'thing of beauty', a substantial form dramatically lit. Mauve's *Fishing Boat on the Beach at Scheveningen* (Cat. 90) caused Van Gogh to meditate on the concept of resignation. In Toorop's case the symbolic content has sharply increased; the boat is no longer a piece of equipment with which the fishermen work, but a sacrificial deity against which man struggles. The picturesque composition has been replaced by a rigid symmetry.

In the catalogue of Toorop's one-man exhibition of 1894 in the Lakenhal at Leiden, Bremmer, who was one of Toorop's earliest supporters, drew the following comparison between Mesdag's work and a pastel of a fishing boat by Toorop.

If you just compare a painting by Mesdag with it, you will realize that Mesdag is someone who records things coldly like an automaton, showing only what is observable and that Toorop, by contrast, penetrates more deeply into the matter and makes of that drawing a very piece of the character of that fisherman's life, with a great and sharp power of observation.34

In Toorop's *Collecting Shells* the general mood is fundamentally no different from that of works by Maris or Israëls, despite the use of the divisionist technique and more decorative line work. The world of Jozef Israëls's *Bringing in the Anchor* is not far away from another work by Toorop, *High Tide*, which depicts a man hauling an anchor on to the shore through 'the strong tide, the prismatic water striped with hissing foam that surges past the fisherman in his oilskins and drops back into the trough of the waves.'35

In Toorop's remarkable pastel, *Motherhood* (fig. 90) the world of Israëls seems to have merged with that of Matthijs Maris. In a Katwijk interior that is devoid of the picturesque qualities lent by a Rembrandtesque chiaroscuro, a young mother sits suckling her child. Her dress and long wavy hair are reminiscent of the pre-Raphaelites and Matthijs Maris's princesses, but the straightforward, almost severe frontal perspective of the high chair with the baby has none of the playfulness and sentiment that constitute the principal ingredients in Jozef Israëls's work (Cat. 33).

There is an equally fundamental difference in the strong social commitment of Toorop's work. If one compares the heavily burdened women trudging through Israëls's dunes with the gloomy procession in Toorop's *After the Strike* (fig. 91) the sombreness of the younger artist's tone is striking despite his use of pointillism. Israëls's attitude is one of compassion; Toorop's implies an indictment.

From 1892 onwards Toorop's realist themes – if one may use that term for work that is so heavily charged with symbolism – were replaced by the more stylized and overtly symbolist work for which Toorop is principally remembered.

fig. 91 TOOROP *After the Strike* 1886–87
(Rijksmuseum Kröller-Müller, Otterlo)

fig. 92 J. ISRAËLS *Woman and Children in the Dunes*
(Haags Gemeentemuseum, The Hague)

fig. 93 TOOROP *The Prayer before the Meal* 1907
(Zeeuws Museum, Middelburg)

Divisionism was replaced by a strongly linear style and the subject-matter was drawn from complex literary and mystical sources. However, for as yet inexplicable reasons, the themes from the life of the fishing people returned after 1896, first in one or two etchings. In an etching of his daughter, *Charley at the Window* (1898), a line of fishermen struggling through bad weather may be seen in the background, and in *Child Gathering Wood* of 1899 a group of people collecting shellfish below the dunes seems to have been intended as a direct quotation from Hague School iconography in the same way that a group of olive trees that appear in some of Toorop's symbolist work were an overt reference to Van Gogh.[36]

With this return to realistic subjects Toorop took up pointillism again, sometimes in combination with Van Gogh's hatching. He painted net-menders, woodcutters, and girls in dunes and orchards. In general, these are sunny paintings and only occasionally is there a return to the gloom of the 1890s, as in his *Watching on the Threshold of the Sea* (Boymans-van Beuningen Museum), which is a direct descendant of his earlier *Calvinists at Katwijk*. Once again, this second realist phase began in Katwijk, but Toorop continued to work in this style at Domburg (Zeeland). The distance of his work from that of the Hague School, particularly in his treatment of light, is clearly illustrated by an interior such as *The Prayer before the Meal* (fig. 93), where, despite a striking similarity in subject-matter, Israëls's dim light filtering through the window is replaced by sunlight flooding the whole room.

Johan Thorn Prikker

Toorop's confrontation with the themes and subject-matter of the Hague School certainly contained an element of positive appreciation, but his younger colleague, Thorn Prikker, found the Hague School's Impressionism more unacceptable as the 1890s progressed. In his efforts to arrive at a pure art, in which he took Van Eyck, Memling and Van der Weyden as his models, he felt less at home in the sometimes rather rough and ready artistic environment of Pulchri and the Kunstkring.

By 1894–95 Prikker's opinion of the older generation had sunk so low that he referred to the work of Israëls and the Marises as 'a thorough mess', a judgement he applied no less harshly to younger artists like Breitner and Tholen. At that time he felt that there should be a strong unity between a room and the works of art in it and concluded from this that there was simply no place for impressionistic landscapes. Such an object 'from which you feel the wind blowing in your face' made a ridiculous hole in the wall! More seriously, he was struck by the emptiness and lack of feeling in many contemporary paintings, which he considered merely 'imitated nature'. He felt that the light in such paintings did not come from within the artists 'because it is in tune with their spirit as it should have done', but that 'they set about painting it because here and there they have seen the sun shining on a nice bit of white wall and a few trees and a cow'.[37]

Like Bremmer, he spoke of the 'cold representation of reality' sometimes seen in the work of Willem Maris. 'I don't exactly mean his best works, which certainly are sound and full of passion, but more those dubious Marises that you often see at Goupil's on the Plaats'.[38] According to Prikker, the symbolist set his face against those 'who paint a tree because it is a tree, who lack precisely that sense that constitutes the difference between an artist and a painter'.[39] To be fair, Willem Maris himself held the conviction that a cow should be painted for the sake of the light and not because it was a cow, but Thorn Prikker was convinced that the Maris brothers had violated their art by conforming to public demands.

Prikker, who had trained at the Hague Academy, had not always been so negative about his fellow-artists. The works he painted between 1881 and 1888 shared a resemblance to the Hague School's style and one of his earliest works to win a prize bears the significant title *Foggy Weather*. From the diary of his friend Henri Borel and his correspondence with Prikker we know that at the beginning of the 1890s they still held the Marises (including Matthijs) and Mauve in particular in high regard. Prikker waxed enthusiastic 'about that light, about that foliage and those clods of earth' on a visit they made together to the Mauve exhibition at Pulchri Studio in 1890 and although Borel was decidedly sparing in his praise of the *Fishing Boat* that had made such an impression on Van Gogh, Thorn Prikker thought it 'stupendous'.[40] Even Borel could not entirely fail to acknowledge 'the grey melancholy spread over the work, the late afternoon light bowing the heads of these humble folk towards the ground. Everywhere in Mauve one finds weary, down-trodden people'.[41]

Then Borel and Prikker's praise turned to criticism. In 1891 Borel wrote that Thijs Maris was the only artist apart from Mauve whom he admired without reservation, although in his opinion they were closely followed by his brothers and Israëls. Next, he put Breitner, Witsen, Neuhuys, Verster, Veth, Kamerlingh Onnes and Van Looy. Mesdag, De Haas, Artz and Ter Meulen he dismissed as completely finished.[42] A year later after seeing a drawing by Millet, Thorn Prikker concluded that 'the best Israëls or Jaap Maris is the work of a child by comparison'.[43]

At the end of 1891 Thorn Prikker exhibited *Woman in a Field of Red Cabbages*, also known as *Cabbage Patch* (fig. 94). Seen as a black and white reproduction the picture evokes associations with Millet and Mauve, although the vague forms are perhaps more closely related to Matthijs Maris, but the work was in fact painted in what Borel described as 'strong, beautiful, healthy colours'.[44] It made a great impression on some contemporaries and the painter noted with amusement that Théophile de Bock made desperate efforts to emulate him by adapting the colours of an already finished landscape to resemble those of *Cabbage Patch*.[45]

In June 1893 Thorn Prikker gave up his membership of the Hague Art Society, where his high ideals and symbolist paintings met with little sympathy. His determination to render the essence of emotions on canvas went far beyond the often simplistic interpretations of many of his so-called artistic colleagues. With the support of his friend Henry van de Velde, he struck out along a path on which art would be placed at the service of life. Only a few understood 'the difference between nature photography, beautiful because of small incidentals such as a grey sky, a patch of sunlight, etc., and the soul of nature…'.[46]

Matthijs Maris

In the 1890s, the work of Matthijs Maris turned out to be an unexpected trump card that the Hague School could play against the growing criticism of the lack of any deeper significance in their work. This almost completely forgotten artist, who had in the 1880s lamented 'It's all Jaap nowadays', now started receiving public attention.

Lodewijk van Deyssel's account of his visit to the artist in

fig. 94 THORN PRIKKER *Cabbage Patch c.* 1891
(Kaiser Wilhelm Museum, Krefeld)

fig. 95 THORN PRIKKER *The Madonna of the Tulips* 1892
(Rijksmuseum Kröller-Müller, Otterlo)

fig. 96 M. MARIS *The Church Bride*
(Rijksmuseum H. W. Mesdag, The Hague)

London in 1894 is typical of the extreme admiration that people suddenly began to feel for this eccentric recluse. Van Deyssel described Maris's humble abode as 'the most sacred spot that can now be found in Europe'.47 He compared Matthijs's impoverished existence and self-inflicted isolation with the affluence and social recognition accorded to Sir Lawrence Alma Tadema, an artist who had once lived in the same house as the Marises in Antwerp. Van Deyssel, of course, preferred Matthijs, expressing the view that his work embodied 'a sublime extravagance, which is rather more than perfect and thus imperfect – for man is not spirit alone, but a spirit that has taken on beautiful visible forms'.

The painter Richard Roland Holst (1868–1938), who in his earliest days was a great champion of the Hague School, considered Matthijs 'the greatest artist of our time', in whose work one was met by the 'purest child's eyes, which have an expression as if they are gazing at us from a distant, immaterial world'.48 Roland Holst's wife, the poet Henriette van der Schalk, recognized in her husband's lithograph *Helga's Entrée* 'a still, dreamy poetry which was rare in Dutch art before Matthijs Maris'.49

It was above all Matthijs's dream landscapes and brides that attracted much attention. The theme of the virgin and the bride occupied a central place in symbolist iconography, as in Toorop's *Three Brides* and the *Bride* by Thorn Prikker, both of 1893.

Alphons Diepenbrock, the leading Dutch composer of the day and an intimate friend of the painter Antoon Derkinderen, described Matthijs's *The Church Bride* (fig. 96) in the Mesdag Collection in an exalted prose style that reveals that the artist was reading the esoteric works of Sâr Péladan at that time. He perceived in this figure

the mystical virgin of all time, still almost a child in her feelings of exaltation at her growing passion, her spirit of sacrifice and her fearful awe of the bliss of approaching womanhood. The maiden, with anguished lips, a yellowish-white gown and a certain mystery from her gossamer-like, almost invisible veil, seems to loom up out of an atmosphere of dimly glowing darkness. It is utterly and deeply moving in its morbidly refined beauty. Really, when you have seen that face, Jaap and Willem Maris are dead for you for an hour.50

Jan Veth, who particularly admired Matthijs as a graphic artist, found his dreams more powerful than the visions of Odilon Redon: 'The former gives us the blissful mysticism of his golden visions of beauty, whereas in the latter we find the nightmares of an exhausted child of the France of this century.'51 Thorn Prikker too, who was another admirer of Matthijs Maris, considered that Redon lacked his purity.52

Matthijs's influence can be recognized most clearly in the work of numerous minor artists. Brides descend through landscapes shrouded in grey mist in the paintings of Jan Zürcher (1851–1905), P.C. de Moor (1866–1953)53 and H.A. van Daalhoff (1867–1953). Félix Fénéon, the French critic and champion of Neo-Impressionism, also recognized a face such as '*Maris nous l'avait déjà montré*' in addition to elements derived from Monticelli and Gustave Moreau in Toorop's *Hetaere*.54 The children of Matthijs Maris still stare at us, with a slight look of surprise, from Piet Mondriaan's *Spring Idyll* of 1900.55

When Matthijs died in 1917, his obituaries contained some surprisingly negative assessments of his work.56 A fierce argument flared up between the critic Bernard Canter and Theo van Doesburg, who was then about to launch his epoch-

fig. 97 M. MARIS *Head of a Girl*
(John G. Johnson Collection, Philadelphia Museum of Art, Philadelphia)

making periodical *De Stijl*. Canter had denigrated Matthijs Maris's work in no uncertain terms in the *Holland Express*, bringing in his brothers *en passant*. To Canter, Matthijs was a painter of 'sentimental-romantic novelettish whimsies intended to brighten up bourgeois drawing-rooms', while his needy way of life was not 'sacred' as Van Deyssel had suggested, but the affected poverty of a retarded gentleman.57

Van Doesburg took Van Deyssel's view: 'Like Van Gogh he was an end and not a beginning. He was the top of a mountain, veiled in mists'.58 He had, however, also been of real importance for modern art:

Thijs Maris's development has been a pre-eminent model of the *opposite side* for abstract art of our century. What does it matter that this man read *Walter Scott* instead of *Marinetti or Döblin*? It is enough that what he created revealed the Universal. Where was there, either before or in his own time, a single artist who expressed the need *to actually dissolve* reality, even if he depicted it on a small scale and in grey . . . Thijs painted spirit with a minimum of reality'.59

In the *Eenheid* of 15 September 1917 Van Doesburg again emphasized Matthijs's special place in Dutch art, this time in a paean of praise.

When he discovered his true self and explored reality, from personal feelings right through to abstraction; when he came to realize that reality had a different meaning for the artist than for the barber or merchant; when reality became the embodiment of his desire, then people called him mad. He was hounded out of the country. And he took his revenge: he abandoned riches for an old brush.[60]

Epilogue

After 1900 developments in Dutch art became much more closely linked with events outside the Netherlands. The formation and development of the newest generation of artists, such as Van Dongen, Sluyters and Mondriaan – who is discussed elsewhere – was complicated by their international contacts and it becomes almost impossible to identify influences, in particular elements that might be derived from the Hague School, with any certainty. It is clear, however, that the heart of the new movement had shifted to Amsterdam and that only occasionally did the Hague School still play a role in the early formation of artists. Leo Gestel (1881–1941), for example, who received part of his training at the Rijksacademie and became one of the most important innovators of the

pre-First World War period, lived for a short while in Weissenbruch's beloved Noorden,[61] while Lodewijk Schelfhout (1881–1943), grandson of the famous romantic and himself a follower of Van Gogh, Cézanne, Cubism, Futurism and other movements in succession, was early in his career a pupil of Théophile de Bock.

But the *avant-garde* critics had already dismissed the Hague School. In 1907 Steenhoff, curator of the Rijksmuseum and a well-known reviewer, castigated those artists who persisted with the same 'stereotyped range of colours and studied quiet tones' for the 'general drowsiness' of their work.[62] A new interest in colour was proclaimed by the arrival of Luminism. Mondriaan, Toorop and Sluyters were the leading painters of this new school. In November 1910, they set up the Moderne Kunstkring (Circle of Modern Art) in Amsterdam together with the critic Conrad Kikkert. Yet, even though Kikkert had turned against the Hague School, he defined Luminism as 'ultimately, nothing but a by-way of the Maris period.'[63]

NOTES

1. V. de Stuers, 'Holland op zijn smalst', *De Gids* XXXVII (1873), vol. 4, p. 347.
2. See G. Brom, *Hollandse schilders en schrijvers in de vorige eeuw*, Rotterdam 1927, pp. 126–29.
3. This was no less true of Van Gogh's former companion George Hendrik Breitner, who in 1892 dubbed Van Gogh's work 'art for Eskimos', regarding it as 'coarse and crass, without the least distinction, and, moreover, all of it also stuff stolen from Millet and others'. See P. Hefting, 'Brieven van G.H. Breitner aan H.J. van der Weele', *Nederlands Kunsthistorisch Jaarboek* XXVII, 1976, p. 129.
4. Hefting, *op. cit.*, p. 134.
5. In one or two cases Théophile de Bock was the intermediary between Maris and young Dordrecht painters. See exh. cat. *Ik mag lijden dat het morgen grijs is, Dordtse kunstenaars 1880–1940*, Dordrecht Museum, Dordrecht 1980.
6. Ter Meulen's articles 'Der maatstaf der kunst' (1874) and 'Kunstwaarde' (1879) first appeared in *De Gids*. They were reprinted in 1913 by M. Nijhoff in The Hague under the title *Gedachten van een schilder over schilderkunst*.
7. *Onze Kunst* VI (1904), pp. 51–53, cited in A.B. Loosjes–Terpstra, *Moderne kunst in Nederland 1900–1914*, Utrecht 1959, p. 34.
8. W. Moes, *Heilig ongeduld, herinneringen uit mijn leven*, Antwerp 1961.
9. Undated letter from Mauve to his wife, cited in E.P. Engel, *Anton Mauve*, Utrecht 1967, pp. 67–68.
10. See J. Huizinga, *Leven en werk van Jan Veth*, Haarlem 1927, p. 29.
11. Engel, *op. cit.*, pp. 74, 78.
12. Letter dated 12 July 1892, Rijksprentenkabinet, Amsterdam.
13. See catalogue *Witsen en zijn vriendenkring*, Amsterdam n.d., p. 23.
14. Antoon Derkinderen, the leading representative of monumental painting in the Netherlands at the end of the last century, was also an admirer of the Hague School in the early 1880s. At that time he himself painted subjects from the life of the working classes, which show some similarity to the work of Anthon van Rappard. His early etchings reveal the influence of the Hague School the most clearly. As late as 1888 he wrote in a letter to the committee of the Society for the General Good 'I regard our painters the Marises, Israëls and Mauve as the greatest men of our time, to whom no-one in any other country is superior'. However, he went on to add 'but their art is a different art from that which I have in mind'. See exh. cat. *Antoon Derkinderen*, Noordbrabants Museum, Bois-le-Duc etc. 1980–81, p. 20.
15. Members of the Hague Etching Club were, Jan Weissenbruch, L. Hardenburg, J.A. Van der Drift, R. Craeyvanger, J.J. Van der Maaten, L. Meijer, J. Hartogensis, J.F. Van Deventer, J.D. Kruseman and S. van den Berg. See exh. cat. *De Haagsche Etsclub 1848–1860*, Haags Gemeentemuseum, The Hague, 1975–76.
16. Letter of 31 August 1889 from Jan Veth to Ph. Zilcken, cited in exh. cat. *Max Liebermann en Holland*, Haags Gemeentemuseum, The Hague 1980, pp. 112–13. See also J. Giltay, 'De Nederlandsche Etsclub (1865–96)', in *Nederlands Kunsthistorisch Jaarboek*, XXVII, 1976, pp. 91–125.
17. Voerman was a boyhood friend of W.B. Tholen. The two of them took their entrance examination for the Rijksacademie together on 26 September 1876. While the critic Steenhoff saw Voerman's work in 1898 as 'the classic apotheosis of impressionism', the artist himself wrote in 1892, 'My work (especially as regards colour) is a pure reaction to the impressionism of the Dutch artists alive at present. Leaving aside the best works of our great masters of today, everything immediately alongside and under them is *rotten*'. Looking back at the early nineties he says elsewhere, 'The longer I go on the

better I understand that the work of the whole body of Dutch painters was not pure enough in colour – at an exhibition of a selection of their paintings in Arti around '91 or '92 this struck me particularly through the contrast between Jaap Maris and Toorop and almost everything else there'. See further A. Wagner, *Jan Voerman IJsselschilder*, Wageningen 1977.
18. Utrechts Provinciaal en Stedelijk Dagblad (3 Feb. 1884).
19. See exh. cat. *Een schilderij centraal. Arbeiders op steenfabriek Ruimzicht van Anthon G.A. van Rappard*, Centraal Museum, Utrecht 1980, p. 13.
20. A.M. Hammacher, *Amsterdamsche impressionisten en hun kring*, Amsterdam 1946², p. 5.
21. Letters from Thorn Prikker to Henri Borel, postmarked 24 August 1895. See J.M. Joosten, *De Brieven van Johan Thorn Prikker aan Henri Borel en anderen 1892–1904*, Nieuwkoop 1981, p. 226.
22. His *Breton Fisherboy*, for example, (sale Sotheby Mak van Waay, Amsterdam, 17–18 Nov. 1981, no. 241) is clearly derived from his father's *Children of the Sea*.
23. Notes by Jan Veth at the Netherlands Institute for Art History in The Hague, quoted from E. van Schendel, *Museum Mesdag ...*, the Hague 1975, p. 77.
24. A letter of 5 January 1906 regarding this from Willem Maris to Albert Plasschaert is published in Van Schendel, *op. cit.*, p. 187.
25. Mauve's opposition must have been a bitter blow to Breitner, for he had mentioned him as his teacher, along with Jacob and Willem Maris, in a letter to A.P. Van Stolk. See P.H. Hefting, *G.H. Breitner in zijn Haagse tijd*, Utrecht 1970, p. 82 and note 61.
26. Cited by Hefting, *op. cit.*, p. 142.
27. For Wagner and Dutch painting see R. De Leeuw, *Richard Wagner en de Franse schilderkunst van het einde van de negentiende eeuw*, unpublished degree essay, Leiden University 1976 (with an appendix on the Netherlands).
28. See R. de Leeuw, 'Van de Bock tot Berserik' in exh. cat. *Haagse Kunstkring, werk verzameld*, Pulchri Studio/Haags Gemeentemuseum, The Hague 1977, p. 8.
29. H.P. Bremmer, 'De tentoonstelling der werken van Jan Toorop in de Lakenhal', *Dagblad van Zuid-Holland en 's-Gravenhage* 8, 9, 12, 13, 14 and 15 Feb. 1894, cited in J.M. Joosten, 'De eerste solo-tentoonstelling van Jan Toorop', *Antiek* XI (1976–77), p. 584.
30. Bremmer, *op. cit.*, pp. 585–86.
31. This panel of 50 × 37.5 cm in a private collection in The Hague is further analyzed in R. Siebelhoff, *The Early Development of Jan Toorop, 1879–92*, University of Toronto (xerox copy in the Netherlands Institute for Art History in The Hague).
32. Siebelhoff, *op. cit.*, dates Toorop's picture 1879. Gabriël's *In the Month of July* dates from 1889.
33. Bremmer, *op. cit.*, pp. 583–84.
34. *Ibid.*, pp. 584–85.
35. W. Vogelsang in *Onze Kunst* III, 1904, cited in exh. cat. *J. Th. Toorop. De jaren 1885 tot 1910*, Rijksmuseum Kröller-Muller, Otterlo, 1978–79, p. 57.
36. See R. de Leeuw in exh. cat. *Impressionists and Post-Impressionists from the Netherlands*, Seibu-Museum, Tokyo 1980, no. 59.
37. Joosten, *op. cit.*, p. 111.
38. *Idem.*
39. *Idem.*
40. *Ibid.*, p. 24.
41. *Ibid.*, p. 21.

42. *Ibid.*, p. 27.

43. *Ibid.*, pp. 81–82.

44. *Ibid.*, p. 36.

45. *Ibid.*, pp. 93–94.

46. *Ibid.*

47. On 29 September 1894 Van Deyssel wrote to Frederik van Eeden that his visit to Matthijs was one of the 'grandest' parts of his stay in London. Van Eeden replied on 10 October, 'I never visited Thijs Maris, because I was afraid he didn't like being visited'. See *De briefwisseling tussen Frederik van Eeden en Lodewijk van Deyssel, bezorgd en toegelicht door H.W. van Tricht en H.G.M. Prick*, The Hague 1981², pp. 234, 236, and 'Over Thijs Maris' in L. van Deyssel, *Verbeeldingen*, Amsterdam 1908.

48. See Roland Holst's article, 'Over de Haagsche en Leidsche schilderijententoonstelling', *De Amsterdammer* (29–30 June 1890), p. 9.

49. See exh. cat. *Kunstenaren der Idee, Symbolistische tendenzen in Nederland* c. *1880–1930*, Haags Gemeentemuseum, The Hague 1978, p. 127, no. 78.

50. Letter of 21 February 1892, quoted from *Alphons Diepenbrock, brieven en documenten bijeengebracht en toegelicht door Eduard Reeser*, vol. 1, The Hague 1962, p. 331. In the manuscript of an article published in a different form in *De Nieuwe Gids* Diepenbrock mentions 'the art of Beethoven, Wagner, Matthijs Maris and Puvis de Chavannes' in the same breath in that same year.

51. J. Staphorst [J. Veth], 'Odilon Redon', *De Nieuwe Gids* II, vol. 2 (1887), p. 68.

52. Joosten, *op. cit.*, pp. 69–70.

53. When Bernard Canter wrote a damning review of Matthijs Maris's art in the *Holland Express* of 29 August 1917, positing P.C. de Moor as a greater artist, not only Theo van Doesburg's fury was aroused (see note 60), De Moor hastened to disassociate himself from it in a letter published in the *Holland Express* of 12 September 1917: 'Does not this artist deserve any reverence any more then, must his name already be trampled on beside his open grave?' De Moor had written the introduction to the catalogue of the Maris brothers' exhibition in Rotterdam in 1893.

54. 'Maris has already shown us', *Le chat noir* (18 March 1892), quoted from F. Fénéon, *Au-delà de l'impressionisme (Miroirs de l'art)*, Paris 1966, p. 130.

55. See exh. cat. *Kunstenaren der Idee* (note 49), p. 103, no. 27.

56. B. Canter, 'Matthijs Maris', *Holland Express* (29 Aug. 1917), p. 411; C.L. Dake, 'Thijs Maris', *De Telegraaf*, (28 Aug. 1917).

57. Canter, *op. cit.*

58. Th. van Doesburg, 'Thijs Maris', *Eenheid* (15 Sept. 1917).

59. In another article written in 1917 Jan Veth also spoke of Matthijs's tendency to abstraction in connection with his views of Lausanne, which he characterized as 'so many stages towards a visionary abstraction'. See J. Veth, 'Matthijs Maris', *De Gids* LXXXI (1917), vol. 4, p. 150.

60. Th. van Doesburg, Open letter to Bernard Canter, *Holland Express* (12 Sept. 1917), p. 441.

61. Gestel settled in Noorden in 1904 along with his friend C. Vredenburgh (1880–1946), who also came from Woerden. Both artists owed a great deal to W.B. Tholen.

62. Cited in Loosjes-Terpstra, *op. cit.*, p. 34.

63. *Ibid.*, p. 96.

The Vogue for Holland

HANS KRAAN

The Netherlands in the eyes of foreign artists

'There are some landscapes and interiors by German masters, which, if placed among the Dutch entries, would not disturb their unity.' So commented an anonymous art critic writing about the 1892 annual international exhibition of contemporary art held in the Glaspalast at Munich.[1] Looking through the catalogue of this exhibition, one is indeed struck by the number of German artists who were represented by Dutch landscapes, townscapes and genre scenes.[2] Evidently their similarity to the many works by Dutch painters also exhibited there was remarked upon by at least one critic.

Other catalogues of international exhibitions held in Munich and Berlin in the last quarter of the nineteenth century reveal that Dutch landscapes and themes were highly popular, not only among German painters, but also among artists from other countries. French and English artists also showed works inspired by the Netherlands in the exhibitions held at the Paris Salon and the Royal Academy in London at this period. There was evidently a general predilection for things Dutch which can explain in part the international acclaim for the distinctively Dutch character of the work of the Hague School.

This vogue for Dutch themes, which was rooted in the general admiration for Dutch seventeenth-century painting that had long existed in other countries, was not new; it had, however, increased in the nineteenth century, when numerous private collections passed into public hands and thus had become more readily accessible. When it became common to hold exhibitions and transport improved, an increasing number of artists began to pay a visit to the land of Rembrandt in order to refresh themselves at the very source of their inspiration. One can, for example, find the names of hundreds of foreign artists who visited the Netherlands between 1844 and 1885 simply by reading the visitors' book of the Trippenhuis in Amsterdam, where the collection of the present Rijksmuseum was housed at that time.[3]

But even before 1844 foreign artists were drawn to the Netherlands, often visiting precisely those places that they knew from the work of their illustrious predecessors. In a deliberate attempt to compete with the seventeenth-century masters, Turner painted *Van Goyen Looking out for a Subject* and *Port Ruisdael* after his first visit to the Netherlands in 1817.[4] In 1832 – while still a student – Andreas Achenbach (1815–1910), accompanied by his father, visited the Netherlands for the first time in order to study and paint the North Sea, which he had first seen in paintings by Willem van de Velde and Ludolf Backhuysen that he greatly admired.[5]

The interest in the Netherlands and Dutch art, which already existed abroad at an early date, was to be stimulated still further in various ways during the course of the nineteenth century under the influence of Realism and the writings of Arsène Houssaye, Thoré-Bürger and Fromentin.[6] Since the Hague School painters built on a seventeenth-century tradition in their realistic approach to nature and emphasis on the intimacy of the interior, it is not surprising that when they presented their work at exhibitions in other countries, the critics measured it in the first instance against that of their seventeenth-century predecessors. It was soon said that there was a revival of the Golden Age of Dutch painting and the Hague School could boast of international success as early as the 1870s.

The work of the painters of the Hague School can be divided into five categories on the basis of its subject matter: typically Dutch landscapes with polders, canals and windmills or views of well-known cities; landscapes with animals; beach scenes and seascapes; scenes from life in fishing and peasant communities; Dutch interiors. Each of these categories also appears in the work of foreign artists, both contemporaries of the Hague School painters and their predecessors. Closer investigation shows that the international success of the Hague School was to a certain extent part of a generally prevailing taste for Dutch art, which had been anticipated by previous generations and was based on their admiration of Dutch seventeenth-century art.

Dutch landscapes

Dutch seventeenth-century landscape painters enjoyed particular fame in the nineteenth century. In England, as well as in France, Germany, the United States and Canada, they constituted a source of study and inspiration. The painters who came to Holland did not just visit the museums. They also recorded their impressions of the Dutch landscape, which was regarded as particularly picturesque.

In 1867 the critic Paul Mantz wrote in a review in the *Gazette des Beaux-Arts*,

Like Hobbema, Ruisdael and Albert Cuyp, I believe that Holland is a very melancholy land in winter and a very cheerful one in summer, but always very fine in tone or very colourful; the meadows are an intense green, the roofs are red and in the last hours of daylight the sky is ablaze with liquid gold.[7]

In 1887 the American painter George Hitchcock (1850–1913) devoted an article to the 'picturesque quality' of Holland, in which he said,

Holland is the most harmonious of all countries either in sun or shadow. It is never crude, it is always a picture atmospherically as it stands, without change or thought of change; even under the bright light of the sun it does not lose its opalescent attributes, nor are its eternal harmonies impaired. It is often most bright, if sunshine be brightness; the shadows are never the crude, purple, cut-out spots of a southern sun, nor is the blue of its skies ever metallic; the brightness is always diffused even through the shadows, and no matter how sharp the sunlight is, the *tonality* is always fine. The north wind brings with it, summer and winter, a sky of the purest turquoise; with at times a soft sun throwing over everything a yellow saffroned light, softening the lines of cast-shadows and harmonizing every object remote or at hand.[8]

In an essay written in 1901 devoted to Jozef Israëls, of whom he was a good friend, Max Liebermann declared,

Holland has rightly been called the land of painting *par excellence* and it is no accident that Rembrandt was a Hollander. The mists that rise up from the water, enveloping everything as if in a transparent veil, give the landscape its peculiar picturesqueness; the damp atmosphere softens the hardness of the outlines and gives the sky its soft silvery-grey tone; the bright local colours are united, the black of the shadows is dissolved in colourful reflections: everything seems to be bathed in light and air. And then there is that flatness, which lets the eye wander unimpeded for miles and seems made for painting with its gradations from the strongest green in the foreground to the most delicate tones on the horizon.[9]

These quotations show how much the artists who visited Holland were struck by the atmospheric Dutch landscape, which they knew from the work of the seventeenth-century masters and were now rediscovering in the work of the Hague School artists. Liebermann's description of that landscape could serve equally well as a description of a polder landscape by Jacob Maris.

That the Hague School painters, like their seventeenth-century predecessors, were thought to have been outstandingly successful in representing the Dutch landscape is clear from the catalogue of an exhibition of Dutch art including contemporary works that was held in London in 1904.

Maris and Mauve, and the other Dutch landscape painters took the country round them, which they *knew*, instead of rushing off to foreign lands to jog a failing capacity to see with the intoxicant of contrast. . . . They brought to the eyes of the world those subtle, half-hidden beauties that only those who have grown up among such scenes can reveal. The modern Dutch painters, when the revival began, about the middle of the last century, had merely to cultivate the soil of their native land which had lain fallow since the end of the seventeenth century. Like their great ancestors they sought inspiration in their own land and times.[10]

When Daubigny visited the Netherlands in 1871 with his son Karl, he wrote to a friend in Paris, 'We are in blonde Holland, as blonde as Ruben's women. What an enchanting country! We have hired a boat and we're going along the Maas in it to do the windmills of Dordrecht'.[11]

Daubigny made a series of paintings of the windmills near Dordrecht, one of which he showed at the Paris Salon of 1872, where it was somewhat coolly received: 'This canvas, alas, has nothing of the Dutch School about it apart from the simplicity of the subject. Everything is confused and incoherent, done without feeling and as if at random.'[12]

Even before Daubigny, Félix Ziem (1821–1911) had been to the Netherlands. He arrived in Amsterdam from Belgium for the first time in 1850, staying there for about a month before going on to The Hague and Dordrecht.[13] He too immortalized the windmills of Dordrecht, which later became a favourite subject of the painters of the Hague School.

The vogue for Holland is also clearly evident in France from the popularity enjoyed there by the work of Johan Barthold Jongkind (1819–91), who lived in Paris from 1860 onwards. He returned to Holland several times during the 1860s in order to be able to meet the French demand for Dutch landscapes.[14] His Dutch windmills and townscapes, and above all his moonlit scenes, appealed to the taste of the French public even more than his French landscapes and in 1862 he brought out an album of seven etchings, *Vues de Hollande* (Views of Holland).[15]

Eugène Boudin (1824–98), too, decided to go and see Holland with his own eyes as a result of Daubigny's enthusiastic accounts and conversations with Jongkind.[16] In 1873 he visited Rotterdam, in 1875 he went to Rotterdam, Scheveningen and Dordrecht, in 1876 he was back in Rotterdam again and in 1884 he made a series of paintings of the river scenes and windmills around Dordrecht.[17] In a letter dated 23 June 1884 he wrote,

Indeed, things are not going badly at all . . . we are staying near the quay and we've also had the good fortune to find various painters in the neighbourhood, including my friend Yon, the painter-engraver, and other foreigners . . . a real artists' colony. The country is very picturesque and the river is superb.[18]

Boudin was evidently not alone in painting at Dordrecht. It was not only French artists who were attracted by the Dutch polders; the English, in particular the painters of the Norwich School, had preceded them. German artists too came to Holland early in the nineteenth century. Caspar Scheuren (1810–87), for example, attracted by the landscapes of Ruisdael and Hobbema, came for the first time in 1829. He was appointed professor at the Düsseldorf Academy in 1855 and in 1858 he wrote, 'I am going to Holland for a few days to refresh and strengthen myself from the old Netherlanders in preparation for my big picture.'[19]

The picturesqueness of the Dutch polder landscape was discovered by the Austrian painters at the same time as the Germans, but they began to come in large numbers in the 1870s. By the last quarter of the nineteenth century, it had become virtually obligatory for students at the academies in Düsseldorf, Munich, Berlin and Vienna to visit Barbizon and the Netherlands and young artists streamed westwards. One of them was the Viennese Tina Blau (1845–1916), who stayed in the Netherlands for several months in 1875 with her friend, the artist Emil Jacob Schindler.[20] Her letters recount her experiences among the Dutch and the impressions made on her by the old masters. Her paintings of Dutch subjects were shown at the big exhibitions in Munich and Vienna, where they had to compete with the work of Mesdag, Mauve and the Maris brothers.

Also from Vienna came Rudolf Ribarz (1848–1904), who showed at least four paintings of the Netherlands at the Exposition Internationale in Paris in 1878. The critic Charles Blanc wrote of them,

> What can stand comparison with the best Dutch masters are the canvases of M. Ribarz: a *View of Dordrecht* which Vermeer could not have rendered better in its composition, tone values and subtleties; a *Canal in Holland*, which is a transposition out of doors of the paintings of Pieter de Hooch and a work remarkable for its unexpected and telling tones.[21]

What is most striking here is that the comparison is drawn not with the contemporary Hague School artists, who were also well-represented at the exhibition and were accorded rave reviews, but with the Dutch seventeenth-century masters, whose work evidently still served as the criterion for criticism.

In Canada the Hague School painters enjoyed an unprecedented popularity. Collectors in Montreal and Toronto were prepared to pay enormous sums to have work by the Hague masters in their collections.[22] This led a number of young Canadian artists, including Edmund Morris (1871–1913), Curtius Williamson (1867–1944) and William Atkinson (1862–1926), to visit the Netherlands during their student years, in order to see with their own eyes the surroundings in which the Hague School artists worked and to study their pictures. So great was the reputation of the Dutch painters that the first art books published in Canada, both written by E. B. Greenshields, were entitled *The Subjective View of Landscape Painting* (1904), the first monograph devoted to Weissenbruch, and *Landscape Painting and Modern Dutch Artists* (1906).

American artists also made the Netherlands one of the main goals of their trips to Europe and the influence of the Hague School painters is often evident in their work. In addition to George Hitchcock, Robert F. Blum, William Merritt Chase, Gari Melchers, George Henry Boughton and Edwin Austen Abbey, who will be discussed again later, mention may be made of John Henry Twachtman (1853–1902), who during a stay in the Netherlands in 1881 showed his work to Anton Mauve for his opinion.[23]

Landscapes with animals

Paulus Potter's monumental *The Young Bull* in the Mauritshuis was regarded in the nineteenth century as the copybook example of a landscape with animals, but in fact its great fame dated back to the end of the eighteenth century when it was exhibited in the Louvre, having been taken to Paris by the French in 1795 along with the rest of the Stadholder William v's collection.[24] There it attracted so much attention that, after the defeat of Napoleon in 1815, the Dutch brought it back to the Netherlands in triumph. Potter, together with Albert Cuyp, continued to exert a great influence on French animal painters who were particularly prevalent in the Barbizon School.

The Hague School painters also began to study the work of the seventeenth-century masters with new eyes as a result of the admiration they felt for the Barbizon School. Thus there are striking similarities between the early work of Gerard Bilders and Troyon. In Belgium too there were animal painters who based themselves on Dutch seventeenth-century models. This is clearly evident from the work of Eugène Verboeckhoven (1799–1881), Xavier de Cock (1818–96) and Alfred Verwee (1838–95), representatives of three successive generations.[25] Xavier de Cock came to Holland in the early 1840s to study the old masters in the Mauritshuis, including Potter. Alfred Verwee, who was a friend of Troyon, fell heavily under the spell of the meadow landscape around Dordrecht in 1868 and it appears regularly in his work.

A key position between the Belgian painters of animals and the Hague School was occupied by Johannes de Haas (1832–1908) who, after a year in Oosterbeek, lived in Brussels from 1857 to 1869, where he must have been in contact with Verwee. During his Brussels period De Haas, like Gabriël, returned regularly to the Netherlands to gather study material and motifs for his animal paintings. He painted the animals in several landscapes by Roelofs and also collaborated with Gabriël during the time when they were both in Brussels.[26]

The German animal painters of the second half of the nineteenth century were particularly fascinated by the Dutch landscape. Carl Seibels (1844–77), Anton Braith (1836–1905), Josef Wenglein (1845–1919), Victor Weishaupt (1848–1905) and numerous others found inspiration in the green pastures and black and white cattle of the Netherlands. Carl Seibels, who was trained at the Düsseldorf Academy, was also a great admirer of Constant Troyon and the Barbizon School; in 1867 and 1868 he went to Paris to study the work of these artists. In 1874, accompanied by his colleague Gregor von Bochmann (1850–1930), he went to the Netherlands, where they made studies of nature and met Anton Mauve.[27]

Hermann Baisch (1846–94), who was appointed *Professor für Tiermalerei* at the Academy at Karlsruhe in 1881, liked to spend the summer in the Netherlands and visited it many times. The vivid impression made on him by the Dutch meadows, especially those around Rotterdam and Dordrecht, together with his admiration for the work of Troyon, resulted in many animal paintings, which achieved great success at international exhibitions in Munich, Berlin, Vienna and London (fig. 98).

The heath landscape with sheep, so superbly interpreted by Anton Mauve, should be mentioned as a separate genre under animal painting. The Hague School artists discovered the Brabant and Drenthe heathlands as a motif through the Barbizon School, many of whose members painted sheep. Mauve's landscapes with sheep evoked much admiration at exhibitions and were sold for high prices. His influence can be seen in the heath landscapes of the French artist Alphonse Stengelin (1852–1938), who was a faithful visitor to the Netherlands as we shall see later, and the German Julius Bergmann.[28] A dune landscape with sheep, probably in the neighbourhood of Katwijk, painted by German Grobe (1857–1938) who was also from Germany, reveals Mauve's influence very clearly (fig. 99).

Beach scenes and seascapes

The sea with the beach and the dunes constitute a special aspect of the Dutch landscape and were favourite subjects of Weissenbruch, Jacob Maris and Mesdag. The coast had long exerted a great pull on Dutch artists – one need only think of marine painters like Simon de Vlieger, Jan Porcellis, Willem van de Velde and Ludolf Backhuijsen and painters of dune landscapes like Jan van Goyen, Jacob van Ruisdael and Jan Wijnants. In the romantic period the seascape flourished again,

fig. 98 BAISCH *Dutch Meadow with Cattle* 1891 (Bayerische Staatsgemäldesammlungen, Neue Pinakothek, Munich)

the most important stimuli coming from French artists like Claude Joseph Vernet (1714–89) and, later, Eugène Isabey (1803–86). Andreas Schelfhout (1787–1870) and Wijnand Nuyen (1813–39) were the most important Dutch representatives of romantic coastal landscape painting. The views of the beach and fishing boats at Scheveningen by Théodore Gudin (1802–80), who was in the Netherlands in 1844, herald Mesdag's work in the 1860s, (cf. fig. 30) while two prominent English marine painters, Clarkson Stanfield (1793–1867) and Edward William Cooke (1811–80), continued a tradition of marine painting that had first been introduced into England by Willem van de Velde in the seventeenth century.[29]

In the 1870s, precisely when the Hague School was at its peak, the seaside and sea-bathing came into vogue: the North Sea coast was lauded in illustrated periodicals for the beneficial effects of its fresh air, fishing villages like Scheveningen, Katwijk, Noordwijk and Egmond expanded into seaside resorts that were filled by an annual summer influx of well-to-do visitors from all parts of the world, and hotels were built in various places, for example the famous Kurhaus of 1883 at Scheveningen.

That the tourists included many artists is evident from written sources such as the register of visitors to Katwijk for the years 1885–1914.[30] Hundreds of artists, not only from all over Europe, but also from America and even Japan, stayed in boarding-houses or with families in Katwijk during those years. Many of them came back several times, some of them – such as German Grobe, Hermann Bahner, Wilhelm Baisch and Hans von Bartels, all from Germany – almost annually.

Katwijk was also a favourite centre of the painters of the Hague School itself. Jozef Israëls lived there in 1856, painted his famous *Sewing School at Katwijk* there in 1881 and in 1890 campaigned with a number of other painters for the

maintenance of the church there. Some minor masters of the Hague School, such as Blommers, Evert Pieters and Jan Zoetelief Tromp, owned houses there, and because Katwijk was so near to The Hague, many of the artists who worked there came heavily under the influence of the Hague School. Charles Gruppe (1860–1940) from Canada, Gerhard Morgenstjerne Munthe (1875–1927), who was born in Düsseldorf, and the Frenchman Alphonse Stengelin (1852–1938), who lived for some years in Katwijk, were influenced by the painters of the Hague School to such an extent that some people number them among its members. Stengelin felt so much at home in Katwijk that he signed himself *Stengelin van Katwijk*. He was much liked by the local people, who honoured him by naming a street after him.[31]

The American Robert F. Blum (1857–1903) visited Haarlem and Zandvoort during a trip to Europe in 1884.[32] He was so inspired by the beach and dunes at Zandvoort that he rented a house there and produced a series of Dutch landscapes and beach scenes in delicate pastel tints on brown paper. He enjoyed the company of William Merritt Chase (1848–1916), who had already visited the Netherlands in 1882.[33] Chase had been a teacher at the Art Students' League in New York since 1878; this institution regularly organized summer classes for its students in other countries and in 1903 Chase was in charge of such a course in Haarlem. Because of his fascination with the beaches of the Netherlands and a concomitant interest in the work of Mesdag, he decided to visit the latter. He described his visit to The Hague in a letter to his wife:

Mr Townsley and I went to The Hague and went directly to the gallery [Mauritshuis]. There are some superb pictures there and I was just in the mood to enjoy them. After lunch we went to call on Mesdag (you know I have known him for a long time). He said he was

fig. 99 GROBE *Dune Landscape in Holland* 1908 (Location unknown)

glad to see me, that he had heard that I was in Haarlem with a lot of American students and he considered that I was paying Holland a great compliment to come so far to study their pictures. He could not have been more congenial. His collection is very fine, and he is giving it to Holland. . . . We are to have the first private view. We stayed the entire afternoon. Mrs Mesdag joined us with tea and we returned to Haarlem feeling happy over a most enjoyable time.[34]

A few days later Chase did, indeed, take his students to see Mesdag's collection. Of this he wrote, 'the students all came away very enthusiastic, Mr Mesdag and Mrs Mesdag showed their studios and were most hospitable'. They also visited Jozef Israëls's studio: 'We found Mr Israëls a very charming little man (he does not stand as high as my shoulder). The students were all delighted with the man and his pictures.'

Mesdag's contacts in Brussels, where he lived from 1866 to 1869, probably contributed to his development as a marine painter.[35] It was here that he met Paul Jan Clays (1819–1900), a pupil of Théodore Gudin and Horace Vernet, who began by painting romantic seascapes in the manner of his teachers, and then went on to produce river scenes and seascapes in a broadly painted style devoid of any romantic sentiment. Apart from the Belgian coast, he looked for subjects primarily in Zeeland, at the mouth of the Scheldt, but he also worked in Dordrecht. Louis Artan (1837–90) was another marine painter living in Brussels; he worked mainly on the Breton and Belgian coasts. In 1871 he was in the Netherlands where he painted the *Pier at Flushing*, which that year was also chosen as a subject by Mesdag.

Fishing towns and villages

Closely linked to the beach and the sea was the way of life in the fishing villages from which Jozef Israëls and a number of less well-known masters of the Hague School, such as Bernard Blommers (1845–1914) and Philip Sadée (1837–1904), often drew their subjects. A good ten years before Jozef Israëls began to concentrate on this genre in Zandvoort (1855), the picturesqueness of this little coastal town had been discovered by the Düsseldorf artist Rudolf Jordan (1810–87).[36] In a letter that Jordan wrote to his wife from Zandvoort on 28 September 1844, we can read how he set about his work there and the problems with which he had to contend.

I have already painted 5 heads and 1 study of the dunes and it must be remembered here that the seamen I'm concerned with are only at home on Saturday evenings and Sundays. The rest of the time they stay out at sea. When I have got 8 heads I shall be satisfied and I shall leave. Other things I need, such as dune contours and terrains, I sketch in my free time in my sketchbook. The dunes here are wonderful and I am delighted to be able to come back here to paint again.[37]

Jordan's interest in traditional costumes also took him to Marken and Volendam. In an undated letter written on the island of Marken he expressed his enthusiasm for the costumes there, 'The costume, the costume, the costume. Oh! Ah! Hurrah! Heavenly!', and a little further on, 'I shall paint heads. Ah, the costumes! Ah my good folk! That alone makes everything fine!' Jordan's paintings were exceptionally popular in Germany, often winning prizes at international exhibitions, and the prints that were made of a number of his compositions were widely distributed.

The scenes from the life of Dutch fishing people by Max Liebermann (1847–1935), who certainly knew Jordan's work, were also generally popular. Jordan's *Death of the Pilot* of 1856 was a very famous picture in Germany and in 1872, during his very first stay in Holland, Liebermann painted his *In the Pilot's Room*.[38] However, Liebermann's treatment of the subject, as evinced by this painting and his *Net Menders*, is completely different from that of Jordan. Jordan's paintings tell a story in which the fisherman is made a hero and drama is the central element, as is apparent from such titles as *The Burial of the Old Seaman* and *All the Boats Return, Only One is Missing*, which are not without a certain sentimentality. Liebermann in contrast observed the fishing people with a cool objectivity devoid of emotion. In that respect, Jozef Israëls's early paintings in this particular genre, such as *Fishermen Carrying a Drowned Man* and *Passing Mother's Grave* (Cat. 28), are closer to the work of Jordan than that of Liebermann. There is a striking similarity in composition between Israëls's *Passing Mother's Grave* of 1856 and Jordan's *The Unhoped-for Reunion* of 1840. The international success of this composition of two figures walking in the dunes with the sea in the background is clear from *A Fisherman and his Son Returning Home with the Day's Catch* (fig. 100) by Andries Scheerboom (1832–80), an artist who was born in Amsterdam but worked in London from 1863 onwards, and who must certainly have known Israëls's *Passing Mother's Grave*.

The fishermen genre enjoyed tremendous popularity in Germany, particularly from the 1870s onwards. Leafing through the catalogues of the international exhibitions held in Munich and Berlin during this period, one is struck by the number of artists who were represented by scenes from the life of fishermen and their families, very often in a Dutch setting. Sometimes Israëls's influence is apparent, as in *The Drowned Sailor* (fig. 101) by Otto Kirberg (1850–1926) and a watercolour by German Grobe (1857–1938; fig. 102).

At nearly every international exhibition in which the Netherlands was represented, views of the beach with fishing people by Blommers and Sadée hung alongside work by artists such as Israëls and Mesdag. The former two artists are now considered as minor masters of the Hague School, but in their own day they were famous and much imitated. Thus *The Return of the Fishermen* of 1878 by the Belgian artist Henry Bource (1826–99) is strongly reminiscent of Sadée's work, while the beach scenes with fishermen's wives by the English artist Edith Hume (active 1862–96) would have been unthinkable without Blommers's paintings.

Via the Düsseldorf Academy numerous Scandinavian artists, such as the two Swedes August Jernberg (1826–96) and Ferdinand Fagerlin (1825–1907), also came to the Dutch coastal villages.[39] From 1862 onwards Fagerlin came nearly every summer to the coast of the Netherlands, deriving subjects from the daily life of the fishermen. In Düsseldorf he had come into close contact with the work of Rudolf Jordan and the Canadian artist Henry Ritter (1816–53), whose work also reveals an obvious preference for motifs from the life of Dutch fishermen.[40] In a letter of 1892 he wrote, 'That my interest goes out to Holland and the life of the fisherfolk there can be put down to Ritters and also to the picturesque country and people. The Dutch art of the past and the nearness of the country also lure one strongly in this direction.'

fig. 100 SCHEERBOOM *A Fisherman and his Son Returning Home with the Day's Catch* 1880
(Location unknown)

From 1874 in particular, after the publication of Henry Havard's book *La Hollande pittoresque, Voyage aux villes mortes du Zuiderzee (Picturesque Holland, a Journey to the Ghost Towns of the Zuider Zee)*,[41] which appeared shortly afterwards in a Dutch edition, the fishing villages of Marken and Volendam became especially popular among the painting and drawing fraternity because of their colourful traditional costumes. In 1875 George Clausen (1852–1944), an Englishman of Danish origin, spent some time in the province of North Holland, where he found many subjects for his paintings.[42] His first painting to be shown at the Royal Academy in London, *High Mass at a Fishing Village* of 1876, was reproduced, described and praised in various periodicals. He was fairly free in his interpretation of reality: the painting shows the main church at Monnikendam, in front of which a crowd of churchgoers has assembled to attend Mass, decked out in a colourful combination of traditional costumes from various regions and places. The German artist Hans von Bartels (1856–1913) allowed himself similar liberties. His studies of Katwijk and Volendam fishing people are very accurate and carefully observed, but in his paintings and gouaches folklore and customs are fancifully combined.

Dutch interiors

Max Liebermann wrote in 1901,

About thirty years ago the Dutch made their debut as a group in the Glaspalast at Munich and created a tremendous sensation among the artists, who constitute the only public in Munich. What struck us was the painterly culture. Any young man of any energy made the pilgrimage to Holland, bringing back with him a wooden shoe, a white cap and a long clay pipe; the Dutch window with its little leaded lights became the fashion. The revival that German painting underwent in the eighties of the last century was owed not least to the influence of the Dutch and the Munich Sezession gratefully acknowledged its debt by making Israëls an honorary member, for it was Israëls who shaped the modern Dutch school.[43]

The wooden shoes, the white cap, the Gouda clay pipe and the leaded lights are brought together in *Sunday Afternoon in Holland* by Gotthardt Kuehl (1850–1915) who repeatedly visited Holland in the 1870s and 1880s in search of motifs for his genre paintings (fig. 105).[44] Liebermann himself painted various fine Dutch interiors, in which the window with light behind it invariably plays an important role (fig. 103).[45] This device is also seen in the interiors of Jozef Israëls and is ultimately borrowed from seventeenth-century masters like Vermeer and Pieter de Hooch. In contrast to Liebermann and Kuehl, Israëls deployed a restrained palette, although with a rich range of gradations. In this respect Liebermann, who placed Israëls on a level with Millet, was of the opinion that there existed an obvious parallel between the work of Israëls and that of his great predecessor Rembrandt.[46] Israëls's simple people in sober interiors evoked eulogies at the international exhibitions and influenced other artists. A watercolour by Hans von Bartels (1856–1913), showing an old woman by the fire (fig. 104), is inconceivable without Israëls's famous painting, *Growing Old* (Cat. 35), which was exhibited at Munich in 1888.

The influence of Israëls is also unmistakable in the work of Gemmell Hutchison (1855–1936), who belonged to the Glasgow School of painters, a group of Scottish artists who were profoundly affected by the Barbizon School on the one hand and the Hague School on the other.[47] The Hague School was greatly admired in Scotland. Paintings by Israëls, Mauve, Jacob and Matthijs Maris, Bosboom, Roelofs and Van Gogh were to be found alongside works by the painters of Barbizon in a number of Scottish collections, such as those of John Forbes White and Alex Reid.[48] The houses of these collectors served as meeting-places for Scottish artists, who could study the work of their Dutch colleagues there and compare it with that of the Barbizon School.

In 1870 they had an opportunity to meet Israëls, when he was the guest of John Forbes White. Israëls stayed in White's Seaton Cottage, where the Glasgow painter George Reid (1841–1913) began to make a portrait of his admired Dutch colleague. George Paul Chalmers (1833–78) and Hugh Cameron (1835–1918) also worked on this portrait during the various sittings. During the last of them Israëls himself seized a brush, crying, 'Now I'll just show you what Rembrandt would have done', and added a few telling strokes. On the brown sleeve was painted '*A notre ami White*', along with the signatures of the four painters. George Reid had been to the Netherlands as early as 1866, to take lessons from the Utrecht landscape painter Alexander Mollinger (1836–67), in whom White also took a great interest. During his stay Reid had made friends with Israëls, who had a great influence on his work. The paintings of Chalmers, too, sometimes show a striking similarity to those of Israëls. His *An Old Shepherd Reading* (fig. 106) is strongly reminiscent of Israëls's *Alone in the World* of 1880 (fig. 9).[49]

fig. 101 KIRBERG *The Drowned Sailor*
(Location unknown)

fig. 102 GROBE *Young Woman Looking Over the Beach* (watercolour)
(Location unknown)

The influence of Israëls, and still more of the lesser master Albert Neuhuys (1844–1914), is also to be seen in the interiors of the American Gari Melchers (1860–1932), who came to the Netherlands in 1884 on the instigation of George Hitchcock, whom he had met in Paris.[50] He rented a studio at Egmond aan Zee to which he regularly returned over the next 30 years to look for subjects for his paintings.

In France the nineteenth-century painters of interiors had always greatly admired the Dutch seventeenth-century models.[51] Vermeer had been more or less a French discovery and it was in France that his fame reached its peak.[52] Pieter de Hooch and Nicolaes Maes also enjoyed great renown and their influence finds clear expression in the work of François Bonvin (1817–87). There are also striking similarities between some interiors by Pierre Edouard Frère (1819–86) and those of Jozef Israëls.[53] Israëls's work received high praise from the critics at the Salon exhibitions and it is thus very probable that his French colleagues considered him a new scion of the old race of Dutch painters and studied his work even more attentively as a result.

Many foreign artists hoped to find the past in the Netherlands, where everything was said to be fifty years behind the times. Industrialization had begun later in the Netherlands than in its European neighbours and people abroad retained an image of it that had originally been formed by the work of the seventeenth-century masters. The windmills that were still turning, the fishermen and peasants in their gay traditional

fig. 104 VON BARTELS *Old Woman near the Fireplace*
(Location unknown)

fig. 105 KUEHL *Sunday Afternoon in Holland*
(Bayerische Staatsgemäldesammlungen, Munich)

fig. 106 CHALMERS *An Old Shepherd Reading*
(Location unknown)

costumes, the farm kitchens with their copper pots and pans and blue Delft tiles, the fishing boats on the beach; all these exerted an irresistible pull on townspeople and artists in search of the picturesque. But in the 1870s the Netherlands also began to change a great deal, as the artists noted with sorrow. At the beginning of the 1880s the painters of the Hague School protested at the levelling of the Dekkersduin. As early as 1872 François Bonvin wrote in a letter,

On doctors' orders I left for Holland on 17 July. I have become rather worse than before my departure and I think this is to be attributed to the modern element, which overthrows and invades everything in the false name of progress. The Bois de Boulogne in Amsterdam! And the demolition of the windmills and the canals to make way for the stinking smoke of coal. By the sea there is no longer any room for the picturesque cottages of the fishermen: nothing but casinos.

A year later he wrote, 'Nothing is so pleasant as The Hague and its surroundings, especially Scheveningen (as long as it's not too windy). Only there are ever more casinos there.'54

The American artists George Henry Boughton (1833–1905) and Edwin Austen Abbey (1852–1911) commented in their *Sketching Rambles in Holland* of 1885 that they were shocked by the Dutch lack of interest in the old and beautiful and by the way in which they were prepared to raze indiscriminately to the ground any historic building in order to build a new boulevard or railway station.55

fig. 103 LIEBERMANN *Silent Work c.* 1884–85
(Private collection)

But despite that, foreign artists continued to come to the Netherlands after the 1880s in great numbers and from all over the world in search of what they regarded as typically Dutch. It was only with the outbreak of the First World War in 1914 that the stream finally came to a standstill. Thus, the heyday of the Hague School had coincided with a period in which the Netherlands was in vogue, a period in which countless artists visited the country in order to study, to draw and to paint the scenery and people among whom the Hague School artists lived and worked.

NOTES

1. Newspaper cutting, R.K.D., dated 1892, with no further details.

2. Exh. cat. *VI Internationale Kunstaustellung*, Glaspalast, Munich 1892.

3. J. Verbeek, *Bezoekers van het Rijksmuseum in het Trippenhuis 1844–1885. Gedenkboek uitgegeven ter gelegenheid van het honderdvijftigjarig bestaan van het Rijksmuseum*, The Hague, 1958, pp. 60–71.

4. J. Sillevis in exh. cat. *Turner 1775–1851*, Haags Gemeentemuseum, The Hague 1978, p. 11.

5. Exh. cat. *Andreas Achenbach 1815–1910, zum 150. Geburtstag*, Galerie G. Paffrath, Düsseldorf 1965.

6. A. Houssaye, *Histoire de la peinture flamande et hollandaise*, Paris 1847; W. Thoré-Bürger, *Etudes sur les peintres hollandais et flamands*, Brussels 1860; W. Thoré-Bürger, 'Van der Meer de Delft', *Gazette des Beaux-Arts* XXII (1866); E. Fromentin, *Les maîtres d'autrefois, Belgique, Hollande*, Paris 1876.

7. P. Mantz, 'Les Beaux-Arts à l'exposition universelle; II La Hollande', *Gazette des Beaux-Arts* XXIII (1867), p. 21

8. G. Hitchcock, 'The picturesque quality of Holland', *Scribner's Magazine*, (Aug. 1887); cited by L. G. Robinson in 'Mr. George Hitchcock and American Art', *Art Journal* (Oct. 1891), pp. 289–95.

9. S. Fischer, *Max Liebermann, Die Phantasie in der Malerei; Schriften und Reden*, Frankfurt am Main 1978, pp. 83–84.

10. Exh. cat. *Dutch Exhibition*, Whitechapel Art Gallery, London 1904, p. 6.

11. J. Laran, *Daubigny*, Paris 1913, pp. 101–02; R. Hellebranth, *Charles-François Daubigny (1817–1878)*, Morges 1976, pp. 242–44, cat. nos. 738–45.

12. Laran, *op. cit.* (note 11), p. 102.

13. P. Miquel, *Félix Ziem*, Maurs-la-Jolie 1978, pp. 65–69.

14. M. Büchler-Schild, *Johan Barthold Jongkind, Seine Stellung in der Landschafts- und Aquarelltradition des 19. Jahrhunderts*, Bern 1979, p. 24.

15. V. Hefting, *Jongkind, sa vie, son oeuvre, son époque*, Paris 1975, p. 347.

16. G. de Knyff, *Eugène Boudin, raconté par lui-même*, Paris 1976, pp. 126–27.

17. R. Schmit, *Eugène Boudin (1824–1898)*, vol. 1, Paris 1973, pp. XXX–XXXI; for the views of Dordrecht of 1884 see *ibid.*, vol. 2, cat. nos. 1815, 1816, 1818–61.

18. G. Jean-Aubry, *Eugène Boudin*, Neuchâtel 1968, pp. 101–02.

19. R. Puvogel in exh. cat. *Caspar Scheuren (1810–1887), Ein Maler und Illustrator der deutschen Spätromantik*, Suermondt-Ludwig Museum, Aachen 1980.

20. Z. Ebenstein, 'Zum Werk von Tina Blau' in exh. cat. *Tina Blau, eine Wiener Malerin*, Österreichische Galerie im oberen Belvedere, Vienna 1971, pp. 18–19.

21. Ch. Blanc, *Les Beaux-Arts à l'exposition universelle de 1878*, Paris 1878, p. 366.

22. D. Reid, *A concise history of Canadian painting*, Toronto 1973, pp. 118–34.

23. Exh. cat. *John Henry Twachtman, A retrospective exhibition*, The Cincinnati Art Museum, Cincinnati 1966, p. 4.

24. G. Gould, *Trophy of conquest*, London 1965, p. 24; exh. cat. *Het vaderlandsch gevoel*, Rijksmuseum, Amsterdam 1978, p. 148.

25. Exh. cat. *Het landschap in de Belgische kunst 1830–1914*, Museum voor Schone Kunsten, Ghent 1980; *Catalogus schilderijen 19de en 20ste eeuw*, Koninklijk Museum voor Schone Kunsten te Antwerpen, Antwerp 1977.

26. J. de Gruyter, *De Haagse School*, vol. 2, Rotterdam 1969, p. 83.

27. Exh. cat. *Die Düsseldorfer Malerschule*, Kunstmuseum, Düsseldorf 1979, pp. 439–40.

28. P. Clemen, 'Julius Bergmann', *Die Kunst für Alle* XXXVII, (Jan. 1922), pp. 105–18.

29. Exh. cat. *Clarkson Stanfield*, Rheinisches Landesmuseum, Bonn 1979, pp. 185–87. For English artists in Holland see also exh. cat. *Holland, a source of inspiration for British art, Paintings and watercolours selected for Pictura '81*, Eurohal Maastricht, Martyn Gregory, London 1981.

30. Information provided by J.P. van Brakel, president of the *Oud Katwijk* society.

31. E. Christen & R. Oberkampf du Dabrun, *Alphonse Stengelin van Katwijk*, Geneva 1932, p. 24.

32. Exh. cat. *Robert F. Blum, a retrospective exhibition*, Cincinnati Art Museum, Cincinnati 1966.

33. K. Metcalf Roof, *The life and art of William Merritt Chase*, New York 1975 (first published New York 1917), pp. 103–10.

34. Metcalf Roof, *op. cit.*, pp. 204–13.

35. J. Poort, *Hendrik Willem Mesdag, artiste peintre à la Haye*, The Hague 1981, p. 23.

36. G. von Jordan in Strassburg i. Els., *Rudolf Jordan 1810–1887, Sonderabdruck aus der Chronik der Familie Jordan*, Berlin 1902; F.W. Rass, *Rudolf Jordan, der Maler Helgolands*, Hanover 1900.

37. The letters by Jordan from which this quotation and the two given below are taken are to be found in the collection of J. W. Niermans, who has lent me his willing assistance.

38. Exh. cat. *Max Liebermann in seiner Zeit*, Berlin 1979, p. 160. For Liebermann's contacts with Holland see exh. cat. *Max Liebermann en Holland*, Haags Gemeentemuseum, The Hague 1980.

39. Exh. cat. *Düsseldorf und der Norden*, Kunstmuseum, Düsseldorf 1976, pp. 53–54.

40. Exh. cat. *The Hudson and the Rhine*, Kunstmuseum, Düsseldorf 1976, pp. 78–79.

41. H. Havard, *La Hollande pittoresque, Voyage aux villes mortes du Zuiderzee*, Paris 1874.

42. B.W.E. Veurman, *Volendammer schilderboek*, Alphen a.d. Rijn 1972, p. 25.

43. Fischer, *op. cit.*, p. 77.

44. Exh. cat. *Die Münchner Schule 1850–1914*, Haus der Kunst, Munich 1979, p. 262; cat. *Neue Pinakothek München*, Munich 1981; pp. 181–82.

45. Exh. cat. Berlin 1979, *op. cit.*, p. 232.

46. Fischer, *op. cit.*, pp. 78–80.

47. D. & F. Irvin, *Scottish Painters at Home and Abroad 1700–1900*, London 1975, pp. 372–91; W. Hardie, *Scottish Painting 1837–1939*, London 1976, pp. 59–82.

48. J.M. Harrower, *John Forbes White*, Edinburgh, n.d.; exh. cat. *A Man of Influence, Alex Reid 1854–1928*, Scottish Arts Council, Glasgow 1967.

49. Harrower, *op. cit.*, pp. 36–37.

50. Exh. cat. *Gari Melchers, American Painter*, Graham Gallery, New York 1978, p. 10; H. Lewis-Hind, *Gari Melchers, Painter*, New York 1928.

51. P. ten Doesschate Chu, *French Realism and the Dutch Masters*, Utrecht 1974.

52. The first major publication on Vermeer was that by W. Thoré-Bürger in the *Gazette des Beaux Arts* of 1866.

53. Exh. cat. *The Realist Tradition, French Painting and Drawing 1830–1900*, the Cleveland Museum of Art, Cleveland 1981, p. 290, see also p. 106.

54. E. Monceau-Nélaton, *Bonvin, raconté par lui-même*, Paris 1927, pp. 87–89.

55. G. Boughton. *Sketching rambles in Holland, with illustrations by the author and Edwin A. Abbey*, New York 1885; exh. cat. *Edwin Austin Abbey (1852–1911)*, Yale University of Art, New Haven (Conn.) 1974.

Art Dealers and Collectors

CHARLES DUMAS

During the 1870s works by the masters of the Hague and Barbizon Schools were rarely collected on any scale in the Netherlands, the only collector of note being Hendrik Willem Mesdag. However, their rural scenes and peasant interiors, whilst neglected in the Netherlands, were already finding their way into English, Scottish and, to a lesser degree, American collections, most of which were formed by well-to-do barristers, solicitors, accountants and, above all, big industrialists who had made their fortunes in the steel industry or in railway and steamship companies.[1] They had acquired their knowledge of contemporary French and Dutch painting through the art trade and exhibitions, such as the International Exhibitions of 1862 and 1871 in London.

The reviews of such exhibitions in the foreign press were in general exceptionally laudatory. One critic, reviewing an exhibition held at the Grosvenor Gallery in London for *The Times* wrote,

There are few facts in modern art history more remarkable than the revival of Dutch painting in our own time from new contact with familiar life and nature. The art of Joseph Israëls is the tap-root of this revival, which includes both oil and watercolour painting. The master himself is better known here by his oil pictures, many of the best of which, we believe, are in this country.[2]

Artists of both the Hague and Barbizon Schools were represented in most of these foreign collections, their paintings often hanging side by side, but towards the end of the century the Hague School seems to have become more popular, as was reflected in the reviews in the English and American press at that time.

The Dutch are born painters more than the French are. The latter strive for distinction, but the Dutch do not think about it or they take no trouble over it . . . Israëls and Mesdag have done things with more heart than the French. They do, indeed, have more heart; character is their basis. . . . The Dutchman has understood better than anyone else how to translate daily life and nature into art. No people has gone so directly to nature.[3]

The Hague School's increasing popularity and the consequent rise in demand for its paintings and watercolours caused prices to rise to unimaginable heights. Pictures by Israëls fetched about 3,000 guilders around 1890, but by 1910 collectors could expect to pay some 30,000 guilders and

one work was sold for 100,000 guilders.[4] Nor did these prices apply to Israëls alone. A lesser idol such as Bernard Blommers succeeded in selling a painting for 6,000 dollars in Philadelphia in 1904.[5]

During the final decades of the nineteenth century various Hague School collections came into being in the Netherlands although these remained much more modest in scale than those in the English-speaking countries. The Dutch museums had also begun to make hesitant purchases at this time, but there was no question of the formation of large collections of Hague School work; it was only after a number of collections had been privately given or bequeathed to various museums during this century that the new golden age of Dutch painting was properly represented in them.

Collections in Great Britain

The Barbizon School and the Hague School were not very widely admired in the 1870s and 1880s, yet it was at precisely this period that the most important collections were formed in Great Britain. The most extensive was that of James Staats Forbes (1823–1904; fig. 107).[6] On his death he left no fewer than 3,200 paintings and watercolours, the largest private collection that had hitherto existed in Britain, over a third of which consisted of works by Jozef Israëls, Mauve, the Maris brothers, Bosboom, Mesdag, Blommers, Gabriël, Roelofs, Neuhuys, De Bock and other contemporary Dutch masters. Works by French painters, with an accent on Corot, Millet and the Barbizon School, made up almost another third of the collection.[7]

Forbes, who was born in Aberdeen, entered the service of the Great Western Railway Company after training as an engineer in London. When the *Hollandsche Rijnspoorweg*, a Dutch railway company under British management, was teetering on the edge of bankruptcy, he was invited to form part of the staff detailed to take charge of its reorganization. He settled in The Hague, rose to the highest post in a relatively short time and managed to run the company reasonably successfully during the 18 years that he held the post and lived in the Netherlands. This resulted in 1861 in his appointment as general manager of the London, Chatham and Dover Railway, and this line too he helped out of financial difficulties.[8]

Forbes, who had acquired a great love of painting, met

fig. 107 James Staats Forbes (1823–1904)

among other works, his well-known *View of Montigny-sur-Loing* (Cat. 48) and *View of Amsterdam* (Philadelphia Museum of Art). There were only four works by Jacob's brother Matthijs,[12] but an unusually large number of watercolours by Anton Mauve as well as a few of his paintings, such as the *Riders on the Beach at Scheveningen* (Cat. 89).

When Forbes died, his estate was so large that his family were afraid a public sale would flood the market, so they decided to accede to the request of several big collectors and sell it privately. Paintings were sold to the United States, Germany, the Netherlands and France, while a little over half the collection remained in England. In the Netherlands the art dealer Abraham Preyer[13] and the firm of Boussod, Valadon & Co.[14] managed to acquire a large number of works. The individual paintings fetched colossal prices for that period. Israëls's *Sewing School*, for example, which Forbes had acquired from a French dealer for 4,800 guilders, was bought by a London dealer for 36,000 guilders, while three works by Mauve for which Forbes had paid 120, 600 and 650 guilders (around 1880), fetched 4,800, 5,400 and 14,400 guilders respectively in 1905.[15] It can only be regretted that such a unique collection could not remain intact; other important British collections, such as those of Alexander Young and Sir John Charles Day, were also dispersed shortly afterwards.

The collection of the London accountant Alexander Young comprised around 700 works, considerably fewer than that of Forbes, but in general of higher quality,[16] with a stronger accent on Corot and the Barbizon School. Over a period of 30 to 40 years Young had managed to amass more than 60 Corots, which constituted the choicest and most representative collection of the artist's work at that time. The Hague School was represented on a smaller scale, but by works of a high standard with fine pieces by Mauve, Jacob and Willem Maris, Jozef Israëls, Neuhuys, Artz, Bosboom, Mesdag and Jan Hendrik Weissenbruch.[17] The greatest masterpiece in Young's collection of Dutch masters was Israëls's *Fishermen Carrying a Drowned Man* (Cat. 29),[18] which had established Israëls's name with the English public when it was shown at the International Exhibition in London in 1862. At that time, it was sold to Arthur J. Lewis through the agency of the Belgian art dealer Gambart[19] and it only came into Young's possession several decades later. After his death his entire collection was sold,[20] but this picture was bought back by his widow and given to the National Gallery in London in accordance with her late husband's wishes.

The third important English private collection that was sold at the beginning of this century was that of Sir John Charles Frederic Sigismund Day (1826–1908).[21] Day was born in The Hague, brought up in Freiburg and Bath and had a flourishing legal practice in London. He began collecting contemporary paintings at an early age and, like Forbes and Young, he concentrated on works by the Barbizon School and the Hague School. Of the former he possessed primarily a large number of paintings by Daubigny, Dupré and Harpignies and of the latter works principally by Jacob and Willem Maris, Mauve, Jozef Israëls and Mesdag. This exhibition includes two works by Mauve that were formerly in his collection, *The Marsh* (Cat. 104) and *Woman with Kid at Laren* (Cat. 105). The collection, which included a not insignificant number of etchings and engravings, was sold in London in 1909, a year after Day's death.[22]

Two of the collectors already mentioned, Forbes and

numerous well-known artists during his time in the Netherlands and became great friends with Jozef Israëls, whom he regarded as one of the greatest living painters.[9] Although he bought some works of art during the time he lived in the Netherlands, most of his purchases were made later, in the 1880s and 1890s, largely through the agency of Warmington, an assistant appointed specially for this purpose.

Forbes divided his collection between his house in London, called Garden Corner, and his office in Victoria Station. After a visit there Max Rooses wrote the following description for the *Nieuwe Rotterdamsche Courant*.

> Paintings everywhere, from the corridor on the ground floor right up to the top floor, paintings in the dining room and in the bedroom, and up the stairs and in the actual art room, paintings from floor to ceiling, paintings stacked in rows of ten or twelve behind one another on the floor, because there was no more room for them on the walls.[10]

Although the emphasis of the collection lay on the Hague School and the Barbizon School, it did contain a few works by Reynolds and several dozen Constables. However, it is striking that virtually no nineteenth-century English painters were represented in it. Israëls took pride of place among the Hague School artists with around 90 paintings and the same number of watercolours, including well-known works like *The Sewing School*, *Old and Worn Out*, *Out of Darkness into Light* and *The Day before Parting* (Cat. 30). As Forbes himself said, 'I can't resist an Israëls!'[11] Jacob Maris was the next best represented Hague School artist, the collection including,

Young, were Scots by birth. Significantly, nearly all the other British collections in which nineteenth-century French and Dutch painting occupied a dominant place were also brought together by Scots: John Forbes White, John Reid, Alexander MacDonald, R.T. Hamilton Bruce, James Donald[23] and Thomas Glenn Arthur.[24] Of these, the most notable collections of Dutch paintings were those of White and Reid.

Like many others, John Forbes White (1831–1904) visited the International Exhibition in London in 1862 and was much impressed by the work of Dutch painters.[25] He particularly liked the work of Alexander Mollinger (1836–67), a pupil of Willem Roelofs, and bought a landscape by him entitled *Drenthe* at the exhibition. White then commissioned Mollinger to make a pendant to his acquisition, conducting a lengthy correspondence about it with him, as a result of which the two men became friends. White visited Mollinger several times at his home in Utrecht and in 1866 sent the young Scottish painter George Reid (1841–1913) to study under him in the Netherlands. After Mollinger's sudden death in 1867, White again visited the Netherlands, returning to Scotland with a large number of his paintings and drawings, which he sold among his friends for a substantial price. He was thus able to secure for the painter's relatives a much higher sum than they would have received from a sale in the Netherlands. White's trips to the Netherlands became increasingly frequent and he made regular visits to the studio of Jozef Israëls, Bosboom and other artists. Israëls in his turn went to stay with White in Aberdeen in 1870. During this visit George Reid painted a portrait of the celebrated Dutchman; the Scottish painters Chalmers and Cameron also worked on the painting and Israëls himself applied the finishing touches to it (fig. 108).[26]

In addition to paintings by Mollinger and contemporary Scottish and English artists, White's collection included work by Corot, Diaz, Israëls, Bosboom, Mauve and Roelofs. He preferred, whenever possible, to buy directly from the artists, so that each work acquired a personal meaning for him. The collection was sold in London during his lifetime, in 1888.[27]

John Reid, who came from Glasgow, did not begin to acquire his collection until the last quarter of the nineteenth century. It fell into three sections, the British, French and Dutch Schools, and included 11 paintings by Israëls,[28] five by Jacob Maris and four by Willem Maris. There were only a few examples of the work of Mauve, Blommers, Neuhuys, Apol and Mesdag, while Matthijs Maris and Bosboom were unrepresented. It was a relatively small collection, and it was partly due to its size that an exceptionally fine catalogue was produced in 1913.[29]

Another Scottish collection, that of Sir William Burrell (1861–1958) should also be mentioned here.[30] It has remained intact and differs from the collections already discussed in other ways. From around 1880 until the time of his death, Burrell, the scion of a well-to-do family of shipowners, built up a collection of over 8,000 objects – paintings, tapestries, furniture, sculpture, glass, silver, ceramics and suchlike – from various cultures and periods.[31] In 1901 he lent more than 200 works of art to the International Exhibition in Glasgow, including 40 paintings and watercolours, seven of which were by Matthijs Maris, two by Jacob Maris and one by Bosboom.[32] Having already given more than 60 paintings and drawings to the Glasgow Art Gallery in 1925, he gave his entire collection to the City of Glasgow in 1925 along with the sum

fig. 108 REID, CHALMERS, CAMERON AND J. ISRAËLS
Portrait of Jozef Israëls
(Aberdeen Museum of Art, Aberdeen)

of £450,000, earmarked for the building of a new museum that is now (1983) nearing completion. The collection, probably the largest in the world ever to have been amassed by a single individual, contains only a relatively small number of works by Hague School artists, but the important place occupied by Matthijs Maris is unparalleled in any other private collection.

Collections in the United States and Canada

Interest in the Barbizon School and the Hague School were as closely linked in the United States as they were in Great Britain. The United States had maintained special ties with France ever since the American War of Independence[33] and this found expression in, among other things, a steady stream of young artists going to study in France. Thus it is not surprising that in the nineteenth century collectors of contemporary art were inclined to take their cue from the French. After the middle of the century it was the works of the leading French academicians, Bouguereau, Meissonier, Gerôme, Bonnat, Tissot and others, that were most collected, but these artists were gradually supplanted by Corot, Theodore Rousseau, Daubigny, Troyon and Dupré. This shift of interest was largely due to the American painter William Morris Hunt (1824–79), who lived in France from 1844 to 1855, first in Paris, where he worked in the studio of Thomas Couture, and then in Barbizon. On his return to the United States he settled in Boston and urged collectors to buy Barbizon paintings, which could be supplied by the Westminster Art Gallery in nearby Providence.[34]

Initially the American collectors confined themselves mainly to French painting, but similarities between the

fig. 109 LÁSZLÓ
Portrait of Edward Drummond Libbey (1854–1925) 1922
(The Toledo Museum of Art, Toledo, Ohio)

Barbizon and Hague Schools in subject matter and atmosphere led to the acquisition of large numbers of works by Mauve, Israëls and the Maris brothers by American collectors from the 1890s onwards. Strangely enough, however, and in marked contrast to the work of the Barbizon painters, there were scarcely any large concentrations of work by particular artists within these collections.

One exception to this was the collection of Edward Drummond Libbey (1854–1925; fig. 109).[35] Libbey entered the service of the New England Glass Company in East Cambridge, Massachusetts, where his father was general manager, at the age of 20. In 1883 his father, who had bought up the company some years before, died and he became its owner. Five years later he moved to Toledo, Ohio, where he set up first the Libbey Glass Company and then the Toledo Glass Company. He took a particular interest in philanthropic and educational work and in 1901, together with some other interested residents, took the initiative in founding the Toledo Museum of Art, which opened its doors in 1912 with five inaugural exhibitions.[36] It was not until 1925, however, the year of his death, that Libbey's own collection of nineteenth-century European paintings and watercolours, old masters, Egyptian antiquities and a unique collection of glass, acquired mainly during the first two decades of the century, became the property of the museum. There were few works by the Barbizon School, but the Hague School was well represented with work by Mauve (Cat. 88, 92), Jan Hendrik Weissenbruch, Jozef Israëls (Cat. 45), Jacob and Willem Maris,

Bosboom (Cat. 14) and Neuhuys.

Arthur J. Secor, the second president of the Toledo Museum, also bequeathed his collection to it in 1926 and 1933. This was the biggest private collection of paintings ever given to this museum and it included a significant number of paintings and watercolours by Hague School painters,[37] as well as a large number of Barbizon pieces. Thus the Toledo Museum of Art is one of the few in the United States that can offer a representative picture of the two schools.

There were also quite a considerable number of works by both schools in the Frick Collection in New York. This collection, the vast bulk of which was amassed by Frank Frick (1828–1910), still contains a masterpiece by Jacob Maris.[37] The Hague School was originally much better represented, but over the years the owner returned a number of pieces to M. Knoedler & Co., the New York art dealers.

Another American collection was that of Joseph Jefferson (1829–1905), a well-known actor in his day.[38] His collection focused almost entirely on Dutch painting. Bernard Blommers visited him in 1904 in his country house at Barclard Bay near Boston and wrote about this in a letter to Miss Marius, the Dutch painter and author of the first survey of nineteenth-century Dutch art.

He possesses the most beautiful painting by Mauve that I've ever seen . . . *such as to make your mouth water*, also a *splendid* Israëls . . . he had paintings by all of us, Neuhuys, myself, and a good sketch by Kever and a Weissenbruch. . . . His admiration for our Dutch art is out of the ordinary. At his country house he had a model Dutch windmill made, which stood there very nicely. . . . In a fire at his house a few years ago . . . a few Mauves and some other paintings were burnt.[39]

Dutch paintings were greatly admired in Canada towards the end of the nineteenth century. In this case, their value as status symbols played no small part in their popularity.[40] In Montreal the best-known collections were those of E.B. Greenshields,[41] William and Agnes Learmont,[42] Sir George A. Drummond and Sir William van Horne;[43] in Toronto those of E.F.B. Johnston and Sir Edmund Walker. The work of Jan Hendrik Weissenbruch enjoyed particular admiration, far more than it did elsewhere. This found expression in the book by Greenshields published in 1904, entitled *The Subjective View of Landscape Painting. With Special Reference to J.H. Weissenbruch and Illustrations from Work of His in Canada*.[44] Tholen and Blommers were also highly regarded in Canada, collectors generally buying their paintings and watercolours at the French Gallery, a London-based art dealer that had branches in Canada, or directly from dealers in England, Scotland and the Netherlands.[45]

Collections in the Netherlands

It was not until the last quarter of the nineteenth century, rather later than in Great Britain and the United States, that a few private individuals in the Netherlands, such as J. Verstolk-Völcker, F.H.M. Post, Dr T.H. Blom Coster and, last but not least, the painter Hendrik Willem Mesdag, began to collect the works of the Barbizon and Hague Schools.[46]

Mesdag's collection was housed in a specially designed building in the garden of his house on Laan van Meerdervoort in The Hague. In 1903 he presented the building and the collection that it housed to the nation, and it became the Rijksmuseum H.W. Mesdag.[47] The collection falls into two parts: French nineteenth-century painting, including many works by Barbizon painters (the most important collection of their work outside France),[48] and Dutch painting of the second half of the nineteenth century, with an emphasis on the Hague School.[49] Mesdag had become familiar with the work of the Barbizon School in Brussels in the 1860s and had then introduced it to the Netherlands. Dutch painters were able to study the paintings in his house and its influence thus became felt in their own work. The French part of the collection included 12 works by Corot, seven by Millet and seven by Courbet, together with 25 by Daubigny and 12 by Théodore Rousseau. In the Dutch part of the collection, all the Hague School painters, including the minor masters, were amply represented, while there were more than ten works by certain artists – Mauve, Jozef Israëls, Bosboom and Mesdag himself.

Mesdag's preference for unfinished works found expression in the large number of studies and watercolours in the collection, which is, when considered as a whole, rather variable in quality. He made most of his purchases at exhibitions and sales of painters' estates, but he did also buy from Goupil & Co. and from private individuals. During his directorship (1903–11) of the museum named after him he added further paintings to the collection and after his death in 1915 the remainder of his private collection, together with his house, was offered to the State for 200,000 guilders. However, owing to the war there was no money available and the State had to forego the purchase.[50]

Another extremely important collection, consisting almost entirely of Hague School works (most of which are now in the Rijksmuseum in Amsterdam), was made by Jean Charles Joseph Drucker (1862–1944) and his wife.[51] Drucker, who was born in Amsterdam, moved to England in 1883, adopted British nationality and in 1886 married an Englishwoman, Maria Lydia Fraser. He had invested part of the capital he had inherited from his father, the financier Louis Drucker, in South Eastern Railways and acted as honorary secretary to the executive council of the shareholder's committee. The couple lived in London until the First World War, then in Baden, Switzerland and alternately in Zürich and St Moritz after the war, finally settling in Montreux. Meanwhile, in 1919, Drucker became a naturalized Dutchman again.

His first purchases, including works by Gabriël and Jacob Maris, date from the mid-1880s. It is possible that he was encouraged to collect by the example of Rudolf Kijzer from Amsterdam, who himself had a collection of the Hague and Barbizon Schools,[52] but he was perhaps more directly inspired by the Staats Forbes Collection, which he must certainly have known.[53] Drucker bought mainly at the Hague branch of the Paris art dealer Goupil & Co. and also did business, although to a lesser extent, with other leading Dutch art dealers, such as Van Wisselingh, Cornelis van Gogh, Preyer and his friend J. Elion. He was a friend of Jozef Israëls, Mesdag and the Maris brothers, but it is unlikely that he bought direct from their studios, since most of the Hague School painters were under contract to art dealers. Jozef Israëls,[54] Mauve and Jacob Maris are more widely represented than the other masters in Drucker's collection – as was also the case in the large British collections – but where Forbes had a predilection for Israëls, Drucker clearly had a preference for Jacob Maris and he owned more than 40 paintings and watercolours by him.[55]

As early as 1903 Drucker loaned 35 paintings and 20 watercolours to the Rijksmuseum. The following year he bequeathed his whole collection to the museum on condition that suitable accommodation for it would be built on to the existing premises. Dr P.J.H. Cuypers, the architect of the Rijksmuseum, was commissioned to design the extension and a committee of artists, including Willem Maris, Jozef Israëls and Mesdag advised on the decoration and furnishing of the new rooms. The Drucker-Fraser wing was formally opened to the public in 1909 on which occasion Drucker donated the works already on loan; new loans followed in 1911 and succeeding years, and in 1916 a second Drucker extension was completed. In 1941 complete control of the entire Drucker Collection was invested in the Director-General of the Rijksmuseum and in 1947, under the terms of the will, all the loans became the museum's property.

Not all the works from Drucker's collection are in the Rijksmuseum; in 1912 the collector gave a number of works by Jacob Maris, Jozef Israëls and Mauve to the National Gallery in London, so that the Hague School would also be permanently represented in England. Some of those works had already been lent to the gallery in 1907, including Israels's *Philosopher*, which made him the first living painter to acquire a place there.[56]

The generous gift of the Druckers had been preceded by that of the painter Joannes Westerwoudt (1849–1906), who lent part of his collection to the Rijksmuseum in 1902 and left it all to the museum after his death four years later.[57] This relatively small collection included several important works by Jongkind and Gerard Bilders, as well as pictures by the usual Hague School painters, and a few examples of the work of the Barbizon School.[58]

The example of Drucker and Westerwoudt was followed in 1925 by J.P. van der Schilden, who left his Hague School collection to the Museum Boymans in Rotterdam.[59] This collection was less representative, but it did include one or two masterpieces, such as Jacob Maris's *View of Montigny-sur-Loing* from the Forbes Collection (Cat. 48) and Mauve's *In the Vegetable Garden* (Cat. 106).[60]

The Haags Gemeentemuseum in The Hague acquired E.H. Crone's collection in 1947 as a loan from his heirs.[61] This collection, acquired at the beginning of the century, had been accommodated for many years in a specially built picture gallery in the Amsterdam house of the Crone family that stood obliquely opposite the Drucker-Fraser wing of the Rijksmuseum. The bulk of the collection is made up of works by Hague School artists, but there are also some works by Diaz, Vollon and Segantini, and a Corot. The Dutch artists who are best represented are Jan Hendrik Weissenbruch (by, among other works, his *View of Haarlem* [Cat. 133]) and Jacob Maris, but works by Willem and Matthijs Maris, Jozef Israëls, Mauve and Bosboom are also a significant part of the collection. In 1964 most of the collection was bought with the aid of the Vereeniging van Haagsche Museumvrienden (Society of Friends of Hague Museums) and the Vereeniging Rembrandt (Rembrandt Society).[62]

It is impossible to discuss here all the relevant Dutch collections, some of which combine works of the Hague and Barbizon Schools and most of which came into being around the turn of the century or in the following decade. It is sufficient simply to mention those of Dr J.D.C. Titsingh,[63] D.C. Reich, Jr.,[64] W.J. van Randwijk,[65] J. Hidde Nijland,[66] A.L.C. Kleijn,[67] Jonkheer J.R.H. Neervoort van de Poll,[68] C.G. Vattier Kraane[69] and M.P. Voûte.[70] All these collections have been sold and dispersed during the course of the century. A collection which has not been dispersed and which should be mentioned here is that of the Dordrecht notary Willem Hendrik van Bilderbeek (1855–1918) and his wife Johanna Adriana Cornelia van Bilderbeek-Lamaison van Heenvliet; in effect, it later became the Rijksmuseum Van Bilderbeek-Lamaison at Dordrecht,[71] Van Bilderbeek's collection, acquired between 1885 and 1918 and originally housed in his home, at 78, Wijnstraat, mainly comprised work by the Hague and Amsterdam Schools, with important paintings by Jacob and Willem Maris and George Hendrik Breitner.

The role of the art trade

The role played by the art trade in the creation of all these collections should not be underestimated. During the eighteenth and nineteenth centuries the European art trade, which had remained largely in the hands of artists in the previous two centuries, developed into an autonomous branch of commerce in which the art dealer served as a link between artist and collector.[72] From the middle of the nineteenth century onwards the power of the art dealer grew enormously owing to the disappearance of the old system of contracts between patron and artist, the growth in demand for works of art among the newly wealthy bourgeoisie, the increase in the number of artists and their need to exhibit and sell their work.

One of the most important art dealers of the middle of the century was Maison Goupil in Paris, founded in 1827 by Adolphe Goupil (1806–93) with the aim of publicizing French painting. The firm began by publishing reproductions in the form of steel engravings and, later, lithographs, but gradually began dealing in pictures itself and from 1848 onwards began opening establishments in Berlin, New York, London and The Hague for this purpose. In 1842 the Belgian Ernest Gambart (1814–1902) had gone to England as Goupil's agent in order to sell prints of famous paintings and in 1845 he had set up on his own in London as printseller and picture dealer;[73] not long afterwards the Goupil Gallery in London opened its doors to the public. They were quickly followed by other galleries that were likewise devoted to nineteenth-century painting: Thomas Wallis's French Gallery, Hollender & Cremetti's Hanover Gallery, the Grafton Galleries and the Continental Gallery. Later on the Holland Fine Art Gallery (Cornelis Marinus van Gogh and W.J. van Hoijtema) and the Dutch Gallery (which began in 1892 as a branch of the Amsterdam firm Van Wisselingh) were founded, concentrating on Dutch art. In addition, mention must be made of the firms of Arthur Tooth & Sons, Alexander R. Peacock[74] and Daniel Cottier.[75]

In Scotland, the leading art dealers, especially in French and Dutch art, were to be found in Glasgow: James Connell and, more important, Craibe Angus (1830–99), who opened his business in 1874. Through the marriage of his daughter Isabella to the Dutch art dealer Van Wisselingh he acquired influential connections on the continent, who were able to keep him regularly supplied with Dutch paintings.

However, the Scottish trade in modern pictures was primarily concentrated around the figure of Alex Reid (1854–1928).[76] As Sir William Burrell remarked 'He did more than any other man has ever done to introduce fine pictures to Scotland and to create a love of art'.[77] In order to learn the trade Reid went to live in Paris in 1887 and got a job with Boussod & Valadon, the sons-in-law and successors to Goupil,

fig. 110 VAN GOGH *Portrait of Alex Reid (1854–1928)* 1887 *(Glasgow Art Gallery and Museum, Glasgow)*

on the Boulevard des Italiens. They had a second smaller branch on the Boulevard Montmartre; this was run by Theo van Gogh (1857–91),[78] who suggested that Reid should live for a time with Vincent van Gogh, his brother, at 6 Place d'Anvers. Two portraits of Reid painted by Van Gogh in 1887 still remind us of this (fig. 110).[79] A year later Reid returned to Glasgow and in 1889 he opened his gallery, La Société des Beaux-Arts, which continued until 1931.

A comparable development is to be seen in the United States. This began in 1846 when Michel Knoedler went to America as the representative for Maison Goupil. Eleven years later he set up on his own as an art dealer in New York, reversing the normal pattern of events by later opening a branch in Paris.[80] Meanwhile, in 1848, Maison Goupil had started its establishment in New York under the name of Vibert Goupil & Co.

Then, in 1857, George Aloysius Lucas (1824–1909), who had formerly been in the service of the New York, New Haven Railroad and the Central Railroad of New Jersey, crossed the Atlantic and decided to remain in Paris in order to buy works of art, which he would then export to clients in America.[81] He continued to live in the French capital until his death and during those years he served a small but exclusive group of clients, including William Thomas Walters (1820–94), Samuel Putnam Avery (1822–1904), William Henry Vanderbilt (1821–85), Henry Field (1814–90) and John Taylor Johnston (1820–93), the first president of the Metropolitan Museum in New York.

In 1860 Frank Frick of Baltimore visited Lucas, who was a personal friend, in Paris and together they made a journey through Italy, Switzerland, Germany, the Netherlands and Belgium.[82] A year later William T. Walters, a civil engineer working for the Baltimore to Savannah Steamship and Railway Companies, went with his family to Paris, where he was to remain until 1865.[83] He had begun collecting paintings at an early age and during this period and the years that followed he bought a great deal, mostly through the agency of Lucas. But only a small part of what he bought, mainly paintings by French academicians and the Barbizon School, was intended for his own collection; he resold most of his purchases in the United States.[84]

In 1878, Walters was again in Europe, this time as United States commissioner for the Exposition Universelle in Paris. He made a journey with Lucas and Avery through Belgium, the Netherlands, Germany and Austria, arriving in The Hague on 20 June. They spent two days there during which, among other activities, they visited the Tentoonstelling van Levende Meesters (Exhibition of Living Masters), admired Rembrandt's *Anatomy Lesson* in the Mauritshuis, made a visit to the studio of Christoffel Bisschop (1828–1904) and took a trip to Scheveningen by tram.[85] During this journey they came into contact with the work of a large number of nineteenth-century artists who were unknown or scarcely known in Paris. But, despite that, the majority of the works of art shipped back to America via Le Havre by these gentlemen were confined to the French School and the Barbizon painters, with a notable number of works by the sculptor A.L. Barye.[86]

Meanwhile, there were new developments in the United States itself. The successful Westminster Gallery in Providence (already mentioned on p. 127) was founded in 1841 by Joseph Vose, but in 1897 moved to Boston where it was continued by Robert C. Vose under the name of The Vose Gallery. The English Duveen Brothers, who at that time were still specializing primarily in decorative art, also opened a business in Boston, but in 1884 moved to New York, as this city increasingly became the centre of the art trade.[87] Two years later Paul Durand-Ruel (1831–1922) arrived there and in 1901 Wildenstein, then still part of Gimpel & Wildenstein, settled on 28th Street and Fifth Avenue, the area favoured by the New York art trade at that time. Henry Reinhardt and Arthur Tooth & Sons, who had branches in Milwaukee and London respectively, also settled in New York. Several decades before that the International Art Union had been created in New York, partly on the initiative of Goupil, in order to promote the importation of French and other European works of art into the United States. It should, however, be stressed that these galleries dealing in modern art were until the end of the century primarily concerned with the work of French artists; it was only around the turn of the century that the Dutch painters became very important.

The Netherlands also had a flourishing art trade. In 1917 Albert Plasschaert wrote of the three largest dealers, E.J. van Wisselingh & Co. and C.M. van Gogh, both in Amsterdam, and Goupil & Co. in The Hague,

I must in all honesty set it down here that I regarded the third firm [Goupil] as the least in its leader, Mr Tersteeg. (Wisselingh was surer in his judgement, Van Gogh more refined). But the firm of Goupil & Co. in The Hague was nonetheless, through its achievements and its actions, of great importance in the history of the Hague School.[88]

Goupil & Co. (fig. 111), later called Boussod, Valadon & Co., had indeed established a great reputation for their

promotion of the Hague School.[89] It had various Hague painters under contract, supplied great collectors such as Forbes, Young and Drucker, organized exhibitions and acted as auctioneers at sales of important collections and painters' estates.[90] The head of the firm, H.G. Tersteeg, was on very friendly terms with the artists and in 1910, on the occasion of the fiftieth anniversary of his collaboration with Jozef Israëls, he published a book entitled *A Half Century With Jozef Israëls*, for which his son wrote the text.[91] However, the company's days were numbered. In 1917, having already sold its New York, London and Berlin branches, Boussod, Valadon & Co. closed its gallery in The Hague.[92] However, its main branch in Paris did continue to exist.

Although the second main art business in the Netherlands, E.J. van Wisselingh & Co. was not established in Amsterdam until 1892, it had actually been in existence since 1838 when Van Wisselingh took over a business in artists' materials and at the same time began to deal in pictures.[93] Van Wisselingh was the first dealer to sell paintings of the Barbizon School in the Netherlands, although interest in them was minimal there at that time. He became friendly with various French artists, including Gustave Courbet who painted a portrait of him.

His son, Elbert Jan van Wisselingh (d. 1912), joined the business as an apprentice at an early age. He afterwards worked at Goupil's in Paris, where he made friends with Jacob and Matthijs Maris, who were living there at that time. From there he sent his father the newest French paintings and sometimes also work by the two Dutchmen. In 1875 the Scottish dealer Daniel Cottier (1838–91), who had a gallery in London, persuaded Van Wisselingh to work for him. After much persuasion Matthijs Maris also decided to make the crossing. He lodged with Van Wisselingh at first, but was soon invited to move into Cottier's home and lived there for some ten years, despite the steady worsening of their relationship.[94] When the situation finally became intolerable, Van Wisselingh removed Maris from Cottier's and gave him a monthly allowance, without expecting anything in return. The hatred Maris had conceived for Cottier had become a generalized hatred of all art dealers and all those who earned a living from the trade, but it did not extend to Van Wisselingh, of whom he wrote, 'He is no ordinary thieving dealer, whose only aim is to line his own coffers.'[95]

In 1880, after his father's death, Van Wisselingh continued his business on the Buitenhof in The Hague. Having successfully set up a branch in Amsterdam, he returned to London and settled there for good as an art dealer, leaving the management of the Amsterdam business to his partner Groesbeek, who was assisted by P.C. Eilers Jr.

The third important art business in the Netherlands was that of Cornelis Marinus van Gogh (1824–1908), which was established in Amsterdam, first in Leidsestraat and then at 453 Keizersgracht, with a branch in The Hague at 16 Kneuterdijk. Together with W.J. van Hoijtema he also started a gallery in London: the Holland Fine Art Gallery, originally situated in Regent Street, but later in Grafton Street. In addition to works by the Barbizon School Van Gogh handled numerous paintings by Hague masters, such as Jacob Maris's *Girl Knitting on a Balcony* (Cat. 47) and Willem Maris's *Herdboys with Donkeys* (Cat. 81). After his death in 1908 the business continued under his son, another Vincent (1866–1911).

However, Cornelis Marinus was not the only member of

the Van Gogh family who was involved in the art trade. His oldest brother Hendrik Vincent (1814–77) had an art business in Rotterdam, later taken over by the Oldenzeel firm, before he moved to Brussels. The second brother Vincent (1820–88), who had started with a small painting and drawing materials shop in the Lange Kranenstraat in The Hague, shortly afterwards opened a bigger one in the busy Spuistraat, where he added paintings and drawings by Hague artists to his stock.[96] Van Gogh, 'a quick, lively young man, dressed with care and whose intelligent eyes and finely drawn features were indicative of a calculating salesman',[97] did not hesitate to take advantage of the fact that 'loose living' caused many a young artist to be in urgent need of money. As Johan Gram related in an anecdote, Van Gogh

> made his art gallery at the Spuistraat a refuge for the owners of empty purses. The care-free painters never applied to him in vain, money was readily available on the condition that in the famous backroom they signed a receipt ... taking the form of a small drawing in sepia or colour, for which the pen or brush lay ready to hand. ...[98]

Yet Van Gogh was not always as calculating. He also helped young artists to get ahead in the world, for instance by introducing Frederik Hendrik Kaemmerer to the atelier of Gérôme, and Jacob Maris to that of Ernest Hébert.

In the course of time the sale of painting materials was entirely pushed aside for that of works of art. This necessitated another change of address, this time to an imposing building at no. 20, Plaats. The firm was now re-christened Internationale Kunsthandel Van Gogh. Vincent, in emulation of Van Wisselingh, travelled to France with great regularity in order to get work from the Barbizon painters. He praised his acquisitions by Corot and Daubigny – not yet very popular with the general public – in the following terms: 'It is like caviar and oysters; when they first touch your palate, you are inclined to make faces; the second time you get used to it, and shortly afterwards you start to appreciate the refinement and delicacy.'[99] In 1869 Van Gogh made an agreement with Goupil's and moved to Paris, while his business in The Hague continued under the name of Goupil & Co. His nephews, Theo and the painter Vincent van Gogh, the sons of his older brother Dominie Theodorus van Gogh, both worked for Goupil's. Vincent worked for the firm from 1869 to 1876 in The Hague, London and Paris in succession, while Theo, having likewise started in The Hague, moved to Paris in 1885, where he was put in charge of a small branch that dealt mainly in the work of the French Impressionists and more modern painters such as Toulouse-Lautrec and Gauguin.

In Amsterdam there were two other art firms – the Larensche Kunsthandel and, more important, Frans Buffa & Zonen – that endeavoured, often by means of commericial exhibitions, to popularize the Hague School with a wider public. Frans Buffa, a native of Italy, had arrived in the Netherlands with his brother at the end of the eighteenth century as an intinerant printseller and in 1806 opened an art business in Amsterdam at the corner of Kalverstraat and Gapersteeg.[100] In 1830 he withdrew from the firm and was succeeded by his sons Jan and Bastiaan. They, in turn, made Pierre Adrien Beguin, a Frenchman who had been working for them as an apprentice since 1825, a partner in the firm and on their return to Italy in 1836 appointed him as their successor. Beguin entered into an agreement with Alberto

Caramelli, who was largely responsible for making the firm one of the most flourishing art businesses in Amsterdam. It had a reputation not only for dealing in prints and pictures, but also for publishing high quality limited editions, which were highly regarded, especially in London and Paris.

Beguin and Caramelli tried to ensure that young artists acquired more recognition. For example, they helped Jozef Israëls while he was still living in Amsterdam by introducing his *Symptômes d'amour* to the public. After Beguin's death in 1860 Caramelli continued the business on his own; in 1865, his son Giovanni became a partner in the firm and Beguin's son Theo succeeded his father. When Theo died four years later, his place was taken by F. Tessaro. This was the beginning of the heyday of the Hague School and in the years that followed many works by Israëls, Bosboom, the Maris brothers and Mauve reached their eventual owners via Buffa.

In 1895 Tessaro made the firm over to J. Slagmulder, who remained the owner until his death in 1921. Slagmulder, who was a collector as well as an art dealer, greatly admired Jan Hendrik Weissenbruch.[101] He owned the latter's *Sunset at Boskoop* (Cat. 127), for example, and on the occasion of Weissenbruch's seventy-fifth birthday in 1899 he organized a large commercial exhibition of his work.[102] This was a tremendous success and greatly contributed to the general recognition and appreciation of the artist. After Slagmulder's death the firm continued under the direction of J. Sierdenburg until 1951, when it was obliged to close its doors for good.

The Larensche Kunsthandel was in comparison a very short-lived company; it only existed from 1905 to 1918. As the company's name indicated, it concentrated mainly on pictures by painters who had worked in Laren, such as Mauve and Neuhuys.[103] It was founded in 1905 by N. van Harpen, former editor-in-chief of the *Amsterdamsche Courant* in the Villa Mauve at Laren, and two years later a large branch was opened in Amsterdam at 495 Herengracht. The artist Theo Neuhuys (1878–1921) was appointed director and in the years that followed he organized various exhibitions. Three of these were devoted to individual Hague School painters: Gabriël (1910), Roelofs (1911) and Bosboom (1917, the centenary of his birth).[104] The Larensche Kunsthandel ceased trading in 1918, ending its short existence on a suitable note with a 'liquidation exhibition'.[105]

Three art firms in The Hague, which likewise failed to withstand the test of time, but deserve a mention because of their importance in disseminating the work of the Hague School, were Maison Artz, Kunstzaal Kleykamp and Abraham Preyer.

Maison Artz was established at 14 Lange Vijverberg, by Mrs A.T.A. Sues, née Schemel, whose first husband was the painter Adolphe Artz. Most of the pictures she handled were paintings by Artz, Gabriël, Roelofs and the Maris brothers, and watercolours by Bosboom and Neuhuys. In 1901 she published a small English dictionary of nineteenth-century Dutch painters illustrated with portrait photographs.[106] She spent the following two years with Mrs Gruppé in the United States, where she organized a travelling exhibition of Mesdag's work at his request. The exhibition was shown in museums and commercial galleries in Boston, Pittsburgh, Philadelphia and New York, but because of the bad organization and high cost of transport, insurance, commission and the like, it was not a financial success.[107] Mrs Sues and her 15-year-old daughter lost their lives in 1907 in the sinking of the steamship

fig. 111 Interior of Goupil & Co., 20 Plaats, The Hague

Berlin; her collection was sold in the same year and the firm itself continued for only a few years after that.[108]

Kunsthandel Kleykamp, the second such company, was based at 9 Oranjestraat until 1917 and after that at 3 Oude Scheveningseweg. The firm was trading mainly in the first quarter of this century, when the Hague School was already established. After the Larensche Kunsthandel ceased to exist, its former director Neuhuys ran this company, which not only organized exhibitions, including one-man shows of such artists as Gabriël and Matthijs Maris,[109] but also held auction sales on a regular basis. The works of art that came under the hammer here included the contents of Mauve's estate[110] and the important collection of the art dealer Abraham Preyer.

Preyer, who had had an art gallery in The Hague since 1880, took over the Amsterdam gallery of Pappelendam & Schouten, that was located in Kalverstraat and held its exhibitions in the room of 'Pictura' at 19 Wolvenstraat. He did much to popularize the work of the Hague School in the United States.[111] In 1893 he acted as the government commissioner for Dutch art at the International Exhibition in Chicago and in this capacity succeeded in arousing much public interest in the School. He was also a keen collector, acquiring an important part of the collection of Staats Forbes in 1905.[112] His collection, in which all the painters of the Hague School were represented, concentrated in particular on

the work of Bosboom, Weissenbruch, Jacob and Willem Maris, Mauve, De Bock and Kever; it was sold in two parts in 1918 at Kunstzaal Kleykamp.[113] Meanwhile Preyer had closed down his own art business and moved to Paris. In 1926, a year before his death, he gave five paintings – by Bosboom, Blommers, Jozef Israëls, Mauve and Jacob Maris – to the Musée du Luxembourg in Paris. They are now among the few examples of the work of the Hague School owned by the Louvre.

The exact relationship that existed between the artists, art dealers and collectors has not yet been clearly established. The lack of readily available sources – should they actually exist – has made it impossible to find out precisely where the three stood in relation to each other and so the topic has in the past either been treated anecdotally or merely mentioned in passing.

We do, however, know that most artists generally entered into an agreement to supply an art dealer with their work for a fixed period of longer or shorter duration and that normally the agreement did not allow the art artist to sell to third parties outside the firm. John Forbes White, for example, asked the painter George Reid, who was then studying in the Netherlands, to visit Jacob Maris and buy a landscape from him, but Maris was under contract to Goupil's, to whom he was obliged to send all his work. White entered into negotiations with Goupil's in an effort to release the painter from his contract, but to no avail.[114]

Although collectors bought works directly from the artists, the art dealers were none the less their most important source. Some collectors showed a preference for a given firm: Mesdag, Drucker, Staats Forbes and Young bought a great deal at Goupil's in The Hague,[115] while Reid favoured Craibe Angus in Glasgow, Libbey and Secor used Reinhardt's in New York and Milwaukee and Frick bought at Knoedler's in New York. These preferences were probably largely determined by financial considerations. Drucker, for example, had an agreement with H.G. Tersteeg of Goupil's in The Hague, whereby he had the right to exchange a painting, or recover its purchase price less ten per cent, for up to three years after the original sale.[116] The collectors also bought outside the art trade at the Tentoonstellingen van Levende Meesters (the International Exhibitions of Living Masters, where work could be purchased on the spot), and at sales of private collections or painters' estates, but the art dealers also made grateful use of these opportunities.

After the 1920s and 1930s interest in the Hague School declined slowly but quite markedly. A number of collections, such as those of Willem van der Vorm (1873–1957) in Rotterdam[117] and R.J. Veendorp in Wassenaar, did come into

being at this period,[118] but they were few and far between.[119] It was not until the years immediately after the Second World War that appreciation of, and interest in, Dutch nineteenth-century art began to revive. This renewal of interest began in 1945 with an exhibition organized by Pulchri Studio under the title *Den Haag eert de Nederlansche schilders van de 19de eeuw* (The Hague honours the Dutch painters of the nineteenth century). Although the critics' attention was at first focused only on the romantic painters of that century, the Hague School began to receive its share of attention in the 1960s. A Jozef Israëls memorial exhibition took place in 1961 and an exhibition entitled 'Masters of the Hague School' in 1965; both of these were organized by Jos. de Gruyter, who more than any other single person should take credit for the recent revival of interest.[120]

Naturally the art trade has not been far behind. Indeed, in one instance, it virtually anticipated the new appreciation of the Hague School; Pieter A. Scheen, an art dealer in The Hague, began collecting works by the Hague School artists and making them known to a wider public as early as the 1950s.[121] Many others have subsequently contributed to this general reappraisal of the Hague School, which has also been marked by small exhibitions at home and abroad. All these have prepared the way for the present international exhibition.

NOTES

For the complete titles of the exhibition catalogues cited below in an abbreviated form, see pp. 322–3.

1. The survey that follows is concerned only with collections in the Netherlands, Great Britain, United States of America and Canada; by comparison those in France, Germany and Italy cannot be considered as being of any great significance.
2. 'The Grosvenor Gallery', *The Times* (1 Jan. 1880).
3. Cutting from an unknown Dutch newspaper (3 Feb. 1894), in which this text had been reprinted from a Boston paper on the occasion of an exhibition in that city (Netherlands Institute for Art History [R.K.D.], The Hague, Press Documentation Department).
4. The work in question was a *Meal in a Farmhouse*. L. Brandt Corstius and others in exh. cat. Haarlem 1981–82, p. 16. For the prices of these Hague School works at auction, see Ch. Carter, 'Where Stands the Hague School Now?' *Apollo* LXXI (June 1960), pp. 173–76; LXXII (July 1960), pp. 7–10.
5. D.A.S Cannegieter, 'Blommers een schilder uit de Haagse School', *Antieck* VII (1972–73), p. 448.
6. See Sir S. Lee (ed.), *Dictionary of National Biography. Second Supplement*, vol. 2, London 1912, pp. 37–39. For the collection see [M. Rooses], 'Bij den Heer Staats Forbes', *N.R.C.* (10 Sept. 1895) and 'Nog eens bij den Heer Staats Forbes', *N.R.C.* (12 Sept. 1895); E.G. Halton, 'The Staats Forbes Collection', *The Studio* XXXVI (1905), pp. 30–47 ('The Barbizon Pictures'), pp. 107–17 ('The Modern Dutch Pictures'), pp. 218–30 ('Third and Concluding Article').
7. Forbes was one of the first British collectors to acquire a great interest in the Barbizon School. See Halton, *op. cit.*, p. 33.
8. Forbes, who also got the Metropolitan District Railway out of financial difficulties, was at the same time involved in various other railway companies, such as the Hull and Barnsley Line, the Didcot, Newbury and Southampton Line, the Whitechapel and Bow Railway and the Regent's Canal, City and Docks Railway. In addition he was chairman of three important electricity companies and one of the directors of the Lion Fire Insurance Company.
9. A photogravure after the portrait painted of Forbes in 1881 by Sir Hubert von Herkomer hung in Israëls's studio. It bore a presentation inscription from Forbes to him. H.E. van Gelder, *Jozef Israëls*, Amsterdam [1946] (Paletserie), p. 35, note 1.
10. Rooses, *op. cit.*
11. [J. Tersteeg], *Een halve eeuw met Jozef Israëls*, The Hague 1910, p. 16.
12. For example, *Washday* (Cat. 70).
13. Some of these were exhibited at Pulchri Studio in The Hague in 1905. See exh. cat. The Hague 1905 (2).
14. In particular a large number of works by Israëls, see Tersteeg *op. cit.*, p. 20. Another important part of the collection was acquired by the Grafton Galleries, London: see exh. cat. London 1905[2]. Nonetheless, in the years that

followed many works came up at sales, e.g. Munich (Fleischmann) 20–21 March 1906; London (Christie's) 2 June 1916, 14 June 1918, 8 December 1919.
15. For the prices fetched by the paintings sold, see 'De collectie Staats Forbes', *N.R.C.* (2 September 1911).
16. See E.G. Halton, 'The collection of Mr Alexander Young', *The Studio* XXXIX (1907), pp. 3–32 ('The Corots'), pp. 99–118 ('The Daubigny's'), pp. 193–210 ('Some Barbizon Pictures'), pp. 287–306 ('The Modern Dutch Pictures').
17. The collection did not include a single work by Matthijs Maris.
18. Another famous canvas by Israëls in the Young Collection was *The Cottage Madonna* (Cat. 32).
19. J.C.J. Drucker related the following anecdote in 1924: 'He [Arthur J. Lewis] was so proud of his purchase that he gave a banquet in the painter's honour. He took Israëls aside and said, "Well, for a young foreigner you have not done so badly in selling me your picture for . . .", mentioning the amount that had been agreed by Gambart. This sum differed quite considerably from the price that Jozef Israëls would get for it, but he philosophically reasoned that he was extremely grateful that this had happened to him so early in his career and that he had acquired a lesson to be on his guard against art dealers in future so cheaply (one of the most experienced of them declared of his colleagues, "It takes two horse dealers to make a picture dealer")'. See J.C.J. Drucker, 'Jozef Israëls in Engeland', *N.R.C.* (26 Jan. 1924).
20. Auct. London (Christie's), 30 June–4 July 1910, 13–14 March 1913. The 1910 auction saw a record price for a sale of modern art: £153,891. See Carter *op. cit.*, p. 7.
21. See Lee, *op. cit.*, vol. 1, pp. 481–83. For the collection see R.A.M. Stevenson, 'Sir John Day's Pictures', *The Art Journal* N.S. (1893), pp. 261–65, 309–13.
22. Paintings and watercolours: auct. London (Christie's), 13–14 May 1909. Etchings and engravings: auct. London (Christie's), 17–18 May 1909.
23. See Cat. 59. James Donald's collection was bequeathed to the Glasgow Art Gallery in 1905.
24. See Cat. 65, 77.
25. See D. Forbes White, 'Private Picture Galleries. The Collection of John Forbes White, Esq.', in D. Macleod (ed.), *Good Words*, London 1896, pp. 813–19; I.M. Harrower, *John Forbes White*, Edinburgh/London 1910; *idem*, 'Josef Israëls and his Aberdeen Friend', *Aberdeen University Review* XIV (1927), pp. 107–22; Ch. Carter, 'Art Patronage in Scotland: John Forbes White. 1831–1904', *The Scottish Art Review* VI (1957), no. 2, pp. 27–30.
26. See p. 121. Four years later, Israëls sent Bosboom a New Year greeting in the form of a piece of doggerel in which he advised him not to keep his work on hand too long, but to sell it in Aberdeen, since it was possible to get a good price for it there: 'At the New Year, prompt as ever, I wish you all the best, but I have seen from Aberdeen that they are still minus what you sketched for them.

Is it still in town? Hasn't it set off yet? What a long time it's taking! Or have you sent it? Have no fear, it will get there one of these days and it won't miss its mark! Jozef Israëls.' Cited in J. Bosboom Nzn., 'Enkele brieven van Jozef Israëls', *N.R.C.* (29 Jan. 1924).

27. Auct. London (Sotheby's), 14–15 Dec. 1888.

28. Including *Growing Old*, a variant of the work exhibited here (Cat. 35).

29. *Catalogue of the Collection of Pictures of the British, French & Dutch Schools Belonging to John Reid, with Notes by James L. Caw*, Glasgow 1913.

30. See E. Fagg, 'Modern Masters in the Burrell Collection on Loan at the Tate Gallery', *Apollo* I (1925), pp. 22–26; W. Wells, in E.T. Williams & H.M. Palmer (eds.), *The Dictionary of National Biography 1951–1960*, London 1971, pp. 161–63; W. Wells, 'Sir William Burrell', in exh. cat. *Treasures from the Burrell Collection*, Hayward Galleries, London 1975, pp. 6–11.

31. Burrell began his career in the family firm at the age of 15. Although, working in conjunction with his brother he was exceptionally successful in expanding the business, he decided in 1917 to sell most of the fleet and devote himself entirely to collecting.

32. Including Matthijs Maris's *The Butterflies* (Cat. 77) and Jacob Maris's *Souvenir of Dordrecht* (Cat. 65).

33. See W.G. Constable, 'French Art: Salon, Barbizon, Impressionism', in *Art Collecting in the United States of America*, London etc. 1964, pp. 69–82.

34. One of the most important collections formed under Hunt's advice was that of Quincy Adams Shaw at Boston. This included, among other things, 60 paintings and 50 pastels by Millet, which were bequeathed to the Museum of Fine Arts at Boston and now constitute the largest assemblage of Millets within a single collection. Other important Barbizon School collections belonged to Martin Brimmer and Samuel D. Warren (both at Boston), William T. Walters (Baltimore), W.P. Wilstach (Philadelphia) and Henry Field (Chicago; given to the Art Institute there in 1893). See also p. 131.

35. See B.-M.G., in Dumas Malone (ed.), *Dictionary of American Biography*, vol. II, London/New York 1933, pp. 233–34; *Museum News. The Toledo Museum of Art* (April 1954).

36. One of them was devoted entirely to Jozef Israëls. See exh. cat. Toledo 1912.

37. For instance Mauve's *A Dutch Road* (Cat. 97).

38. See J.G. Wilson & J. Fish (eds.), *Appleton's Cyclopaedia of American Biography*, vol. 3, New York 1888, pp. 414–15; Dumas Malone, *op. cit.*, vol. 10, pp. 15–17.

39. Letter from Bernard Blommers to Miss G.H. Marius, dated 27 April 1905 (Gemeentearchief, The Hague). See also Cat. 100.

40. See p. 128.

41. See Cat. 76.

42. See Cat. 13, 50, 140, 144.

43. See Cat. 67.

44. This art-historical publication, the very first in Canada, was brought out again in 1906 in a greatly expanded new edition under the title *Landscape Painting and Modern Dutch Artists*.

45. See also E.F.D. Johnston, 'Canadian Collectors and Modern Dutch Art', *Canadian Magazine* XXXVI (March 1911), no. 5. A publication on this subject by Marta H. Hurdalek, Assistant Curator of Old Master Art at the Art Gallery of Ontario, Toronto, will be published shortly in exh. cat. *The Hague School: Collecting in Canada at the Turn of the Century*, Art Gallery of Ontario, Toronto, and elsewhere, 1983.

46. A selection was made from these collections in 1886 for an exhibition at Arti et Amicitiae in Amsterdam. See exh. cat. Amsterdam 1886 (3); Samuel [J. Veth], 'Tentoonstelling van enige schilderijen uit particuliere verzamelingen in Arti et Amicitiae', *De Nieuwe Gids* I (1886), vol. 2, p. 304. The first three mentioned were all sold: Verstolk-Völcker Coll.: Amsterdam (F. Muller & Co.), 17 Oct. 1939; Post Coll.: Amsterdam (C.F. Roos & Co.), 14 April 1891; Blom Coster Coll.: The Hague (Boussod, Valadon & Co.), 31 May 1904. See Cat. 20, 60, 68, 94, 135 (Verstolk-Völcker Coll.), 86 (Post Coll.), 16 (Blom Coster Coll.).

47. See P.A.M. Boele van Hensbroek & G.H. Marius, *Het Museum Mesdag en zijn stichters*, Amsterdam [1890].

48. See P.N.H. Domela Nieuwenhuis, 'H.W. Mesdag et la peinture française', in *Catalogue des collections du Musée Mesdag, Écoles étrangères XIX siècle*, [The Hague] 1964, pp. 7–13.

49. See E. van Schendel, 'Inleiding', in *Museum Mesdag. Nederlandse negentiende-eeuwse schilderijen, tekeningen en grafiek*, The Hague 1975, pp. 9–15.

50. Part of the remainder of the collection was sold: New York (American Art Association), 10 March 1920.

51. See C.G.'t Hooft, *Verzameling J.C.J. Drucker in het Rijksmuseum*, n.p. n.d. (Special publication of the Society for the Promotion of the Fine Arts); W. Steenhoff, 'De collectie Drucker in het Rijksmuseum', *Elsevier's Geïllustreerd Maandschrift* XX (1910), vol. XL, pp. 361–74; M. Eisler, 'De collectie Drucker in het Rijksmuseum te Amsterdam', *ibid.*, XXIII (1913), vol. XLVI, pp. 241–55, 409–27; D. de Hoop Scheffer, 'Het Rijksmuseum en zijn begunstigers', *Bulletin van het Rijksmuseum* VI (1958), pp. 99–100; E.P. Engel, 'Het onstaan van de verzameling Drucker-Fraser in het Rijksmuseum', *ibid.*, XIII (1965), pp. 45–66.

52. Hooft, *op. cit.* The Kijzer Collection was sold: Amsterdam (F. Muller & Co.), 8 Nov. 1904.

53. Drucker later managed to acquire various works from this collection, including Mauve's *Riders on the Beach at Scheveningen* (Cat. 89).

54. See F. Vermeulen, 'Jozef Israëls (in de collectie Drucker)', *Eigen Haard* XXXVII (1911), pp. 485–89, 504–07.

55. See Cat. 51, 55. For other works from the Drucker Collection in this exhibition, see Cat. 16, 41, 43, 89, 98, 104, 107.

56. The couple also gave a number of works by Giovanni Segantini to the museum at St Moritz.

57. See [J.F.M.] Sterk, in *Nieuw Nederlandsch biografisch woordenboek*, vol. 5, Leiden 1921, col. 1117; De Hoop Scheffer, *op. cit.*, pp. 95–97.

58. See Cat. 7, 8. See also Cat. 1, 2.

59. See 'Kunstverzameling van Van der Schilden', *Verslag van het Museum Boymans te Rotterdam over het jaar 1925*, pp. 2–4

60. See also Cat. 5, 46, 132.

61. See B., 'Kunstverzameling Crone', *N.R.C.* (19 July 1907); exh. cat. Amsterdam 1909 (2); C. Kikkert, 'Collectie E.H. Crone. Arti et Amicitiae', *Onze Kunst* VIII (1909), vol. XVI, pp. 138–40; Giovanni, 'De verzameling Crone in Arti', *Algemeen Handelsblad* (24 June 1909) and 'De collectie-Crone', *ibid.* (31 July 1909); G.H. Marius, 'De verzameling-Crone te Amsterdam', *Elsevier's Geïllustreerd Maandschrift* XX (1910), vol. XXXIX, pp. 1–14.

62. See Cat. 47, 62, 66, 105, 126, 133. See also *Agenda Haags Gemeentemuseum* (April 1964).

63. See Cat. 18. The collection was sold: The Hague (Boussod, Valadon & Co.), 12 March 1902.

64. See Cat. 40, 53. See H.F.W. Jeltes, 'De collectie-Reich *Elsevier's Geïllustreerd Maandschrift* XXXIV (1924), vol. LXVII, pp. 6–16, 161–70.

65. See Cat. 73. Part of the collection was given to the Rijksmuseum in Amsterdam in 1914 by the Van Randwijk Heirs. Another part was sold: Amsterdam (F. Muller & Co.) 11 April 1916. See H. de Boer, 'Collection de M. van Randwijk à la Haye', *Les Arts* VI (Aug. 1907), pp. 1–32; exh. cat. Rotterdam 1908–09; M. Eisler, 'The Van Randwijk Collection', *The Studio* LV (1912), pp. 96–107 ('The School of The Hague'), pp. 199–209 ('The Barbizon School'); W. Steenhoff, 'Randwijk-collectie in het Rijksmuseum te Amsterdam', *Onze Kunst* XIV (1915), vol. XXVII, pp. 89–97.

66. See Cat. 130. This collection, which included a large number of watercolours by J.H. Weissenbruch, was sold in two stages: Amsterdam (F. Muller & Co.), 18 Nov. 1914 and The Hague (Venduhuis der Notarissen) 5–6 Oct. 1937. On several occasions separate exhibitions were devoted to the work of Weissenbruch from this collection; see exh. cats. Rotterdam 1906 (2), Dordrecht 1909–10, The Hague 1924 (3). See also exh. cat. Dordrecht 1904 (2). In the Rijksbureau vour Kunsthistorische Documentatie (R.K.D.) in The Hague there is a manuscript for a publication on this collection by A. Plasschaert.

67. See Cat. 72, 143. See also exh. cat. The Hague 1913 (4).

68. See Cat. 70. The collection was sold: Amsterdam (F. Muller & Co.), 29 Nov. 1921. See C. Veth, 'Willem Maris, Mauve, Poggenbeek in de collectie Neervoort van de Poll, Rijksmuseum', *Eigen Haard* XLIII (1918), pp. 745–48.

69. See Cat. 15. The collection was sold: Amsterdam (F. Muller & Co.), 22–25 and 28–29 March 1955. See H.F.W. Jeltes, 'De collectie Vattier Kraane', *Elsevier's Geïllustreerd Maandschrift* XXXII (1922), vol. LXIII, pp. 73–77,

70. See Cat. 58. The collection was sold: Amsterdam (F. Muller & Co.), 17–20 and 23–25 April 1956. See H.F.W. Jeltes, 'De collectie-Voûte', *Elsevier's Geïllustreerd Maandschrift* XXXII (1922), vol. LXIV, pp. 289–96.

71. See H. de Boer, *Schilderijen uit de verzameling Van Bilderveek*, Dordrecht [1915] and exh. cats. Dordrecht 1904 (1), Dordrecht 1957 (2), Dordrecht 1978. The collection of the Van Bilderbeek-Lamaison Museum has now been integrated into that of the Dordrechts Museum.

72. For art-dealing in general see J. Russell Taylor & B. Brooke, *The Art Dealers*, London 1969; G. Savage, *The Market in Art*, London 1969. For the 19th and 20th centuries see G. Seligman, *Merchants of Art: 1800–1960. Eighty Years of Professional Collecting*, New York 1961; G. Bernier, *L'Art et l'argent. Le marché de l'art au XXe siècle*, Paris 1977. For prices see G. Reitlinger, *The Economics of Taste, Vol. 1. The Rise and Fall of Picture Prices 1760–1960*, London 1960.

73. See J. Maas, *Gambart. Prince of the Victorian Art World*, London 1975.

74. Peacock was one of the first to take a great interest in the watercolours of J.H. Weissenbruch and to buy them in great quantities, often direct from the artist.

75. See p. 131.

76. See R. Pickvane, 'Introduction', in exh. cat. *A Man of Influence: Alex Reid 1854–1928*, The Scottish Arts Council, Glasgow 1967, pp. 5–16; D. Cooper, 'A Franco–Scottish Link with the Past', in *Alex Reid & Lefevre. 1926–1976*, [London 1976], pp. 3–26.

77. Letter from Sir William Burrell to A.J. MacNeill Reid, dated 14 Jan. 1946, cited by Pickvane, *op. cit.*, p. 5.

78. See also p. 132. Meanwhile Goupil had opened four branches in Paris: Rue Chaptal, Boulevard Montmartre, Avenue de l'Opéra and Rue Tessis.

79. Van Gogh painted three or possibly four portraits of Reid. Up to now two have been identified as such. J.-B. de la Faille, *The Works of Vincent van Gogh. His Paintings and Drawings*, Amsterdam 1970, pp. 136 (no. F 270), 162 (no. E343).

80. Seligman, *op. cit.*, pp. 18–19.

81. See L.M.C. Randall, *The Diary of George A. Lucas: An American Art Agent in Paris, 1857–1909*, 2 vols., Princeton 1979.

82. See F. Frank, *A Traveller's Diary*, vol. 1, 20 May–19 July (George Peabody Department, Enoch Pratt Free Library, Baltimore). Cf. Randall, *op. cit.*, vol. 1, p. 33.

83. See Dumas Malone, *op. cit.*, vol. 19, London/New York 1936, pp. 400–01; D. Sutton, 'Connoisseur's Heaven', *Apollo* LXXXIV (Dec. 1966), pp. 422–32; Randall, *op. cit.*, vol. 1, pp. 11–16.

84. The first two sales took place in the Dusseldorf Gallery in New York in 1862 and 1864 (Randall, *op. cit.*, vol. 1, p. 12). The collection of Walters himself was considerably expanded by his son Henry (1848–1931) and after his death it was given to the city of Baltimore. See W.R. Johnston, 'William and Henry Walters: Collectors and Philanthropists', *The Walters Art Gallery Bulletin* XXVII (Dec. 1974).

85. Randall, *op. cit.*, vol. 2, p. 457.

86. Lucas was in fact thoroughly familiar with the work of the Hague School. He had already been given a seascape by Jacob Maris as a present by Goupil in 1868, in 1890 he bought a work by this painter at Boussod & Valadon's and three years later he carried on a correspondence with him (Randall, *op. cit.*, vol. 2, pp. 282, 719, 779).

87. After 1884 establishments were also opened in London and Paris. See S.N. Behrman, *Duveen*, London 1952.

88. [A.] Plasschaert, 'Kunst- en letternieuws. Goupil & Co.', *N.R.C.* (12 June 1917).

89. This firm was situated at 20, Plaats. Until 1869 this had been where the Internationale Kunsthandel Van Gogh had had its premises; see p. 132.

90. For example, the following collections were sold by the firm: that of the widow of F.H.M. Post and others (13 Nov. 1894), that of Dr J.D.C. Titsingh (12–13 March 1901) and that of J.H. Henkes Jr. (10–11 Nov. 1903). The following painters' estates were also sold there: contents of the studios of D.A.C. Artz (27–28 Jan. 1891), W. Roelofs (8–9 Feb. 1898, 3–4 May 1910), P. Stortenbeker (15–16 Nov. 1898), M. Bilders van Bosse (16–17 April 1901), P. Sadée (14–15 March 1905). See G. [H. Marius], 'Veiling van de collectie Post en anderen', *De Nederlandse Spectator* (1894), pp. 371–72.

91. The book was published without an author's name and the text has always been wrongly attributed to H.G. Tersteeg. See G. Colmjon, 'J. Tersteeg', in *Jaarboek van de Maatschappij der Nederlandse Letterkunde*, Leiden 1955, p. 91. A Dutch edition of the book also appeared in the same year. See note 11.

92. See 'Het Huis Goupil', *N.R.C.* (4 and 7 June 1917). The paintings from this firm's collection were sold in The Hague on 12 June 1917 by Kunstzaal Kleykamp.

93. See *E.J. van Wisselingh & Co. Kunsthandel. Fine Art Dealer Amsterdam*, [Amsterdam 1914] (with Dutch, English, French and German text); E.J. van Wisselingh & Co., *Half a Century of Picture Dealing. An Illustrated Record with a note on the connection between the Barbizon and The Hague Schools by Jan Veth*, Amsterdam 1923.

94. For this period see W. Arondéus, *Matthijs Maris. De tragiek van den droom*, Amsterdam 1945², pp. 138–43; J. de Gruyter, *De Haagse School*, vol. 1 [Rotterdam 1969], pp. 42–43.

95. Arondéus, *op. cit.*, p. 143. Matthijs's admiration of Van Wisselingh led him to make the latter's widow Isabella Angus his sole heir.

96. J. Gram, 'De kunstverzameling Vincent van Gogh in Pulchri Studio', *Haagsche Stemmen* II (1889), pp. 371–82.

97. Gram, *op. cit.*, p. 372.

98. Gram, *op. cit.*, p. 373.

99. Gram, *op. cit.*, p. 376.

100. See J.H.R., 'De kunsthandel van Buffa te Amsterdam', *Zondagsblad van het Nieuws van den Dag* (25 July 1897); 'Buffa gaat sluiten', *N.R.C.* (3 March 1951); A. Koolhaas, 'De deuren van Frans Buffa 1780–1951 sloten voor goed. Een brok cultur verdween geruisloos in de stroom van de Kalverstraat', *De Groene Amsterdammer* (31 March 1951).

101. The collection was exhibited at the Haagsche Kunstkring (The Hague Art Society) in 1904 as the property of his wife, Mrs J. Slagmulder-van Gent. See exh. cat. The Hague 1904(2).

102. See exh. cat. Amsterdam 1899(3).

103. From the time of its establishment the firm published a periodical entitled *Het Land van Mauve. Bulletin van den Larenschen Kunsthandel*.

104. See exh. cats. Amsterdam 1910(2), 1911(2) and 1917 respectively. The Larensche Kunsthandel regularly joined forces with other dealers when organizing exhibitions. Thus they held several exhibitions in the Haagse Kunstzaal Kleykamp and in 1914 at the art dealer G. Pisko in Vienna.

105. See 'Maatschappij van Beeldende Kunsten. Liquidatie-tentoonstelling van den Larenschen Kunsthandel', *N.R.C.* (24 Jan. 1918).

106. *Souvenir Dedicated to Dutch Art and her Host of Diligent Workers at the Close of the 19th Century. Presented by Maison Artz, Art Dealers, The Hague, Holland*, The Hague 1901.

107. J. Poort, *Hendrik Willem Mesdag, 'artiste peintre à la Haye'*, The Hague 1981, pp. 53–55.

108. Auct. The Hague (C.F. Roos & Co.), 7–8 May 1907.

109. See exh. cat. The Hague 1911(3), 1924(3).

110. Auct. 'The drawings of Anton Mauve and a large self portrait of the master' (22–23 May 1917); auct. contents of Mauve's studio (11 Nov. 1919).

111. See 'Kunstberichten. A. Preyer 1890–1 Januari 1915', *De Hofstad* XVII (9 Jan. 1915); 'A Preyer'.†*N.R.C.* (31 May 1927).

112. See note 13.

113. On 5 March and 8 April. After his death another part was sold: Amsterdam (F. Muller & Co.), 8 Nov. 1927.

114. Harrower, *op. cit.*, p. 35.

115. The handwritten receipt books of Goupil's in The Hague for the period 1880–89 are in the Rijksbureau voor Kunsthistorische Documentatie (R.K.D.), The Hague, Press Documentation Department.

116. Engel, *op. cit.*, p. 47.

117. This collection was begun in 1918. Initially the accent lay on the Hague and Barbizon Schools, but over the years it shifted to the Dutch seventeenth-century painters. After Van der Vorm's death his collection was placed under a separate foundation, which was absorbed into the Museum Boymans-van Beuningen in 1972. See D. Hannema, *Beschrijvende catalogus van de schilderijen uit de kunstverzameling Stichting Willem van der Vorm*, Rotterdam 1972.

118. The collection, built up from the 1930s onwards and focused on Dutch painters of the late nineteenth and early twentieth century, is now on loan to the Groninger Museum. See *Verzameling R.J. Veendorp* [Groningen 1969].

119. The exhibitions devoted to the work of Weissenbruch, the Maris brothers and Gabriël, for example, at this period, were also exceptional. See exh. cats. Amsterdam 1933(3), The Hague 1935–36, Amsterdam 1939(3).

120. See exh. cats. Groningen 1961–62 and The Hague 1965(1) respectively. In 1968–69 De Gruyter published his two-volume standard work on the Hague School (see note 94).

121. Scheen first specialized in the Dutch Romantic School, but soon extended this to include the Hague School, with the accent on J.H. Weissenbruch.

Vincent van Gogh and the Hague School

CHARLES MOFFETT

As Griselda Pollock has shown in *Vincent van Gogh in zijn Hollandse jaren*,[1] the influences underlying Van Gogh's development are complex and wide-ranging, but certainly one of the most important is the Hague School. In Van Gogh's letters there are abundant references to the artists of the Hague School, but certain individuals, for example Anton Mauve and Jozef Israëls, receive a great deal of attention, while others, such as Gerard Bilders and Willem Roelofs, are rarely mentioned. Without question these artists influenced his technique, aesthetic attitudes and choice of subject matter, but even before he decided in 1880 to become an artist he admired several Hague School painters. In January 1874, while working in the London branch of the art gallery Goupil & Co., he included in a letter to his brother Theo a long list of 'some of the painters whom I like especially.' Of the 54 artists cited, five were leading members of the Hague School: Anton Mauve, Jozef Israëls, Jan Hendrik Weissenbruch, Jacob Maris, and Matthijs Maris (*The Complete Letters of Vincent van Gogh*, I, no. 13, p. 17). Eventually Van Gogh displayed an interest in virtually every member of the Hague School, all of whom are included in the present exhibition. His comments about them in this correspondence provide a valuable contemporary view of the Hague School as well as important insights into his own goals as an artist.

Anton Mauve, who was married to one of Van Gogh's cousins, exerted the strongest influence. He advised and taught Van Gogh in 1881–82, but Vincent's familiarity with the older artist's work went back much further than that. In 1869 Vincent went to work for Goupil & Co., first in The Hague, and subsequently in the dealer's branches in London and Paris. In 1872 the stockbooks of Goupil & Co. in The Hague listed 35 pictures by members of the Hague School, 13 of which were by Mauve.[3] Mauve's work clearly made a strong impression on him, because only about a year after deciding to become an artist Vincent appealed to Mauve for guidance.

Van Gogh first approached Mauve for advice in early September 1881. He travelled to The Hague from Etten, where he was living with his parents, to seek the help of Mauve and others. In a letter written to Theo in late August or early September after the trip to The Hague, Vincent described the success of his visit.

I spent an afternoon and part of an evening with Mauve, and saw many beautiful things in his studio. My own drawings seemed to interest Mauve more. He gave me a great many hints which I was glad to get, and I have arranged to come back to see him in a relatively short time when I have some new studies. He showed me a whole lot of his studies and explained them to me – not sketches for drawings or pictures, but real studies, seemingly of little importance. He thinks I should start painting now.

(I, no. 149, p.237; Aug. or early Sept 1881[4])

The visit to Mauve was crucial for two reasons: it helped to precipitate Van Gogh's decision to paint after a year devoted to drawing, and it brought about an important change in his drawing technique and methodology. For about a year he had been making copies after Millet and using manuals by Charles Bargue to teach himself how to draw,[5] but Mauve persuaded him of the importance of working from life. In the letter written immediately after the one quoted from above, Vincent reported:

Though it is only a short time since I wrote to you, I already have some news to tell you.

That is to say, my drawing has changed, the technique as well as the results. Also, as a result of some things Mauve told me, I have begun to work from a live model again.

(I, no. 150, p. 239; c. Sept. 1881)

Working from life became a principal tenet of Van Gogh's technique. Seven years later, at about the time that he was painting some of his best known works in Arles, the question of whether or not to work from reality or the imagination resulted in an interesting exchange between Van Gogh and Emile Bernard. Van Gogh unequivocally stated his position in a letter to Bernard written in October 1888:

I have mercilessly destroyed one important canvas – a 'Christ with the Angel in Gethsemane' – and another one representing the 'Poet against a Starry Sky' – in spite of the fact that the colour was right – because the form had not been studied beforehand from the model, which is necessary in such cases.

(III, no. B19, p. 517; c. 7 Oct. 1888)

Although by 1888 Vincent had developed a highly expressive style and eschewed academically precise rendering in favour of a vocabulary of simplification, his attitude can be traced to Mauve's emphasis on the importance of working from nature. The following passage, written in 1882, clearly identifies Mauve as an important source of such ideas.

It is not the language of painters but the language of nature which one should listen to. Now I understand better than I did six months ago why Mauve said, 'Don't talk to me about Dupré; but talk to me about the bank of that ditch, or something like it.' It sounds rather crude, but it is perfectly true. The feeling for the things themselves, for reality, is more important than the feeling for pictures – at least it is more fertile and more enlivening.

(I, no. 218, p. 416; 22 July 1882)

As early as June 1879, Van Gogh had recognized in Mauve's work the expressiveness and simplifications that he wished to develop in his own work in 1881–82. In short, even before he decided to become an artist, Vincent was committed to the principles that he saw at work in Mauve's pictures. In the summer of 1879 Vincent described to Theo his admiration for art that 'disentangles, sets free, and interprets,' and cited the work of Mauve, Maris and Israëls as primary examples:

I still can find no better definition of the word art than this, 'L'art c'est l'homme ajouté à la nature' nature, reality, truth, but with a significance, a conception, a character, which the artist brings out in it, and to which he gives expression, 'qu'il dégage,' which he disentangles, sets free and interprets. A picture by Mauve or Maris or Israëls says more, and says it more clearly, than nature herself.

(I, no. 130, p. 189; June 1879)

Four years later, in August 1883, Van Gogh continued to espouse similar ideas, and Mauve remained a chief example of what he hoped to achieve.

Simplifying the figures is something which greatly preoccupies me. Well, you will see it for yourself in the figures I show you. . . . Speaking of the expression of a figure, more and more I come to the conclusion that it is not so much in the features as in the whole attitude. There are few things I hate more than most of the academical têtes d'expression. I prefer to look at 'the night' by Michelangelo, or a drunkard by Daumier, or the diggers by Millet, and that well-known woodcut of his, 'The Shepherdess', or an old horse by Mauve, etc.

(II, no. 299, p. 78; c. 11 July 1883)

In addition to influencing Van Gogh's ideas about the nature of art, Mauve also provided much needed technical assistance. As has been noted, their meeting in September 1881, resulted in a straightforward teacher-pupil relationship from which Vincent greatly profited. Following another meeting in December, Van Gogh described an equally fruitful encounter to his brother.

When I came to Mauve my heart palpitated a little, for I said to myself, Will he try to put me off with fair promises, or shall I be treated differently here? And I found that he helped me in every way, practically and kindly, and encouraged me. Not, however, by approving of everything I did or said, on the contrary. But if he says to me, 'This or that is not right,' he adds at the same time, 'but try it this or that way,' which is quite another thing than to criticize for the sake of criticizing.

(I, no. 164, p. 281; Dec. 1881)

The relationship flourished, and for several weeks in late 1881 and early 1882 Mauve continued to provide encouragement and advice about technique. Shortly before Christmas in 1881 Mauve sent Vincent 'a paintbox with paint, brushes, palette, and palette knife, oil, turpentine, in short, everything

necessary' (I, no. 165, p. 289; 23 or 24 Dec. 1881). Early in January 1882, Mauve told him that he would propose him for special membership of the Pulchri Studio. Later that month Van Gogh described a lesson with Mauve; it was undoubtedly one of several.

Yesterday I had a lesson from Mauve on drawing hands and faces so as to keep colour transparent. Mauve knows things so thoroughly, and when he tells you something, he exerts himself and doesn't just say it to hear himself talk; and I exert myself to listen carefully and to put it into practice.

(I, no. 172, p. 310; 22 Jan. 1882)

During the next month, however, Vincent learned that Mauve harboured doubts about his work. Mauve was not well in early February, and after Van Gogh had not seen him for a while he decided to visit Jan Hendrik Weissenbruch for news about their mutual friend. Weissenbruch had visited Vincent in the latter's studio not long before, and Van Gogh learned that the visit was at Mauve's behest:

I have already told you in a previous letter that I had a visit from Weissenbruch. At present Weissenbruch is the only one allowed to see Mauve, and I thought I would go and have a talk with him. So today I went to his studio, the attic which you know too. As soon as he saw me he began to laugh and said, 'I am sure you have come to talk about Mauve'; he knew at once why I came, and I did not have to explain.

Then he told me the reason for his visiting me was really that Mauve, who was doubtful about me, had sent Weissenbruch to get his opinion about my work.

And Weissenbruch then told Mauve, He draws confoundedly well, I could work from his studies myself.

And he added, 'They call me "the merciless sword", and I am; I would not have said that to Mauve if I had found no good in your studies.'

(I, no. 175, p. 314; 13 Feb. 1882)

The approval of both Mauve and Weissenbruch should have been enough to assure Van Gogh's success, but Vincent's relationship with Mauve soon assumed a less favourable character. Indeed, the relationship may not always have been as smooth as implied in Vincent's letters. In a description of Van Gogh's Nuenen period, written in 1912 by his friend Anton Kerssemakers, we learn that Vincent did not always accept Mauve's criticism with the equanimity described to Theo (I, no. 172, p. 301; 22 Jan. 1882).

He [Vincent] always spoke of Anton Mauve with the highest respect, although in the past he had been unable to get along with him, and had worked in his studio for only a short time. According to what he told me, Mauve once made a disapproving remark because he touched the canvas too often with his fingers while painting; this caused him to lose his temper, and he snapped at Mauve, 'What the hell does it matter, even if I did it with my heels, as long as it is good and has the right effect!'

(De Amsterdammer, Weekblad voor Nederland [De Groene], 14–21 April 1912)

The friendship cooled considerably during February and March 1882, and Mauve refused to see Vincent. Mauve's poor health was the ostensible reason, but he may have been influenced by one of Van Gogh's chief detractors, H.G. Tersteeg, the manager of Goupil & Co. in The Hague. Their last meeting took place in May when the two apparently met accidentally in the dunes. It was an especially painful experience for Vincent who found himself irrevocably rejected by the man who only three months before had been his main source of encouragement:

Today I met Mauve and had a very painful conversation with him, which made it clear to me that Mauve and I are separated forever. Mauve has gone so far that he cannot retract, at least he certainly wouldn't do it. I had asked him to come and see my work and then talk things over. Mauve refused point-blank: 'I will certainly not come to see you, that's all over.'

At last he said, 'You have a vicious character.' At this I turned around – it was in the dunes – and walked home alone.

(I, no. 192, pp. 348–49; 3–12 May 1882)

The potential for difficulty had existed since at least early January. On 7 January Vincent wrote to Theo that although he admired Mauve and his work, he felt the need for a broader point of view than that which Mauve had to offer:

As to Mauve – yes, certainly I am very fond of Mauve, and feel in sympathy with him; I love his work and I consider myself fortunate in being able to learn from him, but I can't confine myself within a system or a school any more than Mauve himself, and apart from Mauve and Mauve's work, I also love others who are quite different from him and work quite differently. And as to myself and my work, perhaps there is similarity, but there certainly is a difference, too. When I like somebody or something, I do so in all seriousness, and sometimes positively with passion and fire; but I do not systematically think only a few persons perfect, and all the others worthless – far be it from me!

(I, no. 169, p. 300; 7 Jan. 1882)

Nevertheless, Van Gogh appreciated Mauve throughout his career, and, ultimately, was able to see beyond their differences. When Mauve died in the spring of 1888, Vincent dedicated a painting to him: *Pink Peach Tree in Blossom*, also known as *Souvenir de Mauve* (fig. 112). This picture apparently symbolized Van Gogh's feelings about the artist who had encouraged him to 'blossom' seven years earlier. It is possible that he meant the flowering peach tree to signify his own birth as an artist, just as he later chose a flowering almond branch to celebrate the birth of his nephew in 1890.

Van Gogh's final act of homage to Mauve occurred in February 1890, when he wrote to the Symbolist critic Albert Aurier to comment on a laudatory article that the latter had written about him. He was both pleased and perplexed that Aurier had written so glowingly about him, but he also wished him to understand that he did not agree with everything that he had said. Furthermore, he indicated clearly that he owed a great debt to Mauve and others:

I declare that I do not understand why *you* should speak of Meissonier's 'Infamies'. It is possible that I have inherited from the excellent Mauve an absolutely unlimited admiration for Meissonier; Mauve's eulogies on Troyon and Meissonier used to be inexhaustible – a strange pair.

I say this to draw your attention to the extent to which people in foreign countries admire the artists of France, without making the least fuss about what divides them, often so damnably. What Mauve repeated so often was something like this: 'If one wants to paint colours, one should also be able to draw a chimney corner or an interior as Meissonier does.'

(III, no. 626a, p. 257; 10 Feb. 1890)

fig. 112 VAN GOGH *Pink Peach Tree in Blossom (Souvenir de Mauve)* 1888 (Rijksmuseum Kröller-Müller, Otterlo)

Clearly, then, Mauve's influence extended to Van Gogh's attitude toward art and technique generally. Although for a time Vincent worked in a manner quite close to Mauve, as is apparent in watercolours such as *The State Lottery Office* (Cat. 149) and *The Beach at Scheveningen* (Cat. 150), finally we must not forget the independence and wide-ranging interests that he expressed in his letter of 7 January 1882, to Theo: 'I can't confine myself within a system or a school any more than Mauve himself, and apart from Mauve and Mauve's work, I also love others who are quite different from him and work quite differently.' The catholicism revealed by the 54 painters that Vincent listed for Theo in January 1874 remained characteristic of him throughout his life, and, in addition to the numerous references to Mauve, his letters suggest that he was influenced, in varying degrees and at different times, by every artist in the present exhibition.

After Mauve the Hague School artist in whom Van Gogh showed the greatest interest was Jozef Israëls. He had a first hand knowledge of his work since at least the age of 16 when he went to work for Goupil & Co. in The Hague. Israëls, like Mauve, was one of the artists that Van Gogh acknowledged as a 'force' in nineteenth-century painting:

there used to be a body of painters, authors, artists, who were united, notwithstanding their differences, and they were a force. They did not walk in the dark but were enlightened: they certainly knew what they wanted, and they did not waver. I'm talking about the time when Corot, Millet, Daubigny, Jacque, Breton, were young; in Holland, Israëls, Mauve, Maris, etc.

(I, no. 247, p. 492; 24 Nov. 1882)

Moreover, Israëls was, in Van Gogh's opinion, the equal of

Millet and Jules Breton, two painters that Van Gogh felt could not be bettered.

> In my opinion, up to Millet and Jules Breton there was, however, always progress; but to surpass these two – don't even talk about it.
>
> Their genius may have been equalled in the past, may be equalled now or in the future, but it is impossible to surpass it. There is an equality of genius on that high plane, but one cannot climb higher than the top of the mountain. Israëls, for instance, may equal Millet, but with genius, superiority or inferiority is out of the question.
>
> (I, no. 241, p. 477; 2 or 3 Nov. 1882)

Van Gogh's admiration for Israëls was based on a strong sympathy for his subject matter as well as the conviction that his style was an especially effective vehicle for the expression of a quality that Van Gogh called 'soul'. His description of a painting by Israëls depicting an old man seated in a corner (fig. 113) is typical of his interest in this artist; moreover, the subject had already appeared in two of Van Gogh's drawings, *Peasant Reading by the Fireplace* (late October 1881) and *Old Peasant by the Fireplace* (November 1881; both in the Rijksmuseum Kröller-Müller, Otterlo).

> Israëls's 'An Old Man' . . . is sitting in a corner near the hearth, on which a small piece of peat is faintly glowing in the twilight. For it is a dark little cottage where that old man sits, an old cottage with a small white-curtained window. His dog, which has grown old with him, sits beside his chair – those two old friends look at each other, they look into each other's eyes, the dog and the man. And meanwhile the old man takes his tobacco pouch out of his pocket and lights his pipe in the twilight. That is all – the twilight, the silence, and the loneliness of those two old friends, the man and the dog, the understanding between those two, the meditation of the old man – what he is thinking of, I do not know, I cannot tell, but it must be a deep, long thought, something but I do not know what; it comes rising from a past long ago – perhaps that thought gives the expression to his face, an expression melancholy, contented, submissive, something that reminds one of Longfellow's famous poem with the refrain: But the thoughts of youth are long, long thoughts.
>
> (I, no. 181, pp. 325–26; *c.* 11 March 1882)

When Van Gogh treated the theme of an old man seated by a hearth in a peasant home he did not include the dog, but it is clear that his intentions are the same as those of Israëls. However, Vincent manages to avoid the hint of sentimentality that often characterizes Israëls; he heroizes the old man and emphasizes his dignity, but his expressiveness has a broader appeal than that of Israëls whose work often has the character of genre painting. For example, Israëls's *An Old Man* lacks the universality of Van Gogh's drawing *Worn Out* (September 1881; P. and N. de Boer Foundation, Amsterdam), which has an appeal not unlike that of Rodin's *The Thinker*.

In November 1882 Van Gogh executed a lithograph of an old man drinking coffee, which had evolved from the theme of the old man seated by the hearth in a peasant's cottage (fig. 113). The composition is not as elaborate as either Israëls's painting or Van Gogh's earlier drawings of old men by a hearth, but in the following passage from a letter of late November 1882, he indicates a connection with Israëls's treatment of the subject. Equally important, the passage underscores Van Gogh's understanding of the spiritual significance of such seemingly straightforward genre subjects.

> It seems to me it's a painter's duty to try to put an idea into his

fig. 113 J. ISRAËLS *Old Friends*
(William Elkins Collection, Philadelphia Museum of Art, Philadelphia)

> work. In this print [*Old Man Drinking Coffee*, lithograph, The Hague, November 1882] I have tried to express (but I cannot do it well or so strikingly as it is in reality; this is merely a weak reflection in a dark mirror) what seems to me one of the strongest proofs of the existence of 'quelque chose là-haut' in which Millet believed, namely the existence of God and eternity – certainly in the infinitely touching expression of such a little old man, which he himself is perhaps unconscious of, when he is sitting quietly in his corner by the fire. At the same time there is something noble, something great, which cannot be destined for the worms. Israëls has painted it so beautifully.
>
> (I, no. 248, p. 495; 26–27 Nov. 1882)

Ultimately, Van Gogh defined his admiration for Israëls as a matter of 'soul' that resulted from a wedding of technique *and* subject, neither of which was sufficient by itself:

> My sympathies in the literary as well as in the artistic fields are most strongly attracted to those artists in whom I see the working of the soul predominating. For instance, Israëls is clever as a technician, but so is [Antoine] Vollon; I prefer Israëls to Vollon, however, because I see something more in Israëls's work . . . , something quite different from the colour – and yet this 'something quite different' is brought about by the exact rendering of the light effects, the materials, the colour. [George] Eliot has this particular 'something different,' which I see so much more in Israëls's work than Vollon's to a high degree, and so does Dickens.
>
> Is this because of the choice of subjects? *No!* for this too is only a *result*.
>
> (III, R43, p. 400; April 1884)

Although Van Gogh believed that 'soul' could be realized in a painting through 'exact rendering', he did not mean academically precise replication of visual truths. For Van Gogh, technique was inextricably linked with expressiveness, and he felt that quasi-photographic illusionism was in itself an empty pursuit. In a letter written in the spring of 1884, he made his position clear for his friend Anthon van Rappard, and he cited Israëls, among others, as an artist whose work transcended his considerable technical prowess:

> And now as regards painters – is it the purpose, the non plus ultra, of art to produce those peculiar spots of colour – that capriciousness of drawing – that are called the distinction of technique? Most certainly

not. Take a Corot, a Daubigny, a Dupré, a Millet or an Israëls – fellows who are undoubtedly the great leaders – well, their work is *outside the paint*; it is as different from that of the elegant fellows as an oratorical tirade by Numa Roumestan, for instance, is different from a prayer or a good poem.

(III, R43, p. 398; April 1884)

Van Gogh believed that style and technique had to be mastered, but they were to be used in the service of expressiveness, feeling, and meaning instead of regarded as ends in themselves, 'reminding me always of the studio and never of nature'; he continued his advice to Van Rappard:

So it is *necessary* to work at the technique, as it is one's duty to express better, more accurately, more earnestly, what one feels – and the less verboseness the better. As for the rest – one need not bother about that. Why do I say this? – because I think I've noticed that you sometimes disapprove of things in your own work which are in my opinion decidedly good. In my eyes *your* technique is better than Haverman's, for instance – because already the stroke of your brush often has something personal, characteristic, accounted for and *willed*, while in Haverman's work it is an everlasting convention, reminding one always of the studio and never of nature.

(III, R43, p. 398; April 1884)

The phrase 'something personal, characteristic, accounted for, and *willed*' is particularly noteworthy, because it paraphrases the words the artist used in 1879 to describe the aesthetic mode that he preferred even before becoming an artist: 'nature, reality, truth, but with a significance, a conception, a character which the artist brings out in it, and to which he gives expression, "qu'il dégage", which he disentangles, sets free and interprets. A picture by Mauve or Maris or Israëls says more, and says it more clearly, than nature herself.' (I, no. 130, p. 189; June 1879). One of Van Gogh's strongest expressions of this point of view was included in a letter of July 1885, in which he again invoked Israëls's work as evidence in support of his argument:

a nude by Cabanel, a lady by Jacquet and a peasant woman, *not by Bastien-Lepage himself*, but a peasant woman by a Parisian who has learned his drawing at the academy, will always indicate the limbs and the structure of the body in one self-same way, sometimes charming – correct in proportion and anatomy. But when Israëls, or when Daumier or Lhermitte, for instance, draws a figure, the shape of the figure will be felt much more, and yet – that's why I like to include Daumier – the proportions will sometimes be almost *arbitrary*, the anatomy and structure often quite wrong 'in the eyes of the academician.' But it will *live*.

(II, no. 418, p. 401; c. 13–17 April 1885)

A painting by Israëls that illustrates the kind of style and sense of 'soul' that Van Gogh admired is *The Fisherman of Zandvoort* (Cat. 28), a picture that he mentioned several times in letters written during October 1885. Moreover, the picture appealed to the interest in social-realist subjects that motivated much of Van Gogh's work during the early 1880s.

In Amsterdam I saw two pictures by Israëls, 'The Fisherman of Zandvoort', and – one of his very latest – an old woman huddled together like a bundle of rags near the bedstead in which the corpse of her husband lies.

Both pictures are masterpieces, I think. Let them jabber about technique as much as they like, in Pharisaical, hollow, hypocritical terms – the true painters are guided by that conscience which is called

fig. 114 J. Israëls *Woman Drinking Coffee* (drawing) (Rijksmuseum Kröller-Müller, Otterlo)

sentiment, their soul: their brains aren't subject to the brush, but the brush to their brains. Besides, the canvas is afraid of a real painter, and not the painter afraid of the canvas.

(II, no. 426, p. 417; 10 or 11 Oct. 1885)

In addition to his admiration for the subject matter, Van Gogh showed particular interest in Israëls's stylistic treatment. A little later in the same letter he commented on Israëls's use of colour; the remarks are especially interesting, because they anticipate by at least three years Van Gogh's own theories about arbitrary colour.

Look at 'The Fisherman of Zandvoort' and see what colours it is painted with – it is painted with red, with blue, with yellow, with black and some dirty white, with brown (everything mixed and broken), or isn't it? When Israëls says that one must not paint black, he certainly never means what they now make of it, he means that there must be colour in the shadows, but that excludes neither a single colour scheme, however dark it may be, nor of course that of the blacks and browns and deep blues.

(II, no. 426, p. 418; 10 or 11 Oct. 1885)

The ideas expressed here were even more clearly articulated a few days later; although Israëls is not mentioned in the following passage, Van Gogh has incorporated the lessons of Israëls's technique into his own aesthetic attitudes. Furthermore, he has made the all-important quantum leap from observation to practice:

Of nature I retain a certain sequence and a certain correctness in placing the tones, I study nature, so as not to do foolish things, to remain reasonable; however, I don't care so much whether my colour is exactly the same, as long as it looks beautiful on my canvas, as beautiful as it looks in nature. . . . Here is another example: suppose I have to paint an autumn landscape, trees with yellow leaves. All right – when I conceive it as a symphony in yellow, what does it matter if the fundamental colour of yellow is the same as that of the leaves or not? It matters *very little*.

(II, no. 429, p. 427; end of Oct. 1885)

Four years later, similar principles were still of paramount concern to Van Gogh. In a letter written to Theo from Saint-Rémy, he paraphrased the ideas that he expressed in his description of an autumn landscape in 1885.

Gauguin and Bernard . . . do not ask the correct shape of a tree at all, but they do insist that one can say if the shape of a tree is round or

fig. 115 VAN GOGH *The Potato Eaters* 1885 (Rijksmuseum Vincent van Gogh, Amsterdam)

fig. 116 J. ISRAËLS *The Frugal Meal* 1876
(Glasgow Art Gallery and Museum, Glasgow)

square – and honestly, they are right, exasperated as they are by certain people's photographic and empty perfection. They will not ask the correct tone of the mountains, but they will say: By God, the mountains were blue, were they? Then chuck on some blue and don't go telling me that it was a blue rather like this or that, it was blue wasn't it? Good – make them blue and it's enough.

(III, no. 607, p. 217; 19 Sep. 1889)

Van Gogh was also influenced by Israëls's work in more fundamental and direct ways. For example, his first great success, *The Potato Eaters* (1885; fig. 115) owed a great debt to

Israëls's *The Frugal Meal*, (1876; fig. 116), at least one version of which Vincent saw in March 1882 (I, no. 181, p. 326; *c.* 11 March 1882). Furthermore, the colour scheme of *The Potato Eaters* was apparently directly affected by remarks made by Israëls in The Hague in 1884 which were subsequently reported to Van Gogh:

when I was last in The Hague I heard things Israëls had said about starting with a deep colour scheme, thus making even relatively dark colours seem light. In short, to express light by opposing it to black. I already know what you're going to say about 'too black,' but at the same time I am not quite convinced yet that a grey sky, for instance, must always be painted in the local tone.

(II, no. 371, p. 295; early June 1884)

Israëls's comments appear to have provided Vincent with at least some of the technical rationale for the palette of *The Potato Eaters*:

It is kept in such a low scale of colours that the *light* colours, smeared on white paper, for instance, would look like ink stains; but on the canvas they stand out like lights because of the great forces opposed to them, for instance by putting on absolutely unmixed Prussian blue.

(III, R57, p. 418; Sept. 1885)

Israëls, then, like Mauve, exerted a profound influence on Van Gogh's early work. Although this influence is not immediately apparent in Van Gogh's mature work, the commitment to an expressiveness based on exaggerations, simplifications and arbitrary colour certainly developed at least in part as a result of Van Gogh's early exposure to Israëls's work. Israëls's paintings seem to have fulfilled the dual role of affirming Van Gogh's own aesthetic inclinations and providing a surrogate pedagogical function as strong as that of the actual teaching of Mauve himself.

Jan Hendrik Weissenbruch, too, influenced Van Gogh's early work. He had admired Weissenbruch's work long before the artist visited him in his studio or he went to Weissenbruch's studio to talk about Mauve in early 1882 (see p. 138). Indeed, Weissenbruch was included in the list of 54 painters 'whom I especially like' that Vincent sent his brother Theo in 1874. The previous year he had even visited Weissenbruch's studio in early June, shortly before leaving to work in the Goupil & Co. branch in London. He later wrote,

I was once at Weissenbruch's studio, a few days before I first left for London, and the memory of what I saw there, the studies and pictures, is still as vivid as that of the man himself.

(I, no. 104, p. 131; 3 Aug. 1877)

From as early as 1873 Van Gogh was attracted by the evocative character of Weissenbruch's work. In July 1873, he mentioned a print of a picture by Weissenbruch that he associated with a walk that he and Theo had taken on the Rijswijk road:

What pleasant days we spent together at The Hague; I think so often of that walk on the Rijswijk road, when we drank milk at the mill after the rain. When we send back the pictures we have from you [Theo was working in the Hague branch of Goupil & Co.], I will send you a picture of that mill by Weissenbruch; perhaps you will remember him, his nickname is Merry Weiss. *That Rijswijk road holds memories for me which are perhaps the most beautiful I have. If we meet again, maybe we shall talk about them once more.*

(I, no. 10, p. 10; 20 July 1873)

Theo later sent Vincent a print after a picture by Weissenbruch depicting the Rijswijk road itself (fig. 117): 'I will hang those prints you gave me, "Le Four" by Th. Rousseau, and "The Road to Rijswijk" by Weissenbruch, in my room' (I, no. 117, p. 159; 9 Jan. 1878). Van Gogh seems to have associated the Rijswijk road with an emotional experience that was conveyed by Weissenbruch's work. His interest in Weissenbruch's pictures of the mill and the road foreshadows his conviction that landscape imagery could embody significances equivalent to those of figure paintings. In stating this idea, Van Gogh referred to Weissenbruch and invoked the familiar image of an old peasant sitting by a hearth.

Well, the same thing that Weissenbruch said about a landscape, a peat bog, Mauve said about a figure, i.e., an old peasant who sits brooding by the hearth, as if he saw things from the past rising in the glow of the fire or in the smoke.

(I, no. 177, p. 316; 25 Feb. 1882)

More than seven years later Van Gogh paraphrased this observation in noting that 'J.H. Weissenbruch knows and does the muddy towpaths, the stunted willows, the foreshortening, the strange and subtle perspective of the canals as Daumier does lawyers; I think that is perfect' (III, no. 605, p. 207; 10 Sept. 1889).

For a time Van Gogh executed watercolours that are remarkably similar in technique, mood, and subject to those of

fig. 117 J. H. WEISSENBRUCH *The Towpath along the Rijswijkseweg* (lithograph)

Weissenbruch. Two typical examples are *A Lane*, executed in The Hague, possibly in 1882 (present owner unknown), and *Landscape Toward Evening*, executed in Drenthe in September 1883 (Rijksmuseum Vincent van Gogh, Amsterdam). There are also paintings from the early 1880s that reflect a strong awareness of Weissenbruch's style, such as *Farmhouses*, painted in Drenthe in September, 1883 (Cat. 155) and *The Hut*, painted in Drenthe in November 1883 (R.W. van Hoey Smith, Rockanje, The Netherlands).

But the unmistakable stylistic similarity to Weissenbruch's work is the result of more than admiration and imitation. In February 1882, Weissenbruch advised Vincent about technique; in fact, Vincent reported to Theo, 'Now as long as Mauve is ill or too busy with his large picture [for the Salon], I may go to Weissenbruch if I want to find out anything, and Weissenbruch told me that I need not worry about Mauve's change in attitude toward me' (I, no. 175, p. 314; 13 Feb. 1882). Vincent then described one of the occasions during which Weissenbruch imparted specific technical advice.

I think it a great privilege to visit such clever people as Weissenbruch occasionally, especially when they take the trouble, as Weissenbruch did this morning, for instance, to show me a drawing that they are working on but which is not yet completed, and explain how they are going to finish it. That is just what I want.

(I, no. 175, p. 315; 13 Feb. 1882)

Weissenbruch, Mauve, and Israëls had a profound effect on Van Gogh's work, while other members of the Hague School, such as Hendrik Willem Mesdag, played a less important role. There were, of course, individual works that Vincent admired greatly; for instance, in a watercolour exhibition in Brussels that included works by Mauve, Maris, Weissenbruch, Roelofs and Gabriël, he was particularly impressed by an example by Mesdag:

Then there was a Mesdag that kept one from looking at any other drawing [sic], at least it did me. The beach at twilight, stormy weather, a sky with grey clouds, and the ruddy glow of the setting sun. In the foreground a fisherman on horseback – a tall, strange, dark silhouette standing out against the white foaming waves. . . . It is a large important drawing, done broadly, and so vigorous that, as I told you, nothing else can really be compared to it.

(I, no. 144, p. 232; 1 May 1881)

fig. 118 VAN GOGH *Windmills on the Weeskinderendijk at Dordrecht* (watercolour, pencil and chalk; Rijksmuseum Kröller-Müller, Otterlo)

Mesdag's *Panorama*, too, impressed Van Gogh as a faultless work, though he found some of his drawings less accomplished:

> I went to see Mesdag's 'Panorama' with [De Bock]; it is a work that deserves all respect. It reminded me of a remark, I think by Burger or Thoré, about 'The Anatomy Lesson' by Rembrandt. This picture's only fault is that it has no fault. The three drawings by Mesdag at the exhibition had perhaps more faults, but aroused immediate sympathy, at least it was so with me.
>
> (I, no. 149, pp. 237–38; Aug. 1881)

As is evident from Van Gogh's comments about the three drawings, his admiration for Mesdag was not unqualified. Furthermore, he criticized Mesdag's apparently 'modernist' approach to contemporary painting; the following remarks, made in reaction to an opinion expressed by Mesdag, are typical of Van Gogh's pluralistic approach to art.

> It is easier to say, as Mesdag did of a certain picture by Heyerdahl, painted with the same sentiment as that of a Murillo or Rembrandt, which he didn't want to buy from you, 'Oh, that's the old style – we don't need that any more,' than it is to replace that old style by something as good, let alone something superior.
>
> ... The expression 'We don't need that any more' – how readily that is used, and what a stupid and ugly phrase it is. In one of his fairy tales Andersen puts it, I think, not in a human being's mouth but in an old pig's mouth. People in glass houses shouldn't throw stones.
>
> (I, no. 247, p. 492; 24 Nov. 1882)

Three years later, however, Van Gogh cited Mesdag's work as confirmation of his belief that technically correct realist pictures were insufficient as works of art; he now found Mesdag's later work consonant with his own interests.

> Meanwhile I am going quietly to the *old Dutch masters*, and to the pictures by Israëls, and to those who have a direct affinity with Israëls, which the modern painters do not have. They are almost diametrically opposed to Israëls.
>
> And I think I have noticed that Israëls himself, and Maris, Mauve, Neuhuys, too, look disapprovingly on a certain tendency which we are talking about now. Mesdag, for instance, who was at first very *realistic*, as you remember, has become in his later pictures and

drawings deeper of tone and often somewhat more mysterious.

> (II, no. 427, p. 421; Oct. 1885)

Van Gogh might easily have repeated about Mesdag's work what he had once said about Mauve's: 'I love his work, and I consider myself fortunate in being able to learn from it, but I can't confine myself within a single system or school . . .'.

None the less, despite Van Gogh's aversion to confining himself to a single school, there was a time in the early 1880s when the Hague School was clearly of paramount importance to him. In May 1883, he wrote to his friend van Rappard: 'Well, I for my part am also trying to find the path I think best, let's say the path of Israëls, Mauve, Maris ...' (III, R34, p. 382; May 1883). The reference to Maris – most probably Jacob Maris – is interesting, because although Vincent cited him as an artist he would like to emulate, Maris played a relatively small role in the discussion in his letters. He was cited in January 1874, as one of the 54 painters 'whom I like especially,' but subsequently he often appeared only as one of a group of artists mentioned to illustrate a particular point. For example,

> today's cold flat greys are technically not worth much, but remain *paint*, and with Israëls one forgets the paint. But remember, I do not mean Jaap Maris, Willem Maris, Mauve, Neuhuys, who work in the right manner, each in his own colour scale, Blommers too.
>
> (II, no. 426, pp. 417–18; mid-July 1885)

Jacob Maris's influence on Van Gogh's early work is apparent, however, in a number of pictures. For example, two drawings – *Windmill by a Canal*, executed in August 1881 (Rijksmuseum Kröller-Müller, Otterlo), and *Windmills on the Weeskinderendijk at Dordrecht*, executed in early autumn 1881 (fig. 118) indicate a consciousness of Maris's work, and the composition of another drawing, *The Windmill*, executed in August 1881 (Mrs M.A.R. van der Leeuw-Wentges, The Hague), suggests that Van Gogh had been influenced by Maris's cropped images of windmills such as *The Truncated Windmill* (Cat. 51). The subject and handling of paintings such as *Water Mill at Gennep*, executed in November 1884 (private collection), also reflect the impact of Maris on Van Gogh's early work.

fig. 119 W. Maris *Winter Landscape* (Stedelijk Museum, Amsterdam)

The influence of a number of other Hague School artists is less easy to demonstrate. Johannes Bosboom, for example, is a figure whom Van Gogh admired but whose work had relatively little impact on him. However, Van Gogh on at least one occasion received some advice from him.

> By chance Bosboom saw my studies and gave me some hints about them. I only wish I had more opportunity to receive such hints. Bosboom is one of those people who has the ability to impart knowledge to others and make things clear to them. There were three or four good drawings of his at the exhibition [probably at the Mesdag Panorama].
>
> (I, no. 149, p. 238; early Sept. 1881)

Bernard Blommers had little impact on Van Gogh's work, but he also provided Van Gogh with some practical advice and encouragement.

> Now I have spoken to Blommers about my painting – he wants me to keep it up; personally I also feel that having finished those last ten or twelve large drawings, I have reached a point where I must change my course instead of making more in the same way.
>
> (II, no. 303, p. 86; 23 July 1883)

The encounter seems to have been incidental, and it clearly had none of the consequence of the meetings that Van Gogh had with Mauve and Weissenbruch. Nevertheless, Blommers was an artist whose work Van Gogh had long admired, and whose working habits, such as drawing from models, he emulated:

> It's all right when somebody with years of experience draws the figure from memory after having studied it a great deal, but it seems to me too risky to work from memory systematically. Even Israëls, Blommers and Neuhuys don't do it, though they have so much experience.
>
> (I, no. 185, p. 335; early April 1882)

As was the case with numerous artists, Van Gogh knew at least some of Blommers's work exclusively from reproductions: 'Don't you like Blommers's picture at the Salon,

"November"? I didn't see the picture, only the reproduction. I think it looks exactly like a Butin, and it has more passion (and something dramatic) than Blommers's pictures usually have' (II, no. 296, p. 66; c. June 23–28 1883). It happened that Van Gogh's interest in reproductions after other artists' work was an interest that he shared with Blommers. In fact, Blommers unsuccessfully attempted to persuade the members of Pulchri Studio to allow Van Gogh to show a selection of his collection of wood engravings.

> Blommers spoke to me about showing a collection of wood engravings after Herkomer, Frank Holl, du Maurier, etc., some evening at Pulchri. I should like very much to do so. I have enough of them for at least two evenings.
>
> (I, no. 183, p. 330; 24 March 1882)

Moreover, it is significant that this interest in artists such as Herkomer and Holl was shared by one of the leading members of the Hague School, Jozef Israëls, who hung reproductions of well-known paintings by Herkomer and Holl in his home:

> Recently I passed Israëls's house – I have never been inside – the front door was open, as the servant was scrubbing the hall. I saw things hanging in the hall, and do you know what they were? The large Herkomer, 'Last Muster, Sunday at Chelsea,' and the photograph of that picture by Roll, 'Grève de Charbonniers,' which you perhaps remember I wrote to you about at the time. I didn't know that there existed a photograph of the 'Last Muster'. I possess the large wood engraving of the two principal figures, and the first rough sketch made long before the picture.
>
> (II, no. 280, p. 26; c. 21–22 April 1883)

The other members of the Hague School included in the present exhibition – Willem Roelofs, Gerard Bilders, Matthijs Maris, and Willem Maris – are artists whose work Van Gogh knew, but they played a minor role in his letters, and their impact on his work was slight. For instance, Van Gogh met Roelofs in October 1880, but the older artist was of little help and suggested that he enroll at the academy. From Brussels Van Gogh reported to his brother:

First, I went to see Mr Roelofs the day after receiving your letter; he told me that in his opinion from now on I must draw principally from nature, that is, from either plaster cast or model, but not without the guidance of someone who knows it well. He – and others, too – have advised me so earnestly to go and work at the academy, either here or at Antwerp or wherever I can, that I felt obliged to try to get admitted to the said academy, though I do not think it so very pleasant.

(I, no. 138, p. 210; 1 Nov. 1880)

Roelofs's reluctance to assist Van Gogh was undoubtedly motivated by the undeveloped character of Van Gogh's work in 1880, but he may also have suffered as a result of the poor opinion of him that certain individuals, such as his uncle the art dealer Cornelis Marinus van Gogh and Tersteeg, held of him:

C.M. [van Gogh] and others should change their opinion of me at least outwardly, but I would much rather it were truly so. For example, somebody like Roelofs doesn't know what to make of such a false position – either there must be something wrong with me, or with the others; but what he is sure of is: anyhow, there is something wrong somewhere. So he is over-prudent and will have nothing to do with me just at the moment when I most need advice or help.

(I, no. 142, pp. 220–21: 4 Feb. 1881)

In complete contrast to Roelofs, whose help he wanted, he had little use for the life and work of Gerard Bilders. In the summer of 1882 Vincent read the *Letters and Diary of Gerard Bilders* and declared his own goals different.

Bilders is very witty, and can lament in a most ludicrous way about 'Manila Cigars' – which he likes and which he cannot afford – about tailors' bills which he cannot figure out how to pay. He describes his anxiety about money affairs so wittily that he himself and the reader have to laugh. But no matter how wittily these things may be told, I dislike it, and have more respect for Millet's private difficulties, 'il faut tout de même de la soupe pour les enfants', he does not talk about Manila cigars or about amusements.

What I want to say is, Gerard Bilders' view of life was romantic, and never got over the illusions perdues . . .

(I, no. 227, p. 444: 20 Aug. 1882–6)

While Van Gogh's feelings about Bilders are well defined, his attitude toward Willem Maris is almost one of benign neglect. He identified him as a painter who worked 'in the right manner' (II, no. 426, pp. 417–18; 10 or 11 Oct. 1885) and, although he met him once at De Bock's studio, Willem Maris elicited only the following comment: 'I met Willem Maris at De Bock's. What a beautiful sketch the latter has by him, a road in winter with a little figure under an umbrella' (I,

no. 149, p. 238; *c.* Aug. or early Sept. 1881; see fig. 119).

Vincent also met Thijs Maris ('I spoke once or twice to Thijs Maris'; (II, no. 332, p. 163 *c.* 12 Oct. 1883), the third of the Maris brothers but he, too, exerted virtually no visible influence on Van Gogh's work. However, Van Gogh long admired him and in 1874 included him in the list of 54 'painters whom I like especially'. In a letter written in February 1883, he likened him to Quasimodo; Van Gogh expressed regret that he was so poorly understood and deprecated those who derided him: 'One of the most stupid things about the painters here is that even now they laugh at Thijs Maris . . . in my opinion a painter cannot mock him without lowering himself' (I, no. 268, p. 548; *c.* 20–24 Feb. 1883). In addition, Van Gogh seems to have identified with him as a kindred spirit, perhaps in anticipation of the increasingly poor reception of his own work. Indeed, later he could have easily written the following passage about himself:

The only thing to do is to go one's own way, to try one's best, to make the thing live.

If they hadn't made Thijs Maris too wretched and too melancholy to work, perhaps he would have found something wonderful.

I think of that fellow so often, Theo, how marvellous his work is. It is as if he dreams – but what an artist he is!

(II, no. 408, p. 381; Oct. 1884)

In conclusion, it is difficult to imagine that Van Gogh's work could have evolved as it did without the existence of the Hague School. All the artists seem to have contributed to Van Gogh's artistic development, but each provided something different; their work combined as a visual and theoretical textbook to which he constantly referred in his early years. In London Van Gogh admired contemporary English artists such as Herkomer and Holl, and in Paris – indeed, throughout his career – he admired the artists of the Barbizon School. But during his first five years as an artist the Hague School constituted a continuous influence that was rivalled only by Millet, who remained crucial to Van Gogh's work even after the Hague School ceased to be a direct influence. In Van Gogh's relations with the members of the Hague School and their work, we are able to watch an aesthetic evolve and we see the artist's extraordinary cogent and analytical mind at work. Without Van Gogh's observations about the Hague School we would know a great deal less about the formative background of his early work, a good knowledge of which is essential to a full understanding of his motives in much of his late work. We would also lack an important eye-witness account of a movement that contributed significantly to the rise of Northern European modernism.

NOTES

1. G. Pollock, in exh. cat. *Vincent van Gogh en zijn Hollandse jaren, kijk op stad en land door van Gogh en zijn tijdgenoten*, Rijksmuseum Vincent van Gogh, Amsterdam 1980.
2. All quotations from the letters are taken from Vincent van Gogh, *The Complete Letters of Vincent van Gogh*, London 1958. All citations to the letters in this essay will take the following form: volume number will be given first as roman numeral I, II, or III, followed by the letter number (e.g., no. 229), and finally the page number: for example, II, no. 229, p. 78. A number of translation errors and the spelling have been adjusted.
3. Marc Edo Tralbaut, *Vincent van Gogh*, New York 1969, p. 37.
4. The dates of all undated letters have been taken from Dr Jan Hulsker, *Van Gogh door van Gogh*, Amsterdam, 1973.
5 For more about the influence of Charles Bargue on Van Gogh, see Anne

Stiles Wylie, 'An Investigation of the vocabulary of line in Vincent van Gogh's Expression of Space', *Oud-Holland* LXXXV, (1970), p. 210 ff.
6. His criticism of other artists' lifestyles was not limited to Bilders. In 1885 he similarly criticized Israëls and Mauve, and again used Millet as a contrast to illustrate his point:

What I hope I shall not forget is that 'il s'agit d'y aller en sabots' [a phrase which he borrowed from Alfred Sensier's book on Millet], which means to be content with the food, drink, clothes and board which the peasants content themselves with.

That's what Millet did and in fact did *not want anything better*, and in so doing he was in his daily life, given an example to painters which, for instance, Israëls and Mauve, who live rather luxuriously, have *not* done . . .

(II, no. 400, p. 363; Apr. 1885)

Piet Mondriaan and the Hague School

HERBERT HENKELS

At first sight, Piet Mondriaan appears to have little direct connection with the Hague School and it may appear strange that his work is included in this exhibition. He has in the past almost invariably been seen as the founder of modern abstract art, which is considered to be the very antithesis of the naturalistic painting that is seen as the main characteristic of the Hague School. However, during the last 30 years Mondriaan's role in the founding of modern abstract art has been reassessed and greater emphasis is now laid on the importance of his final American years and his work during the 1920s. But as yet only a few small exhibitions have been devoted specifically to the link between Mondriaan and the Hague School, and the importance of his early years have been studied only in Robert Welsh's book.[1]

Recently Lazlo Glozer pointed out that the time has come for an entirely fresh reappraisal of the so-called fathers of modern art and that more emphasis should be placed on the consistency of an artist's entire œuvre.[2] This is indeed necessary in trying to avoid grave distortions in art historians' research and theories about an artist's development, and also to become more aware of the imposition of one's own projections on the subject of study. Here is not the place to illustrate this problem at length in relation to Mondriaan; suffice to say that terms like father, founder and the like are indicative of such an approach. The extent to which Mondriaan's image really corresponds with his work can be looked at here in more detail, in the context of the work of the Hague School.

This brief survey will examine various aspects of Piet Mondriaan's life and work and will indicate the ways in which the Hague School was an important influence on him. The topics to consider are Mondriaan's youth and development, stylistic similarities between his work and that of the Hague School, their repertoires of subject matter, their methods and aesthetics and the theoretical basis of their art and, in particular, of their painting.

Youth and development

For an artist of Mondriaan's generation who wanted to receive his training in the Netherlands, the influence and presence of the Hague School were inescapable.[3] As will have been made clear in earlier chapters, the position of most members of this school of painting, which was regarded as a single entity, was almost unassailable by 1890. Not only did they dominate a large part of the art market, but their influence was paramount in the social sector through the offices they held in official and semi-official bodies and committees. The attention devoted to their works by the English-speaking countries further enhanced the prestige of the members of the School at home. The hundreds and sometimes even thousands of interpretations of certain themes – meadows with cows, heath landscapes, windmills and canals and suchlike – found an eager market in the United States or Britain in those cases where they did not sell well in the Netherlands itself.

However, the dominance of the Hague School was soon to end. Indeed, it was inherent in that dominance that the next generation would appeal to different aesthetic principles and strongly oppose the influence of the Hague School. That influence was an unmistakable and important element in Piet Mondriaan's formative years, but it is no less significant that he increasingly turned to principles other than those of the Hague School. Mondriaan's development is characterized not by a radical renunciation of an accepted aesthetic, but by the juxtaposition of the distinguishing features of the Hague School and the innovatory tendencies which had begun to show themselves early in the 1890s and were mainly represented by the rapid rise of symbolist art.

Mondriaan grew up in a family circle that was intensively engaged in intellectual activities and in which the visual arts played an important role. His father had during his own training as a teacher acquired a separate diploma that qualified him to give drawing lessons. For him drawing was, like his literary gifts, just one part of an overall view of life that he believed found its best expression in political activity. The Christian emancipation movement, in which he played an important part, dominated his entire life and he used all his skills and activities to try and further the cause of the political and social liberation of an important part of the Protestant population. Thus his most important works still known to us are political prints, lampoons to propagate the ideas and political demands of the Christian emancipation movement.[4]

Both the function of these drawings and the direct assistance Piet Mondriaan gave his father in their production undoubtedly had a formative influence on Mondriaan. It was a foregone conclusion that Mondriaan would be encouraged to develop his talents as a draughtsman and follow a course that

fig. 120 F. Mondriaan *Watermill at Azelo*
(Oudheidkamer Twenthe, Enschede)

fig. 121 F. Mondriaan *View of Twickel, Delden*
(Private collection)

would equip him to occupy a completely independent position in society. Thus his taking of the drawing teacher's training course, at first a secondary and then a higher level, had a somewhat different significance from that we would ascribe to it nowadays. After all, the teaching of drawing was by no means as specialized then as it is today and the training had to cater for people who would later find themselves in very varied employment, in which they might be required to teach drawing, work as a technical artist (in the contemporary sense of technical drawing) or even make anatomical and other medical drawings, which were then of great importance as illustrative material in research and in training publications. Perhaps this explains why such great emphasis was laid in the teaching not only on perspective drawing, but also on the reproduction of geometrical figures, from the basic forms to the most complicated combinations.5 If one examines and reads the method propounded by Braet von Uberfeldt and Bing, which was largely based on that of the Frenchman Dupuis and served as an important textbook for Mondriaan, it becomes clear how formative this training was for him, especially in his formulation of the theory of Neo-Plasticism (1917–20).

Braet von Uberfeldt lived at Doetinchem, a little place not far from Winterswijk, from the time of his retirement as a teacher at an Amsterdam drawing school until his death in 1894. Mondriaan made regular visits to the old man, not only for help in his studies for the drawing diplomas for which he was working, but also because he must undoubtedly have felt attracted by Braet von Uberfeldt's art collection. In addition to a large number of paintings by masters of the Hague School, this included a collection of reproductions, which Braet kept in portfolios and which Mondriaan regularly took home with him for further study or copying. Thus in Winterswijk, far from the official art centres, Mondriaan was able to form a good idea of developments in contemporary painting. This appealed to him so much that he decided, after gaining his diplomas as a drawing teacher, to go to one of the Dutch art centres, namely Amsterdam, in order to perfect his painting skills and possibly to make it his profession, as his uncle Frits Mondriaan had done.

Frits Mondriaan was undoubtedly the strongest link

between his nephew and the Hague School. He was the youngest of the Mondriaan family, separated by 15 years from Piet's father. He took over a fashionable wig salon in The Hague after the death of its founder and ran it with the aid of his highly energetic wife. Although he lacked the training that his brother had enjoyed, he was so fascinated by drawing and painting that he decided to extend and develop his undoubted artistic talent, leaving the wig salon in the capable hands of his wife. It was greatly to his advantage that numerous prominent members of the Hague School, including the celebrated Willem Maris, regularly patronized his salon, and there gave him advice on his painting.

Frits Mondriaan chose his subjects mainly from what he found near his house in The Hague, but he also ventured further afield, often accompanied by painter friends. It is known from his work that he painted near Amsterdam (along the river Gein), in the Veluwezoom in Gelderland, at Woerden and, of course, in the Achterhoek and at Winterswijk. During his frequent and lengthy visits to his brother at Winterswijk he would go out to draw and paint subjects in the neighbourhood, such as country houses, watermills and windmills, often accompanied by his nephew, Piet. Some of these works are still known, such as the *Watermill at Azelo* and *View of the House 'Twickel' at Delden*6 (figs. 120, 121). Although Frits Mondriaan undoubtedly won recognition principally for his scenes in the Hague Woods, he must also have been a competent painter of still lifes, portraits and flower pieces. Of these last subjects only a few still lifes that have recently come to light are known, but it can confidently be assumed from them that the example set by Frits Mondriaan long determined his nephew's idea of what an artist should be.

From the mid-1880s onwards Frits devoted most of his time to painting. He exhibited regularly from the beginning of the 1890s and his reputation continued to grow until the end of the first decade of the present century, by which time, according to later critics, he was selling dozens of oil sketches, large and small, at each exhibition. The exact course of his stylistic development is difficult to follow, mainly because very few of his known works (totalling about 100) are dated. His work itself has great homogeneity, with little variation in the subject matter and none in technique. The large oil paintings have the

fig. 122 P. MONDRIAAN *Farm and Willows on the River Gein*
(Haags Gemeentemuseum, The Hague)

fig. 123 P. MONDRIAAN *Farm near a Waterway*
(Location unknown)

character of highly finished, smoothly painted salon works, and have been praised mainly for the 'authenticity' of the rendering of light and the seasons. From our point of view the smaller oil sketches are more interesting because it is in them that the similarities with the work of Piet are so conspicuous. In fact these similarities are so striking that it is often extremely difficult, in many cases actually impossible, to attribute these smaller works to one or other of the two artists with complete certainty. It is these spontaneous sketches, often painted on the spot, that constitute the major part of Piet Mondriaan's *œuvre* in the first years of this century (figs. 122, 123).

The 1890s were the period in which Piet Mondriaan's work was most closely linked with the Hague School, in terms of both subject matter and technique. Having taken courses at the Rijksacademie in Amsterdam for a few years, which, as far as we can now tell, had little immediate effect on his work, he earned his living by making copies of Hague School works, and by painting plates for the tourist industry. The first copy that he made in the Rijksmuseum was of Gabriël's *In the Month of July* (fig. 125) which had been bought a few years before.[7] It is noteworthy because it is actually the only copy that can be

fig. 124 P. MONDRIAAN *The Schinkel Quarter c.* 1898
(Private collection)

directly linked with Mondriaan's own work. The sun-drenched mill was, after all, one of Mondriaan's most important motifs, especially in the years 1908–12, not only in terms of his experiments with technique but also as a symbol, as he was to explain later in his articles in *De Stijl.*[8]

Other contacts

The sketch – the most spontaneous form of an artist's impressions – proved to be of great importance to Mondriaan. He was to refer to its importance many years later, when he reflected at length on his own development as a painter and tried to explain the crucial influences in his early development. Thus he wrote in the *Trialogue*, 'By virtue of their first, intuitive emotion the studies and sketches of the naturalistic [i.e. Hague School] painters are generally much stronger and finer than their paintings.'[9] It was above all this technique that Mondriaan wanted to master in his treatment of subjects that may be found also in his uncle's work and that belonged to the repertoire of every artist working in the manner of the Hague School: farmhouses with trees, windmills beside a stream, bridges over canals, meadows with cows and so on. Only a few townscapes by Mondriaan have survived and these are immediately reminiscent of Jacob Maris's urban sketches: impasted oil sketches with little detail, but more attention to the brush work, which is built up in areas of varying size (Cat. 157). However, these more or less obvious similarities to some members of the Amsterdam School, such as Breitner (a superficial resemblance to whom may be seen in the figures placed in the forefront of pictures and the truncated compositions, formal similarities that actually have a completely different significance in Mondriaan's pictures; fig. 126), are not the most striking feature of Mondriaan's work. The most characteristic feature, both at this period and subsequently, was his adherence to the subject matter and painting style of the Hague School and the very absence of any clear conversion or changeover to the aesthetic principles of the Amsterdam School. It is not until much later, around 1905, that one occasionally encounters a work by Mondriaan of which the strong composition and great expressiveness are reminiscent of the work of a contemporary whom Mondriaan appears to have admired, such as Suze Robertson (fig. 127).[10]

At the same time some characteristics of Mondriaan's work

fig. 126 P. MONDRIAAN *Peasant Women in Winterswijk c.* 1898 (Haags Gemeentemuseum, The Hague)

fig. 127 ROBERTSON *The Church at Batenburg*
(Suze Robertson Foundation, Haags Gemeentemuseum, The Hague)

in the 1890s suggest that he should not be considered purely and simply as a follower of the Hague School in his early years. These identifiable characteristics are not stylistic, but are to be found in the composition and general construction of his

fig. 125 GABRIËL *In the Month of July* (Rijksmuseum, Amsterdam)

paintings. If one studies the work of Frits Mondriaan and other members of the Hague School, it is immediately noticeable that the composition frequently follows the same arrangement, almost as if it were a set pattern. A lane, a river, or a group of trees to the left or right of the composition, ensures that the eye has no difficulty in resting easily in the landscape, a simple device that can be found in the early work of many Hague School painters, and which must have contributed in no small degree to the commercial success of these landscapes. After all, the spectator has to make scarcely any effort in order to transport himself into the painter's world, nor is he confronted by the technical means that have produced the illusion: it is as close to reality as it can be and the shared standpoint of the spectator and artist is of minimal importance in the composition of the work (figs. 128, 129).

In Mondriaan's case, however, even his very early works from the beginning of the 1890s reveal his great fascination with composition and the principles that lie behind it. It may justifiably be asked whether this interest cannot be traced back to his highly intensive drawing training, since the principles and practice of composition and perspective took pride of place in the particular textbooks that he would have used. This can be very clearly illustrated in a group of works he painted in Winterswijk at the end of the 1890s. In the first study the subject of a given place is sketched out; Mondriaan sets a single motif in the foreground of the composition, aiming at a strong frontal perspective and letting a tension arise between the

fig. 128 P. MONDRIAAN *Farm* (Location unknown)

fig. 129 P. MONDRIAAN *The 'Weevershuis' ('Weavers House') in Winterswijk* (pencil drawing)
(Collection J.P. Smid, Amsterdam)

motif in the foreground and another in the background of the composition. This frontal perspective and the creation of a strong tension between the foreground and background can also often be found in his landscape sketches of the years around the turn of the century. This unique character of his work can be well illustrated by a work like *The Ditch near Het Kalfje* (fig. 131). The same subject occurs in the work of Jan Hendrik Weissenbruch, (fig. 130) but there the spectator is immediately drawn into a wide perspective; Mondriaan is concerned to prevent precisely that and does so by placing the tree in the foreground to make the spectator aware of the construction of the composition. This compositional principle can also be seen in his *Farm at Nistelrode*.[11]

Apart from those members of the Hague School already mentioned as important influences, Mondriaan was particularly close to Jan Hendrik Weissenbruch, not only in his work, but also in his ideas and conception of the artist's role. The great attention Mondriaan paid to colour – violet-blue and green – and the 'cloudiness' of his gradations of tone around the turn of the century, especially in his larger watercolours of that period show strong similarity to the work of Weissenbruch, who was a latecomer to the success achieved by the other members of the School, but who was more fundamentally concerned with light and colour than any of them.

A new art for a new era

As indicated, there are points of contact at various levels between the work of Mondriaan and that of members of the Hague School.[12] He was unable to break away from the Hague School style of painting until a late stage of his artistic development, as a result of his early introduction to the character of that work by his uncle Frits. Opportunities to paint in a different way did, in fact, present themselves in the artistic climate of Amsterdam, certainly after 1890. But there is a further reason for his adherence to the Hague School principles apart from the strong influence of his uncle in his youth, and that is his desire to find a style that would guarantee him a secure position in society. He tried on two occasions to secure official recognition for his art by entering the competitions for the Prix de Rome. If he had won, he would, after all, have been guaranteed prestigious commissions for several years at the very least. But it was in precisely this type of painting, the depiction of scenes with historical figures in a dramatic situation, that he failed; how could it have been otherwise for a landscape painter? Several years later he declared that since that time he had confined himself to painting landscapes, abandoning figure studies altogether. [13] It was at this period that he tried, just as his uncle had done, to build up a reasonable market for his work by making numerous landscape sketches and so it is not surprising that most of his sketches that are close to the work of the Hague School painters, and in particular to that of his uncle, were produced at this time, after 1900.

Mondriaan's reconsideration of the expressive idiom and the significance of art in general in these years – it has been suggested that he suffered a personal crisis[14] – led him to a direct reckoning with, and reappraisal of, the values of the Hague School. He began to approach a relatively small group of artists who wanted a new art for a new era; as Jan Toorop, the co-founder of the Moderne Kunstkring (Contemporary Art Society), and one of the most important representatives of this group summed up the situation: 'You see, however, that for all our endeavours Dutch art-lovers and the great Dutch collectors still look to the art of our fathers and their respectful followers.'[15] This was particularly applicable to Mondriaan, as we have seen. After his involvement in the foundation of the Moderne Kunstkring in 1910, an epoch-making event in the artistic life of the Netherlands, Mondriaan's efforts were continually directed at developing an art that did not hark back to old aesthetic ideals from a bygone age, but that would be an art of the future, linking up with the new developments in society and even helping to shape them. The years 1910–20 were a very stormy period in the history of Dutch art. The advent of the Moderne Kunstkring was the signal for a great flood of publications on new developments in art, especially in France and Germany, which overwhelmed the eager public.[16] As a result, the reputation of the Hague School and interest in their work plummeted to an unprecedented low, from which they only slowly began to recover some 25 years later.

Frits Mondriaan was also affected by these changes in attitude, of which he was well aware. He was still reacting to them in the middle of the 1920s.

Frits Mondriaan complained about the lack of public interest in what the older painters regarded as the only good painting, that of the Hague, Amsterdam and Laren Schools. He had no use whatever for the ultra-modern movement, Cubist, Futurist and Expressionist. Thus he thought that his nephew Piet and his followers had thrown the art-buying public into confusion with their lines, crosses and right-angles that they called 'painting', an opinion which one hears put forward by many non-ultra-modern painters, in other countries too, and which, in view of the facts, has a certain amount of truth behind it.'[17]

The breakthrough that Mondriaan forced with his art is

fig. 130 J. H. WEISSENBRUCH *Waterway through the Polder* 1897 (Private collection)

fig. 131 P. MONDRIAAN *The Ditch near Het Kalfje* c. 1901–02 (Haags Gemeentemuseum, The Hague)

characteristic of the period. There was a strong feeling, especially in *avant-garde* artistic circles, that a new era, which would mean a complete reappraisal of all values, was about to dawn.[18] The challenge of bringing out of its unfruitful social isolation a personal, subjective art that was cramped by a nationalistic straitjacket was met by Mondriaan with an art that was to be based precisely on the most universal means of expression.[19] He believed that an international community was coming into being and that it would need an art based on the same principles: the greatest possible comprehensibility for the largest possible number of people, with the ultimate objective of art and life developing hand in hand in a future society.

To Mondriaan the Hague School represented a very narrow conception and formulation of the significance of art in society. His starting-points for the formulation of the new art were largely to be found in ideas he had assimilated from the Hague School, but the new art itself was to be based on universal premises. His point of departure was the particular, while his sights were fixed on the universal. These two opposite poles, the national school and international comprehensibility, constituted the field of tension within which his later work was accomplished.

This exhibition demonstrates just how important nationalism and internationalism were as determining factors in artistic developments in the Netherlands at the end of the last century. Out of the tension between these extremes, which were interpreted at that time as mutually antagonistic and inimical, there arose a new art, which proved to be an inspiration to innumerable artists all over the world when they came to formulate their own artistic philosophies.

NOTES

1. R.P. Welsh, *Mondriaan's early Career, the naturalistic Period*, New York 1977 (1963).

2. L. Glozer, *Westkunst*, Cologne 1981.

3. See H. Henkels, 'Mondriaan in his Studio' in exh. cat. *Mondriaan, Drawings, Watercolours, New York Paintings*, Stuttgart, The Hague, Baltimore 1980–81, pp. 219–85.

4. For a survey of these prints see H. Henkels, *Mondriaan in Winterswijk*, The Hague 1979, pp. 21–25.

5. For the drawing methods see B. Koevoet, H.C. van Rheeden (ed.), *Geen dag zonder lijn, honderd jaar tekenonderwijs in Nederland 1880–1980*, Haarlem 1980.

6. Z. Kolks, 'Frits Mondriaan en de Noordmolen in Azelo', *Twickelbulletin* (1980), no. 10, pp. 25–28; exh. cat. *Oost-Nederland Model*, Rijksmuseum Twenthe, Enschede 1980, p. 141. I am very grateful to Zeno Kolks for this information.

7. For the copies that Mondriaan made in the Rijksmuseum see Henkels, *art. cit.*.

8. Henkels, *art. cit.*.

9. *De Stijl* III (1919), no. 2, p. 16.

10. See C. Blok, *Mondriaan in de collectie van het Haags Gemeentemuseum*, The Hague 1968, p. 65.

11. Cf. for example, figs. 10, 15, 51, 52, 65 in C. Blok, *Piet Mondriaan, een catalogus van zijn werk in Nederlands openbaar bezit*, Amsterdam 1974.

12. Mondriaan undoubtedly saw a great deal of work by Hague School painters at their numerous exhibitions in the 1890s.

13. In F. Lurasco, *Onze moderne meesters*, Amsterdam 1907.

14. Mondriaan's friend A.P. van den Briel, in particular, continually spoke about this; Van den Briel file, Haags Gemeentemuseum, The Hague; see also Welsh, *op. cit.*, *passim*.

15. Letter from Jan Toorop to C. Kikkert, 20 August 1910, private collection.

16. One often hears the opinion that the Netherlands was practically closed to international contacts up to 1910, but nothing could be further from the truth. The Hague School painters in particular had numerous foreign contacts. However, the artistic movements that came to the fore after 1880 in France in particular did not become known among a wider public in the Netherlands until much later; it is here that the importance of the Contemporary Art Society lies.

17. N.H. Wolf, 'Frits Mondriaan, Kunstzaal Fetter, Amsterdam', *De Kunst* (1925), pp. 447–48.

18. The relationship between renewal movements in the arts and in other social fields has not yet been adequately studied.

19. A symptom of the rejection of an international character for art can be found in, for example, P. Zilcken, *Enquête sur l'art en Hollande*, Amsterdam 1911.

The Catalogue

Editorial Note

Certain works cannot be shown at all three exhibitions due to loan restrictions and for reasons of conservation:

Cat. 4, 9, 10, 12, 13, 17, 21, 22, 28, 33, 36, 38, 42, 44, 62, 66, 67, 70, 80, 81, 83, 85–7, 93, 94, 96, 102, 106, 108, 111, 112, 114, 118, 119, 124, 130, 138, 140, 144, 149, 151, 152, 155 and 157 will not be shown in London.

Cat. 4, 9, 10, 12, 13, 36, 44, 59, 61, 65, 67, 77, 93, 96, 101, 102, 114, 125, 140, 144, 149, 151, 152, 155 and 157 will not be shown in Paris.

Cat. 16, 41, 53, 55, 61, 65, 77, 93, 98 and 157 will not be shown in The Hague.

Catalogue entries are listed under the artists represented in the exhibition; the artists appear in alphabetical order, with the exception of Vincent van Gogh and Piet Mondriaan who are considered separately at the end of the catalogue. There is a brief biographical introduction for each artist, followed by the paintings listed in approximately chronological order.

Dimensions are given to the nearest 0·5 cm; height precedes width.

Catalogue references within the text refer to pictures in the present exhibition and appear in brackets, thus: (Cat. 10). Figure references are to the illustrations in the introductory essays and to the portraits of the artists in the catalogue section, thus: (fig. 10).

Bibliographical references at the end of each catalogue entry are given in abbreviated form; books and articles are indicated by author and date, exhibition catalogues by location and date. They are listed in chronological order and, for works published in the same year, alphabetically by author or location.

In the catalogue entries for Cat. 146–65 inclusive (Van Gogh and Mondriaan), only the provenance and select bibliography have been given; exhibitions and variations or preparatory studies have been omitted. Quotations from the letters of Vincent van Gogh are taken from *The Complete Letters of Vincent van Gogh*, London, 1958.

Authors of the Catalogue

Charles Dumas:
Biographies of the Hague School artists; all bibliographical references; catalogue entries 38 and 152.

Herbert Henkels:
Biography of Mondriaan; catalogue entries 157–65.

Ronald de Leeuw:
Catalogue entries 28, 37, 39–107, 139, 141, 154.

John Sillevis:
Catalogue entries 1–27, 108–38, 140, 142–46, 154, 155.

Abbreviations

n.d. no date
n.p. no place
R.K.D. Rijksbureau voor Kunsthistorische Documentatie (Netherlands Institute for Art History)

Bibliography abbreviations are given in full on p. 317.

Adolphe Artz (1837-1890)

David Adolphe Constant Artz was born in The Hague on 18 December 1837. In 1855 he went to the Amsterdamse Academie, and was taught drawing and painting by Louis Roijer (1793–1868). In Amsterdam he became friendly with Jozef Israëls who gave him advice and accompanied him to Zandvoort in 1859; that year he showed his work for the first time at the Tentoonstelling van Levende Meesters (Exhibition of Living Masters). He remained a student at the Rijksacademie until 1864, spending the following year in Zweeloo, Drenthe. From 1866 until 1874 he was based in Paris, where he shared a studio with Jacob Maris and Kaemmerer but he also travelled extensively: to Scotland in May and June 1869, to Germany in November that year, to England in 1870 and, finally, to Italy in January 1872.

In Paris, Artz spent much time with Jacob Maris and his brother Matthijs, who painted the portrait of him now in the Haags Gemeentemuseum (see fig. 132). He continued to paint scenes from the lives of fishing people, set either on the beaches or in interiors, just as he had done in the Netherlands, although his interest in the Japanese prints which had recently become available in Paris prompted him to paint one or two genre scenes depicting Japanese subjects. In 1874 he returned to the Netherlands and settled in The Hague, where he spent the rest of his life.

Artz is regarded as Israëls's most important follower and, in his own day, was highly esteemed both by the public and by his colleagues. He worked hard on behalf of his fellow artists and as late as 1889, a year before his death, was vice-president of the jury for the Exposition Universelle (International Exhibition) in Paris. He died in The Hague on 5 November 1890.

fig. 132 M. MARIS *Portrait of Adolphe Artz*
(Haags Gemeentemuseum, The Hague)

1

1 *In the Orphanage at Katwijk-Binnen*

Oil on canvas, 97 × 130 cm
Signed bottom left: *Artz*
Amsterdam, Rijksmuseum (on loan to Dienst Verspreide
Rijkskollekties [State-owned Art Collections Department],
The Hague)

Artz has been called a follower of Jozef Israëls, but their styles were in fact different. *In the Orphanage* is far less atmospheric and the drawing is much crisper than comparable works by Israëls, which gives the painting a somewhat static quality. Artz himself described his contact with Israëls and its significance. 'At the age of nineteen I went to the daytime classes at the Amsterdam Academy and began painting from live models under the guidance of Mr Egenberger. At the evening classes I was privileged to meet Israëls, which had a great influence on my later life. Although he was much older than us and already quite a famous man, Israëls still came to draw with us in the evening along with the other pupils, enjoying the outstanding teaching of Mr L. Roijer, the then director of the Academy. Israëls's powerful conviction and fresh talent made us all admire him. I felt most fortunate when I was allowed to visit his studio from time to time. From these visits there gradually grew a lasting friendship, despite the differences in

age and the great intellectual ascendancy of the older man. It is to that friendship and to those visits to the great master when I saw him at work, that I owe whatever I have produced of any quality.' (P.A. Haaxman Jr., in *Het Schildersboek*, vol. 3, Amsterdam 1899, p. 152).

Artz's work was greatly appreciated in his own day and he won awards at international exhibitions in Amsterdam, Paris, Vienna and Munich.

PROVENANCE
Haarlem, coll. J.B.A.M. Westerwoudt, –1907; on loan to the museum, 1893; bequeathed to the museum, 1907.

BIBLIOGRAPHY
E.H. XIV (1888), pp. 131–32 (with ill.; engraving by Kellenbach after the painting); Heath 1896–97, p. 84, ill. p. 85; J. de Vries in *E.H.* XXXIII (1907), pp. 264–65 (with ill.); Scheen 1946, fig. 111; De Gruyter 1968–69, vol. 2, pp. 83, 95, 104, fig. 107; cat. Rijksmuseum 1976, p. 88 (with ill.).

EXHIBITIONS
?Paris 1880, no. 90; Haarlem 1981–82, not numbered, fig. 125.

VARIATIONS
1) The Strollers' Art Gallery, London; *B.M.* LXXXII (1943), ill. p. XI.
2) copy: 15 × 20 cm, coll. Reusch, Oslo.

2

2 Lulled to Sleep

Oil on canvas, 56 × 39 cm
Signed and dated centre right: *Artz 1871*
Amsterdam, Rijksmuseum (on loan to Dienst Verspreide
Rijkskollekties [State-owned Art Collections Department],
The Hague)

This work was painted during Artz's stay in Paris from 1868 to
1874, when he was sharing a studio in Rue Marcadet with
Jacob Maris and Kaemmerer. Artz's stay was financed by his
patron, Johannes Kneppelhout, who had been Gerard Bilders's
benefactor as well. Bilders had also asked if he could spend
some time in Paris, but Kneppelhout had refused on the
grounds that Paris was a pernicious place. He had obviously
modified his views by the time that Artz made his request.

Even in Paris, Artz did not abandon his native culture and
environment, taking with him a basket full of Scheveningen

costumes for his models. Haaxman later wrote: 'His friends
stared at his baggage. They knew, of course, that Artz intended
to use them in his paintings, but nonetheless they hazarded the
opinion that he ought to have brought Scheveningen with him
as well.' (P.A. Haaxman Jr. in *Het Schildersboek*, vol. 3,
Amsterdam 1899, p.146).

PROVENANCE
Auct. Amsterdam (C.F. Roos & Co), 21–22 March 1899, no. 4 (Dfl. 1, 300); Amsterdam, art dealer A.
Preyer, 1899–; Haarlem, coll. J.B.A.M. Westerwoudt, 1907; on loan to Stedelijk Museum, Amsterdam;
bequeathed to Rijksmuseum, Amsterdam, 1907 (received by the museum, 1909); on loan to Dienst
Verspreide Rijkskollekties, The Hague, 1953–.

BIBLIOGRAPHY
M.K. 1 (1903), no. 19 (with ill.); *Album Amsterdamsch Stedelijk Museum*, Amsterdam, n.d., fig. 57; cat.
Rijksmuseum 1976, p. 87 (with ill.).

EXHIBITIONS
Haarlem 1981–82, not numbered.

VARIATIONS
Oil on canvas, 54 × 37.5 cm, auct. Amsterdam (Sotheby Mak van Waay), 7–23 June 1977, no. 166 (with
ill.).

Gerard Bilders (1838-1865)

Albertus Gerardus Bilders, known as Gerard, was born in Utrecht on 9 December 1838, the son of the landscape painter Johannes Warnardus Bilders (1811–90) and his first wife Luise Friederike Staudenmayer. From 1841 to 1845 the family lived in a house called De Parre in Oosterbeek, and in 1852 returned there, having spent the intervening seven years in Utrecht.

The young Gerard received his first painting lessons from his father; when he was 17 he met Johannes Kneppelhout, the well-to-do man of letters who made his name through the realistic, but often moralizing sketches of student life that he wrote under the pseudonym Klikspaan (Tell-tale). In November 1856, Kneppelhout took Bilders under his wing and sent him to The Hague, where he lived from December 1856 to April 1858 in the house of a Mr Dirksen, a French teacher at the grammar school there. During this period he received language lessons from Dirksen and painting lessons from Simon van den Berg (1821–91); he also drew from plaster models at the Haagse Academie and made copies after Paulus Potter in the Mauritshuis. In the summer of 1857 and those of the years that followed he painted at Oosterbeek.

In May 1858 Kneppelhout sent Bilders to Geneva, where he spent a month studying under the landscape and animal painter Charles Humbert (1813–81), on whose advice he visited the village of St Ange, south of Geneva. During this time he became friendly with the amateur painter Auguste, Comte de Pourtalès, and in July he set off with him on a long walking tour to Meiringen, via Lucerne, Flüelen and Altdorf. In September he made some more excursions into the mountains from Chamonix, returning to the Netherlands in November.

After a year in Leiden and Leiderdorp, Bilders moved to Amsterdam in November 1859. Around this time his patron Kneppelhout decided that the young artist ought to become financially independent and so stopped giving him economic support. The following March Bilders was nominated an honorary Member of the Academie van Beeldende Kunsten (Academy of Fine Arts); that September he visited the Brussels exhibition with his father. Here, he was deeply impressed by the work of the Barbizon painters Troyon, Courbet, Diaz, Dupré and Fleury.

After the death of his mother in 1861 Bilders visited Switzerland for the second time; he stayed with the Pourtalès family in their country house near Geneva and once more went to St Ange with his friend Auguste, Comte de Pourtalès. During the following year he developed symptoms of tuberculosis, and early in 1864 returned to Brussels where he lived with his sister Caroline, who was married to the painter Johannes de Haas (1832–1908). He moved back to Oosterbeek that summer and from November onwards lived with his father in Amsterdam, where his health declined still further. After a slight recovery at the beginning of 1865 he died on 8 March. His funeral took place on 11 May, with Anton Mauve, August Allebé and Adolphe Artz among the pall-bearers.

Gerard Bilders's letters and diary were published in Leiden in 1868 and 1876 with a foreword by Johannes Kneppelhout.

fig. 133 *Portrait of Gerard Bilders* (photograph)
(Gemeentearchief, The Hague)

4

3 Landscape with Cattle in the Betuwe at the Approach of a Storm

Oil on canvas, 89 × 149 cm
Signed bottom left: *Gerard Bilders*
The Hague, P. A. Scheen Gallery
repr. in colour on p. 28

The significance of Bilders as a precursor of the Hague School artists is admirably demonstrated in this landscape, which has no vestiges of any cloying or mannered Romanticism, but manifests the fresh touch of an artist who has studied nature closely. In this respect it is a remarkable contrast to the work of his father Johannes Bilders, who, despite his familiarity with the woods and river scenery around Oosterbeek, maintained an idealized approach to nature, which gave his work an unmistakable studio atmosphere. The struggle for artistic freedom expressed by Gerard Bilders in his letters and diary

was thus perhaps also a reaction against the ideas of his father, although he never explicitly stated this.

PROVENANCE
Auct. Ahlden/Aller (F. Seidel), 26 April–3 May 1980, no. 1044.

4 Swiss Landscape

Oil on canvas, 67.5 × 98 cm
Signed bottom right: *Gerard Bilders f.*
The Hague, Haags Gemeentemuseum

The influence of Gerard Bilders's Swiss teacher Charles Humbert (see fig. 34) can be seen more clearly in this work, especially in the treatment of the group of cows and goats, than in any of Bilders's other paintings.

Gerard had been able to spend some time in 1858 studying near Lake Geneva and in the mountains of Savoy, thanks to the patronage of the connoisseur Johannes Kneppelhout. It is clear from Humbert's letters that the artist was pleased with his pupil, but Kneppelhout's correspondence shows that he was far less satisfied with his protegé, with the result that young Bilders lacked confidence in his own abilities.

In a letter dated 18 November 1859 he wrote to Kneppelhout, probably about this painting, 'I had an attack of mountain fantasies. You may perhaps remember the large painting I began in Leiden with such expectations, which turned out to be nothing but a dirty, yellowish placard. I've now gone over the whole thing with a big brush, painted in high mountains and put in more animals. As a composition it is certainly improved, I fancy, but it does look rather odd. There is undoubtedly something attractive about making big plans on big canvases with big brushes in this way, but one seldom sees one's dreams realized – in this case at least, I fear. Such complex

5

giant mountain ranges are undoubtedly rather beyond my powers. But they make more agreeable compositions than our flat Dutch landscape, in which the foreground, middle distance and far distance are so difficult to depict. It [the Dutch landscape] also lacks the linear contrasts and blocks of light and shade, which are so very beautiful and which are such a great help in painting mountainous regions'.

Bilders's emphasis on the exceptional size of the canvas makes it almost certain that he was referring to this painting.

PROVENANCE
The Hague, coll. H. Schwaerzer; The Hague, priv. coll., –1964; purchased by the museum, 1964.

BIBLIOGRAPHY
Jeltes 1947, pp. 32–33, 72–73, 188 (cat. no. 59), fig. 37 on p. 62; De Gruyter 1968–69, vol. 2, pp. 10, 14, 100, fig. 3; Hefting 1981, p. 78 (with fig. 31).

5 *Meadowland with Cows at Opheusden*

Oil on panel, 30 × 45 cm
Signed bottom left: *Gerard Bilders*
Arnhem, Gemeentemuseum

In August 1860 Bilders went to stay at Opheusden thanks to a small financial contribution from his father. Unfortunately, he was unlucky with the weather. He wrote to Kneppelhout on 25 August 1860, 'It is lush and beautiful here, but freezing cold and damp, especially indoors. . . . I'm lodging with the ferryman near the Rhine. The view of the Greb is beautiful. I shall begin by having a look around and putting my painting equipment in order, and then when it is dry I can make a start'. But the weather did not improve, so Bilders decided, after stopping off briefly in Amsterdam, to go and stay with his grandfather in Utrecht.

His historic trip with his father to Brussels, during which he saw the paintings of the Barbizon School for the first time, took place shortly after this.

PROVENANCE
Oosterbeek, coll. Mrs M. Bilders-van Bosse, 1891; The Hague, art dealer P.A. Scheen, 1950; The Hague, coll. H.J. Smulders, –1958; presented to the museum, 1958.

BIBLIOGRAPHY
Colmjon/Scheen 1950, pp. 36, 77, fig. 3; cat. Gemeentemuseum 1965, p. 21, ill. on p. 22; De Gruyter 1968–69, vol. 2, pp. 9, 10, 14, 100, fig. 6; Hefting 1981, pp. 18, 81 (with fig. 34); Scheen 1981, fig. 429.

EXHIBITIONS
Amsterdam 1891(2), no. 103; Tilburg 1950, no. 1; Leiden 1953–54, no. 1; Delft 1955–56, no. 9; The Hague 1965(1), no. 3 (with ill.).

6 The Haystack (Farm near Wolfheze)

Oil on panel, 29.5 × 42 cm
Signed bottom right: *A.G. Bilders*
The Hague, Haags Gemeentemuseum

This summer scene with its unforced composition illustrates Bilders's perception of everyday experiences as source material that needed no detailed description. He wrote in one of the entries in his diary, 'How could it have come about that in my paintings I always try to represent something pleasant and cheerful, the sunny side of life, whereas I prefer more serious and sombre paintings which touch my soul more deeply? I believe it is because I am inhibited by the idea that I must sell my paintings and that, in spite of myself, my natural inspiration has deserted me. But I shall just try to resolve this and paint as if no one will see my paintings, much less buy them. I propose to do this in a quiet studio arranged for this purpose, where there will be few visitors. This summer I shall devote more time to studying atmospheric variations in nature and the impression made upon me by a particular landscape.' (24 March 1860). This resolution was inspired by an approach to landscape painting also characteristic of the Barbizon School.

PROVENANCE
Coll. P. Stiefelhagen, –1939; purchased by the museum, 1939.

BIBLIOGRAPHY
G. Kn[uttel Wzn.] in *M.D.K.W.* VI (1940), pp. 90–91 (with ill.); Wesselink 1946, p. 32; Jeltes 1947, pp. 75, 116 (cat. no. 48), fig. 38 on p. 63; Pedroza 1948, p. 11 (with ill.); cat. Gemeentemuseum 1962, no. 6; Bilders 1974, fig. 1; Hefting 1981, ill. on frontispiece.

EXHIBITIONS
Arnhem 1954, no. 5; Dordrecht 1955, no. 12; The Hague 1965(1), no. 4 (with ill.); The Hague 1972(1), not numbered.

7 Pond in the Woods at Sunset

Oil on panel, 22 × 35 cm
Signed bottom left: *Gerard Bilders*
Amsterdam, Rijksmuseum
repr. in colour on p. 28

In 1862 Bilders painted many sunsets and evening landscapes. On 26 May he referred in his diary to 'landscapes that stand out *en silhouette* against cadmium skies' and in October he wrote twice to Kneppelhout about a particular sunset, 'I have seen a very beautiful sunset at Lochem and am now doing my best to record that area seen in different lights, all of them very striking, which I shall then use in the finished compositions I want to make from my studies. It often happens that I have sat looking at an empty canvas all morning, then drawn all kinds of lines on it in charcoal and white chalk without achieving anything. Meanwhile I have taken the risk of ordering a large canvas measuring 1½ ells, on which I hope to present this

evening scene to the public. Until now I have always had a vague fear that my ambitions to do this would be frustrated; however, by thinking it over for a long time, by working oneself up every now and then and by leaving youthful imagination to mature with time, one can prevent a good deal of such fine inspiration from foundering. If only I could now capture the light just as I observed it at Lochem!' (1 October 1862).

In a second letter of 10 October Bilders told Kneppelhout that he was working on his 'Evening scene', which, as he remarked with a touch of self-mockery, 'will be a masterpiece, of course'. Since the painting shown here is a panel, we cannot be absolutely certain that the passages quoted above refer to it. There is another version of the same subject, also on panel, with a figure of a girl but without the ducks (see sale London, 1979, as *A Young Girl by a Pond in an Orchard*).

PROVENANCE
Haarlem, coll. J.B.A.M. Westerwoudt, –1907; bequeathed to the museum, 1907 (received by the museum, 1929); on loan to Stedelijk Museum, Amsterdam, 1950.

BIBLIOGRAPHY
Jeltes 1944, p. 6, fig. 6; Jeltes 1947, pp. 76, 92, 116 (cat. no. 44) fig. 40 on p. 67; cat. Rijksmuseum 1976, p. 116 (with ill.); Hefting 1981, p. 85 (with fig. 38).

VARIATIONS
Panel, 21 × 35 cm. auct. London (Sotheby's), 14 Feb. 1979, no. 8 (with ill.).

8 The Herdswoman

Oil on canvas, 61.5 × 53 cm
Signed bottom left: *Gerard Bilders*
Amsterdam, Rijksmuseum

In this painting, Bilders transformed the influence of the few works of the Barbizon School he saw at the Exposition Universelle (International Exhibition) in Brussels into a totally individual vision, which was later to make a great impression on the painters of the Hague School. The masterly construction of the composition is strengthened by the contrasting areas of light and shade.

Bilders wrote to Kneppelhout about this work in a letter dated 13 March 1864, 'A painting showing an orchard with goats and an Oosterbeek girl has given me an enormous amount of trouble of late. I believe that the viewpoint that I chose for the landscape makes a fine composition; I only dare to say this because I followed my sketch minutely and the scene could have been a good painting, if only I could have made it sufficiently pleasing in colour and careful in execution. But there are a lot of things that trip me up.' Bilders, prompted by Kneppelhout – who even observed shortly before Gerard's death that he ought to have become a writer rather than a painter – never came to believe in his own artistic powers.

8

PROVENANCE
Haarlem, coll. J.B.A.M. Westerwoudt, –1907; on loan to the museum, 1902; bequeathed to the museum, 1907.

BIBLIOGRAPHY
Jeltes 1935, p. 93, fig. 11; *De Telegraaf* (25 Dec. 1938; with ill.); Wesselink 1946, p. 30; Jeltes 1947, pp. 43–48, 117 (cat. no. 49), fig. 5 on p. 17; De Gruyter 1968–69, vol. 2, pp. 5, 10, 11, 15, 100, ill. on p. 8; cat. Rijksmuseum 1976, p. 117 (with ill.); Hefting 1981, p. 86, fig. 39 on p. 87.

EXHIBITIONS
Amsterdam 1938–39(2), no. 17 (with ill.); Arnhem 1954, no. 3 (with ill.); Passau 1956, no. 1.

Bernard Blommers (1845-1914)

Bernardus Johannes Blommers was born in The Hague on 31 January 1845, the son of Pieter Blommers and Anna Maria van Balen. His father had a printing business and, since it was originally intended that Bernard would succeed him there, he trained him as a lithographer. However, his interest in painting led him to take lessons from Christoffel Bisschop (1828–1904) and at the Haags Academie. There he met Willem Maris with whom he made a journey along the Rhine in 1865. In the same year his *Scheveningen Interior* was given a place of honour beside a large painting by Jozef Israëls at the Tentoonstelling van Levende Meesters (Exhibition of Living Masters) in Amsterdam. The two painters, who had met each other on the beach at Scheveningen around this time, formed a friendship which lasted all their lives and greatly influenced Blommers's artistic development. Like Israëls, he painted interiors, dune scenes and seascapes in which figures play a leading role, illustrating the life of peasants and fishing people.

After finishing his studies at the Academy in 1868, Blommers moved into a studio on Juffrouw Idastraat with Willem Maris. Willem's older brother Matthijs often came to work in this studio, until his departure for Paris in 1869 and Anton Mauve, whom Blommers had already met in Ooster-beek, was also a frequent guest there.

In 1870 Blommers visited Paris, where he stayed with Jacob Maris. He contemplated settling in France for good, but the outbreak of the Franco-Prussian War forced him to return to the Netherlands. The following year he married Anna van der Toorn from Scheveningen; she appears in many of his paintings. They moved into a house on Jacob Catshofje and here Blommers took on his first pupil, Tony Offermans (1854–1911).

Blommers's work, for which he had already been awarded a gold medal at the Hague exhibition of 1868, enjoyed enormous popularity during his lifetime. By 1880 this success had given him the financial means to build a house in The Hague, where he was to live for the rest of his life (he named his house after his eldest daughter Johanna).

Until the turn of the century, he worked mainly in Scheveningen with occasional visits to Zandvoort, accompanied by Philip Sadée (1837–1904), but as Scheveningen began to develop into a seaside resort, the little fishing village of Katwijk, to which Adolphe Artz had first drawn his attention, became his favourite place of work. At first, Blommers stayed in the house of the collector Hidde Nijland, but later he had a house with two studios built there; it was called the Villa Thérèse. He also spent every autumn at Heeze in North Brabant, from which he made excursions to the nearby town of Bladel with Albert Neuhuys.

Blommers received many honours and medals, in both his own and other countries, and was one of the most highly regarded Dutch painters of his day. From 1868 he was an active committee member of Pulchri Studio and after the death of Israëls in 1911 he was elected president of the Hollandsche Teeken-Maatschappij (Dutch Drawing Society). Many of his paintings and watercolours found their way into foreign collections in both Europe and the United States of America, which he visited with his wife and daughter in 1904 (he was even received by President Theodore Roosevelt). Blommers died in The Hague on 15 December 1914 and was buried at Oud Eyck-en-Duinen.

fig. 134 EAKINS *Portrait of Bernard Blommers* 1904
(The Toledo Museum of Art, Toledo)

9

9 *Women on the Beach*

Oil on canvas, 65 × 120 cm
Signed bottom right: *Blommers*
The Hague, Dienst Verspreide Rijkskollekties
(State-owned Art Collections Department)

The life of the Scheveningen fishing community was one of Blommers's favourite themes and he painted numerous pictures of the fish auctions, which, until the harbour was built, took place on the beach there.

Fish auctions were a popular subject for artists and similar scenes are found in the work of Philip Sadée and the Belgian artists Courtens and Bource. The big, flat straw hats that the fishwives still wore at that time, but which fell into disuse by the end of the century, can be seen in this picture.

PROVENANCE
The Hague, coll. F.H.M. Post –1891; auct. Amsterdam (C.F. Roos & Co), 14 April 1891, no 7; ? coll. Mr and Mrs S.P.D. May–Fuld, –1941; auct. Amsterdam (F. Muller & Co), 14–17 Oct. 1941, no. 353 (Dfl. 4, 100).

BIBLIOGRAPHY
Cannegieter 1972–73, pp. 445–46, ill. on p. 451.

EXHIBITIONS
Amsterdam 1883, no. 25 (gold medal).

VARIATIONS
Oil on panel, 27.5 × 41.5 cm, auct. Amsterdam (F. Muller & Co), 12–15 Dec. 1922, no. 221 (with ill.).

10 *Mother with Two Children*

Watercolour and gouache, 48.5 × 35.5 cm
Signed bottom left: *Blommers*
Private collection

In his own lifetime, Blommers was regarded as one of the great figures of the Hague School; he was particularly popular in England and Scotland and later among American and Canadian collectors. It is said that a Boston minister, the Reverend Philip Brooks, who had been invited to preach at Westminster Abbey in London, made a special detour to The Hague in order to meet Blommers, because he had a painting by that artist in his collection. This popularity abroad can probably be explained by the great demand for figure paintings – in which Blommers specialized – in these countries, even though landscapes were still preferred in the Netherlands. Indeed the Hague School has too often been characterized as a landscape school on the basis of Dutch nineteenth-century taste, despite the fact that artists like Israëls, Blommers, Neuhuys and Artz excelled in figure painting, interiors and scenes from the lives of peasants and fishing people.

This watercolour was once in the collection of the Metropolitan Museum in New York.

PROVENANCE
New York, The Metropolitan Museum of Art, –1979; auct. New York (Sotheby Parke Bernet), 4 May 1979, no. 120 (as *Learning to Share*); The Hague, art gallery P.A. Scheen, 1980.

BIBLIOGRAPHY
Scheen 1981, fig. 557.

EXHIBITIONS
The Hague 1980(2), no. 5 (with ill.); Haarlem 1981–82, fig. 23.

Johannes Bosboom (1817-1891)

Johannes Bosboom and his twin brother Nicolas were born in The Hague on 18 February 1817. As a child, Johannes Bosboom loved drawing and his interest was encouraged when Bart van Hove (1790–1880), the painter of townscapes, came to live next door. In the autumn of 1831, at the age of 14, Johannes became a pupil of Van Hove, assisting him in his studio with the painting of stage sets and similar work. Only two years later Bosboom exhibited two paintings at the Tentoonstelling van Levende Meesters (Exhibition of Living Masters) in The Hague.

Sam Verveer (1813–76), with whom he made a study trip in 1835 via Utrecht and Nijmegen to Düsseldorf, Cologne and Coblenz, was among his fellow pupils in Van Hove's studio. One of Bosboom's paintings inspired by this journey, *View of the Bridge over the Moselle at Coblenz*, was bought at the exhibition in The Hague that year by the painter Andreas Schelfhout (1787–1870), to Bosboom's great satisfaction.

Bosboom left Van Hove's studio around 1836 and moved into one of his own in his parents' house in Dunne Bierkade. That year he took part in a competition organized by the Felix Meritis Society and won the gold medal of honour. This was the first in a long series of distinctions acquired both at home and abroad.

In 1837 Bosboom visited Belgium for the first time and two years later he went to Paris and Rouen with Cornelis Kruseman (1797–1857). In his short autobiography, *Notes on My Career as a Painter*, Bosboom recalled that at this time he came under the influence of the work of Wijnand Nuyen (1813–39) and Antonie Waldorp (1803–66). This influence is seen most clearly in *The Quai de Paris and Cathedral at Rouen*, 1839. At this period he also painted some church interiors, which were such a success that he decided to specialize in this genre. One of the best examples of this early period is the *Communion Service in St Gertrude's Church, Utrecht* of 1852 (Cat. 11). Meanwhile, Bosboom had married Anna Louisa Geertruida Toussaint, then a celebrated writer of historical novels. Four years later, when the Société Belge des Aquarellistes was founded in Brussels, Bosboom was elected as an honorary member.

In 1862 his twin brother Nicolas died, leaving a wife and seven young children; Bosboom was greatly affected by the loss and his health suffered as a result. However, his friend, Jonkheer Ridder van Rappard, persuaded him to take a rest at his country house near Woudenberg and he soon recovered. Here, he made his first sketches of stalls, farmers, cows and chickens. After a short stay at Eyckenrode, the country house of the Hacke van Mijnden family in Nieuw Loosdrecht, he returned to The Hague in good health. The next summer he again spent several weeks with the Rappards and made a visit to Cleves. Shortly afterwards his wife fell seriously ill. She recovered against all expectations, but Bosboom suffered a total collapse and came under the care of a neurologist. After a slow recovery he undertook a journey to Huy, Chaudefontaine, Coblenz and Trier in the summer of 1865.

In 1867–71 Bosboom completed four superb church interiors, including an *Interior of Trier Cathedral* (1867) that is known as 'the small Trier' (Cat. 14). In addition to the church interiors and other subjects already mentioned, he began to choose cloisters and synagogues as subject matter. In August 1873 he rented a room in Scheveningen, where he painted a series of views of the village, beach and sea. Three years later he made visits to Groningen and Zuidlaren, where he made studies of both church interiors and cow sheds, and in 1878 stayed for three weeks in Domburg and on the island of Walcheren. A visit to Hoorn in 1880, during which he concentrated mainly on watercolours, was especially productive.

In 1886 his wife died and in 1890 he himself was the victim of a stroke. After a long period of illness during which he was bed-ridden, he died in The Hague on 14 September 1891.

fig. 135 EHNLE *Portrait of Johannes Bosboom* (lithograph)
(Gemeentearchief, The Hague)

11

11 *Communion Service in St Gertrude's Church,
Utrecht*

Oil on canvas, 92.5 × 115 cm
Signed and dated bottom centre: *J. Bosboom MDCCCLII*
Amsterdam, Amsterdams Historisch Museum
(Bequest of C.J. Fodor)

Johannes Bosboom was well able to attract the attention of
connoisseurs and critics of his own time. In *De levens en werken
der Hollandsche en Vlaamsche kunstchilders, beeldhouwers, graveurs en bouwmeesters* (vol. 1, Amsterdam 1842) Immerzeel
wrote, 'Well-deserved laurels adorn the head of this youthful
master and we are pleased to be able to add to this; his
capabilities as an artist are coupled with outstanding qualities as
a person'.

Bosboom himself described how he decided to devote
himself to the painting of church interiors at the beginning of
his career. 'In the same year [1836] I had made my debut at the
Exhibition in Rotterdam with "St John's at 's-Hertogenbosch,
from the inside", which immediately found a buyer in an art
collector there, Mr de Bije. The approval thus gained and a
further award at Felix [Meritis in Amsterdam, 1838], this time
for a "Church with sunlight falling into it", confirmed my
own inclinations to render the impressions that churches made
on me, and this gradually led me to choose this genre as my
"main avenue"'.

This work is an example of Bosboom's early church
interiors, rich in detail and enlivened by figures in seventeenth-
century costume. The painting was exhibited in Ghent in 1853
and contributed to Bosboom's reputation in Belgium. In 1856
he was decorated with the Order of Leopold for his *St James's
Church, The Hague*.

An almost identical version of this painting, although
without the rounded top corners, appeared in 1972 at a sale in
Amsterdam, while in the Fodor Collection there is a watercolour that may be a highly finished preliminary study for it.

PROVENANCE
Amsterdam, coll. C.J. Fodor, 1852/53–60; bequeathed to the City of Amsterdam, 1860; Amsterdam,
Museum Fodor 1863–1975; moved to Amsterdams Historisch Museum, Amsterdam, 1975.

BIBLIOGRAPHY
K.K. xv (1854), p. 11; cat. Museum Fodor 1863, p. 6, no. 15; Vosmaer 1882–85, vol. 1 (J. Bosboom),
p. 3; P.A.M. Boele van Hensbroek in M. Rooses (ed), *Het Schildersboek*, vol. 1, Amsterdam 1898, ill. on
p. 2; *B.K.* IV (1916–17), no. 30 (with ill.); Marius/Martin 1917, pp. 40, 41, 134, fig. 11; Glavimans 1946,
pp. 10, 12; Veth 1969, p. 242, ill. on p. 243; Hagenbeek-Frey 1974–75, p. 919, fig. 16.

EXHIBITIONS
Ghent 1853; The Hague 1853, no. 66; Arnhem 1974, no. 32 (with ill.); Amsterdam 1979(1), no. 29;
Tokyo 1979, no. 29 (with ill.).

VARIATIONS
1) oil on canvas on panel, 90 × 112 cm, auct. Amsterdam (Mak van Waay), 30 May–15 June 1972, no. 55
(with ill.). 2) watercolour, 46 × 63.5 cm, Amsterdams Historisch Museum, Amsterdam (Bequest of C.J.
Fodor). 3) watercolour, 28.6 × 39.5 cm, Amsterdams Historisch Museum, Amsterdam (Bequest of C.J.
Fodor); Hagenbeek-Frey 1974–75, p. 13, fig. 17. 4) watercolour, 14 × 20 cm, auct. Amsterdam (F.
Muller & Co), 22–25 and 28–29 March 1955, No. 64. 5) watercolour, 14 × 20 cm, auct. Amsterdam (F.
Muller & Co), 22–25 and 28–29 March 1955, no. 59.

12

12 *Pumping Installation; a Mine in the Borinage*

Oil on panel, 34.5 × 51 cm
Signed bottom right: *J. Bosboom*
Rotterdam, Museum Boymans-van Beuningen

According to a letter from Bosboom to Kruseman dated 30
June 1867, this study was made after Bosboom's visit to Trier
in 1865. In the letter he referred to 'a lively study that I
sketched near Chaudefontaine two years ago on the way to
Trier [see Cat. 15], a lime kiln in the quarries, for which I also
planned a pendant, to be painted from a study made in the past
of the Borinage at Namur'. Bosboom is referring here to a
crayon drawing entitled *Le Borinage, Hainaut* and dated 1848
(P.A. Scheen Gallery, The Hague, 1959). There is a
watercolour of the same subject in the Teyler Museum in
Haarlem.

This remarkable choice of a subject that was undoubtedly
prosaic to nineteenth-century eyes shows that Bosboom could
still break away from his main subject matter – church interiors
– and that he was able, in a very free and original way, to evoke
an atmosphere which must have also appealed to other artists
of the Hague School.

PROVENANCE
The Hague, art dealer J.C. Schüller, 1904; The Hague, coll. P. Bosboom, 1916; purchased by the
museum, 1937.

BIBLIOGRAPHY
M.K. II (1904), no. 6 (with ill.); Jeltes 1910, p. 35; Marius/Martin 1917, p. 130; *N.R.C.* (9 Aug. 1931);
cat. Museum Boymans-van Beuningen 1963, p. 23; De Gruyter 1968–69, vol. I, pp. 21, 111, fig. 13; cat.
Museum Boymans-van Beuningen 1972, p. 205, ill. on p. 183; Pollock 1980–81, fig. 4 on p. 32.

EXHIBITIONS
Delft 1958–59, no. 11 (with ill.); Amsterdam 1980–81, no. 4 (with ill.).

VARIATIONS
1) drawing, 51.5 × 67 cm, art dealer P.A. Scheen, The Hague, 1959. 2) drawing, 16.4 × 24.8 cm,
Rijksmuseum Kröller-Müller, Otterlo.

13

13   *Interior of a Church at Delft*

Watercolour, 27 × 19 cm
Signed bottom centre: *J. Bosboom*; inscribed on the verso: *14133*
Montreal, Musée des Beaux-Arts de Montréal
(Bequest of William J. & Agnes Learmont)

Bosboom succeeded in establishing a reputation, not only for his early, highly detailed and carefully drawn oil paintings of church interiors, but also for his later, more freely painted, yet firmly composed, watercolours of Dutch churches. These, like the present one, are notable primarily for their subtle suggestion of space. It was these watercolours that won him international renown.

PROVENANCE
Montreal, coll. William John & Agnes Learmont, –1909; bequeathed to the museum, 1909.

EXHIBITIONS
Montreal 1897; Montreal 1899; Montreal 1962 (no cat.); Montreal 1968.

14   *Interior of Trier Cathedral*

Oil on panel, 85 × 66 cm
Signed bottom left: *J. Bosboom*
Toledo (Ohio), The Toledo Museum of Art
(Gift of Edward Drummond Libbey)
repr. in colour on p. 25

Bosboom visited Trier in 1865. He and his wife, Geertruida Bosboom-Toussaint, a celebrated writer of historical novels, visited Germany and Belgium to look for material, he for his paintings and she for her books. Bosboom did two more paintings of the interior of this cathedral; a large one in 1871 (Rijksmuseum Twenthe, Enschede) and a smaller one dated *c*. 1875 (Rijksmuseum, Amsterdam). They reflect his admiration for Emanuel de Witte, which he mentioned in his letters.

Bosboom wrote of this visit to his friend Kruseman: 'After that I went with my wife to Huy. She was interested in the fortress and wanted to visit it. Having travelled that far, we also intended to go on to Trier, where she had once been with Charles the Bold [the subject of one of her novels: *Een kroon voor Karel de Stoute*, Amsterdam 1842]. Between the two places we chose to stay at Chaudfontaine, a place just right for us: rural and peaceful, with a very comfortable hotel and pleasant company. Trier interesting but not so agreeable.' This letter was dated Whit Monday 1866, with a backward glance at the journey in May 1865 (see H.F.W. Jeltes, *Uit het leven van een kunstenaarspaar*, Amsterdam 1910, p. 26).

The spatial effect in this painting is still determined by careful perspective drawing rather than the play of light.

PROVENANCE
Sold after Bosboom's death (14 Sept. 1891); The Hague, art dealer Boussod, Valadon & Co, 1891; De Bilt, coll. Mrs E.L.E. Roëll-van Rappard; Amsterdam, coll. W.C. Robinson, –1906; auct. Amsterdam (F. Muller & Co), 13 Nov, 1906, no. 21 (Dfl. 7,200); The Hague, art dealer A. Preyer, 1906; New York, art dealer Henry Reinhardt; Toledo (Ohio), coll. Edward Drummond Libbey, 1908–25; presented to the museum, 1925.

BIBLIOGRAPHY
N.S. (1867), p. 185; *K.K.* N.S. IX (1868), p. 47; *K.K.* N.S. XII (1871), p. 15; Jeltes 1910, p. 34; Marius/Martin 1917, pp. 60, 143; *Museum News. The Toledo Museum of Art* (March 1926); *Ohio's Woman Magazine* (Oct. 1926; with ill.); cat. Toledo Museum 1939, p. 122, ill. on p. 123; De Gruyter 1968–69, vol. I, pp. 15, 23, 24, 29, 112, fig. 18; cat. Toledo Museum 1976, pp. 26–27, pl. 149.

EXHIBITIONS
Rotterdam 1867, no. 51; The Hague 1891(2), no. 106; Amsterdam 1900(2), no. 146; The Hague 1965(1), no. 6 (with ill.).

VARIATIONS
1) oil on canvas, 33.5 × 24.5 cm, auct. Amsterdam (F. Muller & Co), 29 Oct. 1918, no. 13 (with ill.). 2) watercolour, 39 × 29 cm, priv. coll., Netherlands, 1980. 3) oil on panel, coll. Jonkheer W.F. Roëll, Amsterdam, 1917.

15   *Limekiln in the Quarry at Chaudfontaine*

Watercolour, 32 × 52 cm
Signed and inscribed bottom left: *J. Bosboom Ch. Fontaine*
Private collection
repr. in colour on p. 26

Bosboom painted this watercolour of Chaudfontaine during the journey that took him to Trier, where he painted the cathedral interior. It is striking for its restrained use of colour, which evokes associations with the later watercolours of

15

Mauve, and in particular the latter's views of the dunes and sandpits. Bosboom presented this work at the third exhibition of watercolours by the members of the Hollandsche Teeken-Maatschappij (Dutch Drawing Society) in The Hague in 1878.

PROVENANCE
Amsterdam, coll. J.M. Rodenberg, –1902; auct. Amsterdam (F. Muller & Co), 11 March 1902, no. 21 (Dfl. 390); Amsterdam, art dealer F. Buffa & Zn., 1902–; Aerdenhout/Amsterdam, coll. C.G. Vattier Kraane, –1955; auct. Amsterdam (F. Muller & Co), 22–25 and 28–29 March 1955, no. 65 (Dfl. 825); The Hague, art dealer P.A. Scheen, 1955.

BIBLIOGRAPHY
Jeltes 1910, p. 35; Marius/Martin 1917, pp. 61, 141; H.F.W. Jeltes in *E.G.M.* XXXII (1922), vol. LXIII, p. 6; De Gruyter 1968–69, vol. I, pp. 17, 28, 111, fig. 14.

EXHIBITIONS
The Hague 1878(2), no. 19; The Hague 1891(2), no. 16; Amsterdam 1900(2), no. 150; Rotterdam 1955, no. 7; The Hague 1955(2), no. 5; Delft 1958–59, no. 62 (with ill.); The Hague 1965(1), no. 13 (with ill.).

16

16 *The Beach at Scheveningen*

Watercolour, 35 × 55 cm
Signed bottom right: *J. Bosboom*
Amsterdam, Rijksprentenkabinet, Rijksmuseum

In 1873 Bosboom stayed with the Van Tienhoven family in the Villa Erica on Scheveningseweg. From there he used to walk to the fishing village and the beach to make sketches. Later that year he stayed at the Zeerust, a hotel in Scheveningen. He wrote to Kruseman: 'Once at Scheveningen, I drew all that the village and the beach had to offer me; so much that I worked almost too hard and thought it just as well that our time was up and other people's baggage stood waiting to take the place of ours. By the time we reached home the weather had changed, so that I was also glad to be back for that reason. But later, when the autumn sun began to shine again, I once more felt like going out and working, and in the last two weeks of September I continually retraced my steps to one or other spot that had attracted me.' (From a letter dated by Jeltes to Sept./Oct. 1873).

The subject echoes Mesdag's beach scenes, but Bosboom also shows that he has ideas of his own and the composition is less frontal than many in Mesdag's work. In this watercolour Bosboom reveals his proficiency in the effortless rendering of a somewhat spatial composition.

PROVENANCE
Sold after Bosboom's death (14 Sept. 1891); The Hague, coll. Dr T.H. Blom Coster, –1904; auct. The Hague (Boussod, Valadon & Co), 31 May 1904, no. 41 (Dfl. 3,300); London, coll. Mr & Mrs J.C.J. Drucker-Fraser, 1904–44; on loan to the museum, 1919; bequeathed to the museum, 1944.

BIBLIOGRAPHY
Zilcken 1908, ill. on p. 267; Marius/Martin 1917, pp. 77, 146; cat. Museum Mesdag 1975, p. 62, under cat. no. 49; cat. Rijksmuseum 1976, pp. 807–08 (with ill.).

EXHIBITIONS
The Hague 1891(1), no. 32; Amsterdam 1900(2), no. 21; Delft 1958–59, no. 83; Amsterdam 1963, no. T 50, fig. 53; Paris 1963, no. 15, fig. x.

17

17 *Barn*

Watercolour, 39 × 55 cm
Signed bottom left: *J. Bosboom*
Laren (N.H.), Singer Museum

The subject of this watercolour, which must have been completed after 1863, is probably the barn behind a farmhouse in Nieuw-Loosdrecht near Hilversum. This theme became a great favourite with other painters of the Hague School, in particular Jozef Israëls and Anton Mauve. But instead of emphasizing the anecdotal elements as Israëls often does, Bosboom places his group of figures in surroundings that are entirely appropriate so that the same picturesque objects which Israëls generally arranged with such care, here acquire a much greater naturalism.

PROVENANCE
Scheveningen, coll. Mrs G. Mesdag-van Calcar, 1917; Amsterdam, art dealer E.J. van Wisselingh & Co, 1937; coll. J. van Herwijnen; Amsterdam, art dealer Huinck & Scherjon, –1955; auct. Amsterdam (F. Muller & Co), 8–11 and 14–15 Nov. 1955, no. 363 (Dfl. 2,900); purchased by the museum, 1955.

BIBLIOGRAPHY
Marius/Martin 1917, p. 140, fig. 23; Hennus 1940, ill. on p. 29; cat. Singer Museum 1962, no. 36 (with ill.).

EXHIBITIONS
The Hague 1917(2), no. 118 (with ill.); Amsterdam 1937(1), no. 10.

18 *Old Pine at Eyckenrode*

Watercolour, 32.5 × 48 cm
Monogrammed bottom left: *J.B.*; inscribed
bottom right: *Huize Eikenro*
The Hague, Haags Gemeentemuseum

This watercolour was painted during a short stay at Eykenrode, the country home at Nieuw-Loosdrecht, near Hilversum, of the Hacke van Mijden family. It occupies a special place in Bosboom's oeuvre because of its subject matter, and because of Bosboom's remarkable observation and forceful composition, which make a strong impression on the spectator.

It is surprising that Bosboom did not take landscapes as his subject more often. No other versions of this tree study are known.

PROVENANCE
Coll. Dr J.D.C. Titsingh, –1901; auct. The Hague (Boussod, Valadon & Co), 12–13 March 1901, no. 39 (Dfl. 550); The Hague, coll. W.P. van Stockum Jr., 1901–28; auct. The Hague (Van Stockum's Antiquariaat), 26–27 June 1928; purchased by the museum, 1928.

BIBLIOGRAPHY
Marius/Martin 1917, p. 139; H. E. van Gelder in *M.D.K.W.* II (1926–31), p. 161; cat. Gemeentemuseum 1935, no. 7–28; Hennus 1940, ill. on p. 39; De Gruyter 1968–69, vol. I, pp. 17, 29, 111, fig. 15; *Tekeningen en prenten uit eigen bezit. 19e Eeuw, Haags Gemeentemuseum* n.p. n.d., no. 12 (with ill.).

EXHIBITIONS
The Hague 1917(2), no. 166; Antwerp 1937, no. 7; Maastricht 1945–46, no. 7; The Hague 1947, no. 77; Delft 1952, no. 223; Delft 1958–59, no. 66; Liège 1961–62, no. 23 (with ill.); Paris 1963, no. 17; The Hague 1963, no. 1 (with ill.); The Hague 1965(1), no. 14 (with ill.); The Hague 1967(1), no. 5; Bonn 1972, no. 5; Antwerp 1979, no. 6 (with ill.); Amsterdam 1980–81, no. 6 (with ill.).

18

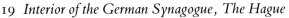

19 Interior of the German Synagogue, The Hague

Oil on panel, 42 × 34 cm
Signed bottom right: *J. Bosboom*
Dordrecht, Dordrechts Museum
repr. in colour on p. 27

Bosboom made a pendant to this painting of the German synagogue on Wagenstraat; it depicts the Portuguese synagogue on Princessegracht, also in The Hague. His work on this theme dates from *c.* 1850 and in 1862 he sent an example to the International Exhibition in London. Here, more than in his earlier work, he has aimed for a chiaroscuro effect in the manner of Rembrandt.

PROVENANCE
Amsterdam, coll. Messchert van Vollenhoven, –1892; auct. Amsterdam (C.F. Roos & Co), 5 April 1892, no. 10 (Dfl. 1,300); Dordrecht, coll. M.C. Lebret, 1892–94; presented to the museum, 1894.

BIBLIOGRAPHY
Jeltes 1917, ill. opp. p. 1; Marius/Martin 1917, pp. 66, 148; cat. Dordrechts Museum 1928, p. 14, no. 35, pl. IX; Knoef 1948, ill. opp. p. 104; cat. Museum Mesdag 1975, p. 47, under cat. no. 40.

EXHIBITIONS
The Hague 1917(2), no. 66; Paris 1921, no. 110; The Hague 1965(1), no. 8 (with ill.).

VARIATIONS
1) oil on panel, 12.5 × 9 cm, auct. Amsterdam (F. Muller & Co), 22–25 and 28–29 March 1955, no. 48 (with ill.). 2) oil on panel, 19 × 15 cm, auct. Amsterdam (F. Muller & Co), 8–11 July 1941, no. 41 (with ill.). 3) oil on panel, 55.7 × 44 cm, Rijksmuseum H.W. Mesdag, The Hague; cat. Museum Mesdag 1975, p. 46, no. 40 (with ill.). 4) watercolour, 39.5 × 30.5 cm, auct. Amsterdam (Mak van Waay), 12 Dec. 1961, no. 24. 5) watercolour, 39 × 31 cm, auct. Amsterdam (F. Muller & Co), 19–20 June 1913, no. 202 (with ill.).

20 The Artist's Studio

Watercolour, 47 × 36 cm
Signed bottom right: *J. Bosboom*
The Hague, Haags Gemeentemuseum
repr. in colour on p. 26

Bosboom was an honorary member of the Société Belge des Aquarellistes in Brussels, of which Willem Roelofs had been a founder. He also belonged to its counterpart in The Hague, the Hollandsche Teeken-Maatschappenij (Dutch Drawing Society), to which he contributed a watercolour of his own studio for their fifth exhibition in 1881. From this it appears that, like other painters of the Hague School, he chose to surround himself with Dutch seventeenth-century objects. Yet the effect is predominantly sober. This studio has none of the sumptuousness usual in the interiors of contemporaries such as Makart or the German *Malerfürsten*.

Several years earlier Bosboom had moved into a house on Veenlaan, which is now called Toussaintkade after his wife. He had a studio built in the back garden by Laarman, who was also responsible for the *faux-terrain* in Mesdag's Panorama. Antique Dutch brass church chandeliers hang from the ceiling, as might be expected from the genre in which Bosboom specialized.

A version of this watercolour, formerly in the collection of Hendrik Mesdag, is in the Fritz Lugt Collection, Fondation Custodia, Paris.

PROVENANCE
Gorssel, coll. J. Verstolk-Völcker, 1909; The Hague, coll. H.G.J. Völcker; Eefde, coll. J.L. Völcker, 1917; Eefde, coll. E.C.K. Völcker, –1939; auct. Amsterdam (F. Muller & Co), 17 Oct. 1939, no. 29 (Dfl. 1,150); The Hague, Vereeniging van Haagsche Museumvrienden (Society of Friends of Hague Museums), 1939; presented to the museum, 1939.

BIBLIOGRAPHY
Marius/Martin 1917, p. 151.

EXHIBITIONS
Amsterdam 1900(2), no. 245; The Hague 1917(2), no. 197; Germany 1955, no. 49; Delft 1958–59, no. 89; Bonn 1972, no. 7, fig. 5; Zeist 1975, no. 32 (with ill.); Antwerp 1979, no. 5 (with ill.).

VARIATIONS
1) watercolour, 37.5 × 27 cm, coll. F. Lugt, Fondation Custodia, Institut Néerlandais, Paris. 2) drawing, 62 × 46 cm, auct. Amsterdam (P. Brandt), 29–30 Sept. 1965, no. 119 (with ill.).

21

21 *View of Hoorn*

Watercolour, 31 × 55 cm
Signed bottom right: *Bosboom*; inscribed bottom left: *Hoorn*
Edinburgh, National Gallery of Scotland

Bosboom often depicted figures in seventeenth-century costume in his townscapes as well as in his church interiors. He had a strong dislike of contemporary dress and regarded it as totally unsuitable for his paintings. It can be assumed that this preference was prompted by his great love for the seventeenth-century Dutch masters and his desire to emulate them.

It must also be said, however, that Bosboom seldom emphasized the historical aspect of his subject matter: his main concern in his depictions of church interiors and other buildings was the overall impression and the atmospheric play of light. When he did introduce an anecdotal element, it was never allowed to dominate the picture.

PROVENANCE
Coll. James Kirkhope; coll. Dr John Kirkhope, –1920; bequeathed to the museum, 1920.

BIBLIOGRAPHY
T.C.M. in *The Studio* LXXXIII (1922), p. 128, ill. on p. 135; cat. National Gallery 1946, p. 81.

EXHIBITIONS
Paris 1963, no. 14, fig. X.

22 *The River Amstel, Amsterdam*

Oil on canvas, 40 × 77 cm
Monogrammed bottom left: *J.B.*
Toledo (Ohio), The Toledo Museum of Art

Bosboom painted only a few townscapes. A view of the Quai de Paris in Rouen dates from the period when he was still following the romantic tradition, and views of The Hague, Nijmegen and Hoorn are later works. This painting shows the Buiten-Amstel and the Amstel Hotel (built in 1867), seen from Amsteldijk with the boathouse of the 'De Amstel' rowing and sailing club. The spire of the Zuiderkerk appears in the centre above the bridge.

De Gruyter dated the work *c.* 1869, but the Toledo Museum of Art changed the date to post-1883 on the basis of information provided by Frits Lugt, whose father, an

22

architect, built the Hogesluisbrug, the bridge shown here, in 1883.

The view chosen by Bosboom was a favourite spot for painters. A watercolour by Johan Conrad Greive (1837–91) shows the Amstel Hotel from a less angled perspective (auct. The Hague [Marcel Diederiks], 13–14 Oct. 1980, fig. 56), while Carel Jacobus Behr also painted a composition similar to that of Bosboom (Scheen 1981, fig. 110).

This townscape by Bosboom lacks any suggestion of a romantic approach to the subject matter, in contrast to his picture of the medieval architecture of Rouen painted in 1839. The present picture is a down-to-earth view of a big city in the process of development: the new hotel and the new bridge are shown in an ordinary Amsterdam setting.

PROVENANCE
Wassenaar, coll. Van Putten, –1935; auct. The Hague (Kunstzaal Kleykamp), 3 Dec. 1935, no. 5 (Dfl. 625); The Hague, art dealer L.J. Krüger; auct. Amsterdam (F. Muller & Co), 2–5 March 1948, no. 373 (Dfl. 4,500); Amsterdam, coll. W.J.R. Dreesmann, 1948–60; auct. Amsterdam (F. Muller & Co), 22–25 March 1960, no. 65; The Hague, art dealer S. Nystad, 1960; purchased by the museum, 1960.

BIBLIOGRAPHY
Hennus 1940, ill. on p. 22; *Verzameling Amsterdam – W.J.R. Dreesmann*, n.p., 1951, vol. 3, p. 759, ill. opp. p. 764; *Museum News. The Toledo Museum of Art* (Autumn 1962), p. 69 (with ill.); Sutton 1967, p. 490, fig. 12; De Gruyter 1968–69, vol. 1, pp. 15, 17, 28, 111, fig. 16; cat. Toledo Museum 1976, p. 27, pl. 150.

EXHIBITIONS
Heerlen 1948, no. 7; Antwerp 1955, no. 2; Amsterdam 1957–58, no. 5 (with ill.); Delft 1958–59, (not in cat.).

Paul Gabriël (1828-1903)

Paul Joseph Constantin Gabriël was born in Amsterdam on 5 July 1828, the eldest son of the sculptor Paulus Joseph Gabriël (1784–1834). From 1840 to 1843 he attended evening drawing classes at the Amsterdamse Academie where he was taught by the architect and amateur painter Louis Zocher (1820–1915); about 1844 he was sent to Cleves to take lessons at the Tekenacademie (Drawing Academy) run by the landscape painter Barend Cornelis Koekkoek (1803–62). However, the young pupil failed to satisfy his master and a year later Gabriël was back in Amsterdam. Some time later he went to the studio of Cornelis Lieste (1817–61) in Haarlem, where, apart from copying the paintings in the Welgelegen Pavilion, he concentrated mainly on portraits. In Haarlem he also met Anton Mauve who, although ten years younger, later become one of his closest companions.

In 1853 he moved to Oosterbeek and took up residence with the Wiesner family, in whose house the artists Johannes de Haas (1832–1908) and Kruseman van Elten (1829–1904) also lived. Gabriël met Johannes Bilders there and with great difficulty devoted his efforts to making studies from nature.

The period 1856–59 was a particularly hard one for Gabriël. He was living in Amsterdam, his paintings were not selling well and he got into financial difficulties. In 1860 he was invited to Brussels by an art-lover, for whom he had carried out a commission, and he did not return to live in the Netherlands until 1884. In Brussels he received much support

and advice from Willem Roelofs, who had been living there since 1847; he also became friends with the marine painter Paul Jan Clays (1819–1900), who gave him advice as well.

In 1862 he spent some time in Amsterdam and later he made trips back to the Netherlands regularly, visiting Veenendaal in 1866, Abcoude and Vreeland in the 1870s, the Kampen polder c. 1879 and Kortenhoef in 1880 and again in 1881.

In 1866 Bilders became a member of the Société Belge des Aquarellistes and a year later married a Miss Urbain, who came from Liège. His well-known landscape *In Groenendaal near Brussels* (Cat. 23) dates from this period. Appreciation of his work, both his landscapes and his flowerpieces, gradually increased and in 1875 he was created a Knight of the Order of Leopold.

Towards the end of the 1870s Gabriël gave lessons in his Brussels studio to Willem Bastiaan Tholen (1860–1931), who may be regarded as his most important pupil. A few years later he left Brussels and settled at Scheveningen where he remained until his death. But he continued to work at several places outside The Hague on the river Vliet near Voorschoten, in Broeksloot (1886), Oosterbeek (around 1887), Kinderdijk and Heeze. During the last 15 years of Gabriël's life, some of his most important works were acquired by various Dutch museums; *Peatcutting at Kampen* (Cat. 27), for example, was purchased by the Haags Gemeentemuseum. Gabriël died at Scheveningen on 23 August 1903.

fig. 136 *Portrait of Paul Gabriël* (photograph by Delboy-Baer) (Haags Gemeentemuseum, The Hague)

23

23 In Groenendaal near Brussels

Oil on canvas, 38 × 61 cm
Signed bottom right: *Gabriël f.*
The Hague, Rijksmuseum H. W. Mesdag
repr. in colour on p. 247

This picture is one of the finest examples of Gabriël's landscape painting during his first ten years in Brussels (1860–70). Mesdag was also a student there and the esteem he felt for Gabriël is reflected by his purchase of this work, dated by De Gruyter to *c.* 1866–67.

In 1867 Gabriël exhibited a painting of a similar view, entitled *Noontide* in Antwerp. Although that picture should not necessarily be identified with the one exhibited here, its title is an indication of Gabriël's preference at this time for painting motifs drenched in sunlight. Gabriël here displays his artistic independence, moving away from the Brussels landscape painters and also from the Dutch romantic tradition, although traces of the influence of Jan Weissenbruch's landscapes and townscapes can still be seen in the picture.

PROVENANCE
The Hague, coll. H. W. Mesdag (purchased in Brussels, *c.* 1866–69; ? directly from the painter).

BIBLIOGRAPHY
Boele van Hensbroek 1890, p. 28; Boele van Hensbroek 1910, p. 28; De Gruyter 1968–69, vol. 1, pp. 83–84, 90, 115, fig. 99; cat. Museum Mesdag 1975, p. 67, no. 132 (with ill.).

EXHIBITIONS
Paris 1891(2), no. 76; The Hague 1965(1), no. 16; The Hague 1967(1), no. 6; Bonn 1972, no. 23.

24

24 Watermill near Leidschendam

Oil on canvas, 65 × 97 cm
Signed bottom left: *Gabriël f.*
Dordrecht, Dordrechts Museum
repr. in colour on p. 247

Gabriël distinguished himself from the painters of the Grey School by his cheerful use of colour and his preference for sunny landscapes. In a letter of 29 May 1901 to the art critic A. C. Loffelt, he wrote: 'Although I may sometimes seem rather grumpy, I really love it when the sun shines on the water; and, quite apart from that, I think my country is colourful. One thing that particularly struck me when I returned from my time abroad was the *colour, lushness* and *richness* of our countryside; hence our beautifully coloured and well-proportioned cattle. Nowhere else do you find meat, milk and butter like theirs, but then they are nourished by our lush, rich and colourful countryside: I have often heard foreigners say that those Dutch painters paint everything grey, yet their country is *green*: when you're young, you're sent out of doors to study in a colourful landscape and then *later* you're obliged to paint grey pictures, cardboard concoctions with the odd bit of colour here and there, and it's called poetry; this strikes me as being akin to cabinet-making that's been dreamed up in a studio, and it's often put forward as if nothing else is possible. . . . An early morning can superficially appear grey, but it isn't, it's more transparent and subtle, the colours delicately greyed, and one looks through the atmosphere; just as an evening with dew on the land is much more colourful than one would imagine, often so intensely coloured that the artist's palette cannot match it . . . the more I observe, the more colourful and translucent nature appears; and then the sky seen

with it, something completely different and yet so much in harmony. It's delightful when one has learned to see, for that, too, does have to be learned. Let me say it again, just one more time, this country is not grey, not even in grey weather; neither are the dunes grey . . . .'.

This diatribe was not only a defence against various art critics' attacks on Gabriëls use of colour, but also a veiled criticism of the Hague School's formula for success which, like the work of Corot and the Barbizon School, at times resulted in a decidedly stereotyped treatment of landscapes. The originality which characterized Gabriël's work was also the direct cause of much of the opposition he encountered.

Piet Mondriaan had a great admiration for the strict, almost geometrical construction of Gabriël's compositions, and in 1895 he made a copy of his painting, *In the Month of July* (Rijksmuseum; cf. fig. 125).

PROVENANCE
Art dealer Holman & Dubourq, –1898; auct. Amsterdam (C.F. Roos & Co), 25 Oct. 1898, no. 21 (Dfl. 670); Amsterdam, art dealer A. Preyer, 1898–; auct. Amsterdam (F. Muller & Co), 20 Nov. 1900, no. 36 (as *Moulin du polder 'De Leidsche Dam' près de la Haye*; for Dfl. 1,050); purchased by the museum, 1900.

BIBLIOGRAPHY
Cat. Dordrechts Museum 1928, p. 23, no. 64.

EXHIBITIONS
The Hague 1965(1), no. 18 (with ill.); Amsterdam 1979(1), no. 41; Seoul 1979, no. 28 (with ill.); Tokyo 1979, no. 41 (with ill.).

VARIATIONS
Oil on panel , 38 × 59 cm, auct. Amsterdam (Sotheby Mak van Waay), 28 Oct. 1980. no. 196 (with ill.).

25

Amsterdam (F. Muller & Co), 29 Oct. 1907, no. 18 (Dfl. 3,550); The Hague, coll. Mrs H. E. L. J. Kröller-Müller, 1907.

BIBLIOGRAPHY
Riat 1904, pp. 61, 164–65, ill. on p. 163; Steenhoff 1906, p. 85, ill. on p. 80; Bénédite 1910, p. 247, ill. on p. 239; Kröller-Müller 1925, p. 83, ill, on p. 81; Kröller-Müller 1927, pp. 72–73 (with ill.); De Gruyter 1968–69, vol. 1, pp. 86–87, 91, 115, fig. 108; cat. Museum Kröller-Müller 1970, p. 116, no. 151; Pollock 1980–81, pp. 71–72, ill. on p. 72.

EXHIBITIONS
Paris 1890; Paris 1891(2), no. 72; The Hague 1904(1), no. 92; Amsterdam 1905, no. 85; Düsseldorf 1928, no. 62; Arnhem 1936, no. 12; The Hague 1945, no. 22 (with ill.); Luxemburg 1948, no. 18; The Hague 1965(1), no. 19 (with ill.); Amsterdam 1980–81, no. 114 (with ill.).

VARIATIONS
Drawing, 31 × 55 cm, coll. Jonkheer De Ranitz, Utrecht; De Gruyter 1968–69, vol. 1, fig. 107.

25   Train in Landscape (Il vient de loin . . .)

Oil on canvas, 67 × 100 cm
Signed bottom left: *Gabriël f.*
Otterlo, Rijksmuseum Kröller-Müller
repr. in colour on p. 248

The critics often lambasted Gabriël for his use of bright colours. One of them wrote about one of his landscapes, 'The strident, blinding blue sky in the painting by Gabriël will appeal to a few. Many a wife and mother may discern such a colour when starching the washing, but Mother Nature never engenders such a frightful colour as that'. Yet Gabriël also proved himself capable of painting the atmospheric landscapes so beloved by the Hague School and could show a complete mastery of the genre, as in the present picture.

Even in the second half of the nineteenth century trains were not popular motifs for paintings. The examples by Turner and the Impressionists are well known; less well known, but closer to this particular painting is *Il treno passa* in the museum at Barletta by De Nittis, an Italian whose work created a sensation in Paris around 1880. The similarity between the two paintings lies mainly in the subtlety with which the smoke from the engine's funnel merges with the misty atmosphere of the landscape.

A preliminary study by Gabriël for this painting, dated November 1886 and inscribed *In Broeksloot*, is in a private collection.

PROVENANCE
Scheveningen, coll. M. Kuyll van Gyn, 1891; The Hague, coll. A. A. Bakker Czn., –1907; auct.

26   Windmill by the Water

Watercolour, 23.5 × 57 cm
Signed bottom left: *Gabriël f.*
Wassenaar, Collection A. A. M. Ruygrok
repr. in colour on p. 248

When Louis de Haes had a conversation with Gabriël around the year 1892, which he later reproduced in an article, he apparently said to Gabriël: 'I believe you continued to paint Dutch landscapes in Brussels. Didn't Belgium appeal to you?' Gabriël answered, 'No, I don't care for it very much. It doesn't have the subtle atmosphere of Holland. It must appear odd that someone should go and live in Brussels in order to study the Dutch lakes, but it just turned out that way, as you know. Actually it was Mr Gericke van Herwijnen, the ambassador, who drew my attention to those lakes. When foreigners came to Belgium, he would take pleasure in showing them something typically Dutch – the polders'. De Haes added 'On hearing the name Gabriël, one involuntarily thinks of our Dutch polders, the wide lakes and endless skies, because recently we have seen a great many such paintings by him; and yet there are few artists who have produced such varied work as this painter.' (L. de Haes in *Het Schildersboek*, vol. 1 Amsterdam 1898, pp. 228, 229).

PROVENANCE
Miami, coll. L. Engers; The Hague, art dealer P. A. Scheen, 1977; purchased by the collector, 1977.
BIBLIOGRAPHY
Scheen 1981, fig. 477.

26

27

27. *Peatcutting at Kampen*

Oil on canvas, 91 × 150 cm
Signed bottom left: *P.J.C. Gabriël fc*
The Hague, Haags Gemeentemuseum

One of Gabriël's pupils was the painter Willem Bastiaan Tholen (1860–1931), who spent several months in Gabriël's studio in Brussels *c.* 1878 improving his skill in landscape painting. When Gabriël went to Kampen in the summer, Tholen joined him on his outings into the countryside, working near the peat banks, sometimes spending the night in barns in order to start work again at first light. The practical advice Tholen received here must have been particularly useful.

Peatcutting at Kampen may well have been the fruit of just such an expedition. Charcoal sketches would have been the basis for this monumental studio version. It was painted shortly before 1890 and bought directly from the artist by the Vereeniging tot het Oprichten van een Museum van Moderne Kunst te 's-Gravenhage (Society for the Foundation of a Museum of Modern Art in The Hague), which presented it to the Haags Gemeentemuseum in 1890.

PROVENANCE
The Hague, Vereeniging tot het Oprichten van een Museum van Moderne Kunst te 's-Gravenhage (Society for the Foundation of a Museum of Modern Art in The Hague), 1890; presented to the museum, 1890.

BIBLIOGRAPHY
De Haes 1893, ill. on p. 466; De Haes 1898, p. 232, ill. on p. 226; *M.K.* I (1903), no. 33 (with ill.); Eisler 1911(I), ill. on p. 221; cat. Gemeentemuseum 1935, p. 73, no. 156, fig. 42; Van Gelder 1937, p. 451 (with fig. 10); Van Gelder 1946(1), p. 696 (with fig. 10); Pedroza 1948, p. 12 (with ill.); Van Gelder 1954–56, vol. 2, p. 402 (with fig. 10); cat. Gemeentemuseum 1962, no. 129 (with ill.); Van Gelder 1963–65, vol. 11, p. 1925, fig. 10 on p. 1929; De Gruyter 1968–69, vol. 1, pp. 86, 88, 91, 115, figs. 113, 115; *O.K.* XVIII (1974), pp. 55–57 (with ill.); *Natuurbehoud* XI (Feb. 1980), ill. on p. 27; E.H. Korevaar-Hesseling, *Het landschap in de Nederlandsche en Vlaamsche schilderkunst*, Amsterdam n.d., p. 78.

EXHIBITIONS
Paris 1889(1), no. 52 (as *Une tourbière en Overijssel*); Antwerp 1937, no. 14 (with ill.); The Hague 1947, no. 136; Dusseldorf 1950, no. 13; Germany 1955, no. 17; Bonn 1972, no. 25, fig. 8; Enschede 1980, no. 40 (with ill.).

Jozef Israëls (1824-1911)

Jozef Israëls was born in Groningen on 27 January 1824 into one of the poorer families in the Jewish community there. After primary school, he went to the French school until he was 15; meanwhile he also took painting and drawing lessons at the Academie Minerva from September 1835 onwards, first under Van Wicheren (1808–97) in 1836 and then under Cornelis Bernardus Buys (1808–72) in 1838. Through the agency of De Witt, the Groningen art dealer, Israëls then entered the Amsterdam studio of the figure and portrait painter Jan Adam Kruseman (1804–62) in 1842; in addition he attended evening classes given by Jan Willem Pieneman (1779–1853) at the Amsterdamse Academie.

In 1845 he went to Paris with his fellow pupil Van Koningsveld (1824–66). Israëls applied himself with great diligence; every morning he worked at Picot's studio from half-past six to eleven o'clock, in the afternoon he copied works by Rembrandt, Velazquez, Raphael and others and in the evening he took lessons from Pradier, Vernet and Delaroche at the École des Beaux Arts.

In 1847 he returned to the Netherlands and went to live in Amsterdam. Three years later he made his name with the large canvas *Ophelia* (also known as *Day Dreaming*). That year, 1850, he also went to Düsseldorf, the centre of German Romanticism, paying a visit to Oosterbeek on his way home.

In 1853 Israëls was again in Paris; this time he paid a visit to Ary Scheffer (1795–1858), whose *Gretchen at the Spinning-wheel* had greatly impressed him when he had seen it at an exhibition eight years before. In 1855 he lodged with a village carpenter at Zandvoort for seven weeks to restore his health. It was at Zandvoort and Katwijk, where he spent some time the following year, that Israëls first became fascinated by the poverty-stricken existence of the fishermen and their families. The fishing communities, together with aspects of Jewish life, were to remain the most important source of inspiration for

Israëls's oils and watercolours.

In 1862 he visited London, where his *Fishermen Carrying a Drowned Man* (Cat. 29) was a great success at the International Exhibition; it finally established his reputation in English-speaking countries. A year later he married Aleida Schaap, by whom he had a daughter and a son, Isaac (1865–1934), who also became a painter (see chapter VI). In 1869 he travelled to Germany (Munich) and Switzerland (Pontresina) and two years later he moved to The Hague with his wife and children. At first they lived at No. 6 Koninginnegracht, but not long afterwards moved to No. 2, where Israëls continued to live until his death. In 1878 he had a spacious studio built in the garden, where his models could pose in what he called his 'fisherman's corner'.

He visited the village of Laren in the Gooi area in the early 1870s, and was followed not long afterwards by Albert Neuhuys, Anton Mauve and many others. In 1877 he toured Europe with his wife and children (Paris, Pisa, Naples, Rome, Milan, Venice, Verona and Munich) and from that time onwards took his entire family to the Paris Salon every year. After his wife's death in 1894, he travelled to Spain and North Africa with Isaac and Frans Erens (a friend of his son) and five years later illustrated and published an account of his experiences.

Throughout his life Israëls was honoured at home and abroad with many medals and decorations, and, in 1904, on the occasion of his eightieth birthday, he was appointed a Commander of the Nederlandse Leeuw (Order of the Dutch Lion). That year, having sent several paintings to the Biennale exhibition, he also visited Venice. His last trip there was in 1910, when he was honoured at the Biennale by a *Mostra individuale*. He died in Scheveningen on 12 August 1911 at the age of 87 and was buried with great ceremony in the Jewish Cemetery in The Hague.

fig. 137 VETH *Portrait of Jozef Israëls* 1895 (Stedelijk Museum, Amsterdam)

28 Passing Mother's Grave

Oil on canvas, 244 × 178 cm
Signed and dated bottom left: *Jozef Israëls Amsterdam 1856*
Amsterdam, Stedelijk Museum

Van Gelder described *Passing Mother's Grave* – also known as *The Way Past the Graveyard* and *The Zandvoort Fisherman* – as 'a genuinely new moment, the obvious beginning of the second period of Israëls's development'. Traces of the historicism which characterized the first period are still evident in the theatrical staging and the flat painting of the landscape. The theme, however, is new: a tragic moment in the life of a Zandvoort fisherman.

The means by which Israëls was converted to genre painting is an indication of the gulf that had opened up between the academic artistic circles in which Israëls had hitherto moved and his own native traditions. The change of subject matter resulted from a suggestion made by Henry Ritter (1816–53), a Canadian genre painter who had trained at Düsseldorf and was a follower of Rudolf Jordan (1820–87), the first German artist to rediscover themes from peasant life. Jordan's work was known through prints, but Israëls may have seen his paintings when in Düsseldorf in 1850; his *Unverhofftes Wiedersehen* (*Unhoped-for Reunion*) of 1840 certainly seems to have been an important source for the present picture.

By rendering this 'simple' subject on a large scale, Israëls clearly distinguished himself from Dutch as well as German genre painters. The size of the painting unmistakably places it in a different sphere from ordinary genre pieces: it not only heralded a new stage in Israëls's work, but was also a milestone in realistic figure painting in the Netherlands, comparable in impact with Courbet's *Stone-breakers*.

According to a note at the Rijksbureau voor Kunsthistorische Documentatie (Netherlands Institute for Art History), The Hague, Klaas Helweg and the two children of his cousin Hendrik Helweg were the models for the painting. The picture won instant popularity: Nicolaas Beets (1814–1903) wrote a poem about it in *Children of the Sea* (Haarlem 1861, no. IX) and a print was made of it on at least three occasions, by Johannes Heinrich Rennefeld and Willem Steelink among other artists.

A witty sketch in the form of a letter from a certain 'Johan', dated October 1856 and published in the *Kunstkronijk*, described the effect of *Passing Mother's Grave* on Johan's wife. 'There were tears in her eyes – ISRAËLS! you have scored a veritable triumph . . .'. Yet Johan accused Israëls of 'superficiality in some parts of his painting, the negligence in the drawing here and there'. Vincent van Gogh, who called the picture 'Delacroix-like and superb' in its technique, countered this accusation some 30 years later in a letter to his brother Theo. 'Let them jabber about technique as much as they like, in Pharisaical, hollow, hypocritical terms – the true painters are guided by that conscience which is called sentiment, their soul: their brains aren't subject to the brush, but the brush to their brains' (no. 426, Oct. 1885).

BIBLIOGRAPHY
K.K. XVIII (1875), p. 76; Thrasbulus, 'Langs het kerkhof (met eene plaat [by W. Steelink] naar eene schilderij van Jozef Israëls)', *Aurora. Jaarboekje voor 1858*, pp. 1–25; Vosmaer 1882–85, vol. I (J. Israëls), p. 3; Veth 1890, pp. 175, 178; De Vries 1894, p. 42; De Meester 1898, p. 94; Kalff 1902, p. 294; Marius 1903, p. 227; Steenhoff 1904, pp. 38, 39, 42, ill. on p. 41; Von Ostini 1904–05, fig. 1; Marius 1906, p. 233; Marius 1908, p. 97; Plasschaert 1909, ill. on p. 103; Bénédite 1910, p. 238; Eisler 1910, p. 36; Dake 1911(1), ill. on p. 39; Dake 1911(2), pp. 27, 41, ill. on p. 7; Eisler 1911(3), pp. 273 (with ill.). 282; *N.R.C.* (14 Aug. 1911); Marius 1920, p. 118; cat. Stedelijk Museum 1922, p. 32, no. 213; Plasschaert 1923(2), ill.; Eisler 1924, pp. 15–16, 19, fig. VI; Van Gelder 1937, p. 443; Knuttel 1938, p. 427; *De Residentie Bode* (29 April 1939; with ill.); Van Gelder 1946(1), p. 687; Van Gelder 1946(2), pp. 10–12, ill. on p. 11; Knoef 1948, p. 85; Knuttel 1950, p. 448; Van Gelder 1954–56, vol. 2, p. 396; exh. cat. Laren 1957, p. 9; exh. cat. Groningen 1961–62, pp. 6, 13; *Het Binnenhof* (28 Oct. 1961); *Friesch Dagblad* (11 Nov. 1961); *De Waarheid* (11 Nov. 1961); *Het Vaderland* (12 Dec. 1961); Van Gelder 1963–65, vol. 11, p. 1919; De Gruyter 1968–69, vol. I, pp. 49–50, 58, 113, fig. 51; Marius/Norman 1973, p. 114.

EXHIBITIONS
Amsterdam 1856(1), no. 205; The Hague 1857, no. 307; Amsterdam 1885(2), no. 2; Groningen 1961–62, no. 6 (with ill.).

VARIATIONS
Oil on canvas, 38 × 32 cm, auct. Vienna (E. Hirschler & Co), 10 April 1907, no. 87 (with ill.).

29 Fishermen Carrying a Drowned Man

Oil on canvas, 128.9 × 143.8 cm
Signed bottom left: *Jozef Israëls*
London, The Trustees of the National Gallery

Fishermen Carrying a Drowned Man signified a breakthrough in Israëls's career and, as he himself realized, firmly established his reputation with the English public. After a successful showing at the Paris Salon in 1861, the canvas, which has now darkened

29

considerably, was acclaimed as a masterpiece at the International Exhibition of 1862 in London. The painter of 'the most touching picture of the whole exhibition' was fêted at a gala banquet and in an extensive review the *Illustrated London News* of 12 September 1863 emphasized that the work was not simply a moving representation of the life of fishermen, but also a silent exhortation to station more lifeboats along the coast in order to prevent further fatalities.

In its composition the painting is a large-scale elaboration of *Passing Mother's Grave* (Cat. 28), in which the contrived spatial composition of the earlier picture has been replaced by a more convincing suggestion of the surrounding landscape: desolate dunes with a view of the sea and a battered ship to the right. It is characteristic of what has been called the 'impassiveness' of Israëls's artistry that he chose the moment after the event rather than the action itself. A generation earlier the romantic artist Wijnand Nuyen had depicted the actual moment of a shipwreck in bold colours; in contrast, Israëls's tones were sober and he painted the emotionally charged moment when the victim was brought ashore. Jan Veth recognized elements borrowed from Raphael in the composition. Its derivation from similar processions depicted by Courbet, such as *Burial at Ornans* (1849–50) and *Return from the Fair* (1850–51) is also evident. Jules Breton's *La Plantation d'un Calvaire* may also have inspired Israëls. This work was exhibited in Antwerp and Paris successively in 1858–59. Funeral subjects were in vogue around 1860, the solemn processions providing younger artists with a suitably serious subject in the realist idiom through which they could challenge the spectacular examples of earlier history painting.

Although this picture remained in England after 1862, it was also very well-known abroad. In March 1879, during his stay in the Borinage, Vincent van Gogh was struck by images that were reminiscent of the works of the Hague School. 'They would find so many things here that would appeal to them. When the cart drawn by the white horse brings an injured man home from the mines, one sees things that remind one of the drowned man by Israëls.' (no. 128).

PROVENANCE
London, art dealer E. Gambart, 1862 (purchased at exh. London 1862; for £200); London, coll. Arthur J. Lewis, 1862–; London/Aberdeen, coll. Alexander Young, –1910; auct. London (Christie's), 30 June–4 July 1910, no. 302 (bought for 4,600 guineas by the widow of Alexander Young); presented to the National Gallery, London by Mrs Alexander Young, in fulfilment of the wish of her husband, 1910; moved to the Tate Gallery, London, c. 1920; taken back to the National Gallery, London, 1956.

BIBLIOGRAPHY
K.K. N.S. IV (1863), pp. 55–56; *The London Illustrated Times* (12 Sep. 1863; with ill. of anonymous engraving after the painting); Vosmaer 1882–85, vol. 1 (J. Israëls), pp. 3–4; De Vries 1894, p. 42; exh. cat. London 1897, p. 9; *Israel: The Jewish Magazine* III (1899), pp. 81, 83; Marius 1903, pp. 228, 230; *B.M.* II (1903), p. 177; Marius 1906, p. 234; Halton 1907, pp. 294–99; *The Daily Telegraph* (26 May 1909); Zilcken 1910, p. 43; *The Art Journal* (1910), p. 310; Dake 1911(1), pp. 36–37; Dake 1911(2), p. 31; *N.R.C.* (2 Sept. 1911); Halton 1912, pp. 92, 102, ill. on p. 93; Marius 1920, p. 119; Plasschaert 1923(2), p. 16; Eisler 1924, p. 19, fig. IX; *N.R.C.* (26 Jan. 1924); Van Gelder 1946(2), p. 12, ill. on p. 13; Ch. Carter, in *Apollo* LXXI (June 1960), pp. 7, 8; cat. National Gallery 1960, pp. 200–01; *Het Vaderland* (12 Dec. 1961); exh. cat. Groningen 1961–62, pp. 6, 13–14; De Gruyter 1968–69, vol. 1, pp. 56, 58; exh. cat. Berlin 1979–80, p. 406, under no. 151; exh. cat. Manchester 1980, p. 10.

EXHIBITIONS
Paris 1861, no. 1596; London 1862, no. 1253; Glasgow 1888, no. 742; London 1889, no. 124; London 1890(1), no. 18; ?London 1896(1), no. 15; London 1903, no. 11; London 1909, no. 18; London 1949, no. 2.

VARIATIONS
1) oil on canvas, 45.5 × 86.5 cm, auct. Amsterdam (Mak van Waay), 15 April 1975, no. 85 (with ill.). 2) oil on canvas on panel, 34.5 × 45 cm, auct. Amsterdam (F. Muller & Co), 29 Nov. 1921, no. 8. 3) oil on canvas, 70 × 107 cm, auct. Heerlen (Hommes), 3 Dec. 1962, no. 199 (with ill.). 4) oil on panel, 23.3 × 33.1 cm, priv. coll., Rijswijk (Z.H.), 1968. 5) drawing, 19.6 × 34.3 cm, Aberdeen Gallery, Aberdeen; *Apollo* LXXII (July 1960), ill. on p. 8.

30 The Day Before Parting

Oil on canvas, 102.5 × 126.5 cm
Signed and dated bottom left: *Jozef Israels 1862*
Boston, Museum of Fine Arts (Gift of Alice N. Lincoln)

The Day Before Parting was one of the last in a series of canvases, with death as their main theme. These paintings showed both realist and romantic tendencies; the present picture still clearly reveals the influence of the tradition of history painting.

The arrangement of the figures parallel to the picture plane

is reminiscent of neo-classical compositions, while the pose of the grieving fisherman's wife would not have been out of place in David's *Oath of the Horatii*. Strong contrasts of light and shade heighten the dramatic tension in this otherwise sober work, a smaller version of which, entitled *Grief*, is in the Glasgow Art Gallery and Museum. There is a watercolour of the same subject in the Teyler Museum at Haarlem.

Although the painting is dated 1862, Israëls himself declared in 1906 that it was painted in 1860: 'I know it was then, because it was the year before I was engaged. It was painted *'pour la gloire'*. It was exhibited in Rotterdam in 1862 and got the gold medal, the last year that medal was given'.

This painting was offered to Queen Sophie of the Netherlands for the sum of 1,600 guilders, but after seeing it in Israëls's studio, she finally decided not to buy it.

PROVENANCE
Utrecht, coll. Jonkheer Van Reede van Oudtshoorn, –1875; auct. Amsterdam, 14 April 1875 (Dfl. 7,150); London, coll. James Staats Forbes, The Hague, art dealer A. Preyer, 1905; coll. Roland C. Lincoln, 1906; coll. Alice N. Lincoln, –1918; presented to the museum, 1918.

BIBLIOGRAPHY
K.K. N.S. IV (1863), pp. 42, 56, 78; K.K. N.S. XVI (1875), p. 40; Vosmaer 1882–85, vol. 1 (J. Israëls), p. 4; De Vries 1894, p. 42; Veth 1911(3), p. 285, ill. on p. 277; cat. Museum Boston 1921, pp. 53–54, no. 125; Plasschaert 1923(2), p. 16; Eisler 1924, p. 19; Van Gelder 1946(2), p. 12, 14 (with ill.); exh. cat. Groningen 1961–62, pp. 6, 14.

EXHIBITIONS
London 1862; Rotterdam 1862, no. 203 (gold medal); Paris 1878; The Hague 1905(2), no. 40.

VARIATIONS
1) oil on canvas, 46 × 58 cm, Glasgow Art Gallery and Museum, Glasgow; cat. Glasgow Art Gallery 1961, vol. 2, ill. on p. 101. 2) painting, exh. cat. Glasgow 1898, no. 43. 3) watercolour, Teyler Museum, Haarlem. 4) watercolour, 31 × 38 cm, formerly coll. James Staats Forbes, London.

31 Ida, the Fisherman's Daughter

Oil on canvas, 76 × 61 cm
Signed bottom left: *J. Israëls*
Antwerp, Koninklijk Museum voor Schone Kunsten

The motif of a girl knitting at the door of a cottage first appears in a painting exhibited by Israëls in 1858 at the Tentoonstelling van Levende Meesters (Exhibition of Living Masters) in Rotterdam. That picture, probably identical with the one shown here, was first reproduced in 1860 in a steel-engraving by J. W. Kaiser, while a year later it appeared as an illustration, this time engraved by Johannes Heinrich Rennefeld, in the album *Children of the Sea, Sketches after Life on the Dutch Coast*. In this popular work, which ran to no less than five editions (the final one appeared in 1901), reproductions after Israëls were accompanied by poems by Nicolaas Beets, one of the most renowned poets of that time. *Passing Mother's Grave* (Cat. 28) was also included in the album.

In the poem by Beets *Ida* is called 'beautiful Kniertje', which

32

is sometimes found as the title of this painting, as is *Knitting Girl*. Another three versions of the subject are known, one painted as late as 1865; of the various watercolours of the subject, that in the Fogg Art Museum, Cambridge, Massachussets is considered the finest. Another watercolour, shown at the 1910 Biennale in Venice, once belonged to Queen Emma of the Netherlands.

In 1885 a much smaller version was exhibited at the Israëls exhibition in the Amsterdam Panorama building; Carel Vosmaer called it 'a little gem in form, full of perfectly harmonious colouring, of detailed handling, as if painted with a brush that produced paint as if it were melting enamel' (*De Nederlandse Spectator*, 18 April 1865). A day later Josephus Alberdingk Thijm, who disliked Israëls's later style and therefore regarded his work of the period 1858–75 as his best, saw in the *Knitting Girl* the auspicious opening of an epoch 'in which the artist still hesitated to fill large areas with the vague blackness that cannot tell us anything; in which he still drew human faces and hands with care, having first selected them with good taste . . .' (*De Amsterdammer*, 19 April 1885).

Ida was indeed the first work in which Israëls depicted the life of the fishing communities with a more optimistic attitude, although some of his more sombre treatments of the subject were still to come. The lighter touch and similar motifs recur later in the works of both Jacob Maris (cf. his *Courtyard* of 1862 and *Villagers* of 1872, both in the Rijksmuseum) and Blommers.

PROVENANCE Coll. Mrs Joostens, –1938; bequeathed to the museum, 1938.

BIBLIOGRAPHY
Cat. Museum Antwerpen 1977, p. 214, no. 2411 (with ill.).

EXHIBITIONS
Rotterdam 1858, no. 165 (*as Ida het visschermeisje aan de deur*).

VARIATIONS
1) painting, 64.7 × 48.8 cm, auct. Laren (Christie's), 10 April 1978, no. 381 (with ill.). 2) oil on panel, 28 × 20 cm, auct. Amsterdam, 17 Oct. 1899, no. 36 (with ill.). 3) oil on canvas, 58 × 44.5 cm, auct. New York (American Art Galleries), 10 Jan. 1922, no. 14 (with ill.).

32   The Cottage Madonna

Oil on canvas, 134.6 × 99.7 cm
Signed bottom left: *Jozef Israels*
Detroit, Detroit Institute of Arts (Bequest of Mrs Harry N. Torrey)
repr. in colour on p. 29

In an attempt to emphasize the intrinsic value of everyday life, realist painters often chose themes that were essentially secularized versions of popular religious subjects. Thus the high pedestal on which motherhood was placed in the last century may be seen as a more or less pointed iconographical reference to the divinity of Mary, as Mother of God. In this painting of a peasant woman feeding her baby (*c.* 1867), even the colours of her garments are reminiscent of the Madonna.

In 1912 Frank Gunsaulus related an anecdote told to him by Israëls. When *The Cottage Madonna* was on exhibition at the Salon, the Archbishop of Paris instantly recognized its religious sentiments. He is said to have called out to its Jewish author, 'Mr Israëls, you are a great Catholic.' In Israëls's own country the Nijmegen minister Haverkamp even devoted a special publication in 1899 to 'Jozef Israëls, who preaches the Gospel with his brush'.

PROVENANCE
London/Aberdeen, coll. Alexander Young, –1902; Detroit, coll. Mrs Harry N. Torrey, 1902; bequeathed to the museum.

BIBLIOGRAPHY
Veth 1902, ill. on p. 238; Marius 1903, p. 230; Stahl 1903, ill. on p. 38; *B.M.* II (1903), p. 177; Marius 1906, p. 234; *The Art Journal* (1906), p. 358 (with ill.); Halton 1907, p. 299; Gansaulus 1912, ill. opp. p. 128; Marius 1920, p. 119; *Bulletin of the Detroit Institute of Arts* II (1921), no. 4; Eisler 1924, fig. XVI; Van Gelder 1946(2), pp. 15, 41, ill. on p. 19; exh. cat. Groningen 1961–62, p. 14.

EXHIBITIONS
?London 1890(1), no. 16; The Hague 1895(1), no. 10; London 1903, no. 14; Toledo 1912, no. 241.

VARIATIONS
Oil on canvas, 49.5 × 39 cm, auct. New York (Parke-Bernet), 25 Feb. 1943, no. 27 (with ill.).

33

33   Baby in a High Chair

Watercolour, 43 × 31 cm
Signed bottom right: *Jozef Israels*
Rotterdam, Museum Boymans–van Beuningen
repr. in colour on p. 30

Paintings of children are one of the most important, although not the most striking, of the genres favoured by the Hague School artists. Willem Maris and Anton Mauve depicted children patiently tending animals, while Jacob Maris observed his own children practising music or playing games.

In the work of Jozef Israëls the presence of children serves as a counterpoint in scenes of poverty and sorrow (Cat. 28, 30, 41) and this highlights the emotional charge of the paintings. The contrast of youth and age is the subject of *Army and Navy*, in which the same child and high chair appear as this watercolour of 'Jantje'.

A poem by Israëls in the Kunstkronijk of 1876 reveals how the artist saw this scene in terms of contrasts.

> 'Within the fisherman's dark shack,
> Lonely, decrepit, where the wind
> Rattles the rafters, finds each crack,
> Can there be aught to cheer the mind?
>
> Yes! By the hearth whose smoke and grime
> Bedaub the walls with murky haze,
> Amid the wrack of age and time,
> A child sits in a chair, and plays.'

BIBLIOGRAPHY
Exh. cat. The Hague 1965(1), p. 45, under no. 27; De Gruyter 1968–69, vol. 1, pp. 59, 114, ill. on p. 48.

EXHIBITIONS
Groningen 1961–62, no. 53 (with ill.).

VARIATIONS
1) watercolour, 26 × 18 cm, art dealer Ivo Bouwman, The Hague, 1979. 2) watercolour, 57.5 × 73 cm, formerly art dealer M. Knoedler & Co, New York.

34   Girl in the Dunes

Watercolour, 37.2 × 24 cm
Signed bottom right: *Jozef Israels*
The Hague, Haags Gemeentemuseum
repr. in colour on p. 30

Nowhere are the romantic overtones in Israëls's work seen so clearly as in his countless paintings and watercolours of fishermen's wives and daughters looking out over the sea from the dunes. Life in the fishing villages of the last century was dominated by the constant fear that a husband or son would one day not return from a fishing trip. Israëls, who, as he himself said, always tried to participate in the joys and sorrows of his models, preferred to paint the melancholy moments when the outcome of the vigil was still unknown. His inclination for such meditative pictures can be seen in his earliest work, as for example in *Day Dreaming* (also known as *Ophelia*) in the Dordrecht Museum. In *After the Storm* (Stedelijk Museum, Amsterdam), a large painting of c. 1860, the tension in the family the fisherman has left behind is still palpable. In later works, like this watercolour, the subject is rendered with the utmost simplicity.

This theme recurs in the paintings of Adolphe Artz, Bernard Blommers and Jacob Maris, and around the turn of the century it can be found in the work of Jan Toorop.

PROVENANCE
The Hague, coll. Jonkheer P. A. van der Velden, 1885; Groningen, coll. W. and A.L. Scholtens Jr., 1912; coll. Dr J.W. van Dijk; coll. Mrs C. van Dijk-Ruempol, –1949; on loan to the museum, 1935–49; presented to the museum, 1949.

BIBLIOGRAPHY
Steenhoff 1910(1), p. 219; Wagner 1974, ill. on p. 5.

EXHIBITIONS
Amsterdam 1885(2), no. 59; The Hague 1911–12, no. 71; Groningen 1924, no. 64; Montpellier 1952, no. 26; Germany 1955, no. 45; The Hague 1963, no. 6 (with ill.; detail); Bonn 1972, no. 12; Antwerp 1979, no. 21 (with ill.); Manchester 1980, no. 6 (with ill.); Florence 1981–82, no. 13 (with ill.).

VARIATIONS
1) watercolour 35.5 × 25.4 cm, formerly art dealer M. Knoedler & Co, New York. 2) watercolour, 9 × 11 cm, art dealer W.S. ten Bosch, The Hague, 1965. 3) watercolour, 17.1 × 29.8 cm, formerly art dealer Jack Niekerk, The Hague. 4) watercolour, 33 × 43 cm, The Metropolitan Museum of Art, New York (Bequest of Isaac D. Fletcher). 5) watercolour, 21.5 × 30.5 cm, auct. Amsterdam (F. Muller & Co), 17 April 1923, no. 25 (with ill.). 6) drawing, 17.5 × 13 cm, auct. Frankfurt (F. von Artus), 24 May 1967, no. 131 (with ill.).

35 Growing Old

Oil on canvas, 160 × 101 cm
Signed bottom right: *Jozef Israels*
The Hague, Haags Gemeentemuseum
repr. in colour on p. 31

The parallel between winter and the old age of man is a very ancient one; it has appeared in Netherlandish art in representations of the four seasons since medieval times. Sixteenth- and seventeenth-century prints and paintings often show an old man warming himself at the fire as a personification of winter and women are also occasionally portrayed in this way. In this work, painted *c.* 1878, Israëls set the traditional theme in his own period with compelling intensity. Israëls's paintings of this kind made a great impression on Van Gogh.

At first, however, the picture was badly received by the public: 'People had all sorts of things to say about it and

nobody understood what I meant by it . . . it was called the apotheosis of a cape, the figure was said to be much too large for the compass, etc. etc. Funnily enough, it was liked enormously at nearly all the exhibitions after that and is still regarded as one of my best.' (notes by Israëls at the Gemeentearchief [Municipal Archives], The Hague).

Israëls painted a number of variations on the theme in oil and in 1883 made an etching (in reverse) of the same subject. Versions are also known in which the composition is worked out more horizontally, with greater attention to the interior. In 1893 Jan Veth made a lithograph after the painting.

PROVENANCE
The Hague, coll. M. Hijmans van Wadenoyen (purchased from the painter); on loan to the Rijksmuseum, Amsterdam by the M. Hijmans van Wadenoyen Heirs, 1909–; on loan to the Haags Gemeentemuseum by the M. Hjmans van Wadenoyen Heirs, –1926; purchased by the museum, 1926.

BIBLIOGRAPHY
Muther 1888, p. 336; Veth 1893, pp. 22–25; *Katholieke Illustratie* (1893), ill. (of an engraving by C.L. Simon after the painting); De Meester 1898, p. 94; *Israël. The Jewish Magazine* III (1899), p. 81; *Die Kunst* (1901), p. 468; Marius 1903, ill. opp. p. 98; Stahl 1903, ill. on p. 25; Steenhoff 1904, p. 39, ill. opp. p. 46; Veth 1904, no. 7 (with ill.); Marius 1906, ill. on p. 219; Marius 1908, ill. opp. p. 68; *E.H.* XXXV (1909), pp. 312–13 (with ill.); Bénédite 1910, p. 240, ill. on p. 232; Martin 1910, ill. opp. p. 145; Dake 1911(1), ill. on p. 24; Dake 1911(2), ill. on p. 43; cat. Rijksmuseum 1918, p. 383, no. 1284 e; Marius 1920, fig. 57; Plasschaert 1923(2), ill.; Eisler 1924, p. 21, fig. XLVI; J. Veth in *Jaarboek Die Haghe* (1924), p. 67; G. Knuttel Wzn. in *M.D.K.W.* II (1926–31), pp. 83–87, ill. on p. 85; H.E. van Gelder in *M.D.K.W.* II (1926–31), pp. 159, 161; cat. Gemeentemuseum 1935, pp. 112–113, no. 72–76, fig. 32; Van Gelder 1937, p. 445; Knuttel 1938, p. 436, ill. on p. 428; Van Gelder 1946(1), p. 689; Van Gelder 1946(2), pp. 41–42, ill. on p. 37; Knoef 1948, p. 104; Knuttel 1950, p. 456 (with ill.); Van Gelder 1954–56, vol. 2, p. 397; Polak 1955, pp. 161, 220–21; exh. cat. Laren 1957, p. 12; exh. cat. Groningen 1961–62, p. 15; *De Waarheid* (11 Nov. 1961); cat. Gemeentemuseum 1962, no. 158; exh. cat. Amsterdam 1963, p. 97, under no. T 63; Van Gelder 1963–65, vol. 11, p. 1919; Zeitler 1966, fig. 141; De Gruyter 1968–69, vol. 1, pp. 47, 59, 113, fig. 62; Pollock 1980–81, ill. on p. 31.

EXHIBITIONS
The Hague 1884(1), no. 182; Amsterdam 1885(2), no. 27; Munich 1888, no. 1328; The Hague 1895(1), no. 20; The Hague 1899(1), no. 52; The Hague 1900(2), no. 20; Berlin 1901, no. 112; The Hague 1909(2), (no cat.); ?London 1912(2), no. 17; Paris 1921, no. 121; The Hague 1924(1), no. 5; Maastricht 1945–46, no. 22 (with ill.); The Hague 1947, no. 185; Laren 1957, no. 102; Groningen 1961–62, no. 13; The Hague 1965(1), no. 28 (with ill.) Berlin 1979/80, no. 151 (with ill.).

VARIATIONS
1) oil on canvas, priv. coll., The Hague; exh. cat. The Hague 1911–12, no. 32. 2) oil on panel, 28.5 × 19.5 cm, auct. Amsterdam (Mak van Waay), 15 April 1975, no. 82 (with ill.). 3) oil on canvas, 41 × 28.5 cm, formerly coll. Alexander Young, London/Aberdeen. 4) oil on canvas, 31 × 46.5 cm, auct. Munich (Neumeister), 17–19 Sept. 1975, no. 1452 (with ill.). 5) oil on canvas, 94 × 66 cm, formerly coll. John Reid, Glasgow; Halton 1912, ill. on p. 98. 6) drawing, Rijksprentenkabinet, Rijksmuseum, Amsterdam; E.R. Meyer, *De tekening zien en vergelijken*, Bilthoven 1959, ill. 7) drawing; *E.H.* XX (1894), ill. on p. 43. 8) etching, 41.3 × 29.4 cm; Hubert 1909, no. XXIX (with ill.).

36 The Bashful Suitor (Primula Veris)

Watercolour, 87.6 × 65 cm
Signed bottom left: *Jozef Israels*
Montreal, Musée des Beaux-Arts de Montréal
(Gift of George Summer)

Around 1879 Israëls painted the theme of a young couple taking a stroll several times. In 1904 he described it in a note to Jan Veth as 'a youth with a sprig in his hand walking beside a young girl in silent love. The landscape is the road to Rijswijk. . . . The picture was painted numerous times in many small sizes, under trees or along a canal'. Israëls clearly also made watercolours of it, this carefully drawn example probably being one of the earliest. A version with a more horizontal composition was sold in Amsterdam in 1899 as *Idylle Pastorale*.

Loving couples taking a walk, lying on a dune top or talking at a window constituted a separate and highly popular genre known as 'fisherfolk's courtships' ('*vissersvrijages*'). They occur in the work of artists such as Artz, Bisschop, Blommers, Neuhuys, De Haas and even Jan Toorop, although the pastoral idyll loses its innocence in Toorop's *The Seduction* (Rijksmuseum Kröller-Müller, Otterlo). Toorop's drawings, which show a couple reposing in the dunes with a graveyard in the background, are no less disquieting.

PROVENANCE
Amsterdam, art dealer F. Buffa & Zn.; coll. George Summer, –1920; presented to the museum in memory of his wife, 1920.

BIBLIOGRAPHY
Eisler 1910, pp. 35–36.

EXHIBITIONS
Montreal 1914.

VARIATIONS
1) watercolour, 53 × 68 cm, auct. Amsterdam (C.F. Roos & Co), 21–22 March 1899, no. 37 (with ill.; as *Idylle Pastorale*). 2) watercolour, 41 × 53 cm, auct. The Hague (Kunstzaal Kleykamp), 5 March 1918, no. 47 (with ill.; as *Lente-idylle*). 3) oil on canvas, 116.9 × 172.8 cm, auct. New York (Sotheby Parke Bernet), 27 March 1956, no. 69 (with ill.). 4) drawing; De Meester 1898, ill. on p. 93.

36

dealer F. Buffa & Zn., 1933; Almelo/Oldenzaal, coll. H.E. ten Cate; Wassenaar, coll. R.J. Veendorp; on loan to the museum.

BIBLIOGRAPHY
Berckenhoff 1901, ill. on p. 166; Rössing 1903, ill. on p. 217; Greenshields 1904, ill. on p. 39; *Sale of the works of J.H. Weissenbruch to be sold March First in Pulchri Studio The Hague*, The Hague 1904, ill. on p. 3; exh. cat. Rotterdam 1906(2), ill. on p. 4; exh. cat. Dordrecht 1909–10, ill. on p. 2; exh. cat. The Hague 1924(3), ill. on p. 2; Van Gelder 1940, p. 38, ill. on p. 39; Van Gelder 1946(2), p. 51; cat. Coll. H.E. ten Cate 1955, vol. 1, p. 92, no. 151, vol. 2, fig. 140; De Gruyter 1968–69, vol. 1, pp. 68, 113, fig. 60.

EXHIBITIONS
The Hague 1882, no. 51; Amsterdam 1885(2), no. 66; Rotterdam 1894(2), no. 52; The Hague 1895(1), no. 28; Amsterdam 1906(2), no. 60; Venice 1910, no. 30; The Hague 1911–12, no. 83; The Hague 1924(1), no. 42; Amsterdam 1933(2), (with ill.); Almelo 1956, no. 61; Laren 1960–61, no. 80; Breda 1961, no. 75; Groningen 1969, no. 96 (with ill.).

38

37 *Portrait of Jan Hendrik Weissenbruch*

Watercolour, 34 × 22 cm
Signed bottom right: *Jozef Israëls*
Groningen, Groninger Museum
(on loan from Collection R.J. Veendorp)

Jozef Israëls, the figure painter, was not always successful as a portraitist. In his earliest Amsterdam period his portraits, which he sold for five to ten guilders, for a long time constituted his main source of income, but the first portrait he exhibited – that of the actress Mme Taigny – was dismissed as a failure by the *Kunstkronijk* in 1848. Another early portrait, that of *Eleazer Herschel* (Stedelijk Museum, Amsterdam), is, however, worth noting.

Nevertheless, Israëls's strength lay in the rendering of general types, rather than specific people; certainly his more formal portraits often appear wooden and forced. It is well known that Israëls struggled with the likeness of the writer Conrad Busken Huet in 1863, and even used photography as an aid, but the final result pleased neither the painter nor the sitter. Israëls's most successful portraits were undoubtedly those of other artists; fellow-painters like Roelofs (Cat. 38) and Blommers, the actor Louis Veltman or the pianist Zeldenrust. The series of watercolour portraits that includes the present picture of Weissenbruch, as well as portraits of Neuhuys and Stortenbeker, is also notable. Israëls first exhibited this portrait at a Hollandsche Teeken-Maatschappij (Dutch Drawing Society) exhibition in 1882. He may have painted it during a visit to the artist at Noorden.

PROVENANCE
The Hague, coll. J.H. Weissenbruch, –1903; Bussum, coll. W.J. Weissenbruch, 1903–; Amsterdam, art

38 *Portrait of Willem Roelofs*

Oil on canvas, 77 × 63 cm
Signed bottom right: *Jozef Israels*
The Hague, Haags Gemeentemuseum

Ten years after Israëls completed the watercolour portrait of Jan Hendrik Weissenbruch (Cat. 37) he painted a likeness of another colleague, Willem Roelofs. The portrait was commissioned in 1892 by the committee set up to honour Roelofs's seventieth birthday and they presented it to the Haags Gemeentemuseum that same year. Although Van Gelder counted it among 'the very best that portraiture – not only that of Israëls! – has produced', neither Roelofs nor his family were very taken with it.

PROVENANCE
The Hague, Commissie tot Huldiging van Roelofs, 1892; presented to the museum, 1892.

BIBLIOGRAPHY
J. Veth in *De Nieuwe Gids* VII (1892), vol. 2, pp. 141–42; G.[H. Marius] in N.S. (1894), pp. 244, 308; G.H. Marius in E.G.M. x (1900), vol. xx, ill, on p. 481; M.K. 1 (1903), no. 42 (with ill.); Jeltes 1911, p. 149; Plasschaert 1923(1), p. 20; Plasschaert 1923(2); ill.; cat. Gemeentemuseum 1935, p. 113, no. 245, fig. 33; Van Gelder 1946(2), p. 51, ill. on p. 55; Pedroza 1948, p. 12 (with ill.); cat. Gemeentemuseum 1962, no. 161 (with ill.); Van Hall 1963, p. 279, no. 1; De Gruyter 1968–69, vol. 1, pp. 58, 113, fig. 54; Scheen 1981, fig. 485; J. Juffermans, J. Breeschoten & T. Breeschoten-Scheen, *Albert Roelofs, 1877–1920*, The Hague/Wassenaar 1982, ill. on p. 14.

EXHIBITIONS
The Hague 1924(1), no. 40; Amsterdam 1948(2), not numbered; Germany 1955, no. 1; Great Britain 1958, no. 1; Groningen 1961–62, no. 25 (with ill.); Bonn 1972, no. 9, fig. 3.

39

39 Midday Meal in a Cottage
at Karlshaven near Delden

Oil on canvas, 173 × 212 cm
Signed and dated bottom right: *Jozef Israels ft 1885*
Dordrecht, Dordrechts Museum

While the baby slumbers in its rush cradle and the kettle sings
on the coal fire, a peasant couple say grace before the steaming
midday meal. The noble expression on the face of the mother,
and the cow's head in the background, evoke vague associations with the birth of the Christ Child in a lowly stable.

This painting is one of the most ambitious of Israëls's many
treatments of the theme. It has an important place in the
tradition in which the *Frugal Meal* in the Glasgow museum was
an early highlight (see fig. 116) and Van Gogh's *Potato Eaters*
the final outcome.

Israëls had had a replica of a Scheveningen fisherman's
dwelling built in a corner of his studio and his models for such
subjects usually posed here, but the very explicit title of this
painting seems to indicate that he particularly wanted to depict
an actual farm kitchen. The same interior, similarly treated,

crops up in other unidentified farm kitchens by Israëls (for
example in the Stedelijk Museum, Amsterdam).

The picture was bought directly from the artist for the
Dordrechts Museum in 1885 and soon became more widely
known through the engraving by H. Sluyter Jr which was
published by the art dealer Buffa in 1886.

PROVENANCE
Purchased from the painter, May 1885 (with the aid of a donation by the Dowager Jonkheer F.J. van den
Santheuvel-Jantzon van Effrenten in Aug. 1884).

BIBLIOGRAPHY
Veth 1890, pp. 186–88; E.E. Haagens, *Album Dordrechts Museum*, Dordrecht [1898], no. 22 (with ill.);
Marius 1903, p. 232; Veth 1904, p. 17, fig. 8; Marius 1906, pp. 237–38; Tersteeg 1910, p. 26; Veth
1911(3), p. 273; Marius 1920, p. 121; Eisler 1924, p. 25, fig. XLII; Kahn 1925, p. 73; cat. Dordrechts
Museum 1928, p. 32, no. 89.

EXHIBITIONS
Groningen 1961–62, no. 19.

41

40 The Sandbargeman

Oil on canvas, 62 × 90 cm
Signed bottom left: *Jozef Israels*
Amsterdam, Rijksmuseum

Jan Veth identified the location of this painting as the Scheveningen canal and dated it shortly before 1890. Thanks to a letter written by the artist to the art dealer F. Buffa & Zn on 2 May 1887, in which the picture was mentioned under the title *On the Canal*, it is possible to be more precise. On 7 July of that year Israëls asked the sum of 5,000 guilders for the work, by then entitled *The Barge* (letters at Rijksprentenkabinet, Rijksmuseum, Amsterdam).

More expressive than all these titles is an old English name for the work, *The Long Way*. The figures in Israëls's landscapes often labour under heavy loads or are bent by the weight of years. Their toil is reflected in the melancholy landscape around them.

In 1894 an etching of *The Sandbargeman* was made by Graadt van Roggen as the twenty-fifth in a series of reproductions of Israëls's works published by Buffa.

PROVENANCE
Amsterdam, coll. C.D. Reich Jr., 1894.

BIBLIOGRAPHY
G. [H. Marius] in *N.S.* (1894), p. 38; J. [Veth] in *Kunst und Künstler* 1 (1902–03), p. 443 (with ill.); Steenhoff 1904, ill. opp. p. 50; Veth 1904, fig. 14; Jeltes 1924, p. 161; Knoef 1948, p. 105, ill. after p. 100; exh. cat. Groningen 1961–62, p. 46; De Gruyter 1968–69, vol. 1, p. 113, fig. 59.

EXHIBITIONS
Rotterdam 1894(2), no. 20; Amsterdam 1895(2), no. 11; Krefeld 1903, no. 42; Amsterdam 1906(2), no. 55; The Hague 1911–12, no. 59; Amsterdam 1923(1), no. 176; The Hague 1924(1), no. 11; Potsdam 1925, no. 61; Düsseldorf 1950, no. 16; Antwerp 1955, no. 24; Amsterdam 1963, no. s 64, fig. 66; The Hague 1965(1), no. 29 (with ill.); Regina 1969–70, no. 6 (with ill.); Amsterdam 1979(1), no. 34; Tokyo 1979, no. 34, (with ill.).

41 A Son of the Chosen People

Watercolour, 56 × 43 cm
Signed bottom right: *Jozef Israels*
Amsterdam, Rijksprentenkabinet, Rijksmuseum

In 1902 Israëls wrote that an artist paints 'the beggar not for his poverty, but for his riches'. Like Rembrandt, he sometimes found his subjects in the Jewish quarter of Amsterdam, although he himself lived in The Hague from 1871 onwards. The watercolours *The Rabbi* (1885) and *A Son of the Chosen People* were the first works Israëls had painted for many years which referred to his Jewish background, with which he always maintained close links. *The Jewish Wedding* (Rijksmuseum, Amsterdam) and *The Jewish Scribe* (Stedelijk Museum, Amsterdam) were among similar later works.

Israëls himself seems to have preferred the oil version of this watercolour, which was also entitled *A Son of the Chosen People* (Stedelijk Museum, Amsterdam). The oil is certainly more intense, since the figure is represented in isolation: Israëls wrote to Jan Veth, 'After I had made a watercolour, in which the Jew sits in the doorway with a child beside him and in which there is a great deal of the house and a large foreground, I decided that the man . . . was more interesting on his own.' Nowadays most writers prefer the watercolour, which has suffered less from the ravages of time. Once again it is striking how the artist has emphasized the man's passivity and apparently complete acceptance of his fate.

The model for the watercolour has been identified as Jacob Städel, of whom Israëls also painted a portrait. Although Israëls himself dated the oil version 1885, 1888 is generally accepted as the date for the watercolour and 1889 that for the painting.

PROVENANCE
London, coll. Mr and Mrs J.C.J. Drucker-Fraser, –1912; on loan to the museum, 1911; presented to the museum, 1912.

BIBLIOGRAPHY
Vermeulen 1911, pp. 486–87 (with ill.); Eisler 1913(1), p. 251; Eisler 1924, p. 28, fig. LXVII; Van Gelder 1946(2), p. 42, ill. on p. 38; exh. cat. Groningen 1961–62, p. 15; De Gruyter 1968–69, vol. 1, pp. 53, 55, 113, fig. 61; cat. Rijksmuseum 1976, p. 811 (with ill.).

EXHIBITIONS
The Hague 1895(1), no. 6; Amsterdam 1934(1), no. 55; Groningen 1961–62, no. 59; Amsterdam 1963, no. T 64; Paris 1963, no. 42, fig. XIV; Amsterdam 1963–64, no. 49; The Hague 1965(1), no. 34 (with ill.); Bonn 1972, no. 13.

VARIATIONS
1) oil on canvas, 178.5 × 137.5 cm, Stedelijk Museum, Amsterdam; cat. Stedelijk Museum 1922, pl. 57. 2) oil on canvas, 90 × 68 cm, art dealer Borzo, Bois-le-Duc, 1979; exh. cat. Bois-le-Duc, 1979, no. 29 (with ill.). 3) oil on panel, 40 × 29 cm, art dealer P.A. Scheen, The Hague, 1971. 4) watercolour, formerly coll. Isaac Israëls, Amsterdam/The Hague.

42 The Harp

Oil on canvas, 50.5 × 61 cm
Signed bottom left: *Jozef Israëls*
The Hague, Rijksmuseum H. W. Mesdag

The motif of a man or woman – the sex is not entirely clear – playing the harp had appeared in Israëls's work as early as 1851, and after this early romantic period it appeared again *c.* 1885. On 12 November of that year Israëls reported that he had sent 'the harpist' to the art dealer Buffa. However, this was a drawing and this oil version is mentioned for the first time at the Tentoonstelling van Levende Meesters (Exhibition of Living Masters) in 1893.

The Harp is reminiscent of the painting *Saul and David* (Stedelijk Museum, Amsterdam), which was finished in 1899 and for which it can be called not so much a preliminary study as a prefiguration. 'This subject has preoccupied me from my youth onwards because of the contrast between the gloomy Saul and the ideal singer David', Israëls wrote in 1904 to Jan Veth, who considered it a bad picture (letter in Gemmeentearchief [Municipal Archives], The Hague). Israëls's assertion that he worked hard over the *Saul and David* for three years, indicates that he began it before Rembrandt's famous *Saul and David* was exhibited in Amsterdam in 1898 and acquired by Dr Abraham Bredius.

PROVENANCE
The Hague, coll. H. W. Mesdag.

BIBLIOGRAPHY
Boele van Hensbroek 1890, p. 16; A.C Croiset van der Kop in *Dietsche Warande* N.S. VI (1893), p. 504; G. [H. Marius] in *N.S* (1893), pp. 248, 254–55; *Bredasche Courant* (12 Aug. 1893); *De Portefeuille* XV (1893–94); Knuttel-Fabius 1894, p. 193; G. [H. Marius] in *N.S.* (1895), p. 45; *Het Vaderland* (21–22 June 1896); Boele van Hensbroek 1910, p. 16; Pythian 1912, pp. 93–94; F. Smit-Kleine in *E.H.* XL (1914) pp. 651–52 (with ill.); Plasschaert 1923(2), ill.; Eisler 1924, fig. LIX; Brom 1959, p. 46; *De Waarheid* (11 Nov. 1961) (with ill.); exh. cat. Groningen 1961–62, p. 16; cat. Museum Mesdag 1975, pp. 84–85, no. 156, fig. on p. 86.

EXHIBITIONS
The Hague 1893(1), no. 177; Groningen 1961–62, no. 27 (with ill.).

43 Meditation

Oil on canvas, 50 × 61 cm
Signed bottom left: *Jozef Israels*
Amsterdam, Rijksmuseum
repr. in colour on p. 32

From the moment Israëls began to depict the life of the fishing people, his subject matter included women gazing out to sea, sometimes from a dune (Cat. 34) and elsewhere from a window. In this late canvas he achieved his most timeless treatment of the subject. In 1961 De Gruyter spoke of 'a generalized human expression' painted with 'brushwork that heralds Expressionism'. The title *Meditation* is characteristic of Israëls, who allows the spectator a certain latitude in interpreting the thoughts of the woman. Thus, in 1896 he refuted one attempt to interpret his *Woman at a Window* (Museum Boymans-van Beuningen) specifically as a widow. However, in a letter of 10 April to Haverkorn van Rijsewijk, the director of the museum, he proved himself quite capable of giving an accurate definition of what he had intended. 'What is represented here is not the mild despair of a widow. It is more an abandoned woman of the people, who feels herself innocently ill-used and downtrodden and does not know how to carry on in this situation.' (letter in Rijksprentenkabinet, Rijksmuseum, Amsterdam).

Meditation has been regarded as a preliminary study for the painting in the Museum Boymans-van Beuningen, but since Israëls frequently handled the theme in the 1890s, there is little point in trying to define the relationships between the innumerable versions more precisely.

PROVENANCE
London, coll. Mr and Mrs J.C.J. Drucker-Fraser, –1944; on loan to the museum, 1919; bequeathed to the museum, 1944.

BIBLIOGRAPHY
Het Binnenhof (28 Oct. 1961); *De Groene Amsterdammer* (28 Oct. 1961); *De Warrheid* (11 Nov. 1961); *Rotterdams Nieuwsblad* (1 Dec. 1961); *Het Vaderland* (12 Dec. 1961), ill.; *De Maasbode* (16 Dec. 1961), ill.; exh. cat. Groningen 1961–62, p. 6; De Gruyter 1968–69, vol. I, p. 113, fig. 56; cat. Rijksmuseum 1976, p. 229 (with ill.).

EXHIBITIONS
? The Hague 1895(1), no. 12; Groningen 1961–62, no. 28 (with ill.); The Hague 1965(1), no. 30 (with ill.); Amsterdam 1979(1), no. 35; Tokyo 1979, no. 35 (with ill.).

44 The Fisherman's Return

Watercolour, 75.2 × 62 cm
Signed bottom right: *Jozef Israels*
Montreal, Musée des Beaux-Arts de Montréal
(Bequest of Mrs William Forrest Angus)

Although Israëls himself sometimes made fun of the contemplative character of his subjects ('My son [Isaac] paints the soldiers going off to battle, I the weeping widows'), he did occasionally handle more robust subjects, as in the present picture and *Bringing in the Anchor*, exhibited in Paris in 1889.

In the Dienst Verspreide Rijkskollekties (State-owned Art Collections Department) in The Hague there is a black chalk drawing of a man whose pose is very close to that of the figure in the *Fisherman's Return*. It has hitherto been dated around 1890. However, in 1904 Israëls wrote to Jan Veth: 'I had at that time [1900] seen my son and Liebermann making studies of horses and was stirred by them to do likewise. Thus, latterly, paintings and watercolours with horses have repeatedly appeared.' (letter in the Gemeentearchief, The Hague).

PROVENANCE
The Hague, art dealer Goupil & Co; Montreal, art dealer Scott & Sons; Montreal, coll. R.B. Angus, before 1903; Montreal, coll. William Forrest Angus, –1962; bequeathed to the museum by Mrs William Forrest Angus, 1962.

VARIATIONS
1) watercolour, 78 × 56 cm, auct. Bern (Dobiaschofsky), 30 April 1980, no. 406 (with ill.). 2) oil on canvas, 82 × 120 cm, auct. The Hague (Koninklijke Kunstzaal Kleykamp), 3 Dec. 1935, no. 20 (with ill.). 3) drawing, 31.5 × 20.3 cm, Dienst Verspreide Rijkskollekties (State-owned Art Collections Department), The Hague (on loan to the Haags Gemeentemuseum, The Hague); exh. cat. Groningen 1961–62, no. 95 (with ill.).

45 Self Portrait

Watercolour and gouache, 79 × 54.3 cm
Signed, dated and inscribed bottom left: *Jozef Israels fecit for mr.
Libbey 28 Oct 1908*
Toledo (Ohio), The Toledo Museum of Art
(Gift of Edward Drummond Libbey)

This late self portrait shows the artist at the age of 84 standing in front of his painting *Saul and David* of 1899 (Stedelijk

Museum, Amsterdam). His choice of this ambitious canvas as a background indicates that the artist regarded it as the crowning achievement of his career (see also Cat. 42).

The watercolour is dated 28 October 1908 and dedicated to Edward Drummond Libbey, an American industrialist and collector who, with a group of friends, had put on a banquet for Israëls in Scheveningen earlier that year. In a letter of 7 October to Libbey, Israëls referred to the painting, for which Libbey paid $3,000, as 'one of my best works' (he evidently had no inhibitions about offering collectors favourable opinions of his own work).

Libbey's collection formed the basis for the Toledo Museum of Art and it is an indication of the great admiration felt for Israëls in the United States of America that when the museum was inaugurated in 1912 with a series of five exhibitions, the only one-man show there was devoted to Israëls, who had just died. Later, the second director of the museum, Arthur J. Secor, presented it with another of Israëls's 'best pictures'.

In December 1908 Israëls completed an oil version of the self portrait (Stedelijk Museum, Amsterdam), in which the composition was slightly shortened at the bottom.

PROVENANCE
The Hague, art dealer Boussod, Valadon & Co, 1908; New York, art dealer Henry Reinhardt, 1908; Toledo (Ohio), coll. Edward Drummond Libbey, 1908–14; presented to the museum, 1914.

BIBLIOGRAPHY
Tersteeg 1910, p. 36, note 1, ill. on p. 37; Veth 1911(3), ill. on p. 280; Gunsaulus 1912, ill. opp. p. 107; Eisler 1924, fig. LXXVIII; Goldscheider 1937, no. 421; cat. Toledo Museum 1939, p. 130, ill. on p. 131; Boon 1947, p. 74; Van Hall 1963, p. 152, no. 3; Engel 1967, p. 75; Sutton 1967, p. 490, fig. 13; De Gruyter 1968–69, vol. 1, pp. 56, 113, fig. 49; cat. Toledo Museum 1976, p. 83, fig. 154.

EXHIBITIONS
The Hague 1908(1); Toledo 1912, no. 243; Toledo 1937, no. 35; The Hague 1965(1), no. 35 (with ill.; also ill. on p. 43).

VARIATIONS
1) oil on canvas, 97 × 70 cm, Stedelijk Museum, Amsterdam; exh. cat. Groningen 1961–62, no. 36 (with ill.). 2) drawing; *Wereldkroniijk* (1911), vol. 2, ill. on p. 28; 3) drawing, *De Amsterdammer* (31 Jan. 1909), ill.

45

Jacob Maris (1837-1899)

Jacob Hendricus Maris was born in The Hague on 25 August 1837 as the eldest son of Mattheus Maris and Hendrika Bloemert; of their five children all three sons, Jacob, Matthijs and Willem, became artists. In 1849, at the age of 12, Jacob became the pupil of Johannes Stroebel (1821–1905) and a year later he also took lessons at the Haagse Academie under Jacobus van den Berg (1802–61). After that he became the pupil of Huib van Hove (1814–64), and moved to Antwerp with him in 1854, the same year in which he first showed work at the Tentoonstelling van Levende Meesters (Exhibition of Living Masters). In Antwerp he attended evening classes at the Academy where he was taught by Nicaise de Keyser (1813–87) and came into contact with the marine painter Louis Meijer (1809–66).

In his second year of study there he was joined by his brother Matthijs, whose grant, on which they both tried to live, made him independent of Van Hove. The brothers rented a studio together in a house where shortly afterwards, their friend and fellow-student Alma Tadema (1830–1912) also took a room. There Jacob and Matthijs Maris painted pictures intended for the American market, which they sold for five to ten guilders apiece.

In 1857 Jacob returned to The Hague, where he shared a studio first with Jan Swijser (1835–1912), then with Ferdinand Sierich (1839–1905) and, after 1858, with Matthijs. In the following years the brothers received a series of commissions from Princess Marianne, the youngest daughter of King William I, to copy eight portraits of members of the House of Orange. This enabled them to spend some time in Oosterbeek and Wolfheze in 1859 and 1860, and in 1861 to make a trip to Germany (Cologne, Mannheim, Heidelberg, Karlsruhe),

Switzerland (Basle, Lausanne, Neufchatel) and France (Dijon, Fountainebleau, Paris). After their return lack of funds compelled them to give up the studio they shared and to move in with their parents. That year Jacob again studied at the Haagse Academie, this time under Johan Philip Koelman, (1818–93) and he also helped Louis Meijer, who had become partially crippled by rheumatism, to finish his paintings.

In the spring of 1865 Jacob moved to Paris, where he remained until 1871. He lived in Rue Marcadet, first with Frederik Hendrik Kaemmerer (1839–1902) and later with Adolphe Artz. During this period he worked for some months in the studio of Ernest Hebert (1817–1908), who he emulated with a series of paintings of Italian peasant girls (Cat. 47). In 1867 Jacob married Catharina Hendrika Horn and two years later, at their insistence, Matthijs came to live with them. In 1871, after the Franco-Prussian War and the Commune that followed Jacob returned to The Hague. Although he had originally intended only a short visit, the family settled there and Jacob lived there for the rest of his life.

Meanwhile he devoted more and more time to painting landscapes. In The Hague he moved into a studio on Noordwest Binnensingel. Many of his subjects were drawn from the immediate vicinity of this studio and he painted *The Truncated Windmill* (Cat. 51) from its window. As well as landscapes, he painted an impressive series of townscapes, many of which are *capriccio* views that drew elements from Amsterdam, Dordrecht, Rotterdam and Delft.

Jacob Maris was an important influence on later artists but had only one real pupil, Willem de Zwart (1862–1931). He died on 7 August 1899 at Carlsbad, where he had gone for a health cure.

fig. 138 VETH *Portrait of Jacob Maris* (black chalk drawing) (Rijksmuseum, Amsterdam)

46

46 The Butcher's Shop

Oil on paper on panel, 52 × 43 cm
Signed bottom right: *J. Maris*
Rotterdam, Museum Boymans-van Beuningen

This interior of a butcher's shop (a large chopping-block can be seen on the right) has been dated *c.* 1870 on the basis of a comparison with a work illustrated in *Elsevier's Geïllustreerd Maandschrift* in 1913. But although the same atmosphere and lighting, derived from the interiors of Pieter de Hooch, can be found in both pictures, there seem to be more arguments in favour of placing the present work somewhat earlier, in Jacob Maris's Antwerp period or shortly afterwards. The free style of painting, which has been thought to indicate a later date, is not uncommon in similar early sketches on paper, which Maris is known to have kept in his studio for many years.

Dutch genre paintings of the seventeenth century were the most important models in the work of the contemporary Antwerp artist, Henri Leys, and his circle. Indeed, one finds the same close attention to the texture of a tiled floor or a plastered wall in the work of countless other contemporary artists. In this connection, one is reminded of the early Antwerp work of Laurens (or Lawrence) Alma Tadema, Maris's friend, who lived in the same house and was later to apply his passion for the extremely precise rendering of textures in his scenes drawn from classical antiquity.

Maris's teachers Huib van Hove and Johannes Stroebel had a similar approach; the latter in particular paid great attention to light and the atmosphere it created. The lack of any anecdotal elements and the dominance of the play of light in the interior

are typical of Jacob Maris's early work. Engel has pointed out in his dissertation on Anton Mauve that his greater attention to light effects in his early interiors of stables can undoubtedly be traced to his association with Jacob Maris.

PROVENANCE
The Hague, coll. of the painter; Rotterdam, coll. J.P. van der Schilden, –1925; bequeathed to the museum, 1925.

BIBLIOGRAPHY
W. V[ogelsang] in *Onze Kunst* II (1903), vol. 2, p. 22 (with ill.); *M.K.* IV (1906), no. 3 (with ill.); *Verslag van het Museum Boymans te Rotterdam over het jaar 1925*, p. 3 (with ill.); Koomen 1949, pp. 127, 142; cat. Museum Boymans-van Beuningen 1963, pp. 81–82; cat. Museum Boymans-van Beuningen 1972, p. 215, ill. on p. 185.

EXHIBITIONS
Amsterdam 1906(2), no. 89; Amsterdam 1923(1), no. 231; The Hague 1935–36, no. 6; The Hague 1945, no. 60.

47 *Girl Knitting on a Balcony, Montmartre*

Oil on canvas, 75 × 40 cm
Signed and dated bottom left: *J. Maris ft 1869*
The Hague, Haags Gemeentemuseum

In 1865 Jacob Maris settled in Paris, where he began painting this series of '*Italiennes*' in the studio of Ernest Hébert. In 1866 he made his debut at the Salon with a *Petite Fille Italienne*; and he won a prize with a similar work that he sent to an exhibition of watercolours in Utrecht. This *Girl Knitting on a Balcony* is one of the last of the series and may be identical with the *Tricoteuse* that he sent to the Salon in 1869. The Corot-like background can be seen in his work several years earlier, while the same balcony appears in a picture dated 1867.

The restrained tonality, contrasting with Jacob's earlier, rather colourful palette, has been attributed by De Gruyter to the renewed influence of Matthijs Maris, who joined his brother in Paris early in 1869. However, Matthijs painted very little in his first years in Paris; in fact there can be no question of his influence in this work, since Jacob sold it to Goupil's in March 1869 and Matthijs did not arrive in Paris until May of that year.

PROVENANCE
The Hague, art dealer Goupil & Co, 1869; Amsterdam, art dealer C.M. van Gogh, 1870; Amsterdam, coll. E.H. Crone, 1935; on loan to the museum by the E.H. Crone Heirs, 1947–64; purchased by the museum, 1964.

BIBLIOGRAPHY
A.H. (24 June 1909); *A.H.* (31 July 1909); Marius 1910, pp. 4–5, ill. on p. 2; cat. Gemeentemuseum 1962, no. 184 (with ill.); *Agenda Haags Gemeentemuseum* (April 1964), ill.; De Gruyter 1968–69, vol. 2, pp. 20, 29.

EXHIBITIONS
?Paris 1869, (as *Tricoteuse*); Amsterdam 1923(1), no. 238; The Hague 1935–36, no. 32; The Hague 1964, no. 14; The Hague 1965(1), no. 40 (with ill.); Bonn 1972, no. 31; Amsterdam 1979(1), no. 43; Tokyo 1979, no. 43 (with ill.).

48

48 *View of Montigny-sur-Loing*

Oil on canvas, 45 × 80 cm
Signed and dated bottom right: *J. Maris 1870*
Rotterdam, Museum Boymans–van Beuningen
repr. in colour on p. 65

In Paris, Maris seemed to have become a figure painter, but at
the end of the 1860s he began to show a renewed interest in
landscape painting; we know of 14 landscapes by him from
1869 alone. This painting was initially associated with the little
village of Marlotte, where he spent some time with his family
in the summer of 1869; the location has since been recognized
as nearby Montigny-sur-Loing, a small town near the
southern edge of the Forest of Fontainebleau, on a small
tributary of the Seine some 75 kilometres from Paris. An oil
sketch for the work, without figures and probably painted in
1869, was exhibited in Utrecht in 1897. In the same year Maris
painted *The Angler*, a river scene in which Montigny can again
be seen in the background.

View of Montigny-sur-Loing has won universal praise for its
careful composition and harmonious combination of pale
tones of green, grey, brown and grey-blue. The earliest of
Maris's views of towns on water, it stands on the threshold of
his grey period. Oddly enough, Maris himself did not like the
painting and was irritated by the praise it attracted. He was
probably aware of the numerous influences that are recognizable in it and was thus unwilling to include it in his Dutch
œuvre. The work reveals a similarity to Corot, and the same
predilection for river scenes with buildings that is found
among painters like Pissarro and Bazille at that time. Knoef has
remarked on the painting's striking similarity to a work by
Daubigny, now in the National Gallery of Scotland in
Edinburgh (see fig. 53). Yet a Dutch influence, that of
Johannes Vermeer's *View of Delft*, is also evident. Maris knew
this painting well from the Mauritshuis in his home town;
indeed, it had already inspired his friend Sam Verveer to paint
a townscape, which may be regarded as an intermediate stage
between the Delft master and the artist of *Montigny-sur-Loing*
(see *Tableau* IV [1982], p. 395). Vermeer's *View of Delft* and the
present work share the same general composition and the

lovingly painted reflections, and they also have in common the
foreground on the left with the two washerwomen.

PROVENANCE
London, coll. James Staats Forbes, 1895; Rotterdam, coll. J.P. van der Schilden, –1925; bequeathed to
the museum, 1925.

BIBLIOGRAPHY
Zilcken 1896(1), ill. after p. 6 (etching by Ph. Zilcken after the painting); Kalff 1902, p. 300; De Bock
1902–03, p. 45; Marius 1903, p. 262; Marius 1906, p. 265; *M.K.* IV (1906), no. 8 (with ill.); Marius 1908,
p. 109; Veth 1908, pp. 170–72; Bénédite 1910, p. 251; Marius 1910, p. 4; Veth 1911, p. 23; Eisler
1913(2), p. 34; Veth 1914, pp. 170–72; Plasschaert 1920, pp. 30–31, 59; *Verslag van het Museum Boymans
te Rotterdam over het jaar 1925*, p. 3 (with ill.); Van Gelder 1937, fig. 4, on p. 445; Van Gelder 1939,
pp. 48–49; Maris 1943, p. 136; Knoef 1946, pp. 210, 212, fig. 4; Van Gelder 1946(1), fig. 4 on p. 689;
Maris 1947, p. 124; Knoef 1948, ill. opp. p. 96; Koomen 1949, pp. 127, 134; *Agenda Museum Boymans
Rotterdam* (1952), no. 51 (with ill.); Van Gelder 1954–56, vol. 2, fig. 4 on p. 396; S.H. Levie in *O.K.* III
(1959), no. 30 (with ill.); Gerson 1961, p. 28, fig. 62; A.B. de Vries in *O.K. Televisiecursus* I (1963),
no. 15, fig. 9; cat. Museum Boymans-van Beuningen 1963, pp. 80–81; Van Gelder 1963–65, vol. 11,
fig. 4 on p. 1918; *Agenda Museum Boymans-van-Beuningen Rotterdam* (1967), no. 10, (with ill; detail); De
Gruyter 1968–69, vol. 2, pp. 18, 20–21, 29, 100, fig. 17; cat. Museum Boymans-van-Beuningen 1972,
p. 215, ill. on p. 184; Marius/Norman 1973, p. 126.

EXHIBITIONS
The Hague 1895(2), no. 29; Amsterdam 1899(2), no. 81; Amsterdam 1923(1), no. 230; London 1929,
no. 424; The Hague 1935–36, no. 304; The Hague 1945, no. 61; Luxemburg 1948, no. 55; The Hague
1965(1), no. 41 (with ill.); Amsterdam 1979(1), no. 44; Tokyo 1979, no. 44 (with ill.).

VARIATIONS
Painting, art dealer C.M. van Gogh, Amsterdam, 1896; exh. cat. Utrecht 1896, no. 35.

49 *The Ferry*

Oil on canvas, 38 × 66 cm
Signed and dated bottom right: *J. Maris ft. 70*
The Hague, Gallery P. A. Scheen

The theme of a ferry carrying passengers or cattle across a river is very common in Dutch nineteenth-century painting. It can be found in many works by artists of the romantic era, and occasionally in those of Hague School painters, for example in Paul Gabriël's *Ferry at Driel*. In Jacob Maris's work the subject of a ferry first appears in a sketchbook dating from the early 1860s. A small sketch of this theme, painted in 1864, is now in the collection of H. van Leeuwen, Amerongen. Only at the end of his Paris period, in 1870, did Maris develop the subject fully and paint five variously related versions of it.

The choice of this particularly Dutch theme, made famous by such artists as Esaias van de Velde, Jan van Goyen and Salomon van Ruysdael, has been interpreted as a deliberate statement by Maris. Coming at a time when he definitely opted for a career as a landscape painter, he stressed his allegiance to the traditions of his native land, to which he was to return the next year.

PROVENANCE
Auct. The Hague (Kunstzaal Kleykamp), 5 May 1919, no. 3 (Dfl. 19,000); The Hague, priv. coll., 1919–; Miami, coll. Westerman; The Hague, art dealer P. A. Scheen, 1977.

BIBLIOGRAPHY
Scheen 1981, fig. 495.

EXHIBITIONS
Maastricht 1977 (Pictura; no cat.).

50

50 *The River Waal near Gorcum*

Oil on canvas, 38 × 61.25 cm
Signed and dated bottom right: *J. Maris ft 1871*
Montreal, Musée des Beaux-Arts de Montréal
(Bequest of William J. & Agnes Learmont)

Jacob Maris's later painted views of rivers were generally combined with a view of a town, but in this work of 1871, probably one of the first he produced in the Netherlands after his stay in Paris, the town is little more than an outline on the horizon and attention is still concentrated wholly on the turbulent water and play of light upon it.

This work is a notable departure from the generally very calm river scenes that Maris had painted on the outskirts of Paris, although something similar is seen in his occasional views of the Breton coast. Maris's free use of the palette knife is also striking. An allied interest in the play of light on rough water is later seen in his paintings of Scheveningen.

PROVENANCE
Montreal, coll. William John & Agnes Learmont, –1909; bequeathed to the museum, 1909.

EXHIBITIONS
Montreal 1898; Montreal 1900; Montreal 1962 (no cat.).

51

51 The Truncated Windmill

Oil on canvas, 45 × 112.5 cm
Signed and dated bottom right: *J. Maris fc 1872*
Amsterdam, Rijksmuseum

In his *Memoirs* Willem Maris recalled how his brother Jacob's work later declined in quality because he painted endless views of the same towns and windmills under skies with white clouds. 'His first windmills were just painted from the window on N.W. Binnensingel. Those were his palmy days'.

The Truncated Windmill of 1872 is one of the most remarkable works that Maris 'just painted from the window' of his studio. Another version of the same subject in a private collection in New Jersey (see fig. 56), dated a year later, shows the identical motif in a carefully considered composition. In the last resort, however, that painting lacks the élan of this picture, in which the large scale, unusual elongated format and daring truncation of the top of the mill all confirm Jacob Maris's newly acquired artistic independence. Here, for the first time, the true character of his art is revealed.

The Truncated Windmill united all the elements of the 'elevation of the grey tone to a national sentiment' (Engel) during the 1870s. The subject is a motif pure and simple, the application of the paint as broad and vigorous as it is controlled, the sky heavily overcast, the light diffused, the atmosphere as saturated with moisture as the lush ground. Plasschaert was of the opinion that the metaphor of organ tones, which he considered misused in relation to Maris's work could be used with justice here. The work is the credo of an artist who said that he thought through the medium in which he worked.

PROVENANCE
The Hague, coll. Baron N. A. Steengracht van Moyland, –1895; auct. Amsterdam (A. Preyer), 10 Sept. 1895, no. 73 (Dfl. 4,750); London, coll. Mr & Mrs J.C.J. Drucker-Fraser, 1895–1909/10; on loan to the museum, 1904; presented to the museum, 1909/10.

BIBLIOGRAPHY
Kalff 1902, p. 301; De Bock 1902–03, ill. on p. 1; *Het Leven* (8 Oct. 1909), Bijlage, ill.; Steenhoff 1910(2), p. 366; Veth 1911, ill. on p. 24; Eisler 1913(1), p. 325, ill. on p. 323; Plasschaert 1920, pp. 34, 60; Knuttel 1938, pp. 441–42 (with ill.); Van Gelder 1939, p. 18; Maris 1943, pp. 170, 171, ill. on p. 167; Maris 1947, pp. 156, 157, ill. on p. 145; Knoef 1948, pp. 101, 103; Knuttel 1950, p. 461, ill. on p. 462; Gerson 1961, p. 28; Engel 1967, p. 63; De Gruyter 1968–69, vol. 2, pp. 21, 30, 100, fig. 16; cat. Rijksmuseum 1976, p. 362 (with ill.); Pollock 1980–81, ill. on p. 32.

EXHIBITIONS
Amsterdam 1899(2), no. 4; The Hague 1899(2), no. 4; London 1929, no. 438; The Hague 1935–36, no. 46; Athens 1953, no. 14; Zagreb 1953, no. 15; Israel 1954, no. 13; Passau 1956, no. 24; The Hague 1965(1), no. 44 (with ill.); Regina 1969–70, no. 15 (with ill.); Bonn 1972, no. 32, fig. 12.

52 Dutch Canal, Rijswijk

Oil on canvas, 82.5 × 147.3 cm
Signed and dated bottom left: *J. Maris, 1872*
Philadelphia, The Philadelphia Museum of Art
(John G. Johnson Collection)
repr. in colour on p. 65

The motif of the long wooden bridge from *The Truncated Windmill* (Cat. 51) appears again in this undoubtedly very Dutch scene that includes a milkmaid and bargeman, painted in the same year as the previous picture. Maris painted countless versions of this theme, giving the location as Rijswijk or Loosduinen. The largest and best-known version is the painting dated 1885 in the Frick Collection, New York, which is noticeably freer in its handling than the 1872 work shown here. This painting may be Maris's first version, although there is another painting dated 1872 in a Canadian private collection. One of the two was exhibited at the Paris Salon in 1873.

In later versions Maris left more room for the sky and in general the air was more opaque than in this painting. This is particularly striking in a dark etching (in which the composition is reversed) that retains the oblong format of this painting. A fine watercolour in the Metropolitan Museum, New York is close to the painting in the Frick Collection.

PROVENANCE
England, coll. Barlow; The Hague, art dealer Boussod, Valadon & Co; coll. John G. Johnson.

EXHIBITIONS
? Paris 1873; New York 1892, no. 194 (or 195); Chicago 1893, no. 95 (or 98); Pittsburgh 1902–03, no. 96.

VARIATIONS
1) oil on canvas, 34.5 × 44.5 cm, auct. Amsterdam (A. Mak), 11 March 1930, no. 19 (with ill.). 2) oil on panel, 77 × 55 cm, auct. Amsterdam (Mak van Waay), 25 June 1957, no. 193. 3) oil on panel, 21 × 52 cm, auct. Amsterdam (Sotheby Mak van Waay), 19 Oct. 1976, no. 962 (with ill.). 4) panel, 22 × 28 cm Rijksmuseum, Amsterdam; cat. Rijksmuseum 1976, p. 363 (with ill.). 5) oil on canvas, 113 × 139 cm, The Frick Collection, New York; *The Frick Collection, An Illustrated Catalogue*, vol. 1, New York 1968,

ill. on p. 241. 6) oil on canvas, 25.5 × 35.5 cm, Dienst Verspreide Rijkskollekties (State-owned Art Collections Department), The Hague. 7) oil on canvas, 24 × 39 cm, art dealer P. A. Scheen, The Hague, 1976. 8) oil on canvas, coll. Senator John Connolly, Ottawa; *B.M.* 11 (1903), ill. on p. 183. 9) oil on canvas, 82 × 111 cm, auct. Amsterdam (F. Muller & Co.), 31 Oct. 1916, no. 179 (with ill.). 10) oil on canvas, 42 × 73 cm, Stedelijk Museum, Amsterdam. 11) oil on canvas, 72.1 × 91.5 cm, Allen Memorial Art Museum, Oberlin College, Oberlin; W. Stechow, *Catalogue of European and American Paintings and Sculpture in the Allen Memorial Art Museum, Oberlin College*, Oberlin (Ohio) 1967, p. 103, no. 42. 83, fig. 101. 12) watercolour, 36.8 × 45.5 cm, The Metropolitan Museum of Art, New York; *Bulletin of the Metropolitan Museum of Art* 11 (1903), ill. on p. 188.

53   *The Drawbridge*

Watercolour, 28 × 21.5 cm
Signed and dated bottom right: *J. Maris 1875*
Amsterdam, Rijksprentenkabinet, Rijksmuseum

During the 1870s Jacob Maris repeatedly succeeded in transforming apparently simple motifs into powerful subjective impressions; painters of the previous generation had never dared to present ordinary subjects with such simplicity. Even Matthijs Maris's heartfelt *Souvenir d'Amsterdam* (Cat. 73), painted from a photograph, seems to be a carefully contrived stage-set when compared with this watercolour (although this is not necessarily indicative of the relative merits of the two works).

There are several telling differences between Maris's watercolour and the oil version of the same theme in the National Gallery in London. In the oil small shifts of emphasis stress the implicit monumentality of the simple drawbridge; the contrasts between light and dark are slightly heightened and the whole is given a greater tautness by applying black outlines, also used by Maris in some of his watercolours (cf. Cat. 55). In addition, Maris creates a larger distance between the bridge and the row of houses on the right by placing the masts of one or two boats between them and he replaces the figure on the bridge by a horse and cart.

One is tempted to conclude that the uncompromising simplicity of Van Gogh's *Bridge at Arles* of 1888 would be inconceivable without similar works of the Hague School.

PROVENANCE
Amsterdam, art dealer E.J. van Wisselingh & Co; Amsterdam, coll. C.D. Reich Jr.; bequeathed to the State of the Netherlands by Mrs A.E. Reich-Hohwü; on loan to the museum.

BIBLIOGRAPHY
De Bock 1902–03, ill. on p. 119; Van Wisselingh 1923, ill. on frontispiece; Jeltes 1924, p. 11, fig. VII.

EXHIBITIONS
Amsterdam 1898(2), no. 1 (with ill.); Amsterdam 1899(2), no. 130 (ill. on the cover); Amsterdam 1904, no. 72; Amsterdam 1919–20, no. 89; Amsterdam 1934(2), no. 83; Zeist 1975, no. 48.

VARIATIONS
Oil on canvas, 30.2 × 22.7 cm, National Gallery, London.

54   *View of Old Dordrecht*

Oil on canvas, 106.5 × 100 cm
Signed bottom left: *J. Maris*
The Hague, Haags Gemeentemuseum
repr. in colour on p. 66

Dordrecht had been a flourishing commercial centre and major political force in both the States of Holland and the Synod in the seventeenth century, but had suffered a sharp decline in the eighteenth century and had gradually become one of the sleepy *villes mortes* that appealed to artists' imaginations by virtue of their picturesque poverty. At the beginning of the nineteenth century local artists like the Van Strij brothers had attempted to continue the indigenous tradition of painting, drawing heavily on the work of their fellow-townsman Aelbert Cuyp. But it was left to Jacob Maris to rediscover the contemporary beauty of Dordrecht in the last quarter of the nineteenth century.

The remarkable, almost square format of this painting was one that Maris quite often chose at this period (see also Cat. 55). The painting was originally dated 1876, but this date was later painted out, perhaps by the artist. Several other versions of this composition are known (including a watercolour entitled *A Corner of Amsterdam* in the Montreal Museum of Fine Arts), but none surpass this work in its subtle play of tones of grey and brick red.

PROVENANCE
Auct. London (Sotheby's), 26 Feb. 1975, no. 221 (£5,500); Amsterdam, art dealer P. Lunshof, 1975; The Hague, art dealer Galerie Hoogsteder, 1980; purchased by the museum, 1981.

BIBLIOGRAPHY
B.M. CXVII (March 1975), p. i (with ill.).

VARIATIONS
1) oil on canvas on panel, 34.5 × 29 cm, art dealer Borzo, Bois-le-Duc, 1977; exh.cat. Bois-le-Duc 1977, no. 58 (with ill.). 2) watercolour, 24.3 × 19.7 cm, Musée des Beaux-Arts de Montréal, Montreal (Bequest of William J. & Agnes Learmont). 3) watercolour, 44.5 × 37 cm, auct. Amsterdam (F. Muller & Co.), 8 Nov. 1904, no. 54 (with ill. in separate album).

54

55

55 *City View at Night*

Watercolour, 48 × 43 cm
Signed bottom left: *J. Maris*
Amsterdam, Rijksprentenkabinet, Rijksmuseum

In composition and motif, this splendid watercolour is close to the previous work. The choice of an almost square format and the style also point to a date in the second half of the 1870s and not 1885, as Bremmer noted on a photograph in the Rijksbureau voor Kunsthistorische Documentatie (Netherlands Institute for Art History) in The Hague. The use of heavy lines, which sometimes also act as an additional boundary for areas of colour, is one of the most striking features of this work.

PROVENANCE
London, coll. James Staats Forbes; London, coll. Mr & Mrs J.C.J. Drucker-Fraser, –1944; on loan to the museum, 1919; bequeathed to the museum, 1944.

BIBLIOGRAPHY
E.G. Halton, in *The Studio* XXXVI (1905), p. 112, ill. on p. 117; De Gruyter 1968–69, vol. 2, p. 101, fig. 24; cat. Rijksmuseum 1976, pp. 812–13 (with ill.).

EXHIBITIONS
London 1929, no. 492; The Hague 1935–36, no. 147; Amsterdam 1963, no. T 76, fig. 58; The Hague 1965(1), no. 55 (with ill.).

57

56 Fishing Boat

Oil on canvas, 124 × 105 cm
Signed and dated: *J. Maris 1878*
The Hague, Haags Gemeentemuseum
repr. in colour on p. 67

In the mid-nineteenth century the Dutch fisheries suffered badly from the embargo on herring fishing and general economic climate; by 1855 herring fishing, which had for centuries been a thriving and important trade, was continued by only 140 boats from Scheveningen, Katwijk and Noordwijk. After the embargo on herring fishing was lifted in 1871 and as the economic situation improved during the following decades, the herring fisheries began to experience a new prosperity; by the end of the century the catch was ten times as large as it had been in 1855. The fleet at Scheveningen was responsible for almost half of this. After 1866, most fishing was done from sailing luggers but Scheveningen, which had no harbour of its own until the beginning of this century, remained faithful to the older type of bluff-bowed fishing boat, which had a flat keel and could be hauled up on to the beach by horses (see Cat. 90). Maris, Mauve, Mesdag and Weissenbruch immortalized these fishing boats in a series of brilliant paintings. The most classical interpretation of the theme is seen in this painting by Jacob Maris, which can also be regarded as a perfect work from the Hague School's grey period. The blue of the pennant and a touch of red on the boat constitute the only accents of colour in this symphony in silvery grey.

PROVENANCE
Coll. Mrs C. Hoogeveen van Walchren, –1930; bequeathed to the museum, 1930.

BIBLIOGRAPHY
Plasschaert 1920, p. 61; cat. Gemeentemuseum 1935, p. 160, no. 94–30, fig. 35; Knuttel 1938, ill. on p. 443; Knuttel 1950, ill. on p. 463; cat. Gemeentemuseum 1962, no. 190; *De wereld van de schilder. 37 Schilderijen uit het Haags Gemeentemuseum gezien door Anna Wagner*, [The Hague] 1962, p. 25, ill. on p. 24. De Gruyter 1968–69, vol. 2, pp. 22, 26, 30, 101, fig. 25.

EXHIBITIONS
Paris 1878; Brussels 1932, no. 63 (with ill.); The Hague 1935–36, no. 66; Antwerp 1937, no. 40 (with ill.); Maastricht 1945–46, no. 41; The Hague 1947, no. 241; Athens 1953, no. 16 (with ill.); Zagreb 1953, no. 17; Israel 1954, no. 15; Germany 1955, no. 7; Laren 1957, no. 156; Amsterdam 1963, no. s 75, fig. v; The Hague 1965(1), no. 46 (with ill.); Bonn 1972, no. 33, fig. 10.

57 Allotments near The Hague

Oil on canvas, 62.5 × 54 cm
Signed bottom left: *J. Maris*
The Hague, Haags Gemeentemuseum
repr. in colour on p. 68

In Maris's day the market-gardens near Laan van Meerdervoort depicted in this painting were still on the outskirts of The Hague. This painting originally belonged to the painter Taco Mesdag (1829–1902), the brother of Hendrik Mesdag. Théophile de Bock called it 'one of the most complete expressions of our master' and related how Maris had found the inspiration for it during a walk with Mauve to the Dekkersduin.

Maris is here drawing on the seventeenth-century tradition of the panoramic landscape, exemplified by the work of Philips Koninck and Jacob van Ruisdael, which was revived in the nineteenth century by Andreas Schelfhout, J.J. Destree and the young Jan Hendrik Weissenbruch. In particular there is an unmistakable affinity with Ruisdael's so-called 'Haarlempjes' (small views of Haarlem; see fig. 2).

Like his predecessors, Jacob Maris managed to suggest an immeasurable area within the space of a relatively small canvas. Without recourse to any anecdotal element, the eye is led into the distance by a winding canal and an autumn mist fuses all the motifs – which are in themselves quite insignificant: gardens, pollard willows and vague outlines of the city – into a superbly atmospheric image. The transition from foreground to background and from earth to sky, are accomplished by the strokes of the brush alone.

De Bock says that Maris painted the same panorama in completely different atmospheric conditions. A watercolour version was formerly in the Ten Cate Collection, and the same compositional elements may be seen in the watercolour *Canal and Town* (National Gallery of Scotland, Edinburgh).

PROVENANCE
Scheveningen, coll. Taco Mesdag Kzn., 1895; Scheveningen, coll. Mrs Taco Mesdag; Scheveningen,

58

coll. P.F. Thomsen, –1918; auct. Amsterdam (F. Muller & Co), 3 Dec. 1918, no. 28 (not sold); Scheveningen, coll. P.F. Thomsen, 1918–; The Hague, art dealer D. Sala & Zn., 1935; coll. W. Hoos; on loan to the museum by the W. Hoos Heirs, 1956–67; purchased by the museum, 1967.

BIBLIOGRAPHY
Kalff 1902, p. 290; De Bock 1902–03, pp. 97–98, ill. on p. 75; Eisler 1911(1), ill. on p. 213; Plasschaert 1920, p. 61; cat. Gemeentemuseum 1962, no. 189; De Gruyter 1968–69, vol. 2, p. 101, fig. 28; Fuchs 1978, pp. 165 (with fig. 148), 213; Pollock 1980–81, p. 51, ill. on p. 53.

EXHIBITIONS
The Hague 1895(2), no. 49; Amsterdam 1899(2), no. 51; The Hague 1899(1), no. 65; The Hague 1899(2), no. 60; The Hague 1913(1), no. 38; The Hague 1923, no. 48; The Hague 1935–36, no. 63; Great Britain 1958, no. 20; Bonn 1972, no. 34.

VARIATIONS
Watercolour, 30 × 21.5 cm, auct. Amsterdam (Mak van Waay), 14–16 Sept. 1964, no. 187 (with ill.).

58 The Five Windmills

Oil on canvas, 82 × 129 cm
Signed and dated bottom right: *J. Maris 1878*
Utrecht, Centraal Museum der Gemeente Utrecht

'The right proportions of light and dark, the accurate definition of the outlines, the finish – all this is of prime importance and the public is right in demanding it from the painter – but the beauty of colour, the tone, that we do for one another.'

Neither collector nor painter will find any deficiency in *The Five Windmills*, although in 1920 the critic Plasschaert compared it somewhat unfavourably with Matthijs Maris's *The Four Windmills* (1871), which struck him as being imbued with greater feeling and 'cheerless melancholy'. Jacob's monumental painting is primarily 'classic' and heroic. It is a textbook example of the Grey School, its considered composition and serene atmosphere evoking reminiscences of both Ruisdael and Aert van der Neer, particularly in the carefully arranged logs floating in the water.

PROVENANCE
Coll. Arthur Young, 1901; Amsterdam, coll. M.P. Voûte, 1921; Baarn, coll. M.P. Voûtre Jr., –1956; auct. Amsterdam (F. Muller & Co), 17–20 and 23–25 April 1956, no. 8 (Dfl. 28,000); purchased by the museum, 1956.

BIBLIOGRAPHY
The Art Journal (1900), p. 112 (with ill.); MacColl 1902, p. 184; Croal Thomson 1907, p. XXXIII, fig. J 2; Brunt 1912, p. 350; Plasschaert 1920, pp. 43, 61; H.F.W. Jeltes in *E.G.M.* XXXII (1922), vol. LXIV, p. 292.

EXHIBITIONS
Glasgow 1901; Paris 1921, no. 131; ?Amsterdam 1923(1), no. 246; London 1929, no. 431; Utrecht 1961, no. 63, fig. 27; Amsterdam 1979(1), no. 45; Tokyo 1979, no. 45 (with ill.).

59 Girl Asleep on a Sofa

Oil on canvas, 18.5 × 25.5 cm
Signed bottom right: *J. Maris*
Glasgow, Glasgow Art Gallery and Museum
repr. in colour on p. 69

'One must be able to devote all one's concentration to figure painting in order to produce anything good. Landscape painting largely boils down to the impression that one receives and recreates, but one cannot achieve very much by those means in composing a figure painting. It is true that the fine shades of tone and colour are also of great value here, as is the proportion of the parts to the whole, but it depends to no less an extent on characteristic expression. Constant observation of attitudes and postures is essential; the fine rendering of eyes and hands is an almost insurmountable difficulty.' Such were the views of Jacob Maris.

Although he did paint one or two large figure pieces after 1871 (eg. *The Arrival of the Boats* in the Rijksmuseum, Amsterdam), Maris confined himself mainly to studies of his own children at play and practising music (see Cat. 60, 61). The medium he generally chose for this was watercolour. In this little picture he has painted one of his daughters in a pale greenish-white dress which stands out against the dark reddish-brown background. The texture of the canvas comes through the fine, but rather free, brushwork and plays a part in the texture of the finished painting.

Maris sold the work to Goupil on 27 May 1880, but it is generally dated to the mid 1870s. Knuttel was the first to link it with the elegant work of Alfred Stevens, a painter who was one of Willem Roelofs's circle of friends in Brussels and later enjoyed much success in Paris and London. Later in the century Roelofs's son Albert specialized in painting women in an atmosphere of intimate luxury.

PROVENANCE
The Hague, art dealer Goupil & Co, 1880–81 (purchased from the painter); London, art dealer Daniel Cottier, 1881; coll. James Donald, –1905; bequeathed to the museum, 1905.

BIBLIOGRAPHY
P. Bate, *Art at the Glasgow Exhibition*, Glasgow 1901, p. 79; MacColl 1902, p. 184; Croal Thomson 1907, p. XXXIII, fig. J 21; Knuttel 1938, p. 440; Koomen 1949, pp. 127, 129; cat. Glasgow Art Gallery 1961, vol. 1, p. 85, no. 1113, vol 2, ill. on p. 103; De Gruyter 1968–69, vol. 2, pp. 20, 21, 29–30, 101, fig. 19.

EXHIBITIONS
Glasgow 1901, no. 1296; The Hague 1935–36, no. 31; Edinburgh 1957, no. 35; The Hague 1965(1), no. 43 (with ill.).

60

60 The Duo

Watercolour, 34.7 × 21.8 cm
Signed bottom left: *J. Maris*
The Hague, Haags Gemeentemuseum

This watercolour shows two of the painter's daughters practising music. The Marises were a musical family; in the 1850s the brothers had been habitual guests at the musical evenings of the Sierich family, as shown in another drawing by Jacob in the Haags Gemeentemuseum. Willem Maris was an outstanding pianist, while Jacob's son Willem (see Cat. 61) became a first-class violin-player.

De Gruyter suggested that Jacob probably painted intimate little scenes like this one as presents for his wife, although it is known that some were sold during his lifetime. The ages of the children date most of these watercolours to around the end of the 1870s.

PROVENANCE
Gorssel, coll. J. Verstolk-Völcker; The Hague, coll. H.G.J. Völcker; Eefde, coll. J.L. Völcker; Eefde, coll. E.C.K. Völcker, –1939; auct. Amsterdam (F. Muller & Co), 17 Oct. 1939, no. 61 (Dfl. 1,750); purchased by the museum, 1939.

BIBLIOGRAPHY
Koomen 1949, p. 131.

EXHIBITIONS
London 1888, no. 79; The Hague 1935–36, no. 138; Maastricht 1945–46, no. 44; Montpellier 1952, no. 38; Germany 1955, no. 28; Liège 1961–62, no. 93; Paris 1963, no. 74; The Hague 1963, no. 14 (with ill.); The Hague 1967(1), no. 21; Bonn 1972, no. 36; The Hague 1972(1), (with ill.); Zeist 1975, no. 50 (with ill.); Antwerp 1979, no. 27 (with ill.); Florence 1981–82, no. 16 (with ill.).

61

61 *The Young Artist*

Watercolour, 44.5 × 49.5 cm
Signed bottom right: *J. Maris*
Glasgow, The Burrell Collection,
Glasgow Art Gallery and Museum

This watercolour shows Willem Matthijs Maris (1872–1929), usually depicted by his father as a budding violinist, making his first attempts at painting. He did, in fact, follow his father's profession and received his first instruction from him; subsequently he attended classes at the Haagse Academie and at the Rijksacademie in Amsterdam under August Allebé and Nico van der Waay. His art, unlike the work of his father and two uncles, was never of great significance.

PROVENANCE
Glasgow, coll. Sir William Burrell.

62

62 *The Schreierstoren, Amsterdam*

Oil on canvas, 80 × 148 cm
Signed bottom right: *J. Maris*
The Hague, Haags Gemeentemuseum

Shortly after his return from Paris Jacob Maris paid his first visit to Amsterdam, where he was fascinated by the city's beauty when viewed from the water. In particular the imposing series of houses, warehouses, drawbridges and the striking Schreierstoren inspired him to paint innumerable canvasses. A modest painting of 1872 (formerly with M. Knoedler & Co, New York) opens the series, already containing all the elements found in this version. In the following years a number of slightly varying, but no less distinct, images of this same view evolved from this work; the Rijksmuseum alone possesses four different oil versions, apart from a watercolour of 1875 and a charcoal drawing of the same motif.

Maris did not greatly value topographical accuracy and treated his subjects freely, so that versions of this view may be found with either one or two drawbridges (cf. fig. 8). The composition shown in *The Schreierstoren* is considered the most classic of the various elaborations; another five versions are known, all of similar size, and generally dated to the 1880s.

PROVENANCE
Amsterdam, coll. E.H. Crone; on loan to the museum by the E.H. Crone Heirs, 1947–64; purchased by the museum, 1946.

BIBLIOGRAPHY
De Bock 1902–03, p. 98; cat. Gemeentemuseum 1962, no. 200 (with ill.).

EXHIBITIONS
The Hague 1935–36, no. 85; The Hague 1967(1), no. 18 (with ill.); Bonn 1972, no. 35.

VARIATIONS
1) oil on canvas, 80 × 147 cm, coll. H.S. Southam, Ottawa. 2) oil on canvas, 24.5 × 36.5 cm, Rijksmuseum, Amsterdam; cat. Rijksmuseum 1976, pp. 365–66 (with ill.). 3) oil on canvas, 81.3 × 146.1 cm, The Burrell Collection, Glasgow Art Gallery and Museum, Glasgow. 4) oil on canvas, 79 × 146 cm, auct. Amsterdam (F. Muller & Co), 22–25 March 1960, no. 81; *Verzameling Amsterdam – W.J.R. Dreesmann*, n.p. 1951, vol. 2, ill. on p. 44. 5) oil on canvas, 81 × 147 cm, auct. D. Cottier, London, 27–28 May 1892, no. 72 (with ill.). 6) oil on canvas, 81.25 × 148.5 cm, The Philadelphia Museum of Art, Philadelphia (William L. Elkins Collection); Rishel 1971, ill. on p. 22. 7) oil on canvas, 51.4 × 66 cm, auct. London (Christie's), 6 July 1973, no. 240 (with ill.).

63

63 *View of a Dutch Town on the Water*

Oil on canvas, 73 × 127 cm
Signed bottom left: *J. Maris*
Paris, Musée du Louvre

'Even when his art belongs to the past, Jacob Maris will be mentioned in the same breath as Vermeer ... and his great contemporaries'. Although one may question the general validity of Miss G.H. Marius's remark, it is undoubtedly true for this townscape, which is strongly reminiscent of Vermeer's *View of Delft*. The composition of the town on the water, viewed from the front and dominated by a large expanse of sky, as well as the light touches sparkling among the brick red of the buildings, are reminiscent of the 'Sphinx of Delft', but whereas Vermeer's painting is a detailed representation of a specific town, Maris combines elements from different towns into a new whole.

This painting was formerly on loan to the Haags Gemeentemuseum. It was then bequeathed by the art dealer Abraham Preyer to the Musée du Luxembourg in Paris in 1926, as part of a group of paintings by masters of the Hague School.

PROVENANCE
Amsterdam, coll. P. Langerhuizen Lzn.,–1918; auct. Amsterdam (F. Muller & Co/C.F. Roos & Co), 29 Oct. 1918, no. 60 (Dfl. 31,000); The Hague, art dealer A. Preyer, 1918–26; on loan to the Haags Gemeentemuseum, The Hague, 1919; presented to the Musée du Luxembourg, Paris, 1926; Paris, Musée National d'Art Moderne; on loan to the Haags Gemeentemuseum, The Hague, 1954.

BIBLIOGRAPHY
De Bock 1902–03, ill. on p. 131; *M.D.K.W.* I (1919–25), p. 12; ill. opp. p. 12; cat. Louvre 1979, p. 86 (with ill.).

EXHIBITIONS
Amsterdam 1899(2), no. 55; The Hague 1899(2), no. 64; Amsterdam 1906(2), no. 72; Amsterdam 1910(1), no. 81.

64 *Dordrecht – the Grote Kerk*

Oil on canvas, 100.3 × 80.6 cm
Signed bottom left: *J. Maris*
Montreal, Musée des Beaux-Arts de Montréal
(Gift of William Gardner)

The imposing square tower of the Grote Kerk at Dordrecht has fascinated painters for centuries; its striking silhouette dominates many paintings, from those by Jan van Goyen and Aelbert Cuyp to those of Turner.

Jacob Maris painted the church countless times, often under an evening sky or in stormy weather. In contrast to his predecessors, however, he painted the huge building from a close perspective, with the boats moored along the quay appearing to seek shelter in its shadow. The vigorous brushwork used for the dashing waves anticipated Breitner and Amsterdam Impressionism. Breitner made no secret of his admiration for Jacob Maris and later participated in the organization of two exhibitions devoted to him. The theme of boats moored in wintry city canals was also to engage him for many years.

PROVENANCE
Coll. Dr William Gardner M.D., –1918; presented to the museum, 1918.

VARIATIONS
1) oil on panel, 27.5 × 24.5 cm, auct. Amsterdam (F. Muller & Co), 13 June 1911, no. 7 (with ill.). 2) oil on canvas, 45.5 × 47.5 cm, Rijksmuseum, Amsterdam; cat. Rijksmuseum 1976, p. 365 (with ill.).

65

65 Souvenir of Dordrecht

Oil on canvas, 71.1 × 125.5 cm
Signed bottom left: *J. Maris*
Glasgow, The Burrell Collection,
Glasgow Art Gallery and Museum

Although the subjects of this painting and the view of the
Grote Kerk (Cat. 64) are virtually identical, it is scarcely
possible to imagine a greater contrast between two works of
similar subjects by the same artist. In the previous picture the
Grote Kerk towers powerfully and almost symbolically above
the turbulent elements, whereas in this painting Maris has
chosen a horizontal format and focused his attention on the
stillness and peace of a town enveloped in a misty atmosphere.
On the basis of a photograph in the Netherlands Institute for
Art History Bremmer dated this townscape around 1890, but
it was already in Edinburgh in the collection of Thomas Glenn
Arthur by 1886 and was thus probably painted shortly after the

smaller version in the Rijksmuseum in Amsterdam (dated
c. 1884 by Bremmer). Eduard August Becht (1868–1931)
made an etching after the Rijksmuseum version.

PROVENANCE
Edinburgh, coll. Thomas Glenn Arthur, 1886; Glasgow, coll. William Beattie,–1924; auct. London
(Christie's), 11 July 1924, no. 151 (£1,365); London, art dealer P. & D. Colnaghi & Co; Glasgow, coll. Sir
William Burrell, –1925.

BIBLIOGRAPHY
Zilcken 1900, ill. opp. p. 231; MacColl 1901, p. 184; Croal Thomson 1907, p. XXXIII, fig. J 5; Hols
1907(1), ill.; Eisler 1911(2), ill. on p. 4; E. Fagg in *Apollo* 1 (1925), p. 26.

EXHIBITIONS
Edinburgh 1886(1); Glasgow 1901, no. 1259; Dublin 1907; London 1924.

VARIATIONS
Oil on canvas, 21.5 × 37.5 cm, Rijksmuseum, Amsterdam; cat. Rijksmuseum 1976, p. 365 (with ill.).

Matthijs Maris (1839-1917)

Matthias Maris – later called Matthijs or Thijs – was born in The Hague on 17 August 1839, the second son of Mattheus Maris and Hendrika Bloemert. In 1851 he became a pupil of Isaac Cornelis Elink Sterk (1808–71), then from 1852 to 1855 he attended classes at the Haagse Academie; in 1854 he also worked in the studio of Louis Meijer (1809–66). As a result of Meijer's efforts, Matthijs was given an allowance of 40 guilders a month by Queen Sophie of the Netherlands to enable him to study in Antwerp. There he moved into a studio with his brother Jacob and studied at the Academy under Nicaise de Keyser (1813–87), among others. He also became friendly with the German painter George Laves, who introduced him to the work of the German Romantics.

After three years in Antwerp, Matthijs returned to The Hague, where he shared a studio with Jacob in Kazernestraat. In the years 1859–61 the brothers received a series of commissions from Princess Marianne to copy eight portraits of members of the House of Orange for her country-house *Rusthof*. The money they earned enabled them to spend some time in Oosterbeek and Wolfheze in 1859 and 1860 and to travel to Germany, Switzerland and France in 1861. This journey proved to be of great importance for Matthijs's development; the castle, cathedral and wooden houses of Lausanne made a particularly great impression on him and were to appear repeatedly in his paintings and watercolours. His watercolour entitled *Christening Procession at Lausanne* (Cat. 68) won him an honorary membership of the Société Belge des Aquarellistes in Brussels in 1863.

In the years that followed, however, Matthijs's works were badly received both by the press and public alike at the exhibitions in The Hague and Amsterdam. He missed the support of Jacob, who had moved to Paris in 1865, and became embittered and solitary. On the insistence of his mother and brother he, too, moved to the French capital in 1869.

During the Franco-Prussian War (1870–71) he enrolled in the Municipal Guard and after the capitulation he threw in his lot with the Communards, but he managed to escape the subsequent terror of the military suppression. Jacob went back to The Hague, but Thijs stayed on; the following years were difficult for him, plagued as he was by poverty and loneliness, but he did paint some of his masterpieces then, including *Souvenir d'Amsterdam* (Cat. 73) and *The Butterflies* (Cat. 77).

In the following years, matters seemed to improve. Matthijs's younger sister Henriëtte came to Paris to look after him and his work gradually attracted more interest. The Parisian art dealer Goupil bought nothing from him, but Elbert J. van Wisselingh, an assistant at the firm, occasionally bought a painting; a little later Daniel Cottier, the Scot who ran an art business in London, began to buy his work. In 1875 Cottier persuaded Van Wisselingh to come and work for him in London and two years later he also persuaded Matthijs to cross the Channel.

For a short time Matthijs lived with Van Wisselingh, but later he moved into Cottier's house where he stayed until 1887. Although the art dealer took him on his trips to Norway, Brittany and Paris, Matthijs felt that he had been bitterly let down over the promises Cottier had made to him and relations between the two men steadily worsened. Eventually Thijs moved 'temporarily' to a furnished room in a working-class district, where he remained for 19 years. During this period, when he was supported financially by Van Wisselingh, he produced very few works. Those he did make sometimes remained on his easel for years; they are the grey dream landscapes and veiled figures, which had nothing in common with the work of the Hague School.

In 1908 Matthijs moved for the last time, this time to two comfortable rooms in a better district. He never finished another painting and died nine years later on 22 August 1917.

fig. 139 MATTHIJS MARIS *Self Portrait* 1860 (Rijksmuseum Kröller-Müller, Otterlo)

66

66 Tree Roots (De Oorsprong)

Oil on canvas, 32 × 49 cm
The Hague, Haags Gemeentemuseum

In 1858 Matthijs Maris had returned to The Hague from
Antwerp and moved into a studio on Kazernestraat with his
brother Jacob. The money they earned by copying royal
portraits for Princess Marianne of Orange enabled them to
travel, and around 1859–60 they both worked near Oosterbeek and Wolfheze. The studies they both made *en plein air* at
this time are closely related, but in this study of tree roots it is
not difficult to recognize the hand of Matthijs, whose choice of
subject matter was already revealing his romantic penchant
for the fanciful and the mysterious.

The painting's alternative title comes from the traditional
attribution of its location to the source of a brook on the estate
of *De Oorsprong* (The Source), to the north-west of Oosterbeek, which was laid out by the garden architect Leonard
Springer. The Haags Gemeentemuseum also possesses a black
chalk drawing of the same tree roots.

PROVENANCE
? Rotterdam, coll. F.J.G. Bosman, 1893; Amsterdam, coll. E.H. Crone, 1923; on loan to the museum by
the E.H. Crone Heirs, 1947–64; purchased by the museum, 1964.

BIBLIOGRAPHY
Haverkorn van Rijsewyk 1912, pp. 50–51 (with ill.); cat. Gemeentemuseum 1962, no. 204; Wagner
1974–75, p. 14; Hefting 1981, p. 113, fig. 64.

EXHIBITIONS
? Rotterdam 1893, no. 4; Amsterdam 1923(1), no. 255; London 1929, no. 416; The Hague 1935–36,
no. 167; The Hague 1939(2), no. 7; The Hague 1964, no. 22; Bonn 1972, no. 46; The Hague 1974–75,
no. 48 (with ill.).

VARIATIONS
Drawing, Haags Gemeentemuseum, The Hague.

67 View of Lausanne (I)

Sepia brush drawing, 13.4 × 19 cm
Monogrammed and dated bottom right: *M.M. 61*
Montreal, Musée des Beaux-Arts de Montréal
(Bequest of Miss Adaline Van Horne)

In 1861 Jacob and Matthijs Maris made a long journey along
the Rhine in Germany, visiting a large exhibition of German
art in Cologne en route. This made a great impression on
Matthijs. He had already become familiar with the work of
several German artists, principally through illustrations, but
also through German colleagues, during his stay in Antwerp.

When the brothers called at Lausanne later on their journey,
Matthijs must have been very forcibly struck by the ambience

68

and setting, which closely resembled the work of Ludwig Richter, his favourite artist. The panoramic view of the city, with its medieval castle and cathedral, the picturesque wooden houses and winding stairways, made such an impression on Matthijs that his memories of it can be recognized in his work decades later. Whereas the landscape studies he made in Oosterbeek only shortly before proved to be of no more than passing interest to Matthijs, as the landscape he had in mind was not to be found in nature, the silhouettes of the cathedral and castle of Lausanne were to appear in many of his townscapes and dream landscapes. Invariably they loom up in the distance, separated from the foreground, like a vision from another world.

This sepia drawing is the first of three versions that Matthijs made of the panorama of Lausanne. A fourth version, in oils, is known from a photograph. Matthijs gave this drawing to his patron Von Weckerlin; luckily it escaped the fate of another work which he tore up at the mere suggestion of presenting it to Von Weckerlin; he was suspicious and often appeared ungrateful to those who supported him.

PROVENANCE
Coll. Von Weckerlin (presented by the painter); The Hague, art dealer A.T.A. Artz, 1911; London, priv. coll., 1912; Montreal, coll. Sir William Van Horne; Montreal, coll. Adaline Van Horne, –1945; bequeathed to the museum, 1945.

BIBLIOGRAPHY
Haverkorn van Rijsewijk 1912, p. 54 (ill. opp. p. 52); Maris 1943, p. 113; Maris 1947, p. 103; De Gruyter 1968–69, vol. 2, pp. 36, 47, 101, fig. 38; Braakhuis 1978–79, pp. 176 (note 244), 177 (note 246).

EXHIBITIONS
? Utrecht 1866; The Hague 1965(1), no. 72 (with ill.).

VARIATIONS
1) drawing, 25.5 × 66 cm, Rijksprentenkabinet, Rijksmuseum, Amsterdam; De Gruyter 1968–69, vol. 2, fig. 39. 2) drawing, 35 × 83.5 cm, Burrell Collection, Glasgow Art Gallery and Museum, Glasgow; De Gruyter 1968–69, vol. 2, fig. 40. 3) painting, coll. Mrs J. Goekoop de Jongh, 1912.

68 Christening Procession at Lausanne

Watercolour, 33.3 × 52.7 cm
Monogrammed centre right: *M.M.*
The Hague, Haags Gemeentemuseum

A christening procession passes down the Escalier du Vieux Marché towards the city. A peasant couple, the woman with a baby in her arms, form the centre of the group; they are preceded by a young woman holding a bible and are followed by a girl supporting the barely visible figure of an old man.

Wijsenbeek has suggested that this watercolour is more than a depiction of a christening procession and is intended to be read as a representation of the various stages of human life, in which 'the young woman in the foreground and the young girl, who is accompanying the old man, symbolize the expectation of motherhood, just as the old man represents the passing of the generations. The springtime setting of the scene thus takes on a symbolic signifance, which is reiterated in the doves billing and cooing in the foreground.'

Knoef, followed by Wijsenbeek, and Braakhuis and Van der Vliet, have all cited different wood engravings by Ludwig Richter as the inspiration behind Matthijs's watercolour. The most closely related is Richter's *Taufgang (Christening Procession)* from *Contemplation and Cultivation: a Family Picturebook* (1855), although the girl with the bible and the mother with her baby have changed places in Maris's work. The foreground on the right shows Maris's use of a sketch from his Oosterbeek period (cf. also *Tree Roots*, Cat. 66).

Despite quite extensive borrowings, this watercolour is one of Maris's most successful works of this period. There is no trace of Richter's *Biedermeier* sentimentality, which has been replaced by a very introspective approach to the subject and rather lofty atmosphere. In 1863 the work was sent by its owner, P. VerLoren van Themaat, a friend of Willem Roelofs, to the exhibition of the Société Belge des Aquarellistes in Brussels where it was received very enthusiastically. Matthijs was consequently made an honorary member of the society. The work received the same recognition in the Netherlands only in 1888 when it won an award at Arti et Amicitiae in Amsterdam and Zilcken made an etching of it.

PROVENANCE
Utrecht, coll. P. VerLoren van Themaat, 1863; The Hague, coll. H.G.J. Völcker; Eefde, coll. J.L. Völcker, 1935; Eefde, coll. E.C.K. Völcker, –1939; auct. Amsterdam (F. Muller & Co), 17 Oct. 1939, no. 65 (Dfl. 4,300); Doorn, coll. Lou Bandy, 1939–; auct. Amsterdam (F. Muller & Co), 5–11 May 1953, no. 382 (Dfl. 7,200); The Hague, art dealer P.A. Scheen, 1953; purchased by the museum, 1953.

BIBLIOGRAPHY
Veth 1908, p. 161, Plasschaert 1911, p. 5; Veth 1917(1), p. 160; Arondéus 1939, pp. 49, 54; Van Gelder 1939, p. 10. ill. on p. 14; Maris 1943, pp. 99, 113; Arondéus 1945, p. 52; Knoef 1947, p. 243; Maris 1947, pp. 89, 103; Koomen 1949, pp. 127, 131; L.J.F. W[ijsenbeek] in M.D.K.W. VIII (1953), pp. 54–58; L.J.F. Wijsenbeek in O.K. Televisiecursus III (1965), no. 2 (with ill.); De Gruyter 1968–69,, vol. 2, pp. 36–37, 47, 101, fig. 41; Scheen 1969–70, vol. 2, fig. 332; Braakhuis 1978–79, pp. 158 (note 142), 160–61, ill. on p. 160.

EXHIBITIONS
Brussels 1863(2); ?Utrecht 1866; London 1880, no. 81; Amsterdam 1888(2); London 1888, no. 81; The Hague 1935–36, no. 219; The Hague 1939(2), no. 55; The Hague 1948, no. 942 (with ill.); Delft 1955–56, no. 61; Mönchen Gladbach 1957, no. 40 (with ill.); Amsterdam 1963, no. T 78, fig. 61; Paris 1963, no. 79, fig. XXIII; The Hague 1963, no. 16 (with ill.); Bonn 1972, no. 52, fig. 13; The Hague 1974–75, no. 74 (with ill.); Amsterdam 1979(1), no. 49; Tokyo 1979, no. 49 (with ill.).

69

69 Christening Procession

Sepia brush drawing, 18.5 × 11.5 cm
Monogrammed bottom left: M.M.
The Hague, Haags Gemeentemuseum

This sepia brush drawing of a christening procession is closely related to Christening Procession at Lausanne (Cat. 68), except that the colour scheme here is built around tones of brown rather than of greyish-blue. The emphasis has shifted from the parents with their child, here shown entering the church, to a mother and daughter dressed for Communion. The figure of the daughter is the first intimation of Matthijs Maris's long series of brides. The drawing is dated between 1862 and 1864.

PROVENANCE
The Hague, Vereeninging van Haagsche Museumvrienden (Society of Friends of Hague Museums), 1935; presented to the museum, 1935.

BIBLIOGRAPHY
Van Gelder 1939, ill. on p. 16; L.J.F. W[ijsenbeek] in M.D.K.W. VIII (1953), p. 57 (with fig. 6); L.J.F. Wijsenbeek in O.K. Televisiecursus III (1965), no. 2, fig. 7; De Gruyter 1968–69, vol. 2, pp. 37, 101, fig. 42; Tekeningen en prenten uit eigen bezit. 19e Eeuw. Haags Gemeentemuseum, n.p., n.d., no. 15 (with ill.).

EXHIBITIONS
The Hague 1935–36, no. 220; The Hague 1939(2), no. 56; The Hague 1948, no. 943; The Hague 1974–75, no. 75 (with ill.); Antwerp 1979, no. 31 (with ill.); Florence 1981–82, no. 17 (with ill.).

70 Washday

Oil on canvas, 39 × 28 cm
Signed bottom left: Matthijs Maris
Private collection

It is difficult now to appreciate why this charming little painting of a woman doing her washing should have produced such fierce reactions when it was shown at the Tentoonstelling van Levende Meesters (Exhibition of Living Masters) in 1863. One of the critics who disliked the work, then known under the title Back Street, was Van Westrheene, who wrote for the Kunstkronijk. When he heard that it had been sold, he commented, 'That the painting has quickly found a buyer proves only that even this eccentricity could become a fashion.' Later, however, he revised his opinion and the work was published in the Kunstkronijk as a lithograph. The greyish-green tone of the painting seems to have been the main cause for offence, but perhaps the artificiality of the scene (Dutch, but with Lausanne cathedral in the background) also upset the critics.

There is a pencil sketch of the washerwoman in the printroom of the Haags Gemeentemuseum and a preliminary oil sketch of the whole composition in the Dordrecht Museum. In addition to the lithograph by Frederik Weissenbruch printed in *Kunstkronijk*, there is an etching of the work by Philippe Zilcken.

PROVENANCE

Amersfoort, coll. L. van Walchren van Wadenoyen, 1863– (purchased at exh. The Hague 1863, for Dfl. 250); Amersfoort, coll. H.S. van Walchren van Wadenoyen, –1875; auct. The Hague (Van den Bergh & Stoop), 17–18 Nov. 1875, no. 100 (as *La ménagère*; for Dfl. 850); The Hague, art dealer Goupil & Co. 1875; coll. Jhr. E. van Heemskerck van Beest, 1875–; London, coll. James Staats Forbes, 1886; United States, priv. coll.; Amsterdam, art dealer E.J. van Wisselingh & Co, 1895; Rijsenburg (near Driebergen), coll. Jonkheer J.R.H. Neervoort van de Poll, –1921; on loan to the Rijksmuseum, Amsterdam, 1919; auct. Amsterdam (F. Muller & Co), 29 Nov. 1921, no. 24 (Dfl. 30,000); Netherlands, priv. coll. 1921–; Amsterdam, art dealer E.J. van Wisselingh & Co; Almelo, coll. H.E. ten Cate, 1929; auct. Amsterdam (Mak van Waay), 6–27 June 1973, no. 754 (Dfl. 50,000); Amsterdam art dealer P. Lunshof, 1977; auct. Laren (Christie's), 20 Oct. 1980, no. 558; purchased by the collector, 1980.

BIBLIOGRAPHY

A.H. (4 June 1863); *N.R.C.* (10 June 1863); [T.] v [an] W[esthreene Wzn.] in *K.K.* N.S. v (1864). p. 54; *K.K.* N.S. v (1864), ill. opp. p. 58 (Lithograph by F.H. Weissenbruch after the painting), p. 64; Gram 1876, p. 21; J. Veth in *De Kroniek* 1 (1895), p. 58; Van Deyssel 1898, fig. 6 on p. 252; Marius 1900, p. 6, ill. on p. 20; Marius 1903, p. 267, ill. on p. 251; Marius 1906, ill. on p. 255; Marius 1908, ill. opp. p. 112; Bénédite 1910, p. 255; Plasschaert 1911, p. 5; C. Veth in *E.H.* XLII (1916), ill. on p. 490 (as *Buurtje*); Veth 1917(1), p. 160 (as *Buurtje*); Veth 1917(2), p. 602 (as *Tuintje*); Buschmann 1918(1), p. 9; Haverkorn van Rijsewijk 1918, pp. 124–26 (with ill.); Arondéus 1939, p. 49; Van Gelder 1939, p. 11, ill. on p. 7; Arondéus 1945, pp. 48, 52–53; Koomen 1949, p. 140; cat. coll. H.E. ten Cate 1955, vol. 1, pp. 66–67, no. 98, vol. 2, fig. 58; Gerson 1961, fig. 63; Veth 1969, p. 245; Braakhuis 1978–79, p. 159 (note 149).

EXHIBITIONS

Brussels 1863(1), no. 762 (as *La blanchisseuse*); The Hague 1863, no. 316 (as *Het achterbuurtje*); Edinburgh 1866(1), no. 163; The Hague 1899(1), no. 72; London 1903, no. 79; Amsterdam 1910(1), no. 84; London 1929, no. 420 (with ill.); Amsterdam 1931(2), no. 22 (with ill.); The Hague 1935–36, no. 170; Amsterdam 1938(2), no. 23; Almelo 1956, no. 86, fig. 22.

VARIATIONS

1) oil on canvas, 22 × 16 cm, Dordrechts Museum, Dordrecht; cat. Dordrechts Museum 1928, p. 46, no. 138. 2) drawing, Haags Gemeentemuseum, The Hague.

71 *Townscape*

Oil on canvas, 38 × 63 cm
Signed and dated bottom left: *M. Maris '63*
Amsterdam, Stedelijk Museum (Gift of Vereeniging tot het Vormen van een Openbare Verzameling van Hedendaagsche Kunst)
repr. in colour on p. 69

This townscape, also known as *Village Street*, is closely related to Matthijs's *Washday*, with which De Gruyter confused it in his detailed description of the reception given to the painting by the contemporary press. Van Gelder described the work in 1939 as 'harmonious in colour' and 'peaceful in mood', but this judgement was not shared by the painter's contemporaries, who wrote of its distortion of nature and marvelled that 'the sober truth can be so disagreeable'.

The same elements that were incorporated into the genre scene in *Washday* – the duckpond, busy women in white caps, a child watching everything from behind a gate on a flight of steps, the outline of Lausanne in the distance – are here brought together in a composition that employs horizontals and verticals in a striking way. Matthijs Maris's revolutionary simplicity becomes clearer when the painting is compared with the ordinary townscapes of this period, such as those by Springer or Karssen. Maris's strongly rhythmic style struck the critic

Arondéus as 'a fairy-tale web' and as 'more of a musical delineation than a painting'.

The first owner of the painting was the artist Louwrens Hanedoes, who bought *Townscape* for 250 guilders. He sold it to the Stedelijk Museum in Amsterdam through the dealer Van Wisselingh in 1903, by which time the price had risen to 15,700 guilders – a remarkable indication of Maris's growing reputation.

PROVENANCE

Coll. Louwrens Hanedoes, – 1903 (bought for Dfl. 250); Amsterdam, art dealer E.J. van Wisselingh & Co, 1903; Amsterdam, Vereeniging tot het Vormen van een Openbare Verzameling van Hedendaagsche Kunst (Society for the Formation of a Public Collection of Modern Art), 1903 (bought for Dfl. 15,700); presented to the museum, 1903.

BIBLIOGRAPHY

Plasschaert 1909, ill. on p. 137; Eisler 1911 (1), ill. on p. 217; Eisler 1911 (2), ill. on p. 6; Plasschaert 1911, pp. 5, 7; Veth 1917 (1), p. 160; cat. Stedelijk Museum 1922, p. 42, no. 286, pl. 80; H.K. Westendorp in *M.B.K.* XI (1934), fig. 8 on p. 331; Arondéus 1939, pp. 49–50, ill. opp. p. 32; Van Gelder 1939, p. 11, ill. on p. 8; Maris 1943, p. 99; Arondéus 1945, pp. 48–49, ill. opp. p. 24; Maris 1947, p. 89; Knoef 1948, p. 109; Koomen 1949, p. 147; De Gruyter 1968–69, vol. 2, p. 37; Pollock 1980–81, p. 54, ill. on p. 55.

EXHIBITIONS

The Hague 1865, no. 317; Paris 1921, no. 137; Brussels 1932, no. 69; The Hague 1939 (2), no. 20 (with ill.); The Hague 1945, no. 70; The Hague 1947, no. 249; Luxemburg 1948, no. 56; Düsseldorf 1950, no. 35; Athens 1953, no. 20; Zagreb 1953, no. 21; Israel 1954, no. 19; The Hague 1965 (1), no. 317; The Hague 1974–75, no. 53; Amsterdam 1979 (1), no. 48; Tokyo 1979, no. 48 (with ill.).

72

72 *Woman with Child and Kid (The Introduction)*

Panel, 15 × 19.5 cm
Monogrammed bottom left: *M.M.*
The Hague, Haags Gemeentemuseum
repr. in colour on p. 70

This notable painting, dated to the mid 1860s, is striking primarily for its extreme stylization. It has been compared to the work of Bart van der Leck and described as Cubism *avant la lettre*, but the style is more reminiscent of the Italian-Swiss painter Segantini, in whose later work natural forms were similarly reduced to their bare essentials.

Several other versions of this subject, also painted by Matthijs, are known, but this is one of the most stylized. The earliest of these is an 1861 drawing in the Burrell Collection, Glasgow; there is also a watercolour formerly in the possession of Jozef Israëls and later of his son, Isaac. A painted version in which the stylization is carried even further (formerly in the collection W. Hoos), is dated 1866. De Gruyter believed that the scene should be looked at from the child's point of view, thus giving the kid a toy-like aspect. Braakhuis and Van der Vliet, who attempted a detailed psychological analysis of Matthijs Maris in their article, placed *The Introduction* in the context of his numerous other depictions of children. Thus they saw it as a rendering of the original state of childhood, still protected by the mother figure. The kid thus becomes the symbolic equivalent of the child, just as the child in Philip Otto

73

Runge's *The Mother at the Spring* is looking at his own reflection; in time, the child's acquisition of knowledge would rob him of this early innocence and drive him out of Paradise, severing the bond between human and animal (Matthijs had a very low opinion of education). It is worth noting that in the version formerly in the W. Hoos collection the kid is separated from the child by a wooden branch, creating a greater sense of isolation of the two parties. Braakhuis and Van der Vliet attribute a similar symbolic content to Matthijs's *The Butterflies* (Cat. 77).

PROVENANCE
Amsterdam, coll. E.H. Crone, 1935; on loan to the museum by the E.H. Crone Heirs, 1947–64; purchased by the museum, 1964.

EXHIBITIONS
The Hague 1935–36, no. 174; The Hague 1939 (2), no. 14; The Hague 1964, no. 23.

VARIATIONS
1) oil on panel, 14.5 × 19 cm, auct. Amsterdam (Mak van Waay), 21 Oct. 1974, no. 108; Scheen 1981, fig. 515. 2) watercolour, 13 × 21 cm, formerly coll. H. E. ten Cate, Almelo; cat. coll. H. E. ten Cate 1955, vol. 1, p. 95, no. 160, vol. 2, fig. 138. 3) drawing, 6.5 × 10 cm, The Burrell Collection, Glasgow Art Gallery and Museum, Glasgow; Braakhuis 1978–79, p. 162, fig. 7.

73 *Souvenir d'Amsterdam*

Oil on canvas, 46.5 × 35 cm
Monogrammed and dated bottom left: *M.M. 71*
Amsterdam, Rijksmuseum

This view of the Nieuwe Haarlemse Sluis on the Singel in Amsterdam is one of the many works that Matthijs Maris later dismissed as his 'potboilers'. He painted it in Paris using as his model a stereoscopic photograph of 1859 taken by Pieter Oosterhuis, the well-known photographer of views of Amsterdam.

Careful study, however, reveals that Maris was far from precise in following his model; not only did he add several little figures, but he has also borrowed motifs from Montmartre for the background. He wrote about this with some satisfaction in 1908, with a reference to Ruskin, the truthloving critic, 'Ruskin would have said, "I know where it is", but he would have been mistaken, for *all those houses in the distance* were not there. I believe I just patched them together with *that long bridge*. If all that is there now, then I was a good prophet'.

Van Gogh expressed a quite different opinion in an enthusiastic description of the painting in a letter of 6 April 1875. 'It represents an old Dutch town with rows of brownish-red houses with stepped gables and high stoops, grey roofs and white or yellow doors, window frames and cornices. There are canals with ships and a large white drawbridge under which a barge, with a man at the tiller, passes the little house of the bridgekeeper, who is seen through the window, sitting alone in his little office. Further on is a stone bridge across the canal, over which some people and a cart with white horses are passing . . . there is life everywhere : a porter with his wheelbarrow, a man leaning against the railings of the bridge and looking into the water, women in black with white caps . . . It is a small picture, and the artist was looking down on the scene. The subject is almost the same as that of the big J. [Jacob] Maris, "Amsterdam", which you probably know; but this is talent and the other, genius' (no. 24, vol. 1, pp. 23–24).

In 1908, Jan Veth described the painter George Laurens Kiers's visit to Amsterdam with Jacob and Matthijs Maris in the summer of 1859 or 1860 at some length and asserted that *Souvenir d'Amsterdam* was based on their impressions, but this has been completely invalidated by recently discovered sources. Matthijs Maris began the work in Paris in 1871, when Artz had advised him to earn some easy money. Artz then sold the picture to the art dealer Cottier. Later, when Matthijs saw it in the latter's house, he was embarrassed by it. 'Those things are not me. I did paint it, but against my better judgement, for a bit of money. . . .'

PROVENANCE
London, art dealer Daniel Cottier, 1872–; art dealer William Marchant & Co, 1907; The Hague, coll. W.J. van Randwijk; presented to the museum by the W.J. van Randwijk Heirs, 1914.

BIBLIOGRAPHY
Marius 1903, pp. 267, 268, 270, ill. on frontispiece; Marius 1906, pp. 270, 272–73; Croal Thomson 1907, p. XXXV, fig. M 16; De Boer 1907, p. 16, ill. on p. 3; Marius 1908, pp. 111–12, ill. on frontispiece; Veth 1908, pp. 141–42; Bénédite 1910, p. 255; Eisler 1911 (1), ill. on p. 215; Plasschaert 1911, pp. 8–9; Brunt 1912, p. 348; M. Eisler in *The Studio* LV (1912), p. 100; W. Steenhoff in *Onze Kunst* XXVII (1915), p. 92, ill. opp. p. 92; Veth 1917 (1), p. 161; Veth 1917 (2), p. 604; *The Sunday Times* (26 Aug. 1917); Croal Thomson 1918, ill.; Haverkorn van Rijsewijk 1919, ill. on p. 120; Marius 1920, pp. 142–43; Fridlander 1921, pp. 7–8, 28, 119, 129; Knuttel 1938, ill. on p. 447; Arondéus 1939, pp. 42–43, 50, 96, 97, 98, ill. opp. p. 33; Van Gelder 1939, pp. 18, 20, 34, ill. on p. 36; Maris 1943, pp. 90, 163; Arondéus 1945, pp. 41–42, 48, 93, 96, 155, ill. opp. p. 25; Maris 1947, pp. 82, 151; Knoef 1948, p. 109; Koomen 1949, pp. 131, 143, 147; Knuttel 1950; ill. on p. 466; L.J.F. Wijsenbeek in O.K. 1 (1957), no. 24 (with ill.); H.L.C. Jaffé in *Ons Amsterdam* X (1958), p. 5, ill. on p. 3; Van Gelder 1959, p. 20, fig. 152; Gerson 1961, p. 29, fig. 64, A.B. de Vries in O.K. *Televisiecursus* I (1963), no. 16, fig. 10; De Gruyter 1968–69, vol. 2, p. 42; Veth 1969, p. 245; Novotny 1970, p. 170, fig. 139 B; Marius/Norman 1973, p. 128; Heijbroek 1975 (1), p. 14–18; Heijbroek 1975 (2), p. 279, ill. on p. 280; cat. Rijksmuseum 1976, pp. 366–67 (with ill.); H.E.M. Braakhuis & J. van der Vliet in *Tirade* XXI (1977), p. 336; Braakhuis 1978–79, 159 (note 146), 177 (notes 246, 248, 249); Pollock 1980–81, p. 56 (with ill.).

EXHIBITIONS
Paris 1888 (2); Paris 1891 (2), no. 155; London 1899, no. 39 (with ill.); Rotterdam 1908–09, no. 30; Paris 1921, no. 140; London 1929, no. 417; The Hague 1935–36, no. 182; The Hague 1939 (2), no. 24 (with ill.); The Hague 1945, no. 68; Amsterdam 1957–58, no. 64 (with ill.); The Hague 1974–75, no. 85; Amsterdam 1980–81, no. 87 (with ill.).

74

74 *Quarry at Montmartre*

Oil on canvas, 55 × 46 cm
Monogrammed bottom left: *M.M.*
The Hague, Haags Gemeentemuseum

Following the departure of his brother Jacob for the Netherlands, Matthijs rented accommodation in Montmartre, a district of which he had become very fond. He painted this sunny corner by a quarry in that *quartier*, using a motif to be encountered later, in 1886, in the work of Vincent van Gogh.

Despite the rapid, confident style of painting, it is difficult to maintain that this 'more direct' work reveals the true essence of Matthijs Maris any more than the *Souvenir d'Amsterdam* (Cat. no. 73) painted from an old photograph. On the contrary, in retrospect the painting seems rather a farewell to the period in which the artist derived most pleasure from the direct representation of the world around him. Other paintings of the quarries which he made as 'snapshots' of

Montmartre are treated differently and the colouring is more sombre (cf. similar works in the National Gallery, London, and the Burrell Collection, Glasgow).

PROVENANCE
The Hague, coll. W, Hoos; on loan to the museum by the W. Hoos Heirs, 1956–67; The Hague, art dealer P.A. Scheen, 1967, purchased by the museum, 1967.

BIBLIOGRAPHY
Cat. Gemeentemuseum 1962, no. 210; De Gruyter 1968–69, vol. 2, pp. 39, 42, 47–48, 102, fig. 45; cf. Heijbroek 1975 (2), p. 279; Scheen 1981, fig. 514.

EXHIBITIONS
The Hague 1965 (1), no. 60 (with ill.); The Hague 1974–75, no. 89 (with ill.).

75

75 Kitchenmaid

Oil on canvas, 66.5 × 50 cm
Monogrammed and dated on centre right: *M.M. 72*
The Hague, Rijksmuseum H.W. Mesdag

It is curious that several works from Matthijs Maris's Paris period should have such typically Dutch themes, but the requirements of the art market gave the artist little choice in the matter. Moreover, Goupil mainly wanted figure pieces because there was an assured market for them. Ironically, therefore, Matthijs's most popular works belonged to the category that he himself considered 'potboilers.' In letters of 1905 and 1909 to Plasschaert he declared that he had painted this picture 'entirely against my better judgement. I tried to imitate nature, but I had no heart for it, I didn't feel that was me . . .'

Maris's allusion to the genre paintings of Pieter de Hooch and Johannes Vermeer in this picture played a large part in its success. In 1875 it came into the possession of Hendrik Mesdag and was thereafter regarded as one of the masterpieces in his collection. The girl depicted is Juli Crottard, the daughter of Jacob Maris's maid, who also served as the model for Matthijs's *Girl at the Pump* in the Groninger Museum (Veendorp Collection).

According to Miss Marius, the Maris brothers generally let the art dealers decide the titles for their paintings. The *Kitchenmaid* is also known as *The Pancake Maker* and the *Kitchen Princess*. It was published in the *Kunstkronijk* in 1877, in reverse, with the title *Day Dreaming*.

PROVENANCE
Amsterdam, art dealer C.M. van Gogh, –1875; The Hague, art dealer Goupil & Co, 1875; The Hague, coll. H.W. Mesdag, 1875.

BIBLIOGRAPHY
K.K. N.S. XVIII (1877), ill. opp. p. 75 (lithograph by J. Mesker after the painting); Berckenhoff 1888, pp. 490, 493; Boele van Hensbroek 1890, p. 18, ill. opp. p. 18; Zilcken 1895, ill.; Zilcken 1896 (1), ill. on p. 31; Van Deyssel 1898, fig. 2; Marius 1899, p. 10; J.V[eth] in *De Kroniek* v (1899), p. 220; *N.v.d.D.* (14 June 1899); Marius 1900, p. 10, ill. opp. p. 8; *N.v.d.D.* (22 Jan. 1903); Boele van Hensbroek 1910, p. 18, ill. opp. p. 18; Plasschaert 1911, p. 9; Brunt 1912, p. 350, ill. on p. 351; J. Havelaar in *E.G.M.* XXII (1912), vol. XLIII, pp. 21–22 (with ill.); Henkel 1916–17, p. 497; Veth 1917 (1), pp. 161–62 (as *Vlaamsche Keuken*); Plasschaert 1917–25, vol. I (Oct.), pp. 8–9; Buschmann 1918(2), p. 71; Haverkorn van Rijsewijk 1919, pp. 34, 37, 38 (with ill.); Arondéus 1939, p. 108; Van Gelder 1939, pp. 9, 20–21, ill. on p. 29; Poortenaar 1940, p. 15; Arondéus 1945, p. 104; Scheen 1946, fig. 130; Knoef 1948, p. 109; Koomen 1949, p. 143; 's-Gravenhage XIX (1964), no. 12, ill. on p. 20; Heijbroek 1975 (2), p. 279; cat. Museum Mesdag 1975, pp. 107–09. no. 198 (with ill.); E.M. Bosch (ed), *Van Mesdag tot Mondrian*, [The Hague 1977], p. 15, fig. 4.

EXHIBITIONS
?Paris 1872; London 1888, no. 9 (as *The Young Housekeeper*); Munich 1888, no. 1599 (as *Flämische Köchin*); The Hague 1899 (1), no. 73; Amsterdam 1919–20, no. 91 (with ill.); Paris 1921, no. 143; Potsdam 1925, no. 90; The Hague 1965 (1), no. 62 (with ill.); The Hague 1974–75, no. 86 (with ill.).

76 The Christening

Oil on canvas, 66.4 × 50.5 cm
Signed and dated bottom right: *M. Maris 73*
Utrecht, Centraal Museum der Gemeente Utrecht
repr. in colour on p. 71

From the dark porch of a Gothic church a young woman with a serious expression emerges into the light. In her arms on a finely embroidered pillow she bears her child, who has just been christened. She is followed at a short distance by her husband, whose colourful doublet and hose are the only bright accents in a work built up of muted tones of reddish-brown, ochre, dark blue and grey. The costume of the figures, in contrast to Matthijs Maris's earlier versions of this theme, are now avowedly historical in character; they reminded one critic of Holbein. Matthijs's liking for the costumes of romance and legend was soon to be expressed even more strongly in the medieval attire of Maris's fairy-tale princes and princesses, so strongly reminiscent of the Pre-Raphaelites.

Anna Wagner has linked Matthijs's return to the theme of the *Christening Procession at Lausanne* in this painting (the vague silhouette of the city again appears in the background) with the christening of his sister Henriëtte's baby daughter. Henriëtte had come to Paris in 1871 to look after Matthijs and continued to do so, even after her marriage to the Frenchman Troussard. Matthijs was devoted to her and painted her portrait in 1872.

PROVENANCE
Montreal, coll. E.B. Greenshields, 1907; United States, coll. Drinkwater, 1939; Amsterdam, art dealer E.J. van Wisselingh & Co, 1965; purchased by the museum, 1967.

BIBLIOGRAPHY
Greenshields 1906, fig. XXXVa; Croal Thomson 1907, p. XXXIV, fig. M 1; Veth 1917(1), p. 162; Croal Thomson 1918, ill.; Arondéus 1939, p. 49; Van Gelder 1939, pp. 10, 18, 34 (with ill.); Arondéus 1945, p. 48; L.J.F. W[ijsenbeek] in *M.D.K.W.* VIII (1953), p. 58, fig. 8 on p. 57; *Verslag Gemeente Utrecht* (1967), Bijlage; A. Wagner in *O.K.* XII (1968), no. 18 (with ill.).

EXHIBITIONS
Paris 1888 (2); The Hague 1965(1), no. 63 (with ill.); Laren 1969, no. 34, fig. 20; Utrecht 1971–72, no. 45 (with ill.); The Hague 1974–75, no. 90 (with ill.); Amsterdam 1979(1), no. 50 (with ill.); Tokyo 1979, no. 50 (with ill.).

77 *The Butterflies*

Oil on canvas, 64 × 97 cm
Signed and dated bottom right: *M. Maris 74*
Glasgow, The Burrell Collection,
Glasgow Art Gallery and Museum
repr. in colour on p. 70

This picture is reminiscent of the work of the English Pre-Raphaelites and was painted by Matthijs Maris in Paris. It shows the freer style he began to adopt after 1874, although the forms are not yet as completely dissolved or as hidden in mists as in his later work; the painting still hovers between dream and reality, whereas *He is Coming* (National Museum of Wales, Cardiff), also painted in 1874, definitely belongs to the realm of fantasy.

Braakhuis and Van der Vliet included *The Butterflies* among those works by Matthijs in which the loss of childlike innocence through the acquisition of knowledge is a central theme. The little girl trying to catch the butterflies is still in that paradisial state in which humans and animals are on an equal footing, with the implication that this equilibrium is as fragile and transitory as the frail butterfly. These two authors recognized Cornelis Kruseman's *Captive Butterfly* of 1845 (Haags Gemeentemuseum) as a precursor of Maris's painting.

The critic Bernard Canter's interpretation of the painting was quite different. In an argument with Theo van Doesburg in 1917, he launched a fierce attack on the 'vague romanticism' and 'sickly sentimentality' of Matthijs's work, in an effort to dislodge the aura of 'sanctity' that enveloped the painter. *The Butterflies* came under particularly heavy fire as 'a product of

hysteria bordering on serious perversion' and Canter wound up his polemic with the barbed condemnation, 'One does not paint children in improper postures' (*Holland Express*, 12 September 1917).

A child with butterflies recurs in several other works by Maris, including a small canvas in the Fogg Art Museum, in which the scene is set in a wood. The model for *The Butterflies* was Tine Lefèvre, who lived next door to Maris in Paris.

PROVENANCE
Paris, art dealer Goupil (bought for £50); Glasgow, art dealer Craibe Angus; Edinburgh, coll. Thomas Glenn Arthur, c. 1888; Amsterdam, art dealer E.J. van Wisselingh & Co; coll. Mrs Calkoen-Zeegers Veeckens, 1893 (bought for Dfl. 20,000); coll. Mrs De Man-Calkoen, 1896; Amsterdam, art dealer E.J. van Wisselingh & Co; Glasgow, coll. Sir William Burrell, c. 1901– (bought for Dfl. 25,000).

BIBLIOGRAPHY
Zilcken 1896(1), ill. after p. 23 (etching by Ph. Zilcken after the painting); Marius 1900, pp. 7, 16; MacColl 1902, p. 184; Marius 1903, pp. 272, 274, 275; *B.M.* II (1903), p. 189, ill. on p. 187; Greenshields 1906, p. 166; Marius 1906, pp. 276, 277, 278; Croal Thomson 1907, no. 27 (with ill.); Marius 1908, pp. 113, 114, 115; *Pall Mall Gazette* (24 April 1909); *The Times* (21 May 1909); *The Manchester Guardian* (29 May 1909); Eisler 1911(1), ill. opp. p. 219; Brunt 1912, p. 349 (with ill.); B. Canter in *Holland Express* (12 Sept. 1917); Veth 1971(1), p. 162; Veth 1917(2), p. 604; Buschmann 1918(2), p. 76, Croal Thomson 1918, p. 22 (with ill.); Haverkorn Rijsewijk 1919, p. 124; Marius 1920, pp. 146, 147; Fridlander 1921, pp. 76, 126; Van Wisselingh 1923, no. 27 (with ill.); E. Fagg in *Apollo* I (1925), p. 22; Arondéus 1939, p. 106, ill. opp. p. 65; Van Gelder 1939, pp. 18, 21, ill. on p. 42; Maris 1943, p. 182; Arondéus 1945, pp. 103, 115, ill. opp. p. 57; L. Ansingh in *M.B.K.* XXIII (1947), pp. 82–83 (with ill.); Maris 1947, p. 168; Koomen 1949, p. 143; De Gruyter 1968–69, vol. 2, pp. 31, 39, 41, 48, 102, fig. 51; Marius/Norman 1973, pp. 129, 130, 131; Braakhuis 1978–79, p. 165 (note 169).

EXHIBITIONS
Glasgow 1888, no. 648; Glasgow 1901, no. 1418; London 1903, no. 62; London 1904, no. 77; London 1909, no. 14; London 1924, no. 80; London 1931; Glasgow 1947, no. 54; Glasgow 1967, no. 10.

78

78 *The Enchanted Castle*

Oil on canvas, 21.5 × 33 cm
Monogrammed bottom right: *M.M.*
Oss, Gemeentelijk Jan Cunencentrum

Although Jacob Maris's townscapes combine elements that he himself compiled, they none the less belong to our world in a way that this dream landscape by Matthijs does not. The castle towering high above the enchanted wood is the unattainable castle of the Sleeping Beauty or a vision of Paradise beyond the reach of mere mortals. All links with the Hague School have been lost.

Opinions differ widely on the dating of both this landscape and a closely related second version in the Haags Gemeente-museum. Dates between 1878 and 1888 have been suggested for these two works and also for one or two related etchings by Maris. De Gruyter even puts them – probably mistakenly – as late as 1900.

PROVENANCE
Montreal, coll. James Crathern, –1955; The Hague, art dealer P.A. Scheen, 1955–63; purchased by the museum, 1963.

BIBLIOGRAPHY
Zilcken 1896(1), ill. after p. 23 (etching by Ph. Zilcken after the painting); Croal Thomson 1907, p. XXXV, fig. M 2; *The Daily Telegraph* (26 May 1909); Croal Thomson 1918, fig. 25; Van Gelder 1939, pp. 21, 35, ill. on p. 47; *Vereeniging Rembrandt. Verslag over 1963*, p. 34; De Gruyter 1968–69, vol. 2, pp. 48, 102, fig. 55; Scheen 1969–70, vol. 2, fig. 333; Braakhuis 1978–79, p. 178 (note 264).

EXHIBITIONS
London 1909, no. 5 (with ill.); Dordrecht 1955, no. 93; The Hague 1965(1), no. 66 (with ill.); Nijmegen 1970, no. 19 (with ill.).

VARIATIONS
Oil on canvas, 21.5 × 33 cm, Haags Gemeentemuseum, The Hague; exh. cat. The Hague 1978(1), no. 25 (with ill.).

Willem Maris (1844-1910)

Wenzel Maris – later called Willem – was born in The Hague on 18 February 1844, the youngest son of Mattheus Maris and Hendrika Bloemert. He received his first drawing lessons from his older brothers Jacob and Matthijs; later he attended evening classes at the Haagse Academie for a time and also received advice from the animal painter Pieter Stortenbeker (1828–98). Nevertheless, he was largely self-taught.

In Oosterbeek in 1862 he met Anton Mauve, who became a lifelong friend. That year he also made his debut at the Tentoonstelling van Levende Meesters (Exhibition of Living Masters) in Rotterdam with the painting *Cows on the Heath*, a subject to which he returned many times. A year later the Maris family moved to another house in The Hague, this time in 'The Three Peasants' Slum', at the front of which the three brothers shared a studio.

In 1865 Willem made a journey along the Rhine with Bernard Blommers, partly on foot and partly by boat. No studies are known from this journey, the only reminder of it being the painting *Herdboys with Donkeys* (Cat. 81). In 1867 Willem paid a short visit to Paris on the occasion of his brother Jacob's wedding and in 1871 he went to Norway with Frederik van Seggeren (1825–1900) and Alexander Wüst (1837–76). Apart from these three trips abroad and a few excursions, for example, to Kalmthout in Belgium, Willem spent all his life in the Netherlands, living in or near The Hague.

From 1868 onwards, Maris shared a studio in Juffrouw Idastraat with Blommers and they both copied several paintings in the Mauritshuis. In 1872 he married Maria Jacoba Visser. They had two sons, the elder of whom Simon Willem (1873–1935), also became a painter. In 1876 Willem founded the Hollandsche Teeken-Maatschappij (Dutch Drawing Society) together with Anton Mauve and Hendrik Mesdag.

In both his oils and his watercolours the same subjects constantly recur: cattle in a meadow or beside a pool, ducks at the side of a ditch. His chief concern was always the rendering of the play of sunshine and shadow.

In 1880, when he was living at Oud-Rozenburg, George Hendrik Breitner (1857–1923) was his pupil for a year. Ten years later, a year after the death of Maria, he married the young pianist Johanna Antonia Gijsberta Bijleveld, by whom he had two daughters. He died in The Hague on 10 October 1910.

fig. 140 J. MARIS *Portrait* of *Willem Maris* from the page of a sketchbook (Haags Gemeentemuseum, The Hague)

79

79 *Cows Beside a Pool*

Oil on canvas, 36 × 62 cm
Signed and dated bottom left: *W. Maris 1863*
The Hague, Haags Gemeentemuseum
repr. in colour on p. 72

This delicate early work by Willem Maris already shows his great attention to light, even though here it is still veiled in morning mists. This painting was first shown as *Young Calves Beside a Milktub* at the Tentoonstelling van Levende Meesters (Exhibition of Living Masters) in The Hague in 1863, where it met with no more approval from the critics than Matthijs Maris's *Washday* (Cat. 70), which was shown at the same time. Théophile de Bock cited one of these negative comments in his book on Jacob Maris: 'Such works may have a right to a place in any general assembly of our artists, but it would be a dismal prospect if such excesses were to constitute a school. The light in Willem's work is not a natural light, but that of the music hall.'

Knoef has suggested that the animal painter Johan Daniel Koelman (1831–57) may have inspired Willem Maris's preference for hazy atmospheres and scenes lit from behind.

PROVENANCE
The Hague, coll. J. van Dijk, 1905; coll. Dr A.A. Korteweg, –1924; auct. Amsterdam (F. Muller & Co), 18 Nov. 1924, no. 202 (Dfl. 4,600); Gorssel, coll. Mrs A.C.A. Korteweg-Bloembergen, 1935–52; bequeathed to the museum, 1952.

BIBLIOGRAPHY
K.K. N.S. v (1864), p. 54; N.R.C. (9 April 1905); Knoef 1947, p. 232.

EXHIBITIONS
The Hague 1863, no. 315; London 1911, no. 47 (with ill.); The Hague 1935–36, no. 236.

80 *Farmyard with Chickens*

Watercolour and gouache, 20.6 × 32.3 cm
Signed bottom left: *W. Maris fc.*
The Hague, Haags Gemeentemuseum

This poultry-yard scene probably dates from the early 1860s. The chickens and duck are not as subtly rendered as they are in Maris's later works (see Cat. 83 for instance), but as a whole this watercolour has the characteristic freshness of a rapid improvisation. The reviewer of the *Kunstkronijk*, writing about the two works exhibited by Willem Maris in 1864, commented perceptively, 'The skill of the brushwork here is really surprising; there is also a great deal of truth in the tone of the ensemble; the artist possesses great potential for further development'.

PROVENANCE
Amsterdam, art dealer Van Delden; Rotterdam, coll. A. Vles, –1939; presented to the museum, 1939.

EXHIBITIONS
Montpellier 1952, no. 41; Zeist 1975, no. 55; Antwerp 1979, no. 39 (with ill.); Florence 1981–82, no. 20 (with ill.).

81

81 *Herdboys with Donkeys*

Oil on canvas, 67 × 115 cm
Signed and dated bottom left: *W. Maris ft 1865*
The Hague, Haags Gemeentemuseum

Donkeys accompanied by herdboys are found only occasionally in Hague School paintings; Anton Mauve painted several attractive works with seaside donkeys and Johannes de Haas made a number of donkey studies in Picardy.

Judging from the wide river landscape in this painting, Willem Maris found his inspiration in Germany. It is the only work that recalls his visit there with Blommers. The 1962 catalogue of the Haags Gemeentemuseum suggests that the painting represents a Norwegian subject, but this is incorrect since it is clearly dated 1865 and Maris did not go to Norway until 1871. The detailed rendering of the grass in the foreground anticipates his later interest in the vegetation along ditches (cf. Cat. 83).

In the Printroom of the Haags Gemeentemuseum there is a sheet with composition sketches for this work. Some related works, with the same donkeys and boys in a Scheveningen setting, are also known; they were exhibited in 1866 and 1867 in Brussels, Antwerp and Rotterdam. Although Isaac Israëls made the theme of donkey rides very popular later in the nineteenth century, Willem Maris never returned to it in any later paintings.

PROVENANCE
Rotterdam, coll. E. Suermondt, –1885; auct. Amsterdam (F. Muller & Co), 28 April 1885, no. 63 (Dfl. 240); Amsterdam, art dealer C.M. van Gogh, 1885; Amsterdam, coll. R.S. van Son, –1908; auct. Amsterdam (C.L.C. Vockuil & Co), 5 May 1908, no. 161 (Dfl. 4,000); Amsterdam, art dealer C.L.C. Voskuil & Co., 1908–; The Hague, art dealer A. Preyer, –1927; auct. Amsterdam (F. Muller & Co), 8 Nov. 1927, no. 79; purchased by the museum, 1927.

BIBLIOGRAPHY
H.E. van Gelder in *M.D.K.W.* 11 (1926–31), p. 161; cat. Gemeentemuseum 1935, p. 164, no. 29–27; Maris 1943, p. 195; Maris 1947, p. 177; Pedroza 1948, p. 14 (with ill.); cat. Gemeentemuseum 1962, no. 219 (with ill.); De Gruyter 1968–69, vol. 2, pp. 53, 59.

EXHIBITIONS
London 1888, no. 46; Amsterdam 1910(1), no. 86; London 1911, no. 36 (with ill.); ? The Hague 1911(2), no. 59; The Hague 1935–36, no. 309; Bonn 1972, no. 39; Zeist 1975, no. 51; Amsterdam 1979(1), no. 52; Tokyo 1979, no. 52 (with ill.).

VARIATIONS
1) oil on canvas, 40 × 52 cm, auct. Amsterdam (F. Muller & Co), 8 April 1930, no. 10 (with ill.). 2) oil on canvas, 66 × 116 cm, auct. The Hague (J.J. Biesing), 13 Feb. 1912, no. 89 (with ill.). 3) drawing, Haags Gemeentemuseum, The Hague.

82

82 *Cow Drinking*

Oil on canvas, 50 × 80 cm
Signed bottom right; *Willem Maris f.*
Bois-le-Duc, Noordbrabants Museum
(on loan from a private collection)

This painting from the classic grey period of the Hague School
is close to the work of Anton Mauve in both conception and
mood. It is not easy to establish the chronology of Willem
Maris's work, mainly because of his narrow range of subjects
and the fact that after the 1860s he no longer dated his pictures.
De Gruyter includes this work among the 'relatively early
paintings', primarily on the grounds of the muted tonality –
the sober greyish-white set against a cool, saturated green. Not
until after the 1880s does a broader touch appear in Willem's
work and the restrained tones make way for warmer colours.

PROVENANCE
The Hague, art dealer P.A. Scheen, 1955. Netherlands, priv. coll.; on loan to the museum, 1982–.

BIBLIOGRAPHY
De Gruyter 1968–69, vol. 2, pp. 52–53, 60, 103, fig. 73; Scheen 1981, fig. 525.

EXHIBITIONS
The Hague 1955(1), no. 22 (with ill.); Tilburg 1955, no. 32;? The Hague 1965(1), no. 74 (with ill.).

83 *The Bliss of Summer*

Watercolour, 45 × 64 cm
Signed bottom right: *Willem Maris ft*
Private collection

The ducks in this watercolour are basking in bright sunlight.
Willem Maris managed to capture every nuance of the play of
light on their downy feathers. He had a duck pond of his own
near his house at Voorburg and there he could observe the
birds with ease at close quarters; he painted them in numerous
variations in oil and watercolour.

The genre found a ready market among buyers and Maris's
imitator Constant Artz (1870–1951) made it his speciality for
many years. In Germany, Franz Grässel (1861–1948), who also
painted ducks, took his inspiration from the works of Maris,
copying even the smallest details from them.

PROVENANCE
The Hague, coll. Mrs M.M.A. Tersteeg-Pronk, 1891; The Hague, art dealer Boussod, Valadon & Co,
1898; Amsterdam, coll. F. Tessaro, –1916; auct. Amsterdam (F. Muller & Co) 11 April 1916, no. v;
Rotterdam, coll. A. Poortman, –1924; auct. Amsterdam (F. Muller & Co), 13 May 1924, no. 169 (Dfl.
3,300); The Hague, art dealer P.A. Scheen, 1959; The Hague, priv. coll., 1959–80; The Hague, art dealer
P.A. Scheen, 1980–81; purchased by the collector, 1981.

BIBLIOGRAPHY
Marius 1891, ill. on p. 123; Zilcken 1893, ill. on p. 89; Marius 1898, ill. on p. 108; Scheen 1969–70, vol. 2,
fig. 327; *Tableau* III (1980–81), no. 3, ill. on back cover; Scheen 1981, fig. 518.

83

84 *Summer*

Oil on canvas, 136.5 × 164.5 cm
Signed bottom right: *Willem Maris*
Dordrecht, Rijksmuseum Van Bilderbeek-Lamaison
repr. in colour on p. 72

Summer was bought by the Dordrecht collector Willem van
Bilderbeek in July 1897 at the Second Biennale in Venice. The
subject of the painting is almost as simple as its title: sunlight.
In this late work any traces of the grey school have virtually
disappeared. Roelofs, Weissenbruch and Jacob Maris drew
much of the strength of their landscapes from the piling up of
impressive cloud formations, but for Willem Maris a few
ethereal wisps of cloud are enough to catch the light and create
the illusion of shimmering summer heat.

Willem Maris returned to the same simple motifs time and
again: cows at a pool, a few willows, the vague silhouette of a
windmill on the horizon. Using these elements, he created
with his brush a series of lyrical paintings of unprecedented
brilliance, making good his claim to paint not cows but the
sunlight itself. In his work the Hague School finds its purest
moment of 'art for art's sake'.

84

PROVENANCE
Dordrecht, coll. W.H. van Bilderbeek, 1897 (purchased at exh. Venice 1897).

BIBLIOGRAPHY
Cat. Verz. Van Bilderbeek 1913, p. 20, no. 81; De Boer 1915, no. 62 (with ill.).

EXHIBITIONS
Venice 1897, no. v-27; Dordrecht 1904(1), no. 11; The Hague 1935–36, no. 275; Dordrecht 1957(1),
no. 28; Dordrecht 1978, no. 59 (with ill.); Amsterdam 1979(1), no. 53; Seoul 1979, no. 30 (with ill.);
Tokyo 1979, no. 53 (with ill.).

Anton Mauve (1838-1888)

Anton Mauve was born at Zaandam on 18 September 1838, the fifth child and second son of the Mennonite minister Willem Carel Mauve and his wife Elisabeth Margaretha Hirschig. Shortly after Anton's birth his father was summoned to Haarlem and here the painter spent his youth. When Mauve was 16 he became the pupil of the animal painter Pieter Frederik van Os (1808–92), with whom he remained until 1857. In 1858 he became a pupil of Wouterus Verschuur (1812–74) for a few months and during the summer he stayed with Paul Gabriël in Oosterbeek for the first time. In the years that followed he visited Oosterbeek regularly; here he met Johannes and Gerard Bilders among others, and, in 1862, Willem Maris with whom he was to form a firm friendship.

From 1865 onwards Mauve was continually on the move. He lived in turn in Amsterdam, Haarlem, The Hague and Scheveningen, Oosterbeek, Renkum, Wezep in Drenthe, Alkmaar and Dordrecht, until in 1871 he moved to a studio in The Hague. Two years later he went to Bad Godesberg near Bonn for a health cure and the following year he married Ariette Sophia Jeannette Carbentus, a cousin of Vincent van Gogh. They spent part of their honeymoon in Gabriël's house in Brussels. From this union there were four children, including Anton Rudolf (1876–1962), who also became a painter.

Mauve spent the whole of his life in his home country, apart from his short visit to Bad Godesberg, and after his marriage lived in The Hague until 1885. In 1876 he founded the Hollandsche Teeken-Maatschappij (Dutch Drawing Society) with Willem Maris and Hendrik Mesdag and from 1878 to 1883 he served on the committee of Pulchri Studio, first as Commissioner for the Discussions and then as Treasurer. In the meantime, in 1876, the Museum Boymans in Rotterdam had purchased *Cows in the Shade* and thus became the first Dutch gallery to acquire one of his paintings.

In August 1881 Vincent van Gogh, who had decided to become a painter the previous year, went to see Mauve (his cousin by marriage), for advice. Towards the end of the year Van Gogh even worked in Mauve's studio for three weeks, but in March 1882 the two painters separated. In June that year Mauve went to Laren for the first time; he was to return there every summer, often accompanied by Albert Neuhuys. During this period he also came into contact with the young painters Willem Witsen (1860–1923), Willem Bastiaan Tholen (1860–1931) and Piet Meiners (1857–1903), whilst staying at *Ewijckshoeve*, a country-house at Baarn.

In 1885 Mauve decided to settle in Laren for good, moving with his family to a house called Arietta on Naarderweg, next door to Neuhuys. Three years later, on 5 February 1888, he died of a heart attack in his brother's house during a holiday trip to Dordrecht, Prinsenhage and Arnhem.

fig. 141 ANTON MAUVE *Self Portrait*
(Haags Gemeentemuseum, The Hague)

85

85 Cows at a Pool near Oosterbeek

Oil on canvas, 69 × 95 cm
Signed bottom left: *A. Mauve f.*
Arnhem, Gemeentemuseum

Mauve visited the Oosterbeek area for the first time in the summer of 1858; these brown and white cows are characteristic of the region. However, the influence of Mauve's teachers, Pieter Frederick van Os and Wouterus Verschuur, is stronger than any direct reference to the Oosterbeek area in this painting. The prominent position of the cattle, near a willow tree, is highly reminiscent of compositions by Paulus Potter, in particular his *Young Bull* in the Mauritshuis (fig. 5). But the cloudy sky, here lowering with the threat of a thunderstorm, is already very characteristic of Mauve.

PROVENANCE
Coll. H.J. Romeyn; The Hague, art dealer P.A. Scheen, 1950; purchased by the museum, 1950.

BIBLIOGRAPHY
Steenhoff 1908, ill. opp. p. 14; cat. Gemeentmuseum 1965, p. 95; Engel 1967, pp. 19, 27, cat. no. 31, fig. IV.

EXHIBITIONS
The Hague 1938–39, no. 52; Arnhem 1954, no. 44 (with all.); Laren 1959–60, no. 17 (with ill.).

86 Barge Horses on the Bank of the Rhine

Oil on canvas, 68.5 × 121 cm
Signed bottom right: *A. Mauve f.*
Private collection

As early as 1864 Mauve wrote an enthusiastic letter to his friend Willem Maris, describing horsemen riding against a grey background: 'The men were riding up against the slope and figures of horses advanced, strongly lit against a misty background. . . .' Mauve has been pigeonholed as a painter of sheep for the sake of convenience, but initially he was known as a painter of horses. In 1858 he was for a short while a pupil of Wouterus Verschuur, whose paintings revived the seventeenth-century tradition of Philips Wouwermans. But in contrast to Verschuur's romantic work, in which horses are represented in fine condition with gleaming coats, Mauve generally paints heavy, labouring animals.

The theme of the tow-path, with a man or animal pulling a boat along from the bank, became a *leitmotiv* of the Hague School's work. It is found repeatedly in the work of Jacob Maris and Jan Hendrik Weissenbruch (Cat. 127) and occasionally in the paintings of Jozef Israëls (Cat. 40).

This impressive painting won prizes in 1870 (Arti, Amsterdam) and 1873 (Vienna). No other versions are known.

PROVENANCE
The Hague, art dealer, A. Preyer; The Hague, coll. F.H.M. Post, –1891; auct. Amsterdam (C.F. Roos & Co), 14 April 1891, no. 59; London/New York, art dealer Arthur Tooth & Sons; Pittsburgh, coll. Alexander R. Peacock, –1922; auct. New York (American Art Association), 10 Jan. 1922, no. 38 ($8,000); New York, art dealer Brothers Duveen, 1922; Ohio (United States), coll. Thelma G. Dunham, 1922–; New York, coll. Elbert H. & Emma T. Gary, –1934; auct. New York (American Art Association/Anderson Galleries), 7–8 Dec. 1934, no. 383 ($1,300); California (United States), coll. William Randolph Hearst; auct. New York (Sotheby Parke Bernet), 12 Oct. 1979, no. 113; Bois-le-Duc, art dealer Borzo, 1980–81; purchased by the collector, 1981.

BIBLIOGRAPHY
C. von Lützow (ed.), *Kunst und Kunstgewerke auf der Wiener Weltausstellung 1873*, Leipzig 1875, p. 390; Engel 1967, pp. 55, 56, cat. no. 62 (with ill.); *Apollo* CX (Sept. 1979), ill. on p. 134; *Tableau* II (1979–80), p. 277, ill. on p. 236; *Tableau* III (1980–81), p. 741.

EXHIBITIONS
Amsterdam 1870, no. 163 (gold medal); Vienna 1873 (silver medal); Bois-le-Duc 1980 (no cat.); Maastricht 1981 (Pictura) (no cat.).

VARIATIONS
Watercolour, 25.5 × 40 cm, auct. Amsterdam (Mak van Waay), 1 May 1973, no. 603 (with ill.).

86

7 Homeward Bound

Oil on canvas, 55 × 82 cm
Signed and dated bottom right: *A. Mauve 75*
Wassenaar, Collection A.A.M. Ruygrok

Mauve's art developed very gradually, the same themes continuing to occupy him for years. The principal differences between his Oosterbeek and Hague periods lie in a change of treatment rather than subject matter. If one compares this scene of a countryman trudging through a dune landscape beside a horse and cart with, for example, *The Carter* (*c.* 1867 Museum of Fine Arts, Boston) one is struck not only by the many similarities, but above all by the greater lyricism and expressiveness of the style. The forms are softer, although they still retain their structure; it is no longer the picturesque incident that attracts Mauve, but the characteristic aspect of a given mood. The end result is a greater overall simplicity.

Unhappily, the woodcart theme became a cliché in the hands of followers such as François Pieter ter Meulen, Herman Johannes van der Weele and, in particular, Johan Frederik Scherrewitz.

PROVENANCE
The Hague, art dealer P.A. Scheen.

BIBLIOGRAPHY
Illustrated Record of Barbizon House, London 1928, no. 22; Scheen 1981, fig. 528.

88

88 Retired Sailor Smoking

Watercolour, 30 × 22 cm
Signed bottom right: *A. Mauve*
Toledo (Ohio), The Toledo Museum of Art
(Gift of Edward Drummond Libbey)

Although Mauve made a number of attractive portrait studies during the years of apprenticeship, the human figure at first played only a subordinate part in his landscapes. Not until his Hague period did he place greater emphasis on the men and women tending cows in his compositions and even then the figures remain impersonal; they are usually seen from the back or have rather expressionless faces (cf. Cat. 92).

In this respect the old seaman shown here is certainly exceptional. The isolation and introspective character of the figure is typical of Mauve (even the link with the landscape is not very close) as is the humour in his treatment of the subject. The same trait is to be found in some of Mauve's watercolours of timber sales. It is probably a relic of his romantic beginnings and is inconceivable in the work of his French contemporaries.

PROVENANCE
Amsterdam, art dealer F. Buffa & Zn.; Toledo (Ohio), coll. Edward Drummond Libbey, –1925; presented to the museum, 1925.

BIBLIOGRAPHY
Cat. Toledo Museum 1939, p. 140, ill. on p. 141; *Museum News. The Toledo Museum of Art* IX N.S. (1966), ill. on p. 73; Sutton 1967, p. 491 (with fig. 14).

EXHIBITIONS
Toledo 1966.

89

89 *Riders on the Beach at Scheveningen*

Oil on canvas, 45 × 70 cm
Signed bottom right: *A. Mauve f.*
Amsterdam, Rijksmuseum
repr. in colour on p. 241

From 1874 to 1885 Mauve lived in The Hague, taking the dunes and the beach of nearby Scheveningen for his subjects. He also had an eye for the more fashionable aspects of seaside life, as is evident from a small number of works, including his *Donkeys* and the outdoor café scene *At Scheveningen* (both in the Rijksmuseum H.W. Mesdag).

In this picture, painted in 1876, the bathing-machines in the distance distinguish Scheveningen as an up-and-coming seaside resort; the painter was seldom more successful in representing this other, elegant world. Several horsemen and a horsewoman ride down from the dunes to the beach at a gentle pace. The aristocratic character of the work led some critics to identify two of the riders as King William III and his second wife, Queen Emma, but this has since been refuted. The work was early recognized as Mauve's masterpiece, winning praise for its serenity of mood and controlled painterly technique. Knoef spoke in 1947 of a 'purity of very rare occurrence, which allows of no admission, but equally tolerates no addition'.

The Hague School characteristics in this painting can be appreciated more readily if Mauve's treatment of the theme is compared with related works by Edouard Manet or Max Liebermann, although it should be remembered that Liebermann's equestrian works are generally considered to have been inspired by Mauve.

Engel mentions a preliminary study in black chalk for this painting in the Rijksprentenkabinet, Amsterdam.

PROVENANCE
London, coll. James Staats Forbes, before 1895–; The Hague, art dealer A. Preyer, 1912–18; auct. The Hague (Kunstzaal Kleykamp), 8 April 1918, no. 40 (Dfl. 19,000); auct. Amsterdam (F. Muller & Co), 8 Nov. 1927, no. 88 (Dfl. 10,500); England, art dealer, 1927; Montreux, coll. Mr & Mrs J.C.J. Drucker-Fraser, 1927–44; on loan to the museum, 1929; bequeathed to the museum, 1944.

BIBLIOGRAPHY
The Queen (30 April 1910); *The Morning Post* (3 May 1910); *De Nieuwe Courant* (17 Jan. 1912); *De Controleur* (20 Jan. 1912); *N.v.d.D.* (22 Jan. 1912); *A.H.* (24 Jan. 1912); Plasschaert 1923(1), fig. 11; *Illustrated Record of Barbizon House*, London 1928, p. 16, no. 20 (with ill.); Baard 1947, p. 40, ill. on p. 37; Knoef 1947, p. 270; H.P. Baard in *O.K.* III (1959), no. 15 (with ill.); Gerson 1961, p. 27; J.H. in *Van Tijd tot Tijd* VI (1964–65), no. 70 (with ill.); Engel 1965, pp. 56, 64; Engel 1967, pp. 55, 59, 63, cat. no. 73a (with ill.); De Gruyter 1968–69, vol. 2, p. 61; Wagner 1974, ill. on p. 8; cat. Rijksmuseum 1976, p. 371 (with ill.); Sillevis 1980, p. 18.

EXHIBITIONS
Rotterdam 1895(2), no. 38; The Hague 1895(3), no. 14; London 1910, no. 66 (with ill.); Amsterdam 1912(1), no. 54 (with ill.); The Hague 1912(1), no. 70; The Hague 1913(1), no. 63; London 1929, no. 414 (with ill.); Brussels 1932, no. 72 (with ill.); The Hague 1938–39, no. 10 (with ill.); Amsterdam 1948(2), not numbered, ill. opp. p. 19; Luxemburg 1948, no. 64; Antwerp 1955, no. 35 (with ill.); Laren 1959–60, no. 46; Amsterdam 1963, no. s 82, fig. IV; Amsterdam 1964–65, no. 42; Bonn 1972, no. 57, fig. 18; Berlin 1979–80, no. 155 (with ill.).

VARIATIONS
Drawing, 6.7 × 15.7 cm, Rijksprentenkabinet, Rijksmuseum, Amsterdam.

90 *Fishing Boat on the Beach at Scheveningen*

Oil on canvas, 78.5 × 113 cm
Signed and dated bottom right: *A. Mauve '76*
Dordrecht, Dordrechts Museum
repr. in colour on p. 241

'There is a Mauve, the large picture of the fishing smack drawn up to the dunes; it is a masterpiece.

'I never heard a good sermon on resignation, nor can I imagine a good one, except that picture by Mauve and the work of Millet.

'That is *the* resignation – the real kind, not that of the clergymen. Those nags, those poor, ill-treated nags, black, white and brown; they are standing there, patient, submissive, willing, resigned and quiet. They have still to draw the heavy boat up the last bit of the way – the job is almost finished. Stop a moment. They are panting, they are covered with sweat, but they do not murmur, they do not protest, they do not complain, not about anything. They got over that long ago, years and years ago. They are resigned to living and working somewhat longer, but if they have to go to the knacker tomorrow, well, so be it, they are ready' (letter no. 181).

Between 1872 and 1882, the year in which Van Gogh wrote the above letter, Mauve painted a number of versions of the theme of horses taking a rest while hauling up a fishing boat. An 1874 version in the Burrell Collection, Glasgow, was awarded an honourable mention at the Paris Salon that year and a silver medal at the International Exhibition in Philadelphia in 1876. The work exhibited here is a repitition of the Glasgow painting, but the composition is reversed. De Gruyter preferred it to the 1882 work described by Van Gogh because it is less laboriously painted. In his dissertation on Mauve, Engel pointed out that the paint layer is thinner on the 1876 version and that in it Mauve has built up the nuances of tone by placing different touches of colour beside each other, thus anticipating the methods of the Neo-Impressionists.

PROVENANCE
Coll. Mrs W.B.M. de Roo van Capelle – née Jonkvrouwe Van den Santheuvel; bequeathed to the museum.

BIBLIOGRAPHY
Engel 1967, p. 58, cat. no. 71, fig. X; De Gruyter 1968–69, vol. 2, pp. 66, 71, 103, fig. 80.

EXHIBITIONS
Laren 1959–60, no. 14; The Hague 1965(1), no. 86; Zeist 1975, no. 57; Amsterdam 1979(1), no. 54; Seoul 1979, no. 27 (with ill.); Tokyo 1979, no. 54 (with ill.).

VARIATIONS
1) oil on canvas, 91 × 183 cm, The Burrell Collection, Glasgow Art Gallery and Museum, Glasgow. 2) oil on canvas, 82 × 100 cm, auct. Amsterdam (Mak van Waay), 25 June 1957, no. 199 (with ill.). 3) oil on canvas, 115 × 172 cm, Haags Gemeentemuseum, The Hague; Engel 1967, cat. no. 103 (with ill.). 4) watercolour, 29.7 × 39.6 cm, priv. coll. 5) watercolour, 28 × 63 cm, art dealer A. Preyer, The Hague, 1902.

91

91 *The Shellfish Gatherer*

Oil on canvas, 51 × 71 cm
Signed bottom left: *A. Mauve f.*
Paris, Musée du Louvre

There are many pictures by Hague painters in which the silhouette of a man dragging the seabed with a net for shellfish can be discerned against a background of breakers, while some distance away his horse and cart await the catch. The theme is found primarily in the work of Mauve, Jacob Maris and Jan Hendrik Weissenbruch, although in works of the latter two the fisherman is generally merely a part of a much grander, cosmic whole. Mauve's close-up treatment is characteristic, as is the almost classical composition of the group arranged parallel to the pearl-grey background.

This work was given to the Musée du Luxembourg in 1926 by the art dealer Abraham Preyer, together with other works by Bosboom, Israëls, Blommers and Jacob Maris.

PROVENANCE
Amsterdam, art dealer A. Preyer, –1898; auct. Amsterdam (C.F. Roos & Co), 24 May 1898, no. 57 (Dfl. 10,000); Amsterdam, coll. P. Langerhuizen Lzn., –1918; auct. Amsterdam (F. Muller & Co/C.F. Roos & Co), 29 Oct. 1918, no. 65 (Dfl. 25,500); The Hauge, art dealer A. Preyer, 1918–26; presented to the Musée du Luxembourg, Paris, 1926; Paris, Musée National d'Art Moderne.

BIBLIOGRAPHY
Cat. Louvre 1979, p. 87 (with ill.).

VARIATIONS
1) oil on canvas, 35.5 × 53.3 cm, The Burrell Collection, Glasgow Art Gallery and Museum, Glasgow. 2) oil on panel, 19 × 34 cm, Stedelijk Museum, Amsterdam. 3) oil on canvas, 57 × 101.5 cm, auct. New York (Parke-Bernet), 17 March 1938, no. 27 (with ill.). 4) oil on panel, 21.5 × 29 cm, Museum of Fine Arts, Boston (Gift of Ernest Wadsworth Longfellow). 5) oil on panel, 16 × 21.5 cm, auct. London (Christie's), 30 June–4 July 1910, no. 326.

92

92 *Woman Tending a Cow*

Watercolour, 24.7 × 35.1 cm
Signed bottom right: *A. Mauve f.*
Toledo (Ohio), The Toledo Museum of Art
(Gift of Edward Drummond Libbey)

Women looking after sheep and cows appear occasionally in Mauve's earlier Oosterbeek work, but in the second half of the 1870s he developed them as a separate theme. The subject was familiar through the work of Millet and Mauve may have come across it through reproductions of his work obtainable at Goupil's.

At the Salon of 1876 Mauve exhibited a painting of a woman tending a cow which resembles this watercolour in having a composition parallel to the picture plane. In the painting, too, the group is placed against a background of spindly trees; human beings and animal are thus united by 'invisible bonds of understanding' (De Gruyter).

PROVENANCE
Toledo (Ohio), coll. Edward Drummond Libbey, –1925; presented to the museum, 1925.

BIBLIOGRAPHY
Cat. Toledo Museum 1939, p. 144, ill. on p. 145; *Museum News. The Toledo Museum of Art* IX N.S. (1966), ill. on p. 91; De Gruyter 1968–69, vol. 2, pp. 66, 103, fig. 77.

EXHIBITIONS
Toledo 1966.

93 *Cows at a Ditch*

Oil on canvas, 65 × 120 cm
Signed bottom left: *A. Mauve f.*
Munich, Bayerische Staatsgemäldesammlungen, Neue Pinakothek

A comparison between this painting, which dates from the end

of the 1870s, and *Cows at a Pool near Oosterbeek* (Cat. 85), which dates from the beginning of Mauve's Oosterbeek period – the two are almost identical in subject matter – shows how Mauve had successfully broken away from the formulae of his teachers in the intervening years.

Here he achieves a convincingly unified concept by simple means rather than a theatrical arrangement. A white cow is still the principal but not the only highlight. The entire landscape is bathed in light and the contrasts between light and dark are now distributed without any emphasis. The foreground is no longer an artfully constructed *repoussoir*, but one of the most arresting and detailed parts of the painting. The greater degree of integration and intimacy, which is achieved in the main by closing off the background with a line of trees and reducing the area of the sky to a third of the canvas, is also striking in this later of the two works.

BIBLIOGRAPHY
Von Boetticher 1895–98, vol. 1. p. 952, no. 6; cat. Neue Pinakothek 1981, p. 224, no. 7766 (with ill.).

EXHIBITIONS
Munich 1888, no. 1621 (as *Holländishe Weide*).

94 Sand Pit

Watercolour, 29 × 48.6 cm
Signed bottom right: *A. Mauve*
The Hague, Haags Gemeentemuseum

The picturesque qualities of sand erosion in dunes and excavations had fascinated Dutch painters since the seventeenth century. The critic Anna Wagner has identified the sand pit here as one that was in the vicinity of the present-day Westbroek Park near Scheveningen.

This delicate watercolour was painted in 1879 and sold to Goupil the same year. The subject was very popular later with two of the younger Hague painters, Willem de Zwart and Willem Bastiaan Tholen. Van Gogh also made a series of drawings of excavations in The Hague, but he placed more emphasis on the element of human activity then Mauve does in this atmospheric impression.

However picturesque the possibilities of the sand pit theme, the steady despoilment of the dunes and the expansion of The Hague eventually persuaded Mauve to leave the city and he started to look for other places where he could work.

PROVENANCE
The Hague, art dealer Goupil & Co, 1879 (bought from the painter); Gorssel, coll. J. Verstolk-Völcker, 1879– (bought from Goupil for Dfl. 200); The Hague, coll. H.G.J. Völcker; Eefde, coll. J.L. Völcker; Eefde, coll. E.C.K. Völcker. –1939; auct. Amsterdam (F. Muller & Co), 17 Oct. 1939, no. 72 (Dfl. 1,250); purchased by the museum, 1939.

BIBLIOGRAPHY
Hols 1907 (2), ill. on p. 49; Engel 1967, pp. 60, 61, cat. no. 89; Wagner 1974, p. 11, ill. on p. 10; Pollock 1980–81, pp. 47–48.

EXHIBITIONS
The Hague 1938–39, no. 96; Germany 1955, no. 36; Mönchen-Gladbach 1957, no. 44; Laren 1959–60, no. 75; Liège 1961–62, no. 97 (with ill.); Breda 1962, no. 97; Amsterdam 1963, no. T 83, fig. 57; Paris 1936; presented to the Haags Gemeentemuseum, The Hague, 1936; sold by the Haags Gemeente- (1), no. 33; Bonn 1972, no. 62; Zeist 1975, no. 59 (with ill.); Antwerp 1979, no. 41 (with ill.); Florence 1981–82, no. 23 (with ill.).

95 Wood Gatherers on the Heath

Watercolour, 37 × 62.5 cm
Signed bottom right: *A. Mauve f.*
Groningen, Groninger Museum
(on loan from Collection R.J. Veendorp)
repr. in colour on p. 243

Wood gatherers have traditionally personified winter in Netherlandish landscape painting ever since the medieval illuminated Books of Hours. The nineteenth-century Realist painters continually had recourse to such standard types, which, imbued by tradition with allegorical meaning, endowed paintings with a significance beyond that initially suggested by the extreme naturalism of the handling. Millet's *Sower* (of which Matthijs Maris made an etching) is undoubtedly the most telling example of this approach; he also chose wood gatherers as personifications of winter for his

unfinished cycle of the four seasons (1868–74). Of the Hague School masters, Jozef Israëls often depicted figures lugging bundles of firewood or other burdens in a winter landscape, alluding to old age as the winter of life (see Cat. 35).

Woodcutters, carts transporting timber, and timber sales constitute a separate theme in Mauve's oeuvre. He created some of his finest works on this theme in his watercolours, many of which show woodland interiors in winter; while most of his landscapes are dominated by a uniformly cloudy sky, this one, exceptionally, has a dramatic sky that determines the tension of the composition.

PROVENANCE
Wassenaar, coll. R.J. Veendorp; on loan to the museum.

BIBLIOGRAPHY
Pollock 1980–81, p. 47 (with ill.).

EXHIBITIONS
Paris 1963, no.89, fig. XVIII; Groningen 1969, no. 102 (with ill.); Amsterdam 1980–81, no. 20 (with ill.).

96

96 Old Coach in the Snow

Watercolour, 26.4 × 32.3 cm
Signed bottom right: *A. Mauve*
Philadelphia, The Philadelphia Museum of Art
(George W. Elkins Collection)

'With unflinching courage we have walked through the snow every day, armed with the paintbox, which seldom remained unused.' Mauve's wife thus described a not unusual outing in the winter cold of 1885. Mauve was, together with Jozef Israëls and Jacob Maris, a worthy representative of the Dutch painters who depicted winter scenes, a tradition that began with Pieter Brueghel. He excelled in rendering the silence of winter, especially in his watercolours.

Some of Mauve's favourite subjects in this genre were woodcutters in wintry woods, sheep beside a snow-covered pen and an old couple shuffling through a city park. The coach in this picture is an unexpectedly picturesque and dynamic subject for Mauve.

PROVENANCE
Philadelphia, coll. George W. Elkins.

BIBLIOGRAPHY
Rishel 1971, p. 27, ill. on p. 26.

97 A Dutch Road

Oil on canvas, 50.5 × 36.8 cm
Signed bottom right: *A. Mauve*
Toledo (Ohio), The Toledo Museum of Art (Gift of Arthur J. Secor)
repr. in colour on p. 242

This little painting of a flat Dutch road, virtually symmetrical in composition and almost bare in its economy of motifs, is a brilliant example of Mauve's capacity to evoke a mood of desolation simply from tones of grey. The work exudes dampness, not only from the puddles on the muddy road, but also from the sky heavy with rain. On the right a bright light is trying to break through the clouds.

Mauve painted numerous variations on this theme of the solitary horseman, his brilliant virtuoso technique occasionally drawing him into a search for somewhat superficial dramatic effects. In a number of versions he treated the theme horizontally. One of the finest versions (*Homeward Bound*) is also in the Toledo Museum.

PROVENANCE
Milwaukee, art dealer Henry Reinhardt; Toledo (Ohio), coll. Arthur J. Secor, 1909–22; presented to the museum, 1922.

BIBLIOGRAPHY
Museum News. The Toledo Museum of Art (April 1922), no. 41, ill.; cat. Toledo Museum 1939, p. 142, ill. on p. 143; Sutton 1967, p. 491 (with fig. 16); cat. Toledo Museum 1976, p. 110, pl. 165 on p. 279.

EXHIBITIONS
Toledo 1966.

VARIATIONS
1) oil on canvas, 59.7 × 45 cm, auct. New York (Christie's), 31 Oct. 1980, no. 182 (with ill.). 2) watercolour, 47 × 34 cm, auct. Amsterdam (F. Muller & Co), 17 Oct. 1939, no. 70 (with ill.). 3) panel, 39 × 27.6 cm, Rijksmuseum H.W. Mesdag, The Hague; cat. Museum Mesdag 1975, no. 208 (with ill.).

89 MAUVE *Riders on the Beach at Scheveningen*

90 MAUVE *Fishing Boat on the Beach at Scheveningen*

97 MAUVE *A Dutch Road*

95 MAUVE *Wood Gatherers on the Heath*

100 MAUVE *The Return of the Flock*

101 MAUVE *Women Binding Sheaves*

105 MAUVE *Woman with Kid at Laren*

115 ROELOFS *Meadow Landscape with Cows*

119 ROELOFS *Lake at Noorden (Water-lilies)*

117 ROELOFS *The Rainbow*

122 ROELOFS *May in Noorden*

23 GABRIËL *In Groenendaal near Brussels*

24 GABRIËL *Watermill near Leidschendam*

25 GABRIËL *Train in Landscape (Il vient de loin . . .)*

26 GABRIËL *Windmill by the Water*

98 *The Artist's Daughter Standing on a Garden Path*

Watercolour, 34 × 21 cm
Signed bottom left: *A. Mauve*
Amsterdam, Rijksprentenkabinet, Rijksmuseum
(on loan to Gemeentemuseum, Arnhem)

Mauve and his wife Ariette Carbentus had four children, one of whom, Anton Rudolf, also decided to become an artist. Many of Mauve's watercolours of figures, like those of Jacob Maris, were inspired by his children. His little daughter Elisabeth is represented here with an objectivity peculiar to Mauve's work. This watercolour, probably painted in 1880, was evidently not intended for his own collection, for he sold it to Goupil as early as February 1881.

The critic Victorine Hefting has noted that the influence of Willem Maris, a great friend of Mauve, can be detected in the handling of the grass (cf. Cat. 83).

PROVENANCE
The Hague, art dealer Goupil & Co, 1881; London, coll. Th. Richardson, 1881–; London, coll. Mr & Mrs J.C.J. Drucker-Fraser, –1909; on loan to the museum, 1903; presented to the museum, 1909; on loan to the Gemeentemuseum, Arnhem, 1952–.

BIBLIOGRAPHY
Eisler 1913 (1), p. 419; Engel 1967, p. 75, cat. no. 102 (with ill.); De Gruyter 1968–69, vol. 2, pp. 61, 103, fig. 83; Hefting 1970, under cat. no. 105; cat. Rijksmuseum 1976, p. 816 (with ill.).

EXHIBITIONS
Dordrecht 1955, no. 207; Laren 1959–60, no. 73.

99

99 *A Shepherd with his Flock on the Heath*

Watercolour, 30 × 48 cm
Signed bottom right: *A. Mauve*
The Hague, Ivo Bouwman Gallery

As he came to feel closed in by the advancing urbanization of The Hague, Anton Mauve began to look for new, unspoilt areas, where he could paint in tranquility. He found them at last in the Gooi area and in 1885 he settled in the town of Laren, where he had already been a regular visitor for some time.

Among the new subjects that he painted there, a few are surprisingly close to Jozef Israëls's motifs, or – even closer at hand – those of Albert Neuhuys, his neighbour in Laren. For instance, from this period we know some watercolours of a farmer holding a boy on his knee, and a Laren interior illuminated by the bright light from a window. Both the subject matter and the gloomy colours seem derived from Israëls. However, works like these remain exceptions. Mauve's main interest – or perhaps that of his clients – were scenes depicting the heath: lonely shepherds and flocks of woolly sheep blending into the gently undulating landscape.

PROVENANCE
England, priv. coll.

100 *The Return of the Flock*

Oil on canvas, 101.6 × 160 cm
Signed bottom right: *A. Mauve*
Philadelphia, The Philadelphia Museum of Art
(George W. Elkins Collection)
repr. in colour on p. 243

In a letter of 3 May 1864 to Willem Maris, Mauve described a scene on the heath near Oosterbeek, which he did not paint until much later. 'Towards sunset I ventured out on to the heath. You can understand how it looked there. Kind, moving; kind and bold – grand. Near Oosterbeek that same shepherd came along again with his sheep; the tinkling and tapping noise they made still murmurs in my ears like the most beautiful of Beethoven's music; I watched them slowly crossing the ridges of the heath again, until they finally disappeared from view – Silence –' (letter at R.K.D., The Hague).

Mauve painted sheep with less attention to the individual animals than he gave to either horses or cows, treating them rather as a mass of animals. The rendering of the animals against the light is strongly reminiscent of Millet.

PROVENANCE
Coll. Dr Gerardus H. Mynkoop, –1890; New York, coll. Joseph Jefferson, –1905; art dealer Scott & Fowles; Philadelphia, coll. George W. Elkins.

BIBLIOGRAPHY
Rishel 1971, pp. 21, 27, ill. on p. 14;

EXHIBITIONS
Paris 1887, no. 1636 (as *Moutons dans la bruyère*); Toledo 1966.

101 *Women Binding Sheaves*

Oil on canvas, 47 × 88 cm
Signed bottom right: *A. Mauve*
Wassenaar, Collection A.A.M. Ruygrok
repr. in colour on p. 244

One of the most characteristic contributions of the Realist school to landscape painting was the elevation of the human figure from a subordinate detail in the landscape to become, if

102

not the protagonist, an essential part of the action. In Romantic painting the human presence in a landscape was expressed either through the spectator, as in the work of Caspar David Friedrich, or the emphasis was on human frailty in comparison with natural forces, as in Turner's paintings.

In Realist painting, the artist was concerned almost exclusively with the bond between man and earth. In the eyes of the Dutch Realists this essential unity was present only in the lives of the peasants and fishing people, who had to wrest their living from a daily struggle with the earth itself. The Realists' vision of this struggle invested them with an additional spiritual dimension of their own. In this work Mauve also rendered the unity of figure and landscape by painterly means.

PROVENANCE
The Hague, Vereeniging van Haagsche Museumvrienden (Society of Friends of Hague Museums), 1936; presented to the Haags Gemeentemuseum, The Hague, 1936; sold by the Haags Gemeentemuseum, 1969; The Hague, art dealer P.A. Scheen, 1969–70; Rotterdam, priv. coll., 1970–79; The Hague, art dealer P.A. Scheen, 1979–80; purchased by the collector, 1980.

BIBLIOGRAPHY
Van Gelder 1937, fig. 11 on p. 452; M.D.K.W.IV (1937), p. 18, ill. on p. 19; G. Kn[uttel Wzn.] in M.D.K.W. VI (1940), pp. 88, 89 (with ill.); Van Gelder 1946 (I), fig. 11 on p. 696; Van Gelder 1954–56, vol. 2, fig. 11 on p. 403; cat. Gemeentemuseum 1962, no. 233; Van Gelder 1963–65, vol. 11, fig. 11 on p. 1930; Scheen 1969–70, vol. 2, fig. 321; Tableau II (1979–80), no. 3, ill. on backcover.

EXHIBITIONS
Antwerp 1937, no. 50 (with ill.); The Hague 1967 (I), no. 31.

102 Gathering Potatoes

Watercolour, 42.1 × 52.3 cm
Signed bottom right: *A. Mauve f.*
Montreal, Musée des Beaux-Arts de Montréal
(Bequest of John W. Tempest)

'The figures of a peasant and a labourer began as "genre", but at present, with Millet the great master as a leader, this is the very core of modern art, and will remain so.' (Letter by Van Gogh, no. 418, July 1885). Peasants and farm labourers were a traditional theme in Dutch art, but until the late nineteenth century their role in the landscape was mainly confined to that of a detail. In Gabriël's *In Groenendaal* (Cat. 23), for example, a woman working on the land appears as an important, but small figure. Only in several early landscapes by Jozef Israëls and Alexander Mollinger (who died young), does the role of the figure in the landscape change.

A group of Scheveningen women gleaning in a harvested potato field are first treated as the main theme of a painting in a work painted in 1874 by Philip Sadée (1873–1904, fig. 41). It was not until the 1880s, however, that this subject became really popular and that Mauve also painted it. In doing so he often worked closely with the young Willem Witsen, who shared his admiration for Millet (cf. fig. 82).

PROVENANCE
Coll. John W. Tempest, –1892; bequeathed to the museum, 1892.

103

103 Self Portrait

Oil on canvas, 65 × 43 cm
The Hague, Haags Gemeentemuseum

After producing a number of attractive early portrait drawings, Mauve virtually abandoned the form for a long while. This painting, which can be dated c. 1885, shows the artist in an apparently casual pose against a wall in his studio. His somewhat haughty gaze is reminiscent of two other self portraits by artists of this period; one by Matthijs Maris (1860, see fig. 139) and the other by George Hendrik Breitner (1882).

The opinion of one critic, Boon, that Mauve's self portrait is no more than a 'studio impression . . . in which the essence of the artist has not found expression', is contradicted by Baard, Mauve's biographer, who says that the painting is a sound rendering 'of the physiognomy of a man who had to struggle against severe inner conflicts'. He contrasts the work with the drawing of Mauve on his deathbed made by Le Comte, in which all traces of conflict have gone from the artist's face.

PROVENANCE
Auct. Studio A. Mauve, The Hague (Kunstzaal Kleykamp), 22–23 May 1917, no. 447; The Hague, (Society for the Foundation of a Museum of Modern Art), 1917; presented to the museum, 1917.

BIBLIOGRAPHY
E.G.M. XXXIV (1924), vol. LXVIII, ill. opp. p. 357; H.E. van Gelder in M.D.K.W. II (1926–31), p. 161; cat. Gemeentemuseum 1935, p. 168, no. 330, fig. 40; Baard 1947, p. 28, ill. on p. 44; Boon 1947, p. 74, fig. 53 on p. 75; M.F. Hennus in M.B.K. XXIII (1947), p. 118 (with ill.); Pedroza 1948, p. 14 (with ill.); cat. Gemeentemuseum 1962, no. 234 (with ill.); Van Hall 1963, p. 202; Engel 1967, pp. 74–75, cat. no. 109, ill. on frontispiece; De Gruyter 1968–69, vol. 2, p. 61; Scheen 1981, fig. 527.

EXHIBITIONS
Amsterdam 1924, no. 91; Amsterdam 1929, no. 62; The Hague 1945, no. 80; Maastricht 1945–46, no. 54 (with ill.); The Hague 1947, no. 265; Amsterdam 1948 (2); Luxemburg 1948, no. 63; Düsseldorf 1950, no. 44; Antwerp 1955, no. 34; Germany 1955, no. 14; Amsterdam 1957, no. 43; Gt. Britain 1958, no. 27; Laren 1959–60, no. 19 (with ill.); Dordrecht 1966–67, no. 39; Bonn 1972, no. 60, fig. 17.

104 The Marsh

Oil on canvas, 60 × 90 cm
Signed bottom left: A. Mauve f.
Amsterdam, Rijksmuseum

This desolate painting bears a remarkable affinity to Vincent van Gogh's Wheatfield with Crows painted five years later. Both works are within the northern tradition of landscape painting, in which a spiritual significance formerly reserved for religious painting is conferred upon nature. In his book Modern Painting and the Northern Romantic Tradition Robert Rosenblum writes of the meditative character of this type of landscape, created by its unusual breadth and silence. Baard, Mauve's biographer, recognized in the artist's work an 'identification of his own solitariness with the loneliness of nature'; another critic, Max Eisler, saw in it 'the spiritual struggle of a recalcitrant human being with a melancholy piece of nature, without attaining artistic liberation'.

The lack of any motif in The Marsh makes it quite exceptional, not only within Mauve's oeuvre, but also within the work of the Hague School as a whole. In a number of preliminary drawings even the birds are absent.

PROVENANCE
London/Falkland Lodge, Newbury, Berkshire, coll. Sir John Charles Day, –1909; auct. London (Christie's), 13–14 May 1909, no. 89 (£682 10s); London, coll. Mr & Mrs J.C.J. Drucker-Fraser, 1909–10; on loan to the museum, 1909; presented to the museum, 1909/10.

BIBLIOGRAPHY
Steenhoff 1910 (2), p. 372; Eisler 1913 (1), pp. 410–11; Baard 1947, p. 46, ill. on p. 49; Colmjon/Scheen 1950, p. 46 (with ill.); Engel 1967, p. 76, cat. no. 111, fig. XIV; cat. Rijksmuseum 1976, p. 391. (with ill.).

EXHIBITIONS
London 1903, no. 23; London 1929, no. 418; Passau 1956, no. 33; Laren 1959–60, no. 45; Amsterdam 1980–81, no. 18 (with ill.).

105 Woman with Kid at Laren

Oil on canvas, 50 × 75 cm
The Hague, Haags Gemeentemuseum
repr. in colour on p. 244

In a letter to his wife written in 1882 Mauve gave his first impressions of the Gooi: 'A beautiful area, splendid heath; there are sheep here as well, magnificent thatched roofs and some very intimate spots.' This painting shows just such an intimate spot near a farmhouse. The strong colour contrasts between the Laren costume, the kid and the background of bright green grass show how far Mauve's work had moved away from the grey palette.

A sense of good-natured everyday contact between people and animals is to be found in the work of most of the Hague School painters, from Jacob Maris's Feeding Chickens (Rijksmuseum, Amsterdam) and Matthijs Maris's Woman with Child and Kid (Cat. 72) to Jozef Israëls's Old Friends (fig. 113). Mauve however, avoided any such emphasis and reduced any anecdotal elements to a bare minimum: the expression of the peasant woman in this picture gives little away.

Max Liebermann, who first met Mauve in 1884, drew inspiration from Laren works such as this, but it is striking how his Woman with Kids (fig. 74) of 1891, for example, is dynamic and filled with movement, whereas Mauve preferred to depict the serenity of this simple wordless action.

PROVENANCE
London, art dealer Obach & Co. 1888; London/Falkland Lodge, Newbury, Berkshire, coll. Sir John Charles Day, 1888–1906; London, art dealer Obach & Co, 1906; Amsterdam, art dealer F. Buffa & Zn., 1906; Amsterdam, coll. E.H. Crone; on loan to the museum by the E.H. Crone Heirs, 1947–64; purchased by the museum, 1964.

BIBLIOGRAPHY
Marius 1910, pp. 11–12 (with ill.); cat. Gemeentemuseum 1962, no. 235; Engel 1967, p. 73, cat no. 116a; De Gruyter 1968–69, vol. 2, p. 103, fig. 90; Sillevis 1980, p. 18, ill. on p. 19.

EXHIBITIONS
Amsterdam 1909 (2), no. 35; Laren 1959–60, no. 11; The Hague 1964, no. 30; Bonn 1972, no. 61, fig. 19; Bremen 1978, no. 446; Berlin 1979–80, no. 154 (with ill.); Haarlem 1981–82, not numbered.

VARIATIONS
1) oil on canvas, 35 × 50 cm, auct. The Hague (Groupil & Co.), 13 Nov. 1894, no. 68 (with ill.). 2) drawing, 25 × 34 cm, coll. Mauve Heirs; Engel 1967, cat. no. 116 c (with ill.). 3) drawing, 9.2 × 15.7 cm, coll. R. Seydenzaal, Utrecht; Engel 1967, cat. no. 116 d.

104

105

106

106 *In the Vegetable Garden*

Oil on canvas, 55.5 × 75 cm
Signed bottom right: *A. Mauve f.*
Rotterdam, Museum Boymans-van Beuningen

According to the critic Loffelt a watercolour of this subject was shown in The Hague in August 1886 at the exhibition of the Hollandsche Teeken-Maatschappij (Dutch Drawing Society). This 'miracle of Dutch watercolour painting' reminded Loffelt primarily of Millet whose work was much admired by Mauve. This oil version dates from 1887.

Mauve first painted vegetable gardens in 1884, initially with less emphasis on the figure and greater attention to the varied vegetation. The prominent position of the Laren peasant woman here and the strikingly detailed representation of the vegetables suggest that Mauve was influenced not so much by Millet, as by Camille Pissaro and Jules Bastien-Lepage, both of whom repeatedly painted such subjects at the beginning of the 1880s. Bastien-Lepage in particular was celebrated for similar close-ups of peasant life at this time and the fresh colours in Mauve's painting are strongly reminiscent of his work.

PROVENANCE
Haarlem, coll. G. de Vos, –1893; auct. Amsterdam (C.F. Roos & Co), 25 April 1893, no. 51 (Dfl. 3,025); The Hague, art dealer Goupil & Co, 1893–95; Rotterdam, coll. J.P. van der Schilden, 1895–1925; bequeathed to the museum, 1925.

BIBLIOGRAPHY
Vier en twintig phototypiën vervaardigd tijdens de Mauve-tentoonstelling van den Rotterdamsche Kunstkring, Amsterdam 1896, pl. XXII; Hols 1907 (2), ill. on p. 71; Steenhoff 1908, ill. opp. p. 16; *Verslag van het Museum Boymans te Rotterdam over het jaar 1925*, p. 3 (with ill.); cat. Museum Boymans-van Beuningen 1963, p. 85; *Agenda Museum Boymans-van Beuningen* (1964), no. 26 (with ill.); Engel 1967, pp. 73–74, cat. 122; De Gruyter 1968–69, vol. 2, pp. 69, 103, fig. 91; cat. Museum Boymans-van Beuningen 1972, p. 216, ill. on p. 186.

EXHIBITIONS
Antwerp 1894, no. 901 (with ill.); Rotterdam 1895 (2), no. 56; Amsterdam 1906 (2), no. 117; Paris 1921, no. 152; Amsterdam 1923 (1), no. 277; London 1929, no. 428; Vienna 1929, no. 153; Brussels 1932, no. 71; The Hague 1945, no. 81; The Hague 1947, no. 263; Luxemburg 1948, no. 67; Düsseldorf 1950, no. 45; Dordrecht 1955, no. 94; Laren 1959–60, no. 4; Amsterdam 1979 (1), no. 55; Tokyo 1979, no. 55 (with ill.); Haarlem 1981–82, not numbered, fig. 143.

VARIATIONS
Watercolour; exh. cat. The Hague 1886, no. 57 (cf. Loffelt 1895, p. 594).

107

107 *Heath at Laren*

Oil on canvas, 77 × 104 cm
Signed on bottom right: *A. Mauve f.*
Amsterdam, Rijksmuseum

Mauve lived in the Gooi from 1885 onwards, but Jozef Israëls had already drawn his attention to the beauty of the area some years earlier. When The Hague became less attractive as a result of the pressure of urbanization, the region around Laren became 'the promised land' for Mauve. One of his favourite spots just outside Laren was later called Mauvezand after him.

This painting is the most successful of several versions. Its expressiveness derives from the contrast between the 'woolly' foreground and the monumental group of trees on the horizon, a motif strongly reminiscent of Millet. A drawing of the same subject was shown at the exhibition of the Hollandsche Teeken-Maatschappij (Dutch Drawing Society) in The Hague in 1886.

Mauve's reputation as a painter of sheep became so great towards the end of his career that he once had to promise an English art dealer to supply 12 paintings with sheep in three weeks. Such works were sometimes taken away by impatient dealers while still unfinished. The story goes that works with 'Sheep coming' were priced more highly than those with 'Sheep going', which were considered less attractive, a criterion that hardly seems applicable to *Heath at Laren*.

PROVENANCE
London, coll. Mr & Mrs J. C. J. Drucker-Fraser, 1888–1910 (bought at exh. Rotterdam 1888); on loan to the museum, 1903; presented to the museum, 1910.

BIBLIOGRAPHY
Loffelt 1895, ill. opp. p. 577; Loffelt 1899, ill. on p. 7; Steenhoff 1910(2), p. 372, ill. on p. 370; Eisler 1913(1), pp. 409–10, ill. on p. 411; Engel 1965, p. 47; Zeitler 1966, p. 228, fig. 140 a; Engel 1967, pp. 71, 72, cat. no. 123 (with ill.); A. C. J. de Vrankrijker in *Spiegel Historiael* VII (1972), fig. 7 on p. 527; Baard 1974, p. 48, ill. on p. 55; cat. Rijksmuseum 1976, p. 372 (with ill.).

EXHIBITIONS
Rotterdam 1888, no. 276; Rotterdam 1895 (2), no. 30; London 1903, no. 76; Laren 1959–60, no. 43.

Hendrik Willem Mesdag (1831-1915)

Hendrik Willem Mesdag was born at Groningen on 23 February 1831. He showed an interest in drawing and painting from an early age. After he left school he went to work at his father's banking house, taking drawing and painting lessons in his spare time from C. B. Buys (1808–72) and later from J. W. Egenberger (1822–97), then director of the Minerva Academy at Groningen. In 1856 he married Sientje van Houten (1834–1909), who like himself belonged to an old Groningen Mennonite family. Partly under her influence, he decided at the age of 35, in the spring of 1866, to end his career at Mesdag & Sons in order to devote himself entirely to painting. This had become feasible financially thanks to an inheritance from Sientje's father, D. van Houten, who had died the year before.

The Mesdags spent the summer of 1866 in Oosterbeek, where they made friends with Johannes Warnardus Bilders (1811–90), then moved to Brussels in the autumn. There Mesdag studied under Willem Roelofs, who had been recommended to him by his cousin Alma Tadema (1836–1912), who was also living in Brussels. In the summer of 1868 the couple went to the Netherlands, spending some time at Vries in the Drenthe, before moving on to the German Island of Nordeney, where Mesdag became fascinated by the sea. That winter in Brussels he tried to work up the sketches he had made there into large paintings, but he was only moderately successful. The following year the Mesdags moved to The Hague, where they moved into the house next door to Sientje's brother, the politician Sam van Houten. Every day, Mesdag went to Scheveningen, where he rented a room from which he could study all aspects of the sea and the beach. A year later, in 1870, his painting *Les Brisants de la Mer du Nord* won a gold medal at the Paris Salon, thus establishing his reputation as a marine painter. That year he had a house built on Laan van Meerdervoort in order, among other things, to accommodate his steadily growing collection of works by contemporary French and Dutch painters. Very soon this collection became so large that he erected the present Museum Mesdag in his garden to house it.

In 1874 he was made chairman of the art society, Pulchri Studio, a position he retained until 1892. In March 1881 he began his greatest creation, a commission from a Belgian company to paint a panoramic view from the Seinpostduin at Scheveningen. This 'Mesdag Panorama', on which his wife Sientje, Bernard Blommers, Théophile de Bock (1851–1904) and George Hendrik Breitner (1857–1923) also worked and which was finished in just over four months, is still one of the most popular attractions in The Hague.

In 1903 Mesdag donated the part of his house used as a museum and a large part of his private collection to the State. He died on 10 July 1915 and was buried amid great public mourning at Oud Eyck-en-Duynen in The Hague.

fig. 142 *Hendrik Willem Mesdag in his Studio* (photograph) (Gemeentearchief, The Hague)

108

108 *Winter on the Beach at Scheveningen*

Oil on canvas, 80 × 100.5 cm
Signed bottom right: *H.W. Mesdag*
The Hague, Rijksmuseum H.W. Mesdag

The beach at Scheveningen provided numerous subjects for artists. Mesdag gathered all these together in 1881 in his great Panorama, on which Blommers, Breitner, De Bock and Sientje Mesdag-van Houten, Mesdag's wife, also worked.

It was not usual to paint Scheveningen in the winter, but Mesdag was so inspired by his favourite subject that he chose to spend all his time on the beach.

Repair work on the fishing boats was done at that time on the beach at Scheveningen because of the lack of a proper harbour. When at last a harbour for fishing boats was constructed in 1904, the picturesque sight of the boats on the beach, the subject of masterly portrayals by Jacob Maris and Weissenbruch as well as by Mesdag, became a part of the past.

PROVENANCE
The Hague, coll. H.W. Mesdag.

BIBLIOGRAPHY
Boele van Hensbroek 1890, ill. following p. 4; Zilcken 1896 (2). ill. opp. p. 134; Boele van Hensbroek 1910, ill. following p. 4; *De Schouw* I (1942), ill. on p. 507; *M.D.K.W.* x (1964), ill. on p. 30; *'s-Gravenhage* xix (1964), no. 12, ill. on p. 30; De Gruyter 1968–69, vol. 1, pp. 96, 101, 116, fig. 121; Cat. Museum Mesdag 1975, p. 113, no. 222, ill. on p. 134; Poort 1981, p. 145, no. 3.29 (with ill.).

EXHIBITIONS
The Hague 1965 (1), no. 104 (with ill.).

VARIATIONS
Oil on canvas, 62 × 141 cm, Museum Panorama Mesdag, The Hague (on loan to the Visserijmuseum, Vlaardingen).

109

109   *The Return of the Lifeboat*

Oil on canvas, 95 × 156 cm
Signed and dated bottom right: *H.W. Mesdag 1876*
Rotterdam, Museum Boymans–van Beuningen
repr. in colour on p. 293

Mesdag's success at the Salon of 1870 further convinced him that the sea should be his most important subject. He soon demonstrated his ability to render the sea in all its moods, whether peaceful and serene at sunset in summer or ghostly and threatening on a stormy winter's day.

Sometimes the sea plays the leading role in his work; sometimes the accent falls on the Scheveningen fishermen and their hard existence, busy with their catch or the upkeep of their boats. The subject of this painting is an unusual one for Mesdag. He succeeds in rendering the drama of a rescue at sea without sentimentality, as one of the hazards to which the fishermen were daily exposed.

PROVENANCE
Amsterdam, art dealer E.J. van Wisselingh & Co, 1910; Gorkum, coll. M.C. van Andel, –1912; auct. Amsterdam (F. Muller & Co), 12 Nov. 1912, no. 122 (Dfl. 1,200); Amsterdam, art dealer E.J. van Wisselingh & Co, 1912–; coll. Mrs J.A. Becker-La Bastide, –1961; on loan to the Haags Gemeentemuseum, The Hague, –1927; on loan to the Museum Boymans, Rotterdam, 1927–61; bequeathed to the museum, 1961.

BIBLIOGRAPHY
Cat. Museum Boymans-van Beuningen 1963, p. 88; Poort 1981, p. 113, no. 76.1 (with ill.).

EXHIBITIONS
Amsterdam 1910 (1), no. 98; Amsterdam 1980–81, no.25 (with ill.).

110

110 *Sunset*

Oil on canvas, 140 × 180 cm
Signed bottom right: *H.W. Mesdag*
Paris, Musée d'Orsay

A popular saying of the Hague School artists was the maxim, 'The dunes belong to Weissenbruch, but the sea, that belongs to Mesdag'. Mesdag did, indeed, succeed in establishing an international reputation as a marine painter in a very short time. He quickly became renowned for his skill in rendering rough seas, in a style reminiscent of Courbet's variations of *La vague*. Later, his paintings of calm seas, in which all anecdotal elements have been suppressed and the emphasis is entirely on mood, also won acclaim.

This painting was bought at the Paris Salon in 1887 by the Musée du Luxembourg, where the French collection of modern art was then housed.

PROVENANCE
Paris, Musée du Luxembourg, 1887 (purchased at exh. Paris 1887); Paris, Musée National d'Art Moderne.

BIBLIOGRAPHY
Cat. Louvre 1979, p. 88 (with ill.).

EXHIBITIONS
Paris 1887, no. 1672.

VARIATIONS
Oil on panel, 137.5 × 178.5 cm, Stedelijk Museum, Amsterdam; cat. Stedelijk Museum 1922, p. 45, no. 311

111 *Summer Evening on the Beach at Scheveningen*

Oil on canvas, 178 × 139 cm
Signed and dated bottom right: *H.W. Mesdag 1897*
The Hague, Collection J. Poort

When this painting was exhibited at the second Biennale in Venice in 1897, it attracted considerable attention. Mesdag was now an international celebrity and in Italy he had been awarded the great distinction of a seat on the Dutch Committee for the Venice Biennale at the time of its inauguration in 1895. Later, in 1911, the Italian government bought one of his large-scale paintings at the International Exhibition in Rome. *Summer Evening on the Beach at Scheveningen* was immediately acquired by an Italian collector in 1897 and remained in a collection in Parma until 1977.

PROVENANCE
Italy, coll. Rosselli, 1897; Parma, priv. coll,. –1977; purchased by the collector, 1977.

BIBLIOGRAPHY
Poort 1981, p. 122, no. 97.4 (with ill.), ill. on p. 150.

EXHIBITIONS
Venice 1897.

Albert Neuhuys (1844-1914)

Johannes Albert Neuhuys – generally called Albert – was born in Utrecht on 10 June 1844. He was the youngest in a family of eight children. His eldest brother Jan Antoon (1832–91), who was a friend of Alma Tadema (1836–1912), had studied at the Antwerp Academy and specialized in painting history pieces. Neuhuys wanted to follow his example, but at first his father was opposed to this; he would only allow him to train as a lithographer.

During this training, however, Neuhuys also received painting lessons from his teacher G. Craeyvanger (1810–95); he devoted his efforts to genre and history paintings, and to portraits. From 1868 to 1872 he was in Antwerp, where he studied at the Academy under P. Beaufaux (1829–1904) and G. Geefs (1805–83). On his return to the Netherlands, he lived with his parents in Amsterdam, but in 1875, a year before his marriage to a woman who was his junior by ten years, he settled in The Hague in a house next door to Jacob Maris, from whom he received further advice. During this period, in which he began to concentrate on peasant interiors, he also became friendly with Jozef Israëls, the Marises and Anton Mauve. Although The Hague remained his home until 1893 he worked in Laren, Brabant, North Holland, Belgian Limburg and the Kempen. In 1893 he moved to Laren where he remained until 1897; from 1897 to 1900 he lived in Hilversum, from 1900 to 1910 in Amsterdam and from 1910 until his death, in Zürich, although he continued to spend each summer and autumn in the Netherlands. During the last 20 years of his life he travelled extensively to Italy (1895), Algiers (1896), Austria (1901), Spain (1903), Corfu (1912) and Russia (1913) and three times to the United States (1904, 1908 and 1910), where on the last two occasions he acted as a member of the jury for the International Carnegie Exhibitions at Pittsburgh.

In his own day Neuhuys was an exceptionally celebrated artist, regarded as the true founder of the Laren School. His most important pupils were his elder brother Joseph Hendrikus Neuhuys (1841–1889) and Jan Hendrik Willem van den Brink (1895–1966). He died at Orselina (Locarno) on 6 February 1914.

fig. 143 *Albert Neuhuys in his Studio* (photograph)
(Rijksbureau voor Kunsthistorische Documentatie, The Hague)

112

112 *Winding Wool*

Oil on canvas, 86 × 121 cm
Signed and dated bottom right: *Alb. Neuhuys/74*
Enschede, Rijksmuseum Twenthe

De Gruyter wrote of Neuhuys: 'Figures like Gabriël, Roelofs and Weissenbruch were underrated, preference being given to the expansive, painterly painters who had a great love of paint, among whom Jaap Maris was seen as the central figure. Albert Neuhuys sometimes comes very close to Jaap Maris as a colourist, perhaps even surpasses him in refined, rich delicacy. But he is much more limited in his subjects, which hark back more to Israëls: interiors, mothers with children and suchlike. His emotional range, however, is not as wide as that of Israëls. Unlike him, Neuhuys was no psychologist or dramatist and his paintings recount neither myths, nor Bible legends. His work deals repeatedly with interiors – the peasant interior, the peasant family or the mother with a child on her lap, the nursing mother, the sleeping child, the knitting lesson, the sewing lesson and so forth. But for all that, he was a painter, there is no doubt about that!' (De Gruyter 1968–69, vol. 2, pp. 84–85). De Gruyter's annoyance at Neuhuys's repetition of fixed themes revealed in these words was felt also by artists of following generations, who came to regard the later painters of the Hague School as a group of artists who had stagnated.

PROVENANCE
Auct. Brussels (Palais des Beaux-Arts), 30–31 Oct. 1956, no. 41 (Bfrs. 30,000); auct. Amsterdam (Mak van Waay), 24 June 1958, no. 165 (Dfl. 1,950); coll. G.J. van Heek Jr., –1958; presented to the museum, 1958.

BIBLIOGRAPHY
Cat. Museum Twenthe 1974–76, p. 82, no. 136; L. van Weezel in *Kunstbeeld* VI (Oct. 1981), p. 31.

Exhibitions
Haarlem 1981–82, not numbered, fig. 21.

113 *Laren Woman beside Cradle*

Oil on canvas, 62 × 51 cm
Signed bottom left: *Albert Neuhuys*
Laren (N.H.), Singer Museum

Neuhuys was one of the central figures of the Laren School. He belonged to the generation after Israëls and Mauve, and his work is similar to theirs in certain respects, but his colour is heavier and more strongly accentuated. The play of light, too, is often rather more unusual than in the well-known interiors by Jozef Israëls, who frequently determined the way the light fell in his paintings by the device of a window to the left or right of the composition.

Neuhuys had a greater command of the broad, free brushwork in which atmosphere replaced draughtsmanship, a style that was highly valued by lovers of modern art at that time, than did his fellow artist Artz.

His work won medals in Munich, Vienna, Paris and Chicago and invariably formed part of the large Hague School collections that were amassed around 1900.

PROVENANCE
Amsterdam, art dealer E.J. van Wisselingh & Co; auct. Amsterdam (F. Muller & Co), 8–11 and 14–15 Nov. 1955, no. 221 (as *Joie maternelle*; for Dfl. 3,000); purchased by the museum, 1955.

BIBLIOGRAPHY
Cat. Singer Museum 1962, p. 39, no. 303.

EXHIBITIONS
The Hague 1903 (2), no. 116; Haarlem 1981–82, not numbered, fig. 34.

113

Willem Roelofs (1822-1897)

Willem Roelofs was born in Amsterdam on 10 March 1822, the eldest son of a brick manufacturer, Otto Willem Roelofs, and his wife Wilhelmina Carolina Elisabeth Pronkert; the family moved to Utrecht when Willem was about four. He began drawing and writing verses at a very early age; his first painted landscape dates from 1837 and not long afterwards he was given lessons by the Utrecht amateur painter Abraham Hendrik de Winter (1800–61). He also exhibited for the first time during this period at the Tentoonstelling van Levende Meesters (Exhibition of Living Masters) in Amsterdam and Rotterdam.

In August 1840 he went to The Hague for a year to take lessons from the landscape and animal painter Hendrikus van de Sande Bakhuyzen (1795–1860), with whom he went on a study trip to Germany the following year. Then he returned to his parents' house in Utrecht, where he stayed until 1846. That year he visited The Hague again and made many studies of trees with Jan Gerard Smits (1823–1910), a painter of townscapes. In January 1847 he helped to found the art society Pulchri Studio and later that year he moved to Brussels, where he remained until 1887.

Two of his paintings exhibited at the Brussels Salon in 1848 immediately won him great renown: one of them was awarded a gold medal and the other was bought by the Belgian king. In 1852, the year of his marriage to Johanna Adriana Verstraten, his *Landscape Before a Storm* (Cat. 114) was bought by the Brusselse Museum voor Moderne Kunst (Brussels Museum of Modern Art) at the Salon there. Three years later he helped to found the Société Belge des Aquarellistes. He often worked around Brussels, on the river Senne, in Belgian Limburg, the Kempen and Beaufort, and he made visits to Fontainebleau in 1851, 1852 and 1853. From 1856 onwards he regularly spent the summer in the Netherlands in, among other places, the Gooi area, the region around the rivers Vecht and Gein, Abcoude, Noorden, Kortenhoef, Loosdrecht, Dordrecht, Meerkerk, Gouda, Reeuwijk and Leidschendam. In 1862 he spent a month in Dresden and the Harz mountains and in 1871 he visited London with his friend Henri Hymans (1836–1912).

Roelofs's wife Johanna had died in 1870 and three years later he married Albertina Vertommen, by whom he had two sons, who also became artists: Willem Elisa (1874–1940) and Otto Willem Albertus (1877–1920). Shortly before his second marriage Roelofs spent a few months in Scotland, where he made a great many sketches on the Isle of Skye. He also devoted himself to the study of entomology and acquired a large collection of insects, but in 1880 he felt compelled to sell this to the Brusselse Museum voor Natuurlijke Historie (Brussels Museum of Natural History) since it was distracting him from his painting.

In 1887 Roelofs returned to the Netherlands for the sake of his sons' education and settled with his family in The Hague. From 1892 onwards his health began to decline and two years later it deteriorated sharply, but he was reluctant to give up painting. In April 1897 he left The Hague in order to end his days in his beloved Brussels, but he never arrived; he died on 12 May in his brother-in-law's house at Berchem near Antwerp and was buried three days later at Schaerbeek-Brussels. Hendrik Mesdag, Paul Gabriël, Jan Theodoor Kruseman (1835–95), Alexander Mollinger (1836–67), Carel Nicolaas Storm van 's-Gravesande (1841–1924) and Frans Smissaert (1862–1944) were among his most important pupils.

fig. 144 DE POORTER *Portrait of Willem Roelofs* 1848 (lithograph)
(Gemeentearchief, The Hague)

114

114 *Landscape before a Storm*

Oil on canvas, 136 × 182 cm
Signed and dated bottom left: *W. Roelofs f. 1851*
Brussels, Musées Royaux des Beaux-Arts de Belgique.
Art Moderne

The purchase of this landscape for the Brussels Museum in
1852, after it had been exhibited at the Brussels Salon that year,
signified critical recognition of the importance of Roelofs's
work. It is still clearly linked to the landscape tradition of
Dutch Romanticism dominated by Andreas Schelfhout and
Barend Cornelis Koekkoek. The feeling of threat and
foreboding evoked by the effect of light and shade just before
the outbreak of a thunderstorm is typical of the Romantic
conception of landscape.

PROVENANCE
Purchased by the museum at exh. Brussels 1852.

BIBLIOGRAPHY
Jeltes 1911, p. 21; cat. Musées Royaux 1928, p. 218, no. 854; De Gruyter 1968–69, vol. 1, pp. 35–36, 44,
112, fig. 30.

EXHIBITIONS
Brussels 1852; Amsterdam 1907 (2), no. 14.

115 *Meadow Landscape with Cows*

Oil on canvas, 46 × 70 cm
Signed bottom right: *W.Roelofs*
Amsterdam, Stedelijk Museum (Gift of J.H. van Eeghen)
repr. in colour on p. 245

Hardly any of Roelofs's works shows so skilful an assimilation
of the influence of the Barbizon School as this *Meadow*

Landscape with Cows. The effects of light and the dramatic
contrasts between areas of light and shade are closely related to
the conception of landscape typified by Narcisse Diaz's *Les
Hauteurs du Jean de Paris, Forêt de Fontainebleau* or Théodore
Rousseau's *Le Curé.*

PROVENANCE
Amsterdam, coll. J.H. van Eeghen, –1912; presented to the museum, 1912.

EXHIBITIONS
Amsterdam 1963, no. s 85, fig. 45; Amsterdam 1979 (1), no. 36; Tokyo 1979, no. 36 (with ill.).

116

116 *The Hovel*

Oil on panel, 25 × 35.5 cm
Signed bottom left: *W. Roelofs*
Otterlo, Rijksmuseum Kröller-Müller

Roelofs's choice of insignificant motifs often surprised his contemporaries, understandably so at a time when the imposing 'machines' of the *artistes-pompiers* were still accorded the most praise. His pupil Smissaert paid the following tribute to his teacher's skill: 'You need to know nature through daily contact, as he does, in order, like him, to enjoy it to the full. What you and I would heedlessly pass by as insignificant or ugly, he stands and contemplates in quiet delight, and while you are wondering what there is to be seen, his poet's soul will have absorbed the poetry of this abandoned spot and he will represent it for you just as it struck him' (see H. Smissaert, in *Het Schildersboek*, vol. 1, Amsterdam 1898, p. 79).

PROVENANCE
Auct. Studio W. Roelofs, The Hague (Kunstzaal Kleykamp), 4 June 1918, no. 34; The Hague, coll. Mrs H.E.L.J. Kröller-Müller, 1918.

BIBLIOGRAPHY
Cat. Museum Kröller-Müller 1970, p. 228, no. 591, fig. 34.

EXHIBITIONS
Arnhem 1936, no. 7; The Hague 1965 (1), no. 108 (with ill.).

117

117 The Rainbow

Oil on canvas, 57 × 110.5 cm
Signed bottom left: *W. Roelofs*
The Hague, Haags Gemeentemuseum
repr. in colour on p. 246

When this canvas was exhibited for the first time at the
Tentoonstelling van Levende Meesters (Exhibition of Living
Masters) in 1875, it was still called *Evening of a Rainy Autumn
Day*. Gram, a contemporary critic, called it a 'risky undertak-
ing to paint nature in all her fickleness, after the storm, with the
sun breaking through'.

Although the fleeting effect of the rainbow is reminiscent of
Landscape Before a Storm (Cat. 114), the subject is treated
differently in this later picture owing to the clearly discernible
influence of the Barbizon School. Roelofs had spent some time
in Barbizon and the Forest of Fontainebleau and had also
studied the paintings of Troyon, Rousseau and Dupré. This
painting comes closest to *Le Printemps* by Jean-François Millet
(Musée du Louvre), painted between 1868 and 1874, although
it is not clear whether Roelofs had seen Millet's picture.

PROVENANCE
The Hague, Vereeniging tot het Oprichten van een Museum voor Moderne Kunst te 's-Gravenhage
(Society for the Foundation of a Museum of Modern Art in The Hague), 1875 (bought for Dfl. 1,600);
presented to the museum, 1875.

BIBLIOGRAPHY
K.K. N.S. XVII (1876), p. 35; Gram 1880, pp. 129–30; Vosmaer 1882–85, vol. 1 (W. Roelofs), pp. 2–3;
Plasschaert 1909, ill. on p. 199; Eisler 1911 (1), ill. on p. 207; Jeltes 1911, pp. 43 (note 1), 71; cat.
Gemeentemuseum 1935, p. 219, no. 417, fig. 27; Van Gelder 1937, p. 446, fig. 3 on p. 444; Hammacher
1941, p. 111, fig. 5; Van Gelder 1946 (1), p. 695, fig. 3 on p. 688; Van Gelder 1954–56, vol. 2, p. 402,
fig. 3 on p. 395; cat. Gemeentemuseum 1962, no. 278 (with ill.); De Bruijn 1963, p. 341, ill. on p. 340;
Van Gelder 1963–65, vol. 11, p. 1921, ill. on p. 1917; De Gruyter 1968–69, vol. 1, pp. 35, 37, 44, 112,
fig. 31; Fuchs 1978, pp. 161 (with fig. 142), 163, 214.

EXHIBITIONS
The Hague 1875, no. 339; The Hague 1907 (2), no. 94; Potsdam 1925, no. 113; Antwerp 1937, no. 66
(with ill.); Maastricht 1945–46, no. 64 (with ill.); (The Hague 1947, no. 331; Germany 1955, no. 3; The
Hague 1965 (1), no. 110 (with ill.); Bonn 1972, no. 16; Amsterdam 1980–81, no. 29 (with ill.).

VARIATIONS
Oil on canvas, 46 × 89.5 cm, auct. Laren (Christie's), 20 Oct. 1980, no. 574 (with ill.).

118 Polder Landscape with Windmill near Abcoude

Oil on canvas, 47 × 74 cm
Signed bottom right: *W. Roelofs*
The Hague, Haags Gemeentemuseum

Roelofs lived in Brussels until 1887, but every year he spent
several months drawing and painting in his beloved Netherlands. He once wrote: 'When I've been to Holland, I'm spoilt
for a time and can't adjust back to the idea of staying here for
good. One always remains a foreigner here and I miss the
support one feels from people in one's own country.' (letter of
1 October 1865 to VerLoren van Themaat). In a later letter
(c. 1866) he wrote: 'My great plan to return to the beloved
fatherland becomes firmer the longer I stay here. Between
ourselves – for I daren't carry on so childishly even in front of
my wife – I really believe I am homesick sometimes. You'll
undoubtedly laugh at this, but it is impossible to understand
what it is to long for one's country. I now believe that to be
sent into exile is the worst possible form of punishment.' The
areas in the Netherlands where Roelofs most liked to paint
were Noorden, the area around the river Gein (where Piet
Mondriaan was also to paint) and Abcoude, which is
represented in this landscape.

PROVENANCE
Auct. Studio W. Roelofs, The Hague (Kunstzaal Kleykamp), 4 June 1918, no. 40; The Hague, coll. Mr &
Mrs G.L.F Philips-van der Willigen, –1942; bequeathed to the museum, 1942.

BIBLIOGRAPHY
Bremmer 1909, no. 63; cat. Gemeentemuseum 1962, no. 280.

EXHIBITIONS
Rotterdam 1889, no. 31; The Hague 1907 (2), no. 119; Maastricht 1945–46, no. 65; The Hague 1947,
no. 334; Tilburg 1952, no. 46.

119

collection, but whenever asked about his interest would always reply, 'Yes, but I have painted as well, you know.' (Jeltes 1910, p. 106).

PROVENANCE
Reigersbergen/The Hague, coll. Baron Van Tuyll van Serooskerken, 1907; coll. Mr J. Jochems.

BIBLIOGRAPHY
Smissaert 1891, p. 427; Smissaert 1898 (1), ill. on p. 73; N.H. Wolf in *Het Leven* (4 Oct. 1907), ill. on p. 1267; F. Rutter in *The Studio* XLII (1908), ill. on p. 182; Bremmer 1909, fig. 82; Scheen 1969–70, vol. 2, fig. 269.

EXHIBITIONS
The Hague 1899 (1), no. 19; The Hague 1907 (2), no. 154; Amsterdam 1911 (2), no. 67; The Hague 1982 (1) no. 50 (with ill.).

VARIATIONS
1) oil on canvas, 108 × 173.4 cm, Aberdeen Museum of Art, Aberdeen. 2) watercolour, 45 × 72 cm, formerly art dealer P.A. Scheen, The Hague; Scheen 1981, fig. 436.

119 Lake at Noorden (Water-lilies)

Oil on canvas, 69 × 107 cm
Signed bottom left: *W. Roelofs*
The Hague, P.A. Scheen Gallery
repr. in colour on p. 245

Roelofs had a penchant for views of lakes. In a second version of this picture, the composition is emptier, the clumps of reeds are less dense and a rowing-boat with a fisherman can be seen in the distance. It is now in the Aberdeen Museum of Art. This work is more radiant and the impression it makes is less desolate.

The rather curious, precise rendering of insects is notable in both pictures. In the Aberdeen version two dragonflies hover in the foreground, while in the Hague work Roelofs has painted a damsel fly in great detail. The presence of these creatures, which are painted in almost *trompe l'oeil* style, can be explained by Roelofs's love and knowledge of entomology. He was an international scholar on the subject of weevils and one of the founders of the Société Entomologique de Belgique. He devoted much time to his publications and to his own

120 In Luxembourg (Beaufort)

Oil on paper on panel, 27 × 44 cm
Signed and inscribed bottom left: *W. Roelofs Beaufort (Luxemburg)*
The Hague, Rijksmuseum H.W. Mesdag

This is an example of Roelofs's many studies on sheets of paper or canvases measuring about 25 by 40 centimetres, which he attached to the lid of his paintbox with drawing pins and later stuck on to panels. In this landscape, not a Dutch subject, echoes of the Barbizon School and, in particular Théodore Rousseau, can be clearly detected. Roelofs did not normally use these studies painted on the spot for his large paintings. For these he used drawings, many of which are powerfully composed and reveal a sharp eye for the essential characteristics of a landscape.

PROVENANCE
?Auct. Studio W. Roelofs, The Hague (Boussod, Valadon & Co), 8–9 Feb. 1898; The Hague, coll. H.W. Mesdag, 1898.

BIBLIOGRAPHY
Boele van Hensbroek 1890, p. 28; Boele van Hensbroek 1910, p. 28; *Het Vaderland* (27 April 1910); Jeltes 1911, p. 47; Jeltes 1922, p. 222; cat. Museum Mesdag 1975, p. 158, no. 280 (with ill.).

EXHIBITIONS
Rotterdam 1889, no. 62.

120

121

121 *Lakes near Kortenhoef*

Oil on canvas on panel, 28.4 × 44.8 cm
Signed bottom left: *W. Roelofs*; inscribed bottom right: *no. 3*
The Hague, Rijksmuseum H.W. Mesdag

It is likely that this study came from the sale of the contents of
Roelofs's studio in 1898, at which Mesdag bought several
works. It shows Roelofs's skill in rendering clouds and the
reflection of light in water. The ideals of Gerard Bilders – his
longing to represent the lush, sparkling Dutch landscape –
were fully realized in this work by Roelofs.

PROVENANCE
?Auct. Studio W. Roelofs, The Hague (Boussod, Valadon & Co), 8–9 Feb. 1898; The Hague, coll. H.W.
Mesdag.

BIBLIOGRAPHY
Boele van Hensbroek 1890, p. 28; Boele van Hensbroek 1910, p. 28; Jeltes 1911, pp. 47–48; Jeltes 1922,
p. 223, fig. XLIII; cat. Museum Mesdag 1975, p. 159, no. 281, ill. on p. 160.

EXHIBITIONS
?Amsterdam 1911 (2), no. 69; The Hague 1965 (1), no. 113 (with ill.); The Hague 1967 (1), no. 42.
Regina 1969–70, no. 32.

122 *May in Noorden*

Oil on canvas on panel, 20.5 × 42 cm
Signed and inscribed bottom right: *W. Roelofs. 215*
The Hague, Haags Gemeentemuseum
repr. in colour on p. 246

Roelofs said of landscape painting: '*We* make a distinction
between colour and drawing, because we simply have to, but
nature doesn't. She doesn't give something a form and then
colour it afterwards. Form and colour are both inherent
qualities of the object that we have to paint. If we neglect either
of them, then we give only half of it.' (see H. Smissaert, in *Het
Schildersboek*, vol. 1, Amsterdam 1898, p. 69).

Roelofs's pupil, Smissaert, gave the following description
of his teacher's forays into the Dutch landscape in search of
subjects. 'Not a summer passes without him packing up his
paintbox, chair, easel and umbrella and setting off for
Noorden, for Abcoude or for Voorschoten in order to study
nature once again, as if he still did not know her. If you saw him
walking through the countryside armed with his painting
equipment, you would never think that this vigorous man will
celebrate his seventieth birthday next spring. Sometimes when
he is sitting by the roadside or in a farmyard, a farmer comes
along and shakes his head compassionately over this old man
who has nothing to do but draw a picture of "Ginger Jan's"
house; . . . there have even been passers-by who, on the basis of
his honest face, have wanted to offer him a position in their
business, to give such a poor fellow a profitable job; but not
one of them, on reading in the paper that a glorious landscape
by Roelofs, full of light, full of warmth and full of poetry, was
to be seen at this or that exhibition, can ever have suspected
that *that* was the work of the old gentleman they met (he was
once reckoned as being "at least in his eighties" by the wives of
some Katwijk fishermen; on account of his white hair).'
(Smissaert, *op. cit.*, p. 75).

122

PROVENANCE
Auct. Studio W. Roelofs, The Hague (Kunstzaal Kleykamp), 4 June 1918, no. 53; purchased by the museum, 1918.

BIBLIOGRAPHY
Jeltes 1922, p. 224, fig. 4; cat. Gemeentemuseum 1935, p. 220, no. 421; cat. Gemeentemuseum 1962, no. 282 (with ill.); De Gruyter 1968–69, vol. 1, pp. 38, 44, 112, fig. 36.

EXHIBITIONS
Dordrecht 1916, no. 8; Brussels 1932, no. 89; Antwerpen 1937, no. 65; The Hague 1947, no. 333; Düsseldorf 1950, no. 54; Tilburg 1952, no. 45; Gt Britain 1958, no. 34; Bonn 1972, no. 17, fig. 6.

123 *Summer Landscape with Cows at a Pool*

Watercolour, 38.5 × 72 cm
Signed bottom left: *W. Roelofs*
The Hague, Ivo Bouwman Gallery

Despite his involvement with the Société Belge des Aquarellistes in Brussels, Roelofs was not a confirmed watercolourist, as were Weissenbruch and Jacob Maris. He was chiefly a draughtsman and even in his watercolours his powerful drawing is always evident. Jeltes wrote that 'Roelofs's watercolour drawings are not so very great in number, but when he does practise this genre, he gives it his all'.

PROVENANCE
Auct. Amsterdam (F. Muller & Co), 18 Nov. 1924, no. 109; Netherlands, priv. coll.

BIBLIOGRAPHY
Tableau IV (1981–82), ill, on p. 340.

EXHIBITIONS
The Hague 1982 (2), not numbered.

123

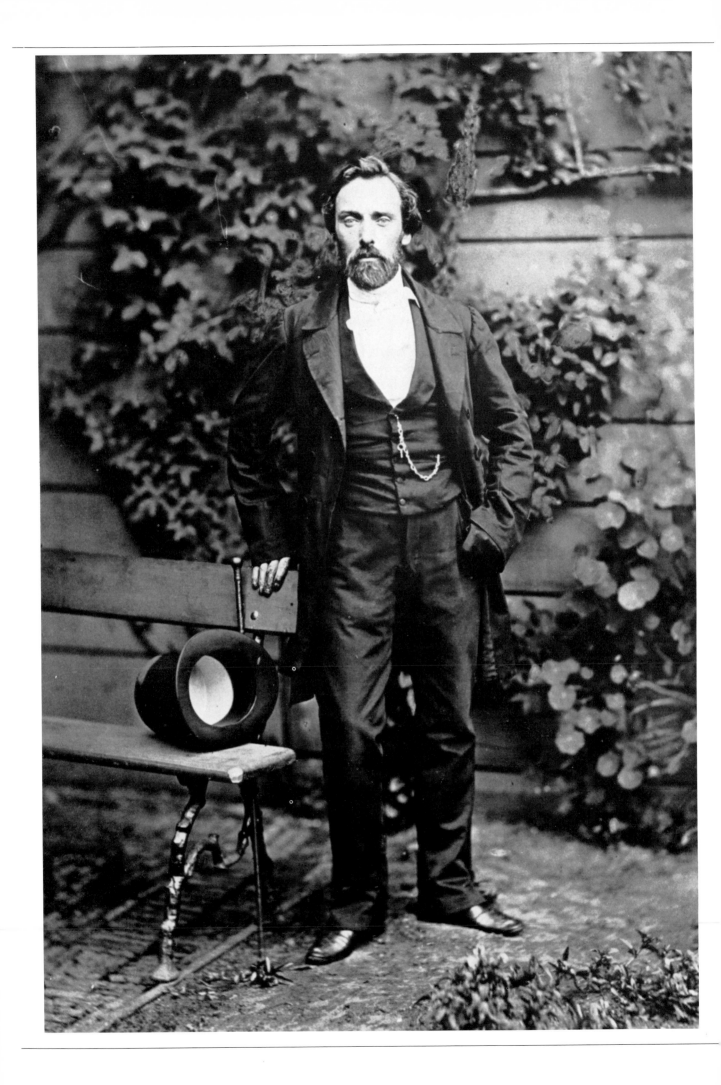

Jan Hendrik Weissenbruch (1824-1903)

Hendrik Johannes Weissenbruch, known as Jan Hendrik, was born in The Hague on 19 June 1824, the second son of Johannes Weissenbruch and Johanna Hendrika Zaag. He came from a very artistic family. His father, who was a chef and restaurateur, painted in his spare time and collected paintings on a modest scale; he owned works by Andreas Schelfhout and Bart van Hove among others. His cousin Jan (1822–80) was a well-known painter of townscapes, another cousin Frederik Hendrik (1828–87) an extremely clever lithographer and his younger brother Frederik Johan, his uncle Daniel and his nephew Isaac (1826–1912) were all engravers.

From the age of 16 Jan Hendrik was given drawing lessons by J.J. Löw and he also attended the evening classes at the Haagse Academie under Van Hove (1790–1880), in whose studio he may also have worked in the daytime, until 1846. Although Weissenbruch's early landscapes were clearly influenced by the work of Andreas Schelfhout (1787–1870), it is not known for certain whether this painter also taught him.

In 1847 he showed his work at the Tentoonstelling van Levende Meesters (Exhibition of Living Masters) for the first time and two years later sold a painting to the Teyler Museum at Haarlem for 250 guilders, a considerable sum at that time. During this period he copied works by Ruisdael and Potter in the Mauritshuis and painted a great deal on the Hague Dekkersduin and on study trips to Arnhem and Haarlem, often in the company of the painter Destree (1827–88).

In 1863 he married Susanna Petronella Geertruida Schouw and a year later they had a son, Willem Johannes, who also became a painter. In 1866 Weissenbruch became a member of the Société Belge des Aquarellistes in Brussels and in the early 1870s his *View of the Trekvliet* (Cat. 128) and *Landscape with Windmill near Schiedam* (Cat. 131) were acquired by the Haags Gemeentemuseum and the Museum Boymans in Rotterdam respectively.

Around this time Weissenbruch gave lessons to Victor Bauffe (1849–1921), Théophile de Bock (1851–1904) and Jan Heppener (1826–98). His friend Sala, an art dealer and framemaker from Leiden, who was also an enthusiastic angler, introduced him in 1875 to the area around Noorden and Nieuwkoop, which he often visited on painting trips in the following years. In January 1882 he visited Vincent van Gogh, whom he had met in 1873, and the following year he was awarded a gold medal at the Internationale Tentoonstelling (International Exhibition) in Amsterdam.

On the occasion of his seventy-fifth birthday in 1899 Buffa en Zn., the Amsterdam art dealers, organized a commercial exhibition of his work. This was a great financial success and apparently also added to his reputation and the popularity of his work.

Weissenbruch made his first and only trip abroad in 1900, to Fontainebleau and Barbizon. In 1903 he died in The Hague on 24 March and was buried there four days later.

fig. 145 *Portrait of Jan Hendrik Weissenbruch* (photograph) (Gemeentearchief, The Hague)

124

bruch and the leading Dutch Romantics; panoramic landscapes in this style were also executed by Andreas Schelfhout and Wijnand Nuyen. The painting shows a view in the immediate vicinity of Oosterbeek and is further evidence of its significance as a meeting place and source of subject matter in the early years of the Hague School.

Weissenbruch has been described as a pupil of Schelfhout, but from various statements that he himself made it is evident that he followed the advice of Bosboom who had told him, 'You must keep on looking out of your own eyes', and deliberately avoided becoming too closely associated with Schelfhout.

PROVENANCE
Coll. Dr H.C. Valkema Blouw, –1954; auct. Amsterdam (F. Muller & Co), 2–4 March 1954, no 716 (with two others); The Hague, art dealer P.A. Scheen, 1954; purchased by the collector, 1954.

BIBLIOGRAPHY
De Gruyter 1968–69, vol. 1, pp. 65, 74, 114, fig. 72.

EXHIBITIONS
Amersfoort 1954, no. 74; Rotterdam 1954, no. 60; The Hague 1954 (2), no. 60; Amersfoort 1955, no. 53; Rotterdam 1955, no. 68; Tilburg 1955, no. 58; Amsterdam 1975–76, no. 136, fig. 31.

124 *Rhine Panorama near Oosterbeek*

Grey brush and pencil, 27 × 73.3 cm
Signed and dated bottom right: *J.H. Weissenbruch 1847*
Amerongen, Collection H. van Leeuwen

This early drawing shows clearly the links between Weissen-

125 *On Dekkersduin, The Hague*

Watercolour, 28 × 33 cm
Signed bottom right: *J.H. Weissenbruch*
The Hague, Haags Gemeentemuseum

125

The Dekkersduin was one of Weissenbruch's favourite places for drawing and painting watercolours. In fact he spent so much time there that his friends used to say they expected to find he had died there one day. He knew the area well because his father, who ran a restaurant, had a market garden there.

The Dekkersduin was one of the first rural areas to suffer from the urban development around The Hague. This area is now the district of Duinoord. When it was being built it was regarded as an ugly addition to the city, but now part of it is protected by the Historical Monuments Act.

PROVENANCE
Coll. Miss Weissenbruch, –1937; presented to the museum, 1937.

BIBLIOGRAPHY
Van Gelder 1940, p. 25, ill. on p. 13.

EXHIBITIONS
Maastricht 1945–46, no. 82; Luxemburg 1948, no. 83; Delft 1952, no. 280; Vancouver 1958, no. 89 (with ill.); Laren 1960–61, no. 114; Breda 1961, no. 106; Bonn 1972, no. 71; Manchester 1980, no. 33; Florence 1981–82, no. 28 (with ill.).

126 View of Haarlem

Oil on panel, 23.5 × 34 cm
Signed bottom right: *J.H. Weissenbruch f.*
The Hague, Haags Gemeentemuseum
repr. in colour on p. 289

This early work is closely related to the panoramic landscapes

that Weissenbruch painted *c.* 1848, such as the *Panorama near Arnhem* and *Panorama near The Hague* (1849, Teyler Museum, Haarlem), and to the watercolour *In Kennemerland* (1849) which also shows the Haarlem skyline in the distance. Schelfhout's influence can still be detected in these detailed landscapes, although Weissenbruch's cool colours and less idealized compositions obviously differ from the work of the older Romantic painter.

The seventeenth-century masters of the Golden Age of Dutch painting are another unmistakable influence in these works. In this connection reference can be made to Ruisdael's *View of Haarlem* (fig. 2) which Weissenbruch must have seen in the Mauritshuis collection. Ruisdael's painting was also illustrated in *Het Koninklijk Museum van 's-Gravenhage op steen gebracht*, published by Desguerrois in Amsterdam in 1833.

PROVENANCE
Amsterdam, coll. E.H. Crone; on loan to the museum by the E.H. Crone Heirs, 1947–64; purchased by the museum, 1964.

BIBLIOGRAPHY
Cat. Gemeentemuseum 1962, no. 303.

EXHIBITIONS
Amsterdam 1948, not numbered; Laren 1960–61, no. 56; The Hague 1964, no. 36; The Hague 1967 (1), no. 49 (with ill.); Amsterdam 1980–81, no. 93 (with ill.).

127

127 Sunset near Boskoop

Oil on canvas, 49 × 85.5 cm
Signed bottom right: *J.H. Weissenbruch*
Private collection
repr. in colour on p. 289

This work was dated 1895 by De Gruyter and Van Gelder, but in the *Kunstkronijk* of 1867 there is a lithograph of an almost identical composition in reverse, and there is also a watercolour of the same subject with a similar composition. In 1864 a painting entitled *Landscape in the Environs of Boskoop: Sunset* was shown at the Tentoonstelling van Levende Meesters (Exhibition of Living Masters).

The painting recalls associations with Daubigny and other artists of the Barbizon School, especially in its composition, but the execution is unmistakably rooted in the Dutch landscape tradition. It is one of Weissenbruch's early masterpieces that attracted little attention at the time.

PROVENANCE
Amsterdam, coll. J. Slagmulder, 1906; Amsterdam, coll. W.F. van Heukelom, –1937; auct. Amsterdam (F. Muller & Co), 12 Oct. 1937, no. 46; Nieuwersluis, coll. B. de Geus van den Heuvel, –1976; auct. Amsterdam (Sotheby Mak van Waay), 26–27 April 1976, no. 334; The Hague, art dealer P.A. Scheen.

BIBLIOGRAPHY
K.K. N.S. VI (1865), p. 48; *K.K. N.S.* VIII (1867), ill. opp. p. 6 (lithograph after the painting), p. 8; Knuttel 1938, ill. on p. 434; Van Gelder 1940, ill. on p. 20, cf. p. 31; Knuttel 1950, ill. on p. 454; Th. H. Lunsingh Scheurleer (ed), *Sprekend verleden*, Amsterdam 1959, fig. 25; De Gruyter 1968–69, vol. 1, pp. 68, 75; Scheen 1981, fig. 645.

EXHIBITIONS
Rotterdam 1864, no. 543; Amsterdam 1906 (2), no. 202; Amsterdam 1923 (1), no. 413; Amsterdam 1933 (2), no. 12; Dordrecht 1951; Amsterdam 1958, no. C 25; Laren 1960–61, no. 59; Breda 1961, no. 57; Laren 1964, no. 98; Laren 1966, no. 116.

VARIATIONS
1) oil on panel, 27.8 × 60 cm, formerly art dealer P.A. Scheen, The Hague; Scheen 1981, fig. 644. 2) watercolour, 24 × 32 cm, art dealer P.A. Scheen, The Hague, 1955; exh. cat. The Hague 1955 (1), no. 43. 3) watercolour, 30 × 54.5 cm, art dealer P.A. Scheen, The Hague; Scheen 1981, fig. 661.

128

128 *View of the Trekvliet*

Oil on canvas, 65 × 100 cm
Signed and dated bottom right: *J. Hendrick Weissenbruch f. 70*
The Hague, Haags Gemeentemuseum

Weissenbruch was no longer a young man when he painted this *View of the Trekvliet*, but it is still considered as a comparatively early work, primarily because of the use of perspective to suggest space and the detailed delineation of all the elements in the landscape. The artist's masterly hand can be detected mainly in the fine play of light, which gives the painting the clarity and freshness characteristic of the Dutch landscape in summer. The Trekvliet is a waterway running between the Rijswijkseplein and the Vliet; on the left looms the tower of a house called De Binckhorst, and on the right the Laak windmill can be seen. By the time this picture was painted railways had replaced barges as the accepted mode of passenger travel, but the picture retains the feel of earlier days when the waterways were also used for general conveyance.

This painting was bought at the Tentoonstelling van Levende Meesters (Exhibition of Living Masters) in Rotterdam in 1870 and given to the Haags Gemeentemuseum by the Society for the Foundation of a Museum of Modern Art in The Hague.

PROVENANCE
The Hague, Vereeninging tot het Oprichten van een Museum voor Moderne Kunst te 's-Gravenhage (Society for the Foundation of a Museum of Modern Art in The Hague), 1870 (bought at exh. Rotterdam 1870); presented to the museum, 1870.

BIBLIOGRAPHY
Vosmaer 1882–85, vol. 2 (H.J. Weissenbruch), p. 4; cat. Gemeentemuseum 1935, p. 276, no. 515, fig. 28; Van Gelder 1940, pp. 1–2 with ill., 27; Van Gelder 1959, fig. 138; Knuttel 1961, pp. 28–30 (with ill.); cat. Gemeentemuseum 1962, no. 305 (with ill.); De Gruyter 1968–69, vol. 1, pp. 67, 71; *O.K.* XVII (1974), p. 56 (with ill.); H. Slechte & M. van der Mast, *75 Jaar Havens Den Haag Scheveningen*, [The Hague 1979], ill. on p. 59.

EXHIBITIONS
Rotterdam 1870, no. 466; Antwerp 1937, no. 76 (with ill.); The Hague 1945, no. 109 (with ill.); Maastricht 1945–46, no. 79 (with ill.); The Hague 1947, no. 437; Düsseldorf 1950, no. 60; Germany 1955, no. 4; England 1958, no. 39.

VARIATIONS
Oil on panel, 31 × 50 cm, Rijksmuseum, Amsterdam; cat. Rijksmuseum 1976, p. 597 (with ill.).

129 *Benoordehoutseweg, The Hague (The White House)*

Oil on canvas, 44 × 78 cm
Signed bottom right: *J.H. Weissenbruch f.*
Private collection
repr. in colour on p. 292

The effects of light achieved by Weissenbruch in many of his paintings established his fame. In his views of The Hague he captured the sharp light that, on a bright day, lends lustre and sparkle to the most banal subjects and scenes. It is this light, so characteristic of coastal areas where haziness alternates with clarity, that give Weissenbruch's paintings a quality lacking in most traditional, topographical townscapes.

PROVENANCE
The Hague, art dealer P.A. Scheen, 1974; purchased by the collector, 1974.

BIBLIOGRAPHY
Scheen 1981, fig. 667.

EXHIBITIONS
Utrecht 1924, no. 43; The Hague 1974 (2), no. 44.

VARIATIONS
1) oil on panel, 21 × 24 cm, auct. Utrecht (Notarishuis), 9 Dec. 1941, no. 182 (with ill.). 2) watercolour, 54 × 37 cm, art dealer P.A. Scheen, The Hague, 1972.

131

130 *Waterway near Rijswijk*

Watercolour, 14.8 × 23.3 cm
Signed bottom right: *J.H. Weissenbruch*
The Hague, Haags Gemeentemuseum

Weissenbruch did not only paint sober renderings of the environs of The Hague; he was also capable of evoking a dreamlike atmosphere in which forms were only summarily represented and were veiled in an evening mist that absorbed all colour. Despite this there is no trace of sentimentality; in Weissenbruch's work the beauty of the landscape is always based on reality.

PROVENANCE
Dordrecht, coll. J. Hidde Nijland, –1937; auct. The Hague (Venduhuis der Notarissen), 5–6 Oct. 1937, no. 225 (as *Avondstemming*; for Dfl. 140); The Hague, Vereeniging van Haagsche Museumvrienden (Society of Friends of Hague Museums), 1937; presented to the museum, 1937.

BIBLIOGRAPHY
Van Gelder 1940, ill. on p. 44.

EXHIBITIONS
Antwerp 1979, no. 50 (with ill.); Florence 1981–82, no. 30 (with ill.).

131 *Landscape with Windmill near Schiedam*

Oil on canvas, 64.5 × 101 cm
Signed and dated bottom left: *J. Hendrik Weissenbruch f. 73*
Rotterdam, Museum Boymans-van Beuningen

E.F.B. Johnston, the nineteenth-century critic, wrote of Weissenbruch: 'There is nothing so expressive of solitude as the clear, sunny, summer day. The stretch of fields bathed in sunlight; the woods casting their deep shadows ...; the peaceful blue sky above, with here and there a fleecy cloud, orphaned and alone, in the deep expanse: all these things appeal to the quiet and sympathetic side of our nature, and find a congenial resting-place in our most reflective moods .... A bit of water, land, or sky was to him [Weissenbruch] as important, as beautiful, and as expressive of nature's moods as the most perfect composition. A few reeds and a glimpse of a canal made a picture; a simple meadow with a few cattle was, in his hands, a poem; a windmill and a lonely farmhouse became a passage of dreamland.' (Quoted in E. B. Greenshields, *Landscape Painting and Modern Dutch Artists*, New York 1906, pp. 192, 193).

PROVENANCE
Rotterdam, Vereeniging van Voorstanders der Kunst te Rotterdam (Society of Supporters of Art in Rotterdam), 1873 (bought at exh. Rotterdam 1873); presented to the museum, 1873.

BIBLIOGRAPHY
Smissaert 1898 (2), ill. on p. 126; Haverkorn van Rijsewijk 1909, p. 183; *Veldhagen & Klasings Monatshefte* (Feb. 1912), ill.; Van Gelder 1940, p. 27, ill. on p. 16; Timmers 1957, p. 210, fig. 543; cat. Museum Boymans-van Beuningen 1963, pp. 146–47; De Gruyter 1968–69, vol. I, pp. 68, 71, 75; cat. Museum Boymans-van Beuningen 1972, p. 226, ill. on p. 187.

EXHIBITIONS
Rotterdam 1873, no. 472; The Hague 1945, no. 111; Laren 1960–61, no. 58; Breda 1961, no. 56; The Hague 1965 (1), no. 117 (with ill.); Amsterdam 1979 (1), no. 38; Tokyo 1979, no. 38 (with ill.).

VARIATIONS
Watercolour, 32.5 × 51 cm, auct. Amsterdam (F. Muller & Co), 3 Dec. 1918, no. 68 (with ill.).

132

133

132 *The Bleaching Green*

Oil on canvas, 38 × 23 cm
Signed bottom right: *J.H. Weissenbruch*
Rotterdam, Museum Boymans-van Beuningen

This enclosed garden, which was used for bleaching and drying laundry, must have been between Kazernestraat where the Weissenbruch family lived and the houses on Lange Voorhout. The house was demolished shortly after Weissenbruch's death. He made attractive paintings and watercolours of the street itself, as well as of the fish-market, which has also been demolished.

PROVENANCE
Rotterdam, coll. J.P. van der Schilden, –1925; bequeathed to the museum, 1925.

BIBLIOGRAPHY
Verslag van het Museum Boymans te Rotterdam over het jaar 1925, p. 3 (with ill.); cat. Museum Boymans-van Beuningen 1963, p. 146; De Gruyter 1968–69, vol. 1, pp. 66, 74, 114, fig. 88; cat. Museum Boymans-van Beuningen 1972, p. 226; Pollock 1980–81, p. 54.

EXHIBITIONS
Laren 1960–61, no. 73; Breda 1961, no. 68; The Hague 1965 (1), no. 119 (with ill.); Amsterdam 1980–81, no. 94 (with ill.).

133 *View of Haarlem (Souvenir de Harlem)*

Oil on canvas, 72.5 × 101 cm
Signed bottom right: *J.H. Weissenbruch f.*
The Hague, Haags Gemeentemuseum

The art critic Albert Plasschaert wrote of this work in 1903: 'Something unusual, a completeness and a precision, was achieved in the composition, which was a harmoniously beautiful whole: but that was not all; there was a finished perfection that made it a "classic" work, one that lives now and will live for all time – a painting in which there is almost no feeling or element of time, only timelessness.' Weissenbruch has stressed the timeless element in this painting by eliminating any reference to a recognizable place. In this respect the French title, *Souvenir de Harlem*, derived from the nineteenth-century tradition in which the subject of the painting came more from the association of ideas and the memory of a mood or state of mind than from a need to record a particular view.

PROVENANCE
Amsterdam, art dealer F. Buffa & Zn.; Amsterdam, coll. E.H. Crone, 1933; on loan to the museum by the E.H. Crone Heirs, 1947–64; purchased by the museum, 1964.

BIBLIOGRAPHY
A. Plasschaert in *Onze Kunst* II (1903), p. 172; *A.H.* (24 June 1909); *A.H.* (31 July 1909); Marius 1910, ill. on p. 13; Van Harpen 1928, p. 18; cat. Gemeentemuseum 1962, no. 311 (with ill.); *Agenda Haags Gemeentemuseum* (April 1964), fig. 2; De Gruyter 1968–69, vol. 1, pp. 63, 69, 75, 114, fig. 89; Fuchs 1978, pp. 161, 215, fig. 143 on p. 162.

EXHIBITIONS
Amsterdam 1899 (3), no. 1; Amsterdam 1909 (2), no. 51; Amsterdam 1933 (2), no. 16; Amsterdam 1946 (2), not numbered, ill. on p. 18; Laren 1960–61, no. 70; Amsterdam 1963, no. s 88; The Hague 1964, no. 41; The Hague 1965 (1), no. 120 (with ill.); Bonn 1972, no. 68, fig. 21.

VARIATIONS
1) oil on panel, 21 × 37 cm, coll. H.W. van Delden, Bloemendaal, 1906; Van Gelder 1940, ill. on p. 31. 2) watercolour, 25 × 43 cm, art dealer E.J. van Wisselingh & Co, Amsterdam, 1937; exh. cat. Amsterdam 1937 (2), no. 60. 3) watercolour, 20 × 28 cm, auct. Amsterdam (F. Muller & Co), 8 Nov. 1904, no. 97 (with ill. in separate album). 4) watercolour, 51 × 71 cm, auct. Amsterdam (F. Muller & Co), 12 May 1908, no. 248 (with ill.). 5) watercolour, 52.5 × 72 cm. Rijksmuseum, Amsterdam; cat. Rijksmuseum 1976, p. 820 (with ill.).

134

134 *Beach Scene*

Oil on canvas, 73 × 103 cm
Signed and dated bottom right: *J.H. Weissenbruch f 87*
The Hague, Haags Gemeentemuseum
repr. in colour on p. 290

This painting, particularly the use of colour, marks a new phase of Weissenbruch's work. He had been searching for new, lighter colour harmonies and in this work he began to see how he could achieve them.

The painting was bought in 1887, the year it was painted, by the Vereeniging tot het Oprichten van een Museum voor Moderne Kunst te 's-Gravenhage (Society for the Foundation of a Museum of Modern Art in The Hague) at the Tentoonstell-ing van Levende Meesters (Exhibition of Living Masters). Tradition has it that Weissenbruch was not at home when the Society decided to purchase it, but was engaged in exercises as a conscript grenadier. The story goes that his father wrote the good news on a piece of cardboard, along with the price (800 guilders), so that his son could read it as he marched back along Kazernestraat past the family home. Dr van Gelder said that this unlikely story originally came from Weissenbruch's son. However, Weissenbruch was no longer 'young' in 1887; he was already 63 years old – a rather advanced age to be taking part in military exercises as a conscript grenadier – and his father would have been a centenarian (he was born in 1787). Thus the story probably relates to another painting.

PROVENANCE
The Hague, Vereeniging tot het Oprichten van een Museum voor Moderne Kunst te 's-Gravenhage (Society for the Foundation of a Museum of Modern Art in The Hague), 1887 (purchased at exh. The Hague 1887 [1] for Dfl. 1,200); presented to the museum, 1887.

BIBLIOGRAPHY
M.K. II (1904), no. 67 (with ill.); Plasschaert 1909, ill. on p. 239; J.G. van Beukenslot Jr. in *Op de Hoogte* VI (1909), ill. on p. 471; Eisler 1911 (1), ill. after p. 230; H.E. van Gelder in *M.D.K.W.* II (1926–31), p. 159; cat. Gemeentemuseum 1935, p. 277, no. 518, fig. 29; Van Gelder 1937, ill. opp. p. 448; H.E. van Gelder in *Prisma der Kunsten* II (1937), ill. on p. 4; Knuttel 1938, p. 434, ill. on p. 435; Van Gelder 1940, pp. 3–4 with ill., 41; Van Gelder 1946 (1), ill. opp. p. 688; Knoef 1948, p. 106; Pedroza 1948, p. 15 (with ill.); Knuttel 1950, p. 454, ill. on p. 455; H.E. van Gelder in *O.K.* II (1958), no. 22 (with ill.); Gerson 1961, fig. 60; cat. Gemeentemuseum 1962, no. 310; Van Gelder 1963–65, vol. 10, ill. opp. p. 1892; De Gruyter 1968–69, vol. 1, pp. 69, 71, 75, 114, ill. on p. 72.

EXHIBITIONS
The Hague 1887 (1), no. 591; Potsdam 1925, no. 147; London 1929, no. 404; Antwerp 1937, no. 79 (with ill.); The Hague 1945, no. 110; Maastricht 1945–46, no. 80 (with ill.); The Hague 1947, no. 439; Luxemburg 1948, no. 75; The Hague 1948, no. 989; Düsseldorf 1950, no. 61; Germany 1955, no. 5 (or 6); Laren 1960–61, no. 66; Breda 1961, no. 63; Amsterdam 1963, no. s 89, fig. 54; The Hague 1965 (1), no. 118 (with ill.).

VARIATIONS
1) oil on canvas, 65.5 × 121 cm, Musée des Beaux-Arts de Montréal, Montreal. 2) oil on panel, 32 × 48 cm, formerly art dealer Huinck & Scherjon, Amsterdam; exh. cat. Amsterdam 1931 (2), no. 12 (with ill.). 3) oil on panel, 21 × 37 cm, auct. Studio J.H. Weissenbruch, The Hague (F. Buffa & Zn.), 1 March 1904, no. 6. 4) painting, priv. coll., Netherlands. 5) watercolour; J. Gram, *Haagsche schetsen*, The Hague 1893, ill. on p. 281. 6) watercolour, 21 × 28 cm, auct. The Hague (Venduhuis der Notarissen), 5–6 Oct. 1937, no. 222 (with ill.).

135

135 *Kitchen*

Watercolour, 32.8 × 48.3 cm
Signed bottom right: *J.H. Weissenbruch*
The Hague, Haags Gemeentemuseum

This watercolour gives us a glimpse into the basement of Weissenbruch's house on Kazernestraat in The Hague; the mood is created by the light at the back, which falls into the kitchen from the street.

Although there is no explicit association with the Dutch seventeenth-century kitchen interiors that also showed glimpses of other rooms through open doors, their atmosphere is not entirely absent from Weissenbruch's work. The introduction to the catalogue of an 1899 exhibition devoted to his work observed: 'In a quiet, peaceful street in The Hague lives the painter Jan Hendrik Weissenbruch. When one enters that tranquil house one finds oneself transported into an old Dutch house by Vermeer of Delft or, even closer, one by Pieter de Hooch.' Weissenbruch drew his inspiration from the Golden Age not from Rembrandt or Frans Hals, as did Israëls and Bosboom, but from Jacob van Ruisdael and Vermeer.

PROVENANCE
Gorssel, coll. J. Verstolk-Völker; The Hague, coll. H.G.J. Völcker; Eefde, coll. J.L. Völcker; Eefde, coll. E.C.K. Völcker, –1939; auct. Amsterdam (F. Muller & Co), 17 Oct. 1939, no. 126 (Dfl. 1,300); purchased by the museum, 1939.

BIBLIOGRAPHY
Exh. cat. Florence 1981–82, p. 19, fig. 6.

EXHIBITIONS
Montpellier 1952, no. 60; Mönchen-Gladbach 1957, no. 62; Laren 1960–61, no. 101; Breda 1961, no. 93; Liège 1961–62, no. 135; The Hague 1963, no. 42; Amsterdam 1963–64, no. 50 (with ill.); Bonn 1972, no. 70, fig. 22; Antwerp 1979, no. 49 (with ill.).

VARIATIONS
Oil on canvas, 39 × 51 cm, Rijksmuseum, Amsterdam; cat. Rijksmuseum 1976, p. 597 (with ill.).

136 *Studio*

Watercolour, 50 × 70 cm
Signed bottom left: *J.H. Weissenbruch*
The Hague, Haags Gemeentemuseum
repr. in colour on p. 290

Weissenbruch rarely depicted interiors and paintings of his studio are even rarer; his kitchen and cowshed interiors are fairly well-known, but this watercolour is quite exceptional. It shows a young man, probably his son Willem, working on a still life. The setting is probably the attic of Weissenbruch's house on Kazernestraat.

The window has been partly pasted over with brown paper in order to darken the room and allow the light to fall through a single pane on to the still life placed on the table. Weissenbruch's rendering of the play of light on the seventeenth-century cupboard and its ebony-inlaid door

panels is masterly. Photographs of Weissenbruch's studio show that, like Bosboom, Israëls and Jacob Maris, he liked to surround himself with seventeenth-century Dutch furniture. The late eighteenth-century chair on which the boy is sitting also appears in photographs of the studio, and serves to confirm that this interior is part of Weissenbruch's own house.

PROVENANCE
Montreal, coll. A.A. Browne, –1980; The Hague, art dealer P.A. Scheen, 1980; purchased by the museum, 1980.

BIBLIOGRAPHY
Scheen 1981, fig. 649.

EXHIBITIONS
The Hague 1980 (2), no. 29 (with ill.); Florence 1981–82, no. 27 (with ill.).

137

137 *The Nieuwkoop Lakes at Noorden*

Watercolour, 39 × 59 cm
Signed bottom left: *J.H. Weissenbruch*
Wassenaar, Collection A.A.M. Ruygrok
repr. in colour on p. 291

The painters who went to Noorden generally concentrated on the open landscape around the lakes and seldom chose the village itself as a subject. This watercolour is an exception. The elegant spire dominating the skyline originally belonged to the 'House at Nieuwkoop' (now demolished) and dated from 1627.

PROVENANCE
The Hague, art dealer P.A. Scheen, 1975; purchased by the collector, 1975.

EXHIBITIONS
The Hague 1975 (1), no. 36.

138

138 Woman near a Farmhouse at Noorden

Watercolour, 51 × 70 cm
Signed bottom right: *J.H. Weissenbruch*
Wassenaar, Collection A.A.M. Ruygrok

Another version of this watercolour, *The Washing Place*, is in the Montreal Museum of Fine Arts. There the farmhouse is less prominent and the peasant woman is standing on a wooden platform rinsing something in the ditch. Both watercolours are notable for the very free brush work.

PROVENANCE
The Hague, art dealer P.A. Scheen, 1976; purchased by the collector, 1976.

BIBLIOGRAPHY
Cf. cat. Museum Mesdag 1975, p. 172, under cat. no. 339; Scheen 1981, fig. 665.

EXHIBITIONS
The Hague 1976 (1), no. 39 (with ill.).

VARIATIONS
1) watercolour, 34.2 × 43 cm, Musée des Beaux-Arts de Montréal, Montreal (Bequest of Lady Allan). 2) gouache and charcoal, 33.1 × 47.2 cm, Rijksmuseum H.W. Mesdag, The Hague; cat. Museum Mesdag 1975, p. 172, no. 399 (with ill.). 3) oil on panel, 33 × 26 cm, *M.K.* v (1907), no. 41 (with ill.). 4) drawing; Smissaert 1898 (2), ill. on p. 131.

139 Noorden

Watercolour, 35 × 50 cm
Signed bottom left: *J.H. Weissenbruch f.*
The Hague, P.A. Scheen Gallery.

The strictly geometrical basis of Paul Gabriël's compositions has often been pointed out. Though this is at first less obvious in Weissenbruch's works, they are in fact equally solidly constructed. The artist time and again used a similar compositional scheme, which is imbued with new meaning in each picture, despite the recurrence of form or motif.

This watercolour, showing a landscape in the Noorden area, is a miracle of finely calculated equilibrium. The placing of the separate elements and the distribution of light and shade, evince a classic sense of balance, and his impetuous brushwork seems effortless – within this framework. The apparent nonchalance and extreme simplicity of the motifs are reminiscent of the works of Johan Barthold Jongkind.

BIBLIOGRAPHY
Scheen 1981, fig. 647.

EXHIBITIONS
The Hague 1971 (2), no. 46; The Hague 1980 (2), no. 28 (with ill.).

VARIATIONS
Drawing; Smissaert 1898 (2), ill on p. 133.

140 *Waterway near Haarlem*

Watercolour, 44 × 66 cm
Signed bottom right: *J.H. Weissenbruch*
Montreal, Musée des Beaux-Arts de Montréal
(Bequest of William J. & Agnes Learmont)

Weissenbruch said in an interview, 'The sky in a painting, now there's a thing! It's the main thing! Sky and light are the great magicians. The sky determines the painting. Painters cannot look at the sky too much. We must get it from the top! Rain and sunshine are our sustenance – we get through the dry patches with our palettes [sic]. . . . I am in my element when it's raining and blowing a gale, when it's thundering and lightening. One must see nature in action. I don my jacket, shove my feet into wooden shoes, stick on a hat of some sort and sally forth. If the showers die down, you make a quick sketch in charcoal or black chalk so as to hang on to what you see. The tone and colour come back on their own when you work it out.

'Going through the polders in a rowing-boat or fishing; that's also the same kind of glorious study of nature. To sit painting in a boat using an old wooden shoe as a water container and with a delicious pipe in your mouth is pure bliss to a painter.' (cat. exh. Amsterdam 1899 [3], p. 2). This watercolour clearly reveals Weissenbruch's enthusiasm for the nuances of the Dutch landscape.

PROVENANCE
Montreal, coll. William John & Agnes Learmont, –1909; bequeathed to the museum, 1909.

EXHIBITIONS
The Hague 1965 (1), no. 127 (with ill.); Regina 1969–70, no. 35 (with ill.).

141 *Dekkersduin*

Watercolour, 30.5 × 56 cm
Signed bottom right: *J.H. Weissenbruch f.*
Wassenaar, Collection A.A.M. Ruygrok

With the exception of Bilders, Bosboom and Israëls, very few painters of the Hague School had any contact with the literary world of their day, in marked contrast to the lively exchange of ideas between writers and painters of the following generation (especially the Amsterdam Impressionists and their circle). It is therefore hardly suprising to find Hague School art almost entirely free of literary content (again with the exception of Israëls and Bosboom). This is particularly true of Weissenbruch, who – in his own words – had only a single book on his shelf, Hildebrandt's *Camera Obscura*.

Weissenbruch's work springs entirely from the direct communication between nature and the artist's temperament. Works like this watercolour lack even the simplest motif, and are particularly striking when compared to earlier treatments of the same subject (*eg.* Cat. 125).

PROVENANCE
The Hague, art dealer P.A. Scheen, 1971; purchased by the collector, 1971.

EXHIBITIONS
The Hague 1971 (2), no. 43.

141

142

142 *Woodland scene near Barbizon*

Oil on canvas, 48.5 × 64 cm
Signed, dated and inscribed bottom left:
J.H. Weissenbruch f. 1900 Barbizon
Amsterdam, Rijksmuseum

Weissenbruch was one of the Hague School artists who seldom travelled. Yet, three years before his death, at an advanced age, he did make a visit to Barbizon, a journey that can be described without exaggeration as a pilgrimage. The Barbizon School had evidently left such a powerful impression and its reputation was still so great that Weissenbruch decided he should go and see the place for himself.

He donated this painting to an art auction organized in 1900 to raise funds for securing new accommodation for Pulchri Studio on Lange Voorhout.

PROVENANCE
Auct. The Hague (H.G. Tersteeg/Pulchri Studio), 16 Oct. 1900, no. 104; bought by the museum, 1900.

BIBLIOGRAPHY
J. de Vries in *E.H.* XXXIV (1908), p. 408, ill. on p. 409; M. Delitzscher, in *Die Kunst* (1960), p. 45 (with ill..); De Gruyter 1968–69, vol. 1, pp. 71, 75, 114, fig. 91; cat. Rijksmuseum 1976, p. 597 (with ill.).

EXHIBITIONS
Passau 1956, no. 44.

143 *View of the Spaarne at Haarlem*

Watercolour, 45 × 68 cm
Signed bottom left: *J.H. Weissenbruch*
Private collection
repr. in colour on p. 291

Weissenbruch – one of the finest watercolourists of the Hague

143

School – was no more concerned with topographical accuracy in his watercolour townscapes than in his oils. This watercolour is closely related in its composition to *At Noorden near Nieuwkoop* (Cat. 145), the bridge with the light behind it ensuring an unusual spatial arrangement.

PROVENANCE
The Hague, coll. A.L.C. Kleijn; The Hague, coll. Mrs C. Kleijn-Eschauzier, –1946; auct. The Hague (Venduhuis der Notarissen), 5–7 Nov. 1946, no. 130 (Dfl. 4,000); The Hague, art dealer D. Sala & Zn., 1946; Wassenaar, coll. Dr A.F. Lodeizen, 1946–80; The Hague, art dealer P.A. Scheen, 1980; purchased by the collector, 1980.

BIBLIOGRAPHY
De Gruyter 1968–69, vol. 1, p. 114, fig. 86; *Tableau* II (1979–80), pp. 389–90, (with ill.); Scheen 1981, fig. 652.

EXHIBITIONS
The Hague 1913 (1), no. 75; Amsterdam 1923 (1), no. 546 d; Amsterdam 1934 (1), no. 132 (with ill.); The Hague 1947, no. 441; The Hague 1965 (1), no. 132 (with ill.); The Hague 1980 (2), no. 31 (with ill.).

144

144 *View of Dordrecht by Moonlight*

Watercolour, 48.5 × 63.7 cm
Signed bottom right: *J.H. Weissenbruch f.*
Montreal, Musée des Beaux-Arts de Montréal
(Bequest of William J. & Agnes Learmont)

Weissenbruch, like Jongkind, regarded Dordrecht as a city
with an unusual atmosphere. Its situation on the river Waal, its
beautiful skyline of towers and houses and with the masts of
the ships on the river inspired many artists.

Here, Weissenbruch has characteristically used a composition in which the light divides the picture in half
horizontally as well as vertically. The same kind of composition is also found in the watercolour *View of the Spaarne at
Haarlem* (Cat. 143) and in the painting *At Noorden near
Nieuwkoop* (Cat. 145).

PROVENANCE
Montreal, coll. William John & Agnes Learmont, –1909; bequeathed to the museum, 1909.

BIBLIOGRAPHY
De Gruyter 1968–69, vol. I, p. 114, fig. 83.

EXHIBITIONS
The Hague 1965 (I), no. 128 (with ill.); Regina 1969–70, no. 40 (with ill.).

145 *At Noorden near Nieuwkoop*

Oil on canvas, 33.5 × 41 cm
Signed and dated bottom left: *J.H. Weissenbruch f 1901*
Dordrecht, Rijksmuseum Van Bilderbeek-Lamaison
repr. in colour on p. 292

The Leiden framemaker and art dealer Sala owned a sailing-
boat, which he used for trips on the lakes in South Holland,
often accompanied by one or other of his artist friends. They
included Willem Roelofs, Paul Gabriël, Julius van de Sande
Bakhuyzen, Pieter Stortenbeker and Weissenbruch; in this
way they discovered the beauty of the area around the little

145

village of Noorden, near the Nieuwkoop Lakes. It was on one such trip that the foundation for this masterpiece was laid.

Weissenbruch especially had felt it necessary to find new subjects, since the area where he had previously worked had changed drastically. Favourite spots like the Dekkersduin and the gardens near the Laan van Meerdervoort had been transformed into new suburbs of The Hague; Scheveningen also had undergone considerable change. Noorden long remained a secret place for Weissenbruch and his friends, who wanted to prevent the 'new era' from encroaching on this rural area. The brilliant light effects in this picture clearly show Weissenbruch's admiration for Vermeer.

PROVENANCE
Amsterdam, art dealer F. Buffa & Zn., 1910; Dordrecht, coll. W.H. van Bilderbeek, 1910–18.

BIBLIOGRAPHY
Cat. Verz. Van Bilderbeek 1913, p. 30, no. 129; De Boer 1915, no. 93; De Gruyter 1968–69, vol. 1, pp. 63, 69, 75, 114, fig. 90.

EXHIBITIONS
London 1929, no. 403; Brussels 1932, no. 111; Dordrecht 1951, no. 6; Dordrecht 1957 (1), no. 34; Laren 1960–61, no. 79; Breda 1961, no. 74; The Hague 1965 (1), no. 123 (with ill.); Dordrecht 1973–74, no. 15; Dordrecht 1978, no. 87 (with ill.); Amsterdam 1979 (1), no. 40; Seoul 1979, no. 31 (with ill.); Tokyo 1979, no. 40 (with ill.); Nieuwkoop 1982, no. 8.

146 *Beach Scene*

Oil on canvas, 102.5 × 128 cm
Signed and dated: *J.H. Weissenbruch 20 October 1901*
The Hague, Haags Gemeentemuseum

Weissenbruch's artistic development was slow and very gradual; he produced several of the works that are now ranked among his masterpieces when he was in his seventies. Appreciation of his work, too, came much later than it had with other artists of the Hague School, such as Israëls and Mesdag. He did not gain international recognition until the turn of the century and his paintings and watercolours were sought by American collectors only after his death.

PROVENANCE
The Hague, art dealer A. Preyer, –1918; presented to the museum, 1918.

BIBLIOGRAPHY
H.E. van Gelder in *M.D.K.W.* II (1926–31), p. 159; cat. Gemeentemuseum 1935, p. 277, no. 519; Van Gelder 1940, p. 4 (with ill.); cat. Gemeentemuseum 1962, no. 317 (with ill.).

EXHIBITIONS
Brussels 1932, no. 112; Maastricht 1945–46, no. 81; The Hague 1947, no. 440; Athens 1953, no. 7; Zagreb 1953, no. 7; Israel 1954, no. 5; Laren 1957, no. 260; Laren 1960–61, no. 78; Breda 1961, no. 73; Bonn 1972, no. 69, fig. 20.

126 WEISSENBRUCH *View of Haarlem*

127 WEISSENBRUCH *Sunset near Boskoop*

134 WEISSENBRUCH *Beach Scene*

136 WEISSENBRUCH *Studio*

137 WEISSENBRUCH *The Nieuwkoop Lakes at Noorden*

143 WEISSENBRUCH *View of the Spaarne at Haarlem*

145 WEISSENBRUCH *At Noorden near Nieuwkoop*

129 WEISSENBRUCH *Benoordehoutseweg, The Hague (The White House)*

109 MESDAG *The Return of the Lifeboat*

148 VAN GOGH *The Beach at Scheveningen in Stormy Weather*

154 VAN GOGH *The Drawbridge at Nieuw Amsterdam*

151 VAN GOGH *Miners' Wives Carrying Sacks of Coal*

157 MONDRIAAN *Slum Area in Amsterdam*

153 VAN GOGH *Fisherman with Pipe*

165 MONDRIAAN *Large Landscape*

Vincent van Gogh
Piet Mondriaan

Vincent van Gogh (1853-1890)

Vincent Willem van Gogh, born in Groot-Zundert on 30 March 1853, was the son of a Protestant clergyman of modest means. He did not decide to become an artist until 1880 when he was 27. At the age of 16 he went to work for the art gallery Goupil & Co. in The Hague, and subsequently worked for branches of the firm in London and Paris. In 1876 he was dismissed and from then until 1880 he worked as a school teacher in England and a clerk in a bookshop in Dordrecht; he studied theology at the University in Amsterdam and preached as a lay missionary in the coal mining district of Belgium known as the Borinage.

His early work reflects a strong admiration for the Barbizon School and the Hague School. He knew several of the Hague School artists whose influence, especially that of Anton Mauve, is particularly evident in his work between 1880 and 1885. Early in 1886 he studied briefly at the Academy in Antwerp before going to live in Paris with his brother Theo, the director of the Montmartre branch of the art gallery Boussod & Valadon. In the spring of 1886 Vincent attended classes in the studio of Fernand Cormon, a professor at the École des Beaux-Arts. During the next two years he was strongly influenced by several different Impressionist and Post-Impressionist artists; among the painters that he is known to have met are Degas , Pissarro, Anquetin, Bernard, Gauguin, Toulouse-Lautrec, Seurat, and Signac.

On 20 February 1888, Van Gogh left Paris and went directly to Arles where he executed his first mature works in a highly personnel Post-Impressionist style. In late September Gauguin arrived for an extended visit but left in December following Vincent's first attack of mental illness. After subsequent attacks he voluntarily entered the Asylum of Saint-Paul-de-Mausole in Saint-Rémy where he remained until his release in mid-May 1890. On 17 May he arrived at his brother's apartment in Paris, and four days later he went to live in Auvers-sur-Oise under the care of the physician Paul Gachet. On 27 July he shot himself in the chest and died two days later.

fig. 146 VINCENT VAN GOGH *Self Portrait at the Easel* (Rijksmuseum Vincent van Gogh, Amsterdam)

147

147 *Young Scheveningen Woman, Seated: Facing Left*

Watercolour, 48 × 35 cm
Signed: *Vincent*
Amsterdam, P. & N. de Boer Foundation

Between 27 November and a few days before Christmas 1881, Van Gogh was in The Hague working under the tutelage of Anton Mauve. In a letter to Theo written *c*. 18 December, Van Gogh included pen-and-ink sketches of two watercolours: *Young Scheveningen Woman, Seated: Facing Left* and *Young Scheveningen Woman, Knitting: Facing Right* (priv. coll., New York), crediting Mauve's assistance with the latter: 'I still go to Mauve's every day – in the daytime to paint, in the evening to draw. I have now painted five studies and two watercolours and, of course, a few more sketches. . . . Enclosed I send you little sketches after the two watercolours. I confidently hope that I shall be able to make something saleable in a relatively short time. Yes, *I even think that these two would be saleable in case of need*. Especially the one which Mauve brushed a little.' (no. 163, vol. 1, pp. 277–79; *c*. 18 Dec. 1881).

The subject of both watercolours is superficially the same as that of Israëls's large canvas, *Expectation* (The Metropolitan Museum of Art, New York). It was a popular theme among certain artists of the Hague School, its origins lying in seventeenth-century Dutch genre painting. However, Vincent's goals in *Young Scheveningen Woman, Seated: Facing Left* seem limited to a demonstration of his rapidly developing technical proficiency. The striking realism was important to him as evidence of his ability as a watercolourist and as proof of the advance that he had made under Mauve's guidance: 'What a splendid thing watercolour is to express atmosphere and distance, so that the figure is surrounded by air and can breathe in it, as it were . . . I think I shall make better progress now that I have learned something practical about colour and the use of the brush.' (no. 163, vol. 1, p. 280).

A few days before Christmas Van Gogh left The Hague and returned to his parents' home in Etten. He took the two watercolours of the young Scheveningen woman, but in a letter written to Theo shortly after his arrival he expressed a less sanguine opinion about them. Nevertheless, he realized that while working in Mauve's studio he had achieved a new standard and decided that the two watercolours would be useful for comparative purposes: 'They may have many imperfections – I am the first to admit that I am very much dissatisfied with them – but still they are quite different from what I made before, and look brighter and clearer. That does not alter the fact that others in the future may become still brighter and clearer, but one cannot do what one wants right away. It will come gradually.

'For the present I want to keep those two drawings [sic] myself in order to compare them with those that I am going to make here, for I must carry them at least as far as the ones I made at Mauve's' (no. 164, vol, 1, p. 282; *c*. 21 Dec 1881).

However, Vincent's use of the two watercolours as comparative material was short lived. At Christmas he had a serious disagreement with his father and returned to The Hague to seek Mauve's advice. On 1 January 1882, he moved into a studio apartment that was a ten-minute walk from the older artist's studio. Naturally Mauve's influence became even stronger and, despite the disintegration of their relationship later that winter, left a lasting impression on Van Gogh's early work (cat. 149–51).

PROVENANCE
Nuenen, coll. Miss M. Begemann; The Hague, coll. H.D. van Stipriaan Luïscius; The Hague, coll. J.F.D. Scheltema, –1963; auct. Amsterdam (P. Brandt), 18–22 Nov. 1963, no. 103.

BIBLIOGRAPHY
De la Faille 1970, pp. 326 (no. F 869), 645 (no. F 869); Hulsker 1980, pp. 26, 28, 29 (no. 83).

148

148 *The Beach at Scheveningen in Stormy Weather*

Oil on canvas on pasteboard, 34.5 × 51 cm
Amsterdam, Stedelijk Museum (on loan from
Collection Miss E. Ribbius Peletier)
repr. in colour on p. 293

This picture clearly emulates the many paintings of the beach at Scheveningen by members of the Hague School such as Israëls, Mauve, Mesdag, and Jacob Maris. It is also significant as one of Van Gogh's earliest attempts at oil painting after two years devoted almost exclusively to drawings and water-colours. It was executed only two weeks after he began to paint regularly. In early August 1882, Theo visited Vincent and gave him money with which to buy art supplies, including oil paints. In letter 222 Vincent thanked him and enumerated his purchases.

A few lines later in the same letter, Van Gogh expressed the desire to paint the subject of this work: 'What we saw in Scheveningen together – sand, sea and sky – is something I certainly hope to express some time.' About two weeks later he realized his wish: 'All during the week we have had a great deal of wind, storm and rain, and I went to Scheveningen several times to see it. I brought two small marines home from there.' (no. 226, vol. 1, p. 439; 19 Aug. 1882).

The Beach at Scheveningen in Stormy Weather is probably one of the two paintings mentioned in letter 226 and is the only one which has survived. Its somewhat primitive character reflects Van Gogh's lack of experience with oil paint, but the conditions under which it was painted may also have affected its appearance: 'One of them is slightly sprinkled with sand – but the second, made during a real storm, during which the sea came quite close to the dunes, was so covered with a thick layer of sand that I was obliged to scrape it off twice. The wind blew so hard that I could scarcely see for the sand that was flying around. However, I tried to get it fixed by going to a little inn behind the dunes, and there scraped it off and immediately painted it in again, returning to the beach now and then for a fresh impression.' (no. 226, vol. 1, p. 439).

Nearly five years later his technique had changed radically, but his motivations were still very similar: 'And in a picture I want to say something comforting, as music is comforting.' (no. 531, vol. 3, p. 25; 3 Sept. 1888).

PROVENANCE
Rotterdam, art dealer Oldenzeel, 1903, Utrecht, coll. J. Ribbius Peletier, 1903–. Scheveningen, coll. Miss E. Ribbius Peletier; on loan to the museum.

BIBLIOGRAPHY
D.B. in *De Kroniek* IX (1903), pp. 19, 20; R. Jacobsen in *Onze Kunst* I (1903), vol. I, p. 116; *M.K.* I (1903), no. 31 (with ill.); De la Faille 1970, pp. 44 (no. F4), 612 (no. 14), Hulsker 1980, pp. 51 (no. 187), 54, 56.

149

149 *The State Lottery Office*

Watercolour, 38 × 57 cm
Amsterdam, Rijksmuseum Vincent van Gogh

Van Gogh's first reference to *The State Lottery Office* appears in a letter written to Theo during the first week of October 1882: 'You remember perhaps Moorman's State Lottery office at the beginning of the Spuistraat? I passed there on a rainy morning when a crowd of people stood waiting to get their lottery tickets. For the most part they were old women and the kind of people of whom one cannot say what they are doing or how they live, but who evidently have a great deal of drudgery and trouble and care. Of course superficially such a group of people who apparently take so much interest in 'today's draw' seems rather ridiculous to you and me, because neither you nor I care in the slightest for the lottery. But that little group of people – their expression of waiting – struck me, and while I sketched it, it took on a larger, deeper significance for me than at first. For it is more significant when one sees in it *the poor and money*. It is often that way with almost all groups of figures: one must think it over before one understands what it all means. The curiosity and the illusion about the lottery seem more or less childish to us – but it becomes serious when one thinks of the contrast of misery and that kind of forlorn effort of the poor wretches to try to save themselves by buying a lottery ticket, paid for with their last ten pennies, which should have gone for food. However it may be, I am making a large watercolour of it.' (no. 235, vol. I, pp. 463, 465; *c.* 1 Oct. 1882).

The technique of the present work and the grouping of the figures is reminiscent of watercolours by Mauve, such as *The Timber Auction* (*De Houtveiling*) in the Rijksmuseum H.W. Mesdag. Van Gogh greatly admired Mauve's work, and he studied with him briefly in late 1881 and early 1882, and here

we can be certain that Van Gogh was conscious of his debt to Mauve. In a letter written to Theo on 22 October 1882, Van Gogh referred to Mauve in a discussion of his own current work, which included both *The State Lottery Office* and *The Beach at Scheveningen* (Cat. 150): 'It is real autumn weather here, rainy and chilly, but full of sentiment, especially splendid for figures that stand out in tone against the wet streets and the roads in which the sky is reflected. It is what Mauve does so often and so beautifully. So I have again been able to work on the large watercolour of the crowd of people in front of the lottery office, and I also started another of the beach . . .' (no. 237, vol. I, p. 467; 22 Oct. 1882).

Although Mauve's influence is unmistakable, Van Gogh's technique is more expressive and supersedes the genre-like character of the older artist's work. In addition a member of the Hague School is unlikely to have depicted such a subject and would not have sought the 'larger, deeper significance' that informs Van Gogh's watercolour.

PROVENANCE
Amsterdam, coll. Mrs J. van Gogh-Bonger; Laren, coll. V.W. van Gogh.

BIBLIOGRAPHY
De la Faille 1970, pp. 362 (no. F 970), 648 (no. F 970); Hulsker 1980, p. 58 (no. 222); Pollock 1980–81, pp. 61–62, 152 (no. 65).

150 *The Beach at Scheveningen*

Watercolour, 34 × 49.5 cm
Baltimore, The Baltimore Museum of Art (Bequest of Etta Cone)

About one week after informing Theo that he had begun the watercolour depicting the State Lottery Office (Cat. 149), Van Gogh wrote that he had started another of 'the last summer guests on the beach – an evening effect' (no. 236, vol. 1, p. 467; Oct. 1882). Like *The State Lottery Office*, this work reflects the influence of Mauve's watercolour technique, but the figure style and the mood are unmistakably Van Gogh's. Moreover, there is an element of straightforward social realism seldom present in the sympathetic peasant figures in the work of Mauve and most other members of the Hague School.

A crowd of figures on a beach is a common subject in the work of the Hague School, but fishermen and their families are usually depicted. Images of 'summer guests on the beach – an evening effect' are more typical of the work of the French painter Eugène Boudin (1824–98), whom Van Gogh described in a letter of January 1874, as one of 'the painters whom I like especially' (no. 13, vol. 1, p. 17; Jan. 1874). However, as one would expect from Van Gogh, the crowd on the beach at Scheveningen is redolent more of the Revolution of 1848 than the upper-class modishness of the figures in Boudin's beach scenes painted in Deauville and Trouville.

PROVENANCE
Rotterdam, art dealer Oldenzeel; The Hague, coll. P. Versteeven; auct. Amsterdam (A. Mak), 27 Oct. 1925, no. 121 (Dfl. 260); Amsterdam, art dealer J. Goudstikker; New York, Tannhauser Art Gallery; Baltimore, coll. Etta Cone, –1949; bequeathed to the museum, 1949.

BIBLIOGRAPHY
De la Faille 1970, pp. 384 (no. F 1038), 650 (no. F 1038); Hulsker 1980, pp. 59 (no. 228, 62; Pollock 1980–81, p. 152 (no. 64).

151 *Miners' Wives Carrying Sacks of Coal*

Watercolour, heightened with white, 32 × 50 cm
Otterlo, Rijksmuseum Kröller-Müller
repr. in colour p. 294

Early in his career Van Gogh considered becoming an illustrator. He discussed the possibility in a letter to Theo from The Hague in early November 1882: 'I think it is possible that, within a relatively short time, there will perhaps be greater demand for illustrators than at present. As for me, if I fill my portfolio with studies from all of the models I can get hold of, I expect to become skilful enough to get a job.' (no. 241, vol. 1, p. 470; *c.* 2 or 3 Nov. 1882). At the end of the same letter, Vincent described his work on 'a watercolour of miners' wives carrying bags of coal in the snow'. He hoped that it would be suitable for publication in an illustrated magazine such as *La Vie Moderne*: 'I again worked on a watercolour of miners' wives carrying bags of coal in the snow. But especially I drew about twelve studies of figures for it and three heads. I am not

ready yet. I think I found the right effect in the watercolour, but I do not think it strong enough in character. In reality it is something like "The Reapers" by Millet, severe, so you understand that one mustn't make a snow effect out of it, which would be just an impression and would then have its *raison d'être* only if it were done as a landscape. I think I will start afresh, though I think you will like the studies I have at present because they succeeded better than many others. It would really be right for the *Vie Moderne*, I think. When I get the paper, I shall have at least *one* of the figures to make a trial, but it must become a group of women, a small caravan.' (no. 241, vol. 1, p. 481).

The paper mentioned at the end of the passage was transfer lithography paper that Theo had evidently promised to secure for Vincent through the printmaker Félix Buhot (1847–98). The specially coated paper was a relatively recent invention that permitted the transfer of a drawn image directly on to lithographic stone. Previously, an artist, illustrator or printmaker had to draw directly on to the stone. Apparently Vincent hoped to use the paper to make an experimental print depicting one of the figures in *Miners' Wives Carrying Sacks of Coal*. It is not known if he ever received the paper, but none of the three lithographs that he made in November 1882, depicts a miner's wife carrying a sack of coal.

151

According to a letter that Van Gogh wrote to his artist friend Anthon van Rappard in autumn 1882, he first became interested in the subject of this watercolour in 1879 while serving as a lay evangelist in the coal-mining region of Belgium known as the Borinage: 'Not without some trouble I have at last discovered how the miners' wives in the Borinage carry their sacks. You may remember that when I was there I made some drawings of it – but they were not yet the real thing. Now I have made twelve studies of the same subjects.' (no. R 16, vol. 3, p. 339; Sept.–Oct. 1882). In the letter he sent a sketch showing exactly how the sacks were carried and identified the source of his information as a coal loader at the Rhine railway station in The Hague, not far from his lodgings on the Schenkstraat. However, the twelve studies mentioned in both letters 241 and R 16 (in addition to which 'three heads' are cited in letter 241) have all disappeared.

The phrase 'when I was there' in letter R 16 probably refers to the period between October 1880 and April 1881, when Van Gogh was living in Brussels. Between March and May 1881, Van Gogh and Van Rappard saw each other regularly, and the drawing *Miners' Women Carrying Sacks (The Bearers of the Burden)*, April 1881, or shortly thereafter (Rijksmuseum Kröller-Müller, Otterlo), is apparently the only one of the early drawings of women carrying sacks of coal to have survived.

152

It is noteworthy that Van Gogh compared *Miners' Wives Carrying Sacks of Coal* to Millet's *The Gleaners*, 1857 (Musée du Louvre), which he referred to in letter 241 as 'The Reapers'. The bent figures in both works are substitutes for mechanical and/or animal labour. Of course Van Gogh's interpretation is more expressive and anticipates the works of artists such as Ernst Barlach and Käthe Kollwitz, but even more significantly this watercolour immediately foreshadows interests analogous to those of Émile Zola's novel about coal miners, *Germinal*, which was published in 1885. In fact, *Miners' Wives Carrying Sacks of Coal* is remarkably similar to the following passage from *Germinal* describing the coal miners' return to work after their strike had been broken: 'Everywhere, in the morning mist, along the shadowy roads, the trampling herd could be seen, lines of men plodding along with their noses to the ground like cattle being driven to the slaughterhouse. They were shivering in their thin cotton clothes, their arms folded for warmth, shambling and hunched up so that the *briquet*, held between shirt and coat, looked like a deformity. But behind this mass return to work, these silent dark shapes with never a smile or a glance to the side, you could sense jaws set in anger and hearts bursting with hatred. They had only knuckled under because compelled to by starvation.'

PROVENANCE
The Hague, coll. J. Hidde Nijland, 1895–1928; The Hague, coll. Mrs H. E. L. J. Kröller-Müller, 1928.

BIBLIOGRAPHY
De la Faille 1970, pp. 368 (no. F 994), 649 (no. F 994); Cat. Museum Kröller-Müller 1980, p. 5 (no. 6); Hulsker 1980, pp. 62, 63 (no. 253), 68; Pollock 1980–81, pp. 92, 150 (no. 52).

152 *Girl under Trees*

Oil on canvas, 39 × 59 cm
Otterlo, Rijksmuseum Kröller-Müller

In the late summer of 1882 Vincent van Gogh often worked out of doors, choosing spots that had been favoured by Hague School painters for many years: the beach and dunes at Scheveningen, and the woods of The Hague. Like the earlier painters he learned to appreciate the beauty of 'bad' weather, particularly striking before, during or just after a rainstorm. He professed to have found in the very heart of the Hague School country a number of motifs so far neglected by these masters. In a letter of 20 August 1882 Van Gogh described a 'study in the wood' of 'some large green beech trunks on a stretch of ground covered with dry sticks, and the little figure of a girl in white. There was the great difficulty of keeping it clear, and of getting space between the trunks standing at different distances – and the place and relative bulk of those trunks change with the perspective – to make it so that one can breathe and walk around in it, and to make you smell the fragrance of the wood . . .' (no. 227, vol. 1, p. 442). The study mentioned is the work shown here, and Van Gogh referred to it again in another letter a few weeks later: 'It is autumn now in the woods, it quite absorbs me. There are two things in autumn which particularly appeal to me. There is sometimes a soft melancholy in the falling leaves, in the tempered light, in the haziness of things, in the elegance of the slender stems. . . . Enclosed is another sketch of the woods. I made a large study of it . . .' (no. 229, vol. 1, pp. 449, 451). Both the sketch and the large study show a girl in white leaning against a tree, a motif that Van Gogh said he had taken from the English illustrator Percy McQuoid (no. R 12, vol. 3, p. 327).

A slightly different study dating from the same period and also showing a girl in a wood (no. F 8a) is in a Dutch private collection.

PROVENANCE
Voorburg, coll. L. C. Enthoven, –1920; auct. Amsterdam (F. Muller & Co), 18 May 1920, no. 200; The Hague, coll. Mrs H. E. L. J. Kröller-Müller, 1920.

BIBLIOGRAPHY
De la Faille 1970, pp. 44 (no. F 8), 612 (no. F 8); Cat. Museum Kröller-Müller 1980, p. 41 (no. 96); Hulsker 1980, pp. 48 (no. 182), 52.

153 *Fisherman with Pipe*

Pen, pencil, black chalk, wash, heightened with white, 46 × 26 cm
Signed bottom left: *Vincent*
Otterlo, Rijksmuseum Kröller-Müller
repr. in colour on p. 295

In January and February 1883, Van Gogh executed several drawings of fishermen, or models dressed as fishermen, in a portrait format. Towards the end of January he reported to Theo: 'Tomorrow I get a sou'wester for the heads. Heads of fishermen, old and young, that's what I've been thinking of for a long time, and I have made one already, then afterward I couldn't get a sou'wester. Now I shall have one of my own, an old one over which many storms and seas have passed.' (no. 261, vol. 1, p. 528; *c*. 21 Jan. 1883). In the next letter, written a few days later, he again referred to the project: 'I am very glad to have my sou'wester; I wonder if you will find some good in those fishermen's heads. The last one I made this week was of a fellow with white throat whiskers.' (no. 262, vol. 1, p. 531; *c*. 25–29 Jan. 1883). The drawing mentioned is probably *Fisherman with Sou'wester, Pipe, and Firepot, Half-Figure*, no. F 1016 (Rijksmuseum Vincent van Gogh, Amsterdam). It depicts the same individual as *Fisherman with Pipe*,

easily recognized by his 'white throat whiskers'. In letter 300 (*c*. 31 July 1883), Van Gogh included a sketch (F 1013) for *Fisherman with Pipe*, and identified the model as the resident of an almshouse, probably the Dutch Reformed Old Men's and Old Women's Home on the Warmoezierstraat: 'Today the almshouse man again posed for a thing that I suddenly felt I had to make before I started anything else' (no. 300, vol. 2, p. 78; *c*. 31 July 1883). Furthermore, the model probably wears the jacket that Van Gogh mentioned having recently acquired: 'a very characteristic Scheveningen jacket with high turn-up collar, picturesque, faded and patched.'

As Jan Hulsker has observed, Van Gogh's drawings of fishermen, dated January and February 1883, were probably inspired by the series of *Heads of the People* by Hubert Herkomer, Matthew White Ridley, and William Small that Vincent had admired when they were published in *The Graphic*. Indeed in letter 252 he wrote, 'I do try my best to make "Heads of the People". You know, Theo, I would like to do the kind of work those who started *The Graphic* did, though I do not count myself their equal: I would take a fellow or woman or child from the street, and draw them in my studio . . .' (no. 252, vol. 1, pp. 511–12; *c*. 11 Dec. 1882). Although *Fisherman with Pipe* seems to have evolved from Van Gogh's own project for *Heads of the People*, the drawing also probably relates to his admiration for Israëls's *Old Friends* (see fig. 113). As is discussed in chapter IX in this catalogue, Vincent greatly admired Israëls's painting of an old man, who sits by a hearth with his dog. Apart from the remarks about the dog, his description of Israëls's paintings in letter 181 (11? March 1882) could easily have been written about *Fisherman with Pipe*: 'Israëls's "An Old Man" (if he were not a fisherman it might be Thomas Carlyle . . .) is sitting in a corner near the hearth. . . . And meanwhile the old man takes his tobacco pouch out and lights his pipe in the twilight. That is all – the twilight, the silence, the loneliness of those two old friends, the man and the dog, the understanding between those two, the meditation of the old man – what he is thinking of, I do not know . . . but it must be a deep, long thought . . . it comes rising from a past long ago – perhaps that thought gives the expression to his face, an expression melancholy, contented, submissive, something that reminds one of Longfellow's famous poem [*Lost Youth*] with the refrain: But the thoughts of youth are long, long thoughts.' (no. 181, vol. 1, pp. 325–26; 11? March 1882)★

Of course many such drawings of isolated and contemplative seated figures appear in Van Gogh's early work, and the type is clearly a significant element in Vincent's personal iconography. However, these images reach beyond the immediate influence of Israëls and are best understood in the broader context of the long tradition of such figures in European art that is epitomized by Rodin's *The Thinker*.

★The editors of *The Complete Letters of Vincent van Gogh*, p. 325, note that the correct quotation from Longfellow's *Lost Youth* is: '*And* the thoughts of youth are long, long thoughts.'

PROVENANCE
Amsterdam, coll. Dr F.J. Michelson, –1918; auct. Amsterdam (F. Muller & Co), 3 Dec. 1918, no. 306; The Hague, coll. Mrs H.E.L.J. Kröller-Müller, 1918.

BIBLIOGRAPHY
De la Faille 1970, pp. 373 (no. F 1010), 649 (no. F 1010) (The editors note on p. 374 that the sketch, no. F 1013, was erroneously published with letter 262 but it belongs with letter 300); cat Museum Kröller-Müller 1980, p. 35 (no. 79); Hulsker 1980, pp. 60, 74, 76 (no. 306).

154

154 *The Drawbridge at Nieuw-Amsterdam*

Watercolour, 38.5 × 81 cm
Groningen, Groninger Museum
repr. in colour on p. 294

In September 1883 Van Gogh left The Hague for the province of Drenthe. His work there, especially the watercolours, reflects the influence of Mauve and Weissenbruch. He took a room in a small quayside hotel from which he could see the drawbridge depicted in this watercolour.

The proportions of the composition and the exactness of the perspective suggest that Van Gogh used a perspective frame for this work. Only a few weeks before he had stressed the importance of a sound understanding of perspective: 'I spoke once or twice to Thijs Maris. I dared not speak to Boughton because his presence overawed me; but I did not find it there either, that help with the very *first* things, the ABC.' (no. 332, vol. 2, p. 163; *c*. 12 Oct. 1883). The reference to Matthijs Maris is particularly interesting in this context, because *The Drawbridge at Nieuw-Amsterdam* is quite similar in subject and mood to Maris's *Souvenir d'Amsterdam* of 1871 (Cat. 73).

PROVENANCE
Groningen, coll. G. Heymans; Groningen, coll. Miss J. van Binnendijk; purchased by the museum, 1961.

BIBLIOGRAPHY
De la Faille 1970, pp. 402 (no. F 1098), 652 (no. F 1098); A. Stiles Wylie in *O.H.* LXXXV (1970), pp. 210 ff.; Hulsker 1980, p. 100 (no. 425; Pollock 1980–81, p. 157 (no. 104).

155 *Farmhouses*

Oil on canvas on cardboard, 36 × 55.5 cm
Amsterdam, Rijksmuseum Vincent van Gogh

In October 1883 Vincent van Gogh was in 'the very remotest part of Drenthe'. He wrote to his brother Theo from Nieuw-Amsterdam (cf. Cat. 154): 'I see no possibility of describing the country as it ought to be done; words fail me, but imagine the banks of the canal as miles and miles of Michels or T. Rousseaus, Van Goyens or P. Konincks. Level planes or strips of different colour, getting narrower and narrower as they approach the horizon. Accentuated here and there by a peat shed or small farm, or a few meagre birches, poplars, oaks . . . . This evening the heath was inexpressibly beautiful. In one of

the Boetzel Albums there is a Daubigny which gives exactly that effect. The sky was of an indescribably delicate lilac white, no fleecy clouds . . . but dashes of more or less vivid lilac, grey, white, a single rent through which the blue gleamed through. Then a glaring red streak at the horizon, below which the very dark stretch of brown moor, and standing out against the brilliant red streak a number of low-roofed little sheds. . . . Before I left Hoogeveen, I painted a few studies there, including one of a large moss-roofed farm.' (letter 330, 6 Oct. 1883).

PROVENANCE
Amsterdam, coll. Mrs J. van Gogh-Bonger; Laren, coll. V. W. van Gogh.

BIBLIOGRAPHY
De la Faille 1970 pp. 48 (no. F 17), 612 (no. F 17); Hulsker 1980, pp. 93, 94 (no. 395).

156 *Peasant Woman Taking her Meal*

Oil on canvas, 42 × 29 cm
Otterlo, Rijksmuseum Kröller-Müller

In Nuenen during the winter of 1885 Van Gogh drew and painted a great number of studies of peasant women in cottage interiors silhouetted against a window. These pictures seem at least indirectly related to the series of works depicting weavers in similarly lit cottage interiors executed the year before. In March 1885, Vincent wrote to Theo about the project: 'I am brooding over a couple of larger, more elaborate things, and if I should happen to get a clear idea of how to reproduce the effects I have in mind, in that case I should keep the studies in question here for the time being, because then I should certainly need them – it would be, for instance, something like this: namely figures against the light of a window. I have studies for it, against the light as well as turned toward the light, and I have worked several times already on the complete figure; spooling yarn, sewing, or peeling potatoes. Full face and in profile, it is a difficult effect.' (no. 396, vol. 2, p. 353; March 1885).

Images of seated peasant women in cottage interiors are common in the work of the artists of the Hague School (cf. Cat. 32, 113), and their origins lie in seventeenth-century Dutch genre painting. Mondriaan, too, undertook the theme in two early works now in the collection of Sidney Janis, New York.

155

Vincent's proposal to execute 'a couple of larger, more elaborate things ... namely figures against the light of a window' was apparently superseded by his project for *The Potato Eaters* (see fig. 115). The first sketch for *The Potato Eaters* was apparently executed during the same period, February to March, 1885, as *Peasant Woman Taking her Meal*. The backlit and sidelit figures in interiors were undoubtedly useful in learning how to realize the strong contrasts of light in the artificially lit interior of *The Potato Eaters*. In early May Van Gogh was evidently fascinated by both effects: 'When I went to the cottage tonight, I found the people at supper in the light of the small window instead of under the lamp – oh, it was splendid! The colour was extraordinary too; you remember those heads painted against the window – the effect was like that, but even darker.' (no. 405, vol. 2, p. 373; early May 1885).

Finally, it is likely that *Peasant Woman Taking her Meal* was at least inspired by Jozef Israëls's images of peasants eating and working in cottage interiors. There are several in which the figures are seen against the back light or side light of a window. Van Gogh was certainly familiar with such pictures and in March 1882 wrote to Theo about one 'with five or six figures, I think, a peasant family at mealtime' (no. 181, vol. 1, p. 326; 11? March 1882). Moreover, there are works by Israëls such as a painting of a woman sewing (auct. London [Sotheby's], 9 May 1924, no. 35) that seem to relate directly to the subject and composition of *Peasant Woman Taking her Meal*.

PROVENANCE
Voorburg, coll. L.C. Enthoven, –1920; auct. Amsterdam (F. Muller & Co), 18 May 1920, no. 228 (Dfl. 1,050); The Hague, coll. Mrs H.E.L.J. Kröller-Müller, 1920.

BIBLIOGRAPHY
De la Faille 1970, pp. 66 (no. F 72), 614 (no. F 72); Cat. Museum Kröller-Müller 1980, p. 70 (no. 177); Hulsker 1980, pp. 154, 158 (no. 718).

156

Piet Mondriaan (1872-1944)

Pieter Cornelis Mondriaan was born in Amersfoort on 7 March 1872. He was the son of Pieter Cornelis Mondriaan (1839–1921) and Johanna Christina Kok (1839–1909). Mondriaan's father trained as a teacher at a Protestant college in The Hague, where he moved in the circle of the Dutch statesman Groen van Prinsterer (1801–76), whose ideas he upheld throughout his life both verbally and in writing. In 1869 he was appointed headmaster of a Protestant primary school at Amersfoort where he taught French and drawing; in April 1880 he became headmaster of the Protestant primary school at Winterswijk and there Piet Mondriaan began to draw, his favourite scenes being the Lappenbrink and the view of the Protestant church, St James's. Piet helped his father to design memorial plates, and after he had gained the Lower Certificate in drawing in 1889, he gave drawing lessons at his father's school. He was in constant touch with the retired drawing teacher Braet von Uberfeldt, whose collection of reproductions he studied and his uncle, Frits Mondriaan (1853–1932) also made regular painting visits to Winterswijk.

In 1892 Mondriaan was awarded the Higher Certificate in drawing and became a student at the Rijksacademie (National Academy) in Amsterdam, where Nico van der Waay and Carel Dake were his professors. He earned his living by making portraits and copying paintings in the Rijksmuseum. In 1892 he became a member of the Utrecht artists' society Kunstliefde and in 1897 he joined the St Lucasgilde and Arti et Amicitiae in Amsterdam, where he exhibited regularly between 1897 and 1910, mainly showing still lifes.

Each year he visited Winterswijk for longer periods, and it was here that he produced his first works with a symbolic content; he competed for the Prix de Rome in 1898 and 1901, but failed both times. He broke away from his family's Protestantism and became interested in esoteric philosophies, of which Theosophy was the most important. Through Albert van den Briel he became familiar with the ethical pantheism of Dr Hugenholz, which had a great influence on the later philosophy of Dr Schoenmaekers.

Landscapes now became the most important subjects in his work, but he also painted Amsterdam townscapes. The immediate vicinity of Amsterdam provided the settings – Watergraafsmeer, Abcoude and the countryside around the little river Gein – and he often worked in the company of painters such as Arnold Gorter and Simon Maris. He adopted his uncle Frits's manner of making landscape sketches.

From 1905 onwards light – sunlight and moonlight – played a very important part in Mondriaan's work; in his series of 'evening and night scenes' the details are blurred and it is the contours of large areas which determine the image. Numerous drawings and small oil sketches culminated in a number of large-scale paintings. The painterly element became very strong, expressing itself primarily in very loose brushwork and a heightened tonality, which was to evolve into strongly contrasted colours after 1908.

In 1906 Mondriaan won the Willink van Collen Prize with four other artists, and in the winter of 1906–07 he stayed with his colleague Albertus Hulshoff Pol at a farm at Oele, just north of Winterswijk. In September 1908, during a stay at the seaside resort of Domburg in Zeeland, he came into contact with a group of painters with a more cosmopolitan viewpoint, in particular Jan Toorop, which led Mondriaan to study French Neo-Impressionism; in 1910 he was one of the founders of the Moderne Kunstkring (Modern Art Society) along with Conrad Kikkert, Jan Sluyters and Jan Toorop. At the beginning of 1912 he settled in Paris.

In 1914 the outbreak of the First World War prevented him from returning to Paris after his annual visit to Domburg. In the Netherlands interest in his work grew and in 1917 the first number of the periodical *De Stijl* appeared, of which Theo van Doesburg was the editor. For many years Mondriaan had been defining his theories on art, compiling his ideas into 'The book', which provided a major contribution to *De Stijl* up to and including 1920; 'The New Plasticism' became the motto of the periodical. In June 1919 Mondriaan returned to Paris. Interest in his work was now international and his ideas appeared in several European avant-garde periodicals.

In 1938 he moved temporarily to London; in 1940, through the agency of the American artist Harry Holtzman, he left for New York, where his ideas became widely disseminated. The significant changes in his work from 1935 onwards continued to evolve radically until his death on 1 February 1944.

fig. 147 *Piet Mondriaan in his Amsterdam Studio c.* 1903 (photograph) (Haags Gemeentemuseum, The Hague)

157

157 *Slum Area in Amsterdam*

Oil on canvas, 50.8 × 76.3 cm
Signed bottom right: *Piet Mondriaan*
Private collection
repr. in colour on p. 295

This is one of the few known townscapes of Amsterdam by Mondriaan, a theme which he took up in the 1890s. This painting aptly illustrates his assimilation of the typical Hague School townscape, and similarities with the work of Jacob Maris can be found; but his style is characterized by brush strokes set down separately alongside one another in gradations of colour and the picturesque element is predominant. It is typical of Mondriaan's method of working that he was simultaneously producing works with houses and streets as their subjects, in which the picturesque element does not appear at all. Here it is the composition that has received his full attention.

158 *View of Winterswijk*

Gouache, 52 × 63 cm
Signed bottom left: *Piet Mondriaan*
Amsterdam, Collection J.P. Smid, Monet Art Gallery

In addition to numerous sketches and finished paintings of houses and streets in Winterswijk itself, there are also a few in which the landscape around the village plays an important

part. This work has a strong composition. The horizon lies slightly above the centre and the girl and the cow are placed below it in the foreground of the picture area. Mondriaan has placed this detail in direct compositional relationship to the severely vertical tower of St James's Church at Winterswijk to create spatial tension. The late evening atmosphere blurs

159

repr. in colour on p. 296

the details, so that the silhouette of the village is heavily accentuated. Both the use of strong colour and the evening atmosphere differ markedly from the works that Mondriaan's uncle, Frits Mondriaan, painted in this area. The theme of evening and night landscapes was taken up again by Mondriaan many years later.

BIBLIOGRAPHY
H. Henkels. *Mondriaan in Winterswijk*, The Hague 1979, p. 52.

159 Landscape with Windmill

Oil on canvas, 75 × 63 cm
Signed bottom left: *Piet Mondriaan*
The Hague, Haags Gemeentemuseum
repr. in colour on p. 296

Like his uncle Frits, Mondriaan painted a great deal in the outskirts of Amsterdam. The little river Gein, where earlier

Gabriël and Roelofs had also worked, was one of the most popular haunts of Mondriaan and many of his artist colleagues. Most of his works dating from the beginning of this century – drawings, oil sketches and finished paintings – have this landscape as their subject. The combination of water, banks, trees and windmills was evidently very inviting. The dozens of studies that exist make it clear that Mondriaan continually returned to the same spots, studying them from different angles. Sometimes we see the group of trees on the right with the mill beside it; another time Mondriaan has concentrated entirely on the trees, seen from a slightly different viewpoint, and their reflection in the water. The elaborate character of this work is strongly reminiscent of the rather conventional renderings of such subjects by followers of the Hague School.

PROVENANCE
Sitio do Regato, Janes-Cascais (Portugal), coll. Dr W.H.D. Nolen, –1978; on loan to the museum, 1968–78; presented to the museum, 1978.

160

160 *The Canal near Het Kalfje*

Oil on canvas on pasteboard, 23.5 × 37.5 cm
Signed bottom right: *Piet Mondriaan*
The Hague, Haags Gemeentemuseum

As we have already seen in the *View of Winterswijk*, Mondriaan was concerned with the construction of the composition and the spatial relationship between foreground and background. Many of his works dating from 1898–1904 are characterized by a very high horizon or the complete absence of a horizon. This also constitutes the most important difference between Mondriaan's work and that of Weissenbruch, which he undoubtedly knew well. Mondriaan makes the spectator strongly aware of the actual boundaries of the picture plane by letting the trunk of the willow in the foreground cut through the whole of it, the reverse of the effect Weissenbruch was aiming for; Mondriaan's intention was to reveal the spatial relationship between different pictorial elements (see fig. 130).

PROVENANCE
De Meern, coll. A.P. van den Briel, –1956; presented to the museum, 1956.

BIBLIOGRAPHY
Blok 1974, pp. 86 (no. 41), 170 (no. 41).

161 *Evening on the Gein*

Oil on canvas, 65 × 86 cm
The Hague, Haags Gemeentemuseum

As in several previous works, Mondriaan often singled out the same spots in a given landscape in order to 'portray' them from different angles. In this work too he draws the spectator's attention to a basic starting-point for the composition of a painting. If we mentally remove the vertical tree, we are left with a scene that is virtually identical: the contours of the trees are reflected exactly in the water, while the dividing line, almost in the centre of the canvas, is barely indicated, so that it

161

is not immediately clear which is the top and which is the bottom of the painting. The net result is that the solitary vertical tree acquires even more power and tension.

PROVENANCE
De Meern, coll. A.P. van den Briel, –1956; presented to the museum, 1956.

BIBLIOGRAPHY
Blok 1974, pp. 106 (no. 103), 172 (no 103).

162 *Landscape with Trees by the Water*

Oil on canvas, 100 × 136 cm
Signed and dated bottom left: *Piet Mondriaan '07*
The Hague, Haags Gemeentemuseum

With a subject similar to that of the previous picture, this canvas is striking for its great overall elaboration and its finished character. It can also be seen as the final culmination of a long series of preparatory works, in which all the experiences

162

of the preceding sketches coalesce, giving the impression of a completeness which the other oil sketches lack. It could also be called a finished painting in the nineteenth-century French academic tradition.

PROVENANCE
Coll. M. Knoops, –1938; auct. Amsterdam (F. Muller & Co), 6–7 Dec. 1938, no. 38; Blaricum, coll. S.B. Slijper, –1971; bequeathed to the museum, 1971.

BIBLIOGRAPHY
Blok 1974, pp. 109 (no. 113), 174 (no. 113).

163 Landscape

Oil on canvas, 78 × 91 cm
Signed bottom left: *Piet Mondriaan*
The Hague, Haags Gemeentemuseum

163

In contrast to the previous work this painting has the character of a sketch, admittedly an oil sketch, but without the finish of *Landscape with Trees by the Water*; this work exhibits several themes with which Mondriaan was much preoccupied. On the one hand there is the vertical tree dominating the composition – a theme that was already present in Cat. 161; on the other this vertical tree is placed not against the contour of a group of trees, but against a cloudy sky.

Various 'cloud studies' by Mondriaan are known, in which the landscape is relegated to the background and all the attention is concentrated on the movement and form of the clouds, sunrise or sunset being the favoured moments of the day. The veiled light of a moonlit night is also often found in Mondriaan's work. Here, too, the light is mysterious: its source – whether the sun or moon – is invisible and shines through the crown of the tree, giving the clouds an agitated character diametrically opposed to the immobility of the tree.

PROVENANCE
Blaricum, coll. S.B. Slipjer, –1971; bequeathed to the museum, 1971.

BIBLIOGRAPHY
Blok 1974, pp. 115 (no. 129), 175 (no. 129).

164

164 *Windmill by Moonlight*

Oil on canvas, 99.5 × 125.5 cm
Signed bottom right: *Piet Mondriaan*
The Hague, Haags Gemeentemuseum

The theme of a windmill in a landscape is one of the most stereotyped subjects in the repertoire of the Hague School. It also appears in Mondriaan's early work. The first copy that he made in the Rijksmuseum, in January 1895, was of Gabriël's *In the Month of July* (see fig. 125), purchased in 1889. It marks the beginning of a long series of works in which a windmill invariably plays the leading role. Sometimes Mondriaan followed the fashionable trend of the Hague School; elsewhere he used the motif in a more symbolic, romantic vision of the landscape.

In this painting he again brought together a number of elements which appear in different combinations in other works: the windmill in a moonlit landscape. Here, even more strongly than in Cat. 163, the position of the sails in the form of a cross is a symbol of eternity, contrasted to the organic transience of the constantly changing phenomena of nature.

PROVENANCE
London, coll. Van Dam, –1929; auct. Amsterdam (F. Muller & Co), 29 Oct. 1929, no. 42 (Dfl. 550); coll. J.H. Gosschalk, 1929–39; on loan to the museum, 1929–39; presented to the museum, 1939.

BIBLIOGRAPHY
Blok 1974, pp. 111 (no. 117), 174 (no. 117); R. Rosenblum, *Modern Painting and the Romantic Tradition. Friedrich to Rothko*, London 1975, p. 187.

165 Large Landscape

Oil on canvas, 75 × 120 cm
The Hague, Haags Gemeentemuseum
repr. in colour on p. 296

This last painting marks the change that occurred in Mondriaan's work at this period. On the one hand it bears the same characteristics that have already been noted in previous works: the subject, the way of rendering it with emphasis on the contours and brushwork and not on the details, the relationships between the various parts of the painting – trees, water and clouds. The composition, too, is familiar.

Later, when Mondriaan was asked about the turning-point in his development as an artist, he said that the abandonment of the 'naturalistic' concept of colour had marked the beginning of a whole series of new experiments and investigations, which ultimately led him to the autonomous expression which he called the 'New Plasticism'. This work is distinguished by this dual character: it is strongly bounded by the traditional principles of the Hague School, while in the application of colour, it reveals a new conception of painting and its significance.

PROVENANCE
Blaricum, coll. S.B. Slijper, –1971; bequeathed to the museum, 1971.

BIBLIOGRAPHY
Blok 1974, pp. 117 (no. 139), 175 (no. 139).

THE NETHERLANDS IN THE NINETEENTH CENTURY

Norderney

NORTH SEA

ZUIDER ZEE

Groningen

Vries
• Zuidlaren

Zweeloo
Nieuw-Amsterdam

Hoorn
• Alkmaar

Kampen

Zaandam

Haarlem

Zandvoort

Amsterdam

THE GOOI

Laren
Katwijk
Noorden
Hilversum
Voorschoten • Leyden
Baarn
Scheveningen
Nieuwkoop
Leidschendam
Utrecht

Reeuwijk

Oosterbeek
Arnhem

The Hague

Rotterdam

Nymegen
Cleves

Dordrecht

Domburg

Nuenen
Heeze

Yssel

Rhine

Antwerp

Meuse

Scheldt

Cologne

Brussels

Liège

Trier

Bibliography

CHARLES DUMAS

The bibliography is arranged as follows:

Select Bibliography: full bibliographical details of books and articles referred to in the text in abbreviated form. Works are listed under the authors' surnames, arranged alphabetically; under each author's name the titles appear in chronological order. Catalogues are listed under the name of the museum or gallery, listed alphabetically.

Exhibition Catalogues: full bibliographical details of exhibition catalogues referred to in the text in abbreviated form. Catalogues are arranged by location and date. The following abbreviations are used:

H.T.M. — Exhibition of drawings by ordinary and honorary members of the *Hollandsche Teeken-Maatschappij* (Dutch Drawing Society), held at the Academy of Fine Arts, The Hague from 1876–87 and at Pulchri Studio, The Hague from 1888–95.

L.M. — Exhibition of paintings and other works of art by *Levende Meesters* (Living Masters), held at least once a year in the Netherlands (generally in Amsterdam, The Hague and Rotterdam, but also in smaller cities) from 1827 onwards.

Salon — Annual international exhibition in Paris organized by the *Société Nationale des Beaux-Arts*.

General Bibliography

I The Nineteenth Century; II The Hague School; III The Artists Works are listed chronologically. The following abbreviations are used for newspapers, periodicals and other publications:

A.H.	*Algemeen Handelsblad*
B.K.	*Beeldende Kunst*
B.M.	*The Burlington Magazine*
B.R.M.	*Bulletin van het Rijksmuseum*
E.G.M.	*Elsevier's Geïllustreerd Maandschrift*
E.H.	*Eigen Haard*
G.B.A.	*Gazette des Beaux-Arts*
K.K.	*Kunstkronijk*
M.B.K.	*Maandbland voor Beeldende Kunsten*
M.D.K.W.	*Mededeelingen van den Dienst voor Kunsten en Wetenschappen der Gemeente 's-Gravenhage*
M.K.	*Moderne Kunstwerken*
N.v.d.D.	*Het Nieuws van den Dag*
N.R.C.	*Nieuwe Rotterdamsche Courant*
N.S.	*Nederlandsche Spectator*
O.E.	*Onze Eeuw*
O.H.	*Oud Holland*
O.K.	*Openbaar Kunstbezit*

Select Bibliography

Arondéus 1939
W. Arondéus, *Matthijs Maris. De tragiek van den droom*, Amsterdam 1939.
Arondéus 1945
W. Arondéus, *Matthijs Maris. De tragiek van den droom*, Amsterdam 1945².
Artz 1901
Souvenir Dedicated to Dutch Art and her Host of Diligent Workers at the Close of the 19th Century. Presented by Maison Artz Art Dealers, The Hague Holland, The Hague 1901.

Baard 1947
H.P. Baard, *Anton Mauve*, Amsterdam [1947] (Palet-serie).
Bénédite 1910
L. Bénédite, *De schilderkunst der XIXde eeuw in Frankrijk, Engeland, Amerika, Nederland* . . . Amsterdam 1910 (Dutch adaptation by G.H. Marius).
Bénézit 1976
E. Bénézit, *Dictionnaire critique et documentaire des peintres, sculpteurs, dessinateurs et graveurs*, 10 vols., Paris 1976,
Berckenhoff 1888
H.L. Berckenhoff, 'De gebroeders Maris', *De Gids* LII (1888), vol. 3, pp. 469–501.
Berckenhoff 1901
H.L. Berckenhoff, 'J.H. Weissenbruch', *Woord en Beeld* (1901), pp. 163–69.
Bilders 1974
G. Bilders, *Vrolijk versterven. Een keuze uit zijn dagboek en brieven door Wim Zaal*, Amsterdam 1974.
Blok 1974
C. Blok, *Piet Mondriaan. Een catalogus van zijn werk in Nederlands openbaar bezit*, Amsterdam 1974.
Boele van Hensbroek 1890
P.A.M. Boele van Hensbroek & G.H. Marius, *Het Museum Mesdag en zijne stichters*, Amsterdam [1890].
Boele van Hensbroek 1910
P.A.M. Boele van Hensbroek, *De Haagsche School in het Mesdag-Museum*, Amsterdam [1910].
Boon 1947
K.G. Boon, *Het zelfportret in de Nederlandsche en Vlaamsche kunst*, Amsterdam [1947].
Braakhuis 1978–79
H.E.M. Braakhuis & J. van der Vliet, 'Patterns in the Life and Work of Matthijs Maris', *Simiolus* X (1978–79), pp. 142–81.
Bremmer 1909
H.P. Bremmer, *Willem Roelofs. 100 Lichtdrukken naar zijn werken vertegenwoordigd op de eeretentoonstelling in 'Pulchri Studio', October 1907*, Amsterdam 1909.
Brom 1959
G. Brom, *Schilderkunst en litteratuur in de 19e eeuw*, Utrecht/Antwerp [1959].
Brunt 1912
A. Brunt, 'Matthijs Maris', *E.H.* XXXVIII (1912), pp. 347–51.
Buschmann 1918 (1)
P. Buschmann, 'Matthew Maris', *B.M.* XXXII (1918), pp. 4–9, 73–75.
Buschmann 1918 (2)
P. Buschmann, 'De Matthijs Maris-tentoonstelling te Londen'. *Onze Kunst* XXXIII (1918), vol. 1, pp. 68–76.

Cannegieter 1972–73
D.A.S. Cannegieter, 'Blommers een schilder uit de Haagse School', *Antiek* VII (1972–73), pp. 446–61.
Cat. Coll. H.E. ten Cate 1955
D. Hannema, *Catalogue of the H. E. ten Cate Collection*, 2 vols., Amsterdam 1955.
Cat. Dordrechts Museum 1928
Dordrechts Museum. Catalogus der kunstwerken, Dordrecht 1928.
Cat. Gemeentemuseum 1935
G. Knuttel Wzn., *Gemeentemuseum 's-Gravenhage. Catalogus van de schilderijen, aquarellen en teekeningen*, [The Hague] 1935.
Cat. Gemeentemuseum 1962
Gemeentemuseum Den Haag. Catalogus schilderijen. Afdeling moderne kunst, [The Hague] 1962.
Cat. Gemeentemuseum 1965
Schilderijen Gemeentemuseum Arnhem, n.p. 1965.
Cat. Glasgow Art Gallery 1961
Dutch and Flemish, Netherlandish and German Paintings. Glasgow Art Gallery and Museum, 2 vols., Glasgow 1961.
Cat. Koninklijk Museum 1977
Catalogus schilderijen 19de en 20ste eeuw. Koninklijk Museum voor Schone Kunsten Antwerpen, [Antwerp 1977].
Cat. Louvre 1979
Catalogue sommaire illustré des peintures du Musée du Louvre. I. Écoles flamande et hollandaise, Paris 1979.
Cat. Musées Royaux 1928
Fierens-Gevaert & A. Laes, *Musées Royaux des Beaux Arts de Belgique. Catalogue de la peinture moderne*, Brussels 1928.
Cat. Museum Boston 1921
Museum of Fine Arts, Boston. Catalogue of Paintings, [Boston] 1921.
Cat. Museum Boston 1949
Catalogue of Paintings and Drawings in Watercolor. Museum of Fine Arts, Boston, Boston 1949.
Cat. Museum Boymans-van Beuningen 1963
Museum Boymans-van Beuningen Rotterdam. Catalogus schilderijen na 1800, [Rotterdam] 1963.
Cat. Museum Boymans-van Beuningen 1972
Museum Boymans-van Beuningen Rotterdam. Old Paintings 1400–1900. Illustrations, Rotterdam 1972.
Cat. Museum Fodor 1863
Beschrijving der schilderijen, teekeningen, prenten, prentwerken en boeken in het Museum Fodor, te Amsterdam, Amsterdam 1863.
Cat. Museum Kröller-Müller 1970
Schilderijen van het Rijksmuseum Kröller-Müller, Otterlo 1970.
Cat. Museum Kröller-Müller 1980
Vincent van Gogh. A Detailed Catalogue of the Paintings and Drawings by Vincent van Gogh in the Collection of the Kröller-Müller National Museum, Otterlo 1980⁴.
Cat. Museum Mesdag 1975
E. Van Schendel, *Museum Mesdag. Nederlandse negentiende-eeuwse schilderijen, tekeningen en grafiek*, The Hague 1975.
Cat. Museum Twenthe 1974–76
O. Terkuile, *Rijksmuseum Twenthe Enschede. Catalogus van de schilderijen*, n.p. 1974–76.
Cat. National Gallery 1946
Catalogue National Gallery of Scotland, Edinburgh, [Edinburgh] 1946.
Cat. National Gallery 1960
N. MacLaren, *National Gallery Catalogues. The Dutch School*, London 1960.
Cat. Neue Pinakothek 1981
Bayerische Staatsgemäldesammlungen. Neue Pinakothek. Erläuterungen zu den ausgestellten Werken, Munich 1981.
Cat. Rijksmuseum 1918
Catalogus der schilderijen, miniaturen, pastels, omlijste teekeningen enz. in het Rijks-museum te Amsterdam, met supplement, Amsterdam 1918.
Cat. Rijksmuseum 1976
Alle schilderijen van het Rijksmuseum te Amsterdam. Volledig geïllustreerde catalogus, Amsterdam/Haarlem 1976.
Cat. Singer Museum 1962
Singer Memorial Foundation Museum. Catalogus, [Laren 1962].
Cat. Stedelijk Museum 1922
Catalogus van schilderijen, teekeningen en beelden in het Stedelijk Museum en andere Gemeentegebouwen bijeengebracht door de Vereeniging tot het vormen van eene openbare verzameling van hedendaagsche kunst te Amsterdam, Amsterdam 1922.
Cat. Toledo Museum 1939
Blake-More Godwin, *The Toledo Museum of Art Founded by Edward Drummond Libbey. Catalogue of European Paintings*, Toledo (Ohio) 1939.
Cat. Toledo Museum 1976
The Toledo Museum of Art. European Paintings, [Toledo (Ohio)] 1976.
Cat. Verz. Van Bilderbeek 1913
Verzameling Van Bilderbeek. Moderne schilderijen, aquarellen, teekeningen en bronzen beelden van Hollandsche en van buitenlandsche meesters . . . Dordrecht 1913.
Colmjon/Scheen 1950
G. Colmjon & P. A. Scheen, *De Haagse School. De vernieuwing van onze schilderkunst sinds het midden der negentiende eeuw*, Rijswijk 1950.
Croal Thomson 1907
D. Croal Thomson, *The Brothers Maris (James-Matthew-William)*, London/Paris 1907 (*The Studio*, Special Summer Number).
Croal Thomson 1918
D. Croal Thomson, E.D. Fridlander, F. Lessore & M.E. Sadler, *Matthew Maris. An Illustrated Souvenir*, London [1918].

Dake 1911 (1)
C.L. Dake, *Jozef Israëls*, Amsterdam [1911].
Dake 1911 (2)
C.L. Dake, *Jozef Israëls*, Berlin [1911].
De Bock 1902–03
Th. de Bock, *Jacob Maris. Met 90 photogravures naar zijne werken en zijn portret door M. van der Maarel*, Amsterdam [c. 1902–03].
De Boer 1907
H. de Boer, 'Collection de M. Van Randwijk à La Haye', *Les Arts* VI (Aug. 1907), pp. 1–32.
De Boer 1915
H. de Boer, *Schilderijen uit de verzameling Van Bilderbeek*, Dordrecht [1915].
De Bruijn 1963
H.C de Bruijn Jr, 'Willem Roelofs 1822–1897. Wegbereider der Haagse School', *Op den Uitkijk* (April 1963), pp. 338–41.
De Gruyter 1968–69
J. de Gruyter, *De Haagse School*, 2 vols., [Rotterdam 1968–69].
De Haes 1893
L. de Haes, 'P.J.C. Gabriël', *E.G.M.* III, vol. v, pp. 453–73.
De Haes 1898
L. de Haes, 'P.J.C. Gabriël', in M. Rooses (ed.), *Het Schildersboek*, vol. I, Amsterdam 1898, pp. 212–36.
De la Faille 1970
J.-B. de la Faille, *The Works of Vincent van Gogh. His Paintings and Drawings*, Amsterdam 1970².
De Meester 1898
J. de Meester, 'Jozef Israëls', in M. Rooses (ed.), *Het Schildersboek*, vol. I, Amsterdam 1898, pp. 82–99.
De Vries 1894
J. de Vries, 'Jozef Israëls', *E.H.* XX (1894), pp. 37–44.

Eisler 1910
M. Eisler, *Von jüdischer Kunst (Jozef Israëls). Ein Vortrag*, Cologne/Leipzig 1910.

Eisler 1911 (1)
M. Eisler, *Die neuholländische Kunst (Die Haager Schule)*, Munich 1911.
Eisler 1911 (2)
M. Eisler, 'Die drei Brüder Maris', *Veldhagen & Klasings Monatsheft* XXV (May 1911), pp. 1–15.
Eisler 1911 (3)
M. Eisler, 'Zandvoort 1855', *E.G.M.* XXI (1911), vol. XLII, pp. 266–85.
Eisler 1913 (1)
M. Eisler, 'De collectie Drucker in het Rijksmuseum te Amsterdam', *E.G.M.* XXIII (1913), XLVI, pp. 241–55, 323–35, 409–27.
Eisler 1913 (2)
M. Eisler, 'Jacob Maris in Parijs', *E.G.M.* XXIII (1913), vol. XLV, pp. 25–40.
Eisler 1924
M. Eisler, *Jozef Israëls*, Londen 1924 (*The Studio*, Special Spring Number).
Engel 1965
E.P. Engel, 'Het ontstaan van de verzameling Drucker-Fraser in het Rijksmuseum', *B.R.M.* XIII (1965), pp. 45–66.
Engel 1967
E.P. Engel, *Anton Mauve (1838–1888). Bronnen verkenning en analyse van zijn oeuvre*, Utrecht 1967 (Utrechtse Kunsthistorische Studiën, no. 9).

Fridlander 1921
E.D. Fridlander, *Matthew Maris*, London/Boston 1921.
Fuchs 1978
R.H. Fuchs, *Dutch Painting*, London 1978.

Gerson 1961
H. Gerson, *De Nederlandse schilderkunst. III: Voor en na Van Gogh*, Amsterdam 1961 (De Schoonheid van ons Land, vol. 17).
Glavimans 1946
Een en ander betrekkelijk mijne loopbaan als schilder, beschreven door Johannes Bosboom. Herdrukt naar de oorspronkelijke uitgave van 1891. Toegelicht door A. Glavimans, Rotterdam/Antwerp 1946.
Goldscheider 1937
L. Goldscheider, *Five Hundred Self Portraits*, Vienna/London 1937.
Gram 1876
J. Gram, 'Matthijs Maris', *K.K.* N.S. XVII (1876), pp. 21–22.
Gram 1880
J. Gram, *Onze schilders in Pulchri Studio*, Rotterdam [1880].
Gram 1904
J. Gram, *Onze schilders in Pulchri Studio (1880–1904)*, Leiden [1904].
Greenshields 1904
E.B. Greenshields, *The Subjective View of Landscape Painting. With Special Reference to J.H. Weissenbruch and Illustrations from Works of his in Canada*, Montreal 1904.
Greenshields 1906
E.B. Greenshields, *Landscape Painting and Modern Dutch Artists*, New York [1906].
Gunsaulus 1912
'An Address Delivered by Frank Wakeley Gunsaulus, D.D. on the Occasion at the Opening of the Memorial Exhibition of the Work of Josef Israëls', in exh. cat. Toledo 1912, pp. 107–32.

Hagenbeek-Frey 1974–75
I. Hagenbeek-Frey, 'Carel Joseph Fodor (Amsterdam 1801–1860) en zijn schilderijenverzameling', *Antiek* IX (1974–75), pp. 908–24.
Halton 1907
E.G. Halton, 'The Alexander Young Collection – IV. Modern Dutch Pictures', *The Studio* XXXIX (1907), pp. 287–306.
Halton 1912
E.G. Halton, 'Josef Israëls: The Leader of the Modern Dutch School', *The Studio* LIV (1912), pp. 89–102.
Hammacher 1941
A.M. Hammacher, *Amsterdamsche impressionisten en hun kring*, Amsterdam 1941².
Haverkorn van Rijsewijk 1909
P. Haverkorn van Rijsewijk, *Het Museum Boymans te Rotterdam*, Rotterdam 1909.
Haverkorn van Rijsewijk 1912
P. Haverkorn van Rijsewijk, 'Matthijs Maris te Wolfheze en Lausanne', *Onze Kunst* XI, vol. XXII (1912), pp. 48–59.
Haverkorn van Rijsewijk 1918
P. Haverkorn van Rijsewijk, 'Matthijs Maris', *Onze Kunst* XVI (1918), vol. XXXIII, pp. 29–43, 85–90, 122–38; vol. XXXIV; pp. 117–27.
Haverkorn van Rijsewijk 1919
P. Haverkorn van Rijsewijk, 'Matthijs Maris', *Onze Kunst* XVII (1919), vol. XXXV, pp. 33–34, 117–30; vol. XXXVI, pp. 92–102.
Heath 1896–97
R. Heath, 'Adolphe Artz', *The Magazine of Art* (1896–97), pp. 80–85.
Hefting 1970
P. H. Hefting, *G.H. Breitner in zijn Haagse tijd*, 2 vols., Utrecht 1970 (thesis).
Hefting 1981
V. Hefting, *Schilders in Oosterbeek 1840–1870*,

Zutphen/Arnhem 1981 (Uitgaven van de Stichting De Gelderse Bloem, vol. 30).
Henkel 1916–17
M.D. Henkel, 'Matthijs Maris †', *Kunstchronik* N.S. XXVIII (1916–17), pp. 495–99.
Hennus 1940
M.F. Hennus, *Johannes Bosboom*, Amsterdam [1940] (Paletserie).
Heijbroek 1975 (1)
J.F. Heijbroek, 'Matthijs Maris en het "Souvenir d'Amsterdam"', *Amstelodamum* LXII (1975), pp. 14–18.
Heijbroek 1975 (2)
J.F. Heijbroek, 'Matthijs Maris in Parijs 1869–1877', *O.H.* LXXXIX (1975), pp. 266–89.
Hols 1907 (1)
M. Hols (ed.), *De meesterwerken van Jacob en Willem Maris. 32 Reproducties naar hun meest bekende schilderijen*, The Hague [1907] (Nederlandsche Meesters, vol. 4).
Hols 1907 (2)
M. Hols (ed.), *De meesterwerken van Mauve. 32 Reproducties naar zijn meest bekende schilderijen*, The Hague [1907] (Nederlandsche Meesters, vol. 3).
Hubert 1909
H.J. Hubert, *De etsen van Jozef Israëls, een catalogus*, Amsterdam 1909.
Hulsker 1980
J. Hulsker, *The Complete Van Gogh*, New York 1980.

Immerzeel 1842–43
J. Immerzeel Jr., *De levens en werken der Hollandsche en Vlaamsche kunstschilders, beeldhouwers, graveurs en bouwmeesters, van het begin der vijftiende eeuw tot heden*, 3 vols., Amsterdam 1842–43.

Jeltes 1910
H.F.W. Jeltes, *Uit het leven van een kunstenaarspaar. Brieven van Johannes Bosboom*, Amsterdam 1910.
Jeltes 1911
H.F.W. Jeltes, *Willem Roelofs. Bizonderheden betreffende zijn leven en zijn werk*, Amsterdam 1911.
Jeltes 1917
H.F.W. Jeltes, 'Johannes Bosboom (1817–1891)', *E.G.M.* XXVII (1917), vol. LIII, pp. 1–25.
Jeltes 1922
H.F.W. Jeltes, 'Willem Roelofs (1822–1922)', *E.G.M.* XXXII (1922), vol. LXIII, pp. 217–27.
Jeltes 1924
H.F.W. Jeltes, 'De collectie-Reich', *E.G.M.* XXXIV (1924), vol. LXVII, pp. 6–16, 161–70.
Jeltes 1935
H.F.W. Jeltes, 'Gerard Bilders', *E.G.M.* XLV (1935), vol. LXXXIX, pp. 73–96.
Jeltes 1944
H.F.W. Jeltes, 'Nadere mededeelingen over Gerard Bilders', *M.B.K.* XXI (1944), pp. 1–11.
Jeltes 1947
H.F.W. Jeltes, *Gerard Bilders. Een schildersleven in het midden der 19de eeuw*, The Hague 1947.

Kahn 1925
G. Kahn, 'Jozef Israëls (1824–1911)', *G.B.A.* 5e pér. XI (1925), pp. 87–94.
Kalff 1902
J. Kalff Jr., 'Jacob Maris', in *Mannen en vrouwen van beteekenis in onze dagen*, vol. 32, Haarlem 1902, pp. 283–308.
Knoef 1946
J. Knoef, 'Fransche invloeden op Jacob Maris', *O.H.* LXI (1946), pp. 204–12.
Knoef 1947
J. Knoef, *Van Romantiek tot Realisme. Een bundel kunsthistorische opstellen*, The Hague 1947.
Knoef 1948
J. Knoef, *Een eeuw Nederlandsche schilderkunst*, Amsterdam 1948.
Knuttel 1938
G. Knuttel Wzn., *De Nederlandsche schilderkunst van Van Eyck tot Van Gogh*, Amsterdam 1938.
Knuttel 1950
G. Knuttel Wzn., *De Nederlandsche schilderkunst van Van Eyck tot Van Gogh*, Amsterdam 1950².
Knuttel 1961
G. Knuttel Wzn., *Jan Hendrik Weissenbruch. naar aanleiding van de tentoonstellingen te Laren, Singer Museum, 11 december 1960–30 januari 1961 en te Breda, Cultureel Centrum, 10 februari – 20 maart 1961*', *Kroniek van Kunst en Kultuur* XXI (1961), no.4, pp. 26–32.
Knuttel-Fabius 1894
E. Knuttel-Fabius, 'Ein Besuch bei dem holländischen Meister Joseph Israëls', *Deutsche Revue* XXII (1894), pp. 187–93.
Koomen 1949
P. Koomen, *In het zand gefixeerd. Beschouwingen over Nederlandse beeldende kunstenaars*, The Hague 1949.
Kramm 1857–64
Chr. Kramm, *De levens en werken der Hollandsche en Vlaamsche kunstschilders, beeldhouwers, graveurs en bouwmeesters van den vroegsten tot op onzen tijd*, 6 vols., Amsterdam 1857–64.
Kröller-Müller 1925
H. Kröller-Müller, *Beschouwingen over problemen in de ontwikkeling der moderne schilderkunst*, Maastricht 1925.
Kröller-Müller 1927.
H. Kröller-Müller, *Die Entwicklung der modernen*

Malerei. Ein Wegweiser für Laien, Leipzig [1927].

Loffelt 1895
A.C. Loffelt, 'Anton Mauve 1838–1888', *E.G.M.* V (1895), vol. IX, pp. 577–604.
Loffelt 1899
A.C. Loffelt, 'Anton Mauve', in M. Rooses (ed.), *Het Schildersboek*, vol. 3, Amsterdam 1899, pp. 1–33.
Luns 1941
H. Luns, *Holland schildert*, Amsterdam [1941].
Lurasco 1907
F.M. Lurasco, *Onze moderne meesters*, Amsterdam 1907.

MacColl 1902
D.S. MacColl, *Nineteenth Century Art. With Illustrations from Pictures and Objects in the Fine Art Loan Collection of the Glasgow International Exhibition*, Glasgow 1902.
Maris 1943
M.H.W.E. Maris, *De geschiedenis van een schildersgeslacht*, Amsterdam [1943].
Maris 1947
M.H.W.E. Maris, *De geschiedenis van een schildersgeslacht*, [Gouda 1947]².
Marius 1891
G.H. Marius, 'Willem Maris', *E.G.M.* I (1891), vol. II, pp. 109–22.
Marius 1898
G.H. Marius, 'Willem Maris', in M. Rooses (ed.), *Het Schildersboek*, vol. 2, Amsterdam 1898, pp. 100–13.
Marius 1899
G.H. Marius, 'Matthijs Maris', *E.G.M.* IX (1899), vol. XVIII, pp. 1–19.
Marius 1900
G.H. Marius, 'Matthijs Maris', in M. Rooses (ed.), *Het Schildersboek*, vol. 4, Amsterdam 1900. pp. 1–21.
Marius 1903
G.H. Marius, *De Hollandsche schilderkunst in de negentiende eeuw*, The Hague 1903.
Marius 1906
G.H. Marius, *Die holländische Malerei im neunzehnten Jahrhundert*, Berlin 1906.
Marius 1908
G.H. Marius, *Dutch Painting in the Nineteenth Century*, London 1908.
Marius 1910
G.H. Marius, 'De verzameling-Crone te Amsterdam', *E.G.M.* XX (1910), vol. XXXIX, pp. 1–14.
Marius 1920
G.H. Marius, *De Hollandsche schilderkunst in de negentiende eeuw*, The Hague 1920².
Marius/Martin 1917
G. [H.] Marius & W. Martin, *Johannes Bosboom*, The Hague 1917.
Marius/Norman 1973
[G.H.] Marius (ed. G. Norman), *Dutch Painters of the 19th Century*, [Woodbridge, Suffolk 1973].
Martin 1910
H. Martin, 'Jozef Israëls te Venetië', *E.G.M.* XX (1910), vol. XL, pp. 145–49.
Muther 1888
R. Muther, 'Die internationale Kunstausstellung in München', *Zeitschrift für Bildende Kunst* XXIII (1888).

Novotny 1970
F. Novotny, *Painting and Sculpture in Europe 1780–1880*, Harmondsworth 1970 (Pelican History of Art).

Pedroza 1948
R. Pedroza, *A pintura Holandesa de 1880 até hoje*, n.p. 1948 (ed. Instituto Brasil-Holanda).
Plasschaert 1909
A. Plasschaert, *XIXde Eeuwsche Hollandsche schilderkunst*, Amsterdam [1909].
Plasschaert 1911
A. Plasschaert, 'M. Maris, een lezing uit 1910', *Kritietien* III (1911), no. 1, pp. 1–14.
Plasschaert 1917–25
A. Plasschaert, *Beschouwingen*, 5 vols., Middelburg 1917–25.
Plasschaert 1920
A. Plasschaert, *Jacob Maris. Een overzicht*, Arnhem 1920.
Plasschaert 1923 (1)
A. Plasschaert, *Korte geschiedenis der Hollandsche schilderkunst van af de Haagsche School tot op den tegenwoordigen tijd*, Amsterdam 1923.
Plasschaert 1923 (2)
[A.] Plasschaert, *Jozef Israëls. Korte, eenvoudig-gehouden biographie en karakteriseering*, Amsterdam [1923].
Polak 1955
B. Polak, *Het fin-de-siècle in de Nederlandse schilderkunst. De symbolistische beweging 1890–1900*, The Hague 1955.
Pollock 1980–81
G. Pollock, 'Geworteld in Hollandse aarde'; 'Van Goghs begintijd en studiejaren'; 'Stad en stadrand: Leven en werk in de moderne stad', 'Drente – het keerpunt'; 'Schilder van boeren op het platteland van Brabant'; 'Nawoord', in exh. cat. Amsterdam 1980–81, pp. 11–134.
Poort 1981
J. Poort, *Hendrik Willem Mesdag. 'artiste peintre à la Haye'*, The Hague 1981.

Poortenaar 1940
  J. Poortenaar, *Matthijs Maris*, Naarden [1940] (De Torenreeks, vol. 5).
Pythian 1912
  J.E. Pythian, *Jozef Israëls*, London 1912.

Riat 1904
  G. Riat, 'P.J.C. Gabriël', *G.B.A.* 3e pér. XXXI (1904), pp. 158–66.
Rishel 1971
  J.J. Rishel, 'The Hague School: Some Forgotten Pictures in the Collection', *Bulletin Philadelphia Museum of Art* LXVI (July/Sept. 1971), pp. 15–27.
Rössing 1903
  J.H. R[össing], 'Jan Hendrik Weissenbruch. Gebite 's-Gravenhage 19 Juni 1824. Gest: Aldaar 24 Maart 1903', *E.H.* XXIX (1903), pp. 216–22.

Scheen 1946
  P.A. Scheen, *Honderd jaren Nederlandsche schilder– en teekenkunst. De Romantiek met voor– en natijd (1750–1850)*, The Hague 1946.
Scheen 1969–70
  P.A. Scheen, *Lexicon Nederlandse beeldende kunstenaars 1750–1950*, 2 vols. The Hague 1969–70.
Scheen 1981
  P.A. Scheen, *Lexicon Nederlandse beeldende kunstenaars 1750–1880*, The Hague 1981.
Sillevis 1980
  J. Sillevis, 'Max Liebermann en Holland', in exh. cat. *Max Liebermann en Holland*, Haags Gemeentemuseum, The Hague 1980, pp. 7–24.
Smissaert 1891
  H. Smissaert, 'Willem Roelofs', *E.G.M.* I (1891), vol. II, pp. 417–31.
Smissaert 1892
  F.A.E.L. Smissaert, 'Jan Hendrik Weissenbruch', *E.G.M.* II (1892), vol. III, pp. 425–40.
Smissaert 1898 (1)
  H. Smissaert, 'Willem Roelofs', in M. Rooses (ed.), *Het Schildersboek*, vol. 1, Amsterdam 1898, pp. 62–80.
Smissaert 1898 (2)
  F.A.E.L. Smissaert, 'Jan Hendrik Weissenbruch', in M. Rooses (ed.), *Het Schildersboek*, vol. 1, Amsterdam 1898, pp. 122–38.
Stahl 1903
  F. Stahl, 'Josef Israëls', in M. Buber (ed.), *Juedische Kuenstler*, Berlin 1903, pp. 17–39.
Steenhoff 1904
  W. Steenhoff, 'Jozef Israëls', *Onze Kunst* III (1904), vol. I, pp. 29–51.
Steenhoff 1906
  W. Steenhoff, 'P.J.C. Gabriël', *E.G.M.* XVI (1906), vol. XXXI, pp. 78–79.
Steenhoff 1908
  W. Steenhoff, 'Anton Mauve en zijn tijd', *Onze Kunst* XIII (1908), pp. 12–20, 58–65.
Steenhoff 1910 (1)
  W. Steenhoff, 'Jos. Israëls. Aus dem Holl. von M. Henkel', *Die Kunst unserer Zeit* XXI (1910), vol. 2, pp. 209–28.
Steenhoff 1910 (2)
  W. Steenhoff, 'De collectie Drucker in het Rijksmuseum', *E.G.M.* XX (1910), vol. XI, pp. 361–74.
Sutton 1967
  D. Sutton, 'Nineteenth-century Painting: Trends and Cross–currents', *Apollo* LXXXVI (Dec. 1967), pp. 486–95.

Tersteeg 1910

[J. Tersteeg], *Een halve eeuw met Jozef Israëls*, The Hague 1910.
Thieme-Becker 1907–50
  U. Thieme & F. Becker, *Allgemeines Lexikon der bildenden Künstler von der Antike bis zur Gegenwart*, 37 vols., Leipzig 1907–50.
Timmers 1957
  J.J. Timmers, *Atlas van de Nederlandse beschaving*, Amsterdam/Brussels 1957.

Van Deyssel 1898
  L. van Deyssel [K.J.L. Alberdingk Thijm]. *Matthijs Maris*, Haarlem [1898].
Van Gelder 1937
  H.E. van Gelder (ed.), *Kunstgeschiedenis der Nederlanden*, Utrecht [1937].
Van Gelder 1939
  H.E. van Gelder, *Matthijs Maris*, Amsterdam [1939] (Paletserie).
Van Gelder 1940
  H.E. van Gelder, *J.H. Weissenbruch*, Amsterdam [1940] (Paletserie).
Van Gelder 1946 (1)
  H.E. van Gelder (ed.), *Kunstgeschiedenis der Nederlanden*, Utrecht 1946².
Van Gelder 1946 (2)
  H.E. van Gelder, *Jozef Israëls*, Amsterdam [1946] (Paletserie).
Van Gelder 1954–56
  H.E. van Gelder (ed.), *Kunstgeschiedenis der Nederlanden*, 3 vols., Utrecht/Antwerp etc. 1954–56³.
Van Gelder 1959
  H.E. van Gelder, *Holland by Dutch Artists in Paintings, Drawings, Woodcuts, Engravings and Etchings*, Amsterdam 1959.
Van Gelder 1963–65
  H.E. van Gelder, J. Duverger, C.J.A.C. Peeters, & Ch. Wentinck (ed.) *Kunstgeschiedenis der Nederlanden*, 12 vols., Zeist/Antwerpen 1963–65⁴.
Van Hall 1963
  H. van Hall, *Portretten van Nederlandse beeldende kunstenaars. Repertorium*, Amsterdam 1963.
Van Harpen 1928
  N. van Harpen, *Menschen die ik gekend heb*, Rotterdam 1928.
Van Wisselingh 1923
  E.J. van Wisselingh & Co, *Half a Century of Picture Dealing, an Illustrated Record, with a Note on the Connection Between the Barbizon and The Hague Schools by Jan Veth*, Amsterdam 1923.
Vermeulen 1911
  F. Vermeulen, 'Jozef Israëls, (in de collectie Drucker)', *E.H.* XXXVII (1911), pp. 485–89, 504–07.
Veth 1890
  J. Veth, 'Jozef Israëls, in E.D. Pijzel (ed.), *Mannen van beteekenis in onze dagen*, vol. 20, Haarlem 1890, pp. 173–98.
Veth 1893
  J. Veth, *Gedenkboek. Keuze-tentoonstelling van Hollandsche schilderkunst uit de jaren 1860 tot 1892, gehouden te Amsterdam in 'Arti et Amicitiae'*, Amsterdam 1893.
Veth 1902
  J. Veth, 'Modern Dutch Art; the Work of Jozef Israëls', *The Studio* XXVI (1902), pp. 239–51.
Veth 1904
  J. Veth, *Jozef Israëls en zijn kunst*, Arnhem/Nijmegen 1904.
Veth 1905
  J. Veth, *Hollandsche teekenaars van dezen tijd*, Amsterdam 1905.

Veth 1908
  J. Veth, *Portretstudies en silhouetten*, Amsterdam [1908].
Veth 1911
  J. Veth, 'Jacob Maris', *Kunst and Künstler* IX (1911), pp. 15–26.
Veth 1914
  J. Veth, *Portretstudies en silhouetten*, Amsterdam [1914]².
Veth 1917 (1)
  J. Veth, 'Matthijs Maris, 1839–1917', *De Gids* LXXI (1917), vol. 4, pp. 158–64.
Veth 1917 (2)
  C. Veth, 'Matthijs Maris 1839–1917', *E.H.* XLIII, pp. 601–04.
Veth 1969
  C. Veth, *De Nederlandse schilderkunst in vogelvlucht*, Rotterdam 1969³.
Von Boetticher 1891–1901
  F. von Boetticher, *Malerwerke der 19. Jahrhundert*, 3 vols., Dresden 1891–1901
Von Ostini 1904–05
  F. von Ostini, 'Jozef Israëls', *Veldhagen & Klasings Monatsheft* XIX (1904–05), no. 1, pp. 1–16.
Von Wurzbach 1906–10
  A. von Wurzbach, *Niederländisches Künstler-Lexikon*, 2 vols., Vienna/Leipzig 1906–10.
Vosmaer 1882–85
  C. Vosmaer, *Onze hedendaagsche schilders*, 2 vols., The Hague [1882–85].

Wagner 1974
  A. Wagner, *Schilders zien de duinen*, The Hague [1974].
Wagner 1974–75
  A. Wagner, 'Matthijs Maris', in exh. cat. The Hague 1974–75, pp. 5–30.
Waller 1938
  F.G. Waller, *Biographisch woordenboek van Noord-Nederlandsche graveurs*, The Hague 1938.
Wesselink 1946
  J. Wesselink, *Schilders van de Veluwezoom*, Amsterdam 1946.

Zeitler 1966
  R. Zeitler, *Die Kunst des 19. Jahrhunderts*, Berlin 1966 (Propyläen Kunstgeschichte, vol. 11).
Zilcken 1893
  Ph. Zilcken, *Peintres hollandais modernes avec facsimilés d'après des oeuvres de ces artistes*, Amsterdam 1893.
Zilcken 1895
  Ph. Zilcken, *Verzameling 'H.W. Mesdag'*, [Amsterdam] 1895 (Premie-uitgave van de Vereeniging tot Bevordering van Beeldende Kunsten).
Zilcken 1896 (1)
  Ph. Zilcken, *Les Maris: Jacob-Mathijs-Willem*, Amsterdam [1896].
Zilcken 1896 (2)
  Ph. Zilcken, *H.W. Mesdag, de schilder van de Noordzee. Etsen naar schilderijen en begeleidende tekst*, Leiden [1896].
Zilcken 1900
  Ph. Zilcken, 'The Late J. Maris', *The Studio* XVIII (1900), pp. 231–40.
Zilcken 1908
  Ph. Zilcken, 'Johannes Bosboom', *The Studio* XLII (1908), pp. 257–69.
Zilcken 1910
  Ph. Zilcken, *Jozef Israëls. Con 66 illustrazioni*, Bergamo 1910.

Exhibition Catalogues

ALMELO **1956** *Van Daumier tot Picasso. Twents particulier bezit*, Kunstkring De Waag (text by D. Hannema).

AMERSFOORT **1954** *Romantische- en Haagse School. Nieuwe aanwinsten collectie Pieter A. Scheen*, 't Oude Wevershuys (leaflet).

AMSTERDAM **1870** Arti et Amicitiae. **1883** *Internationale koloniale en uitvoerhandel-tentoonstelling. Nederlandsche afdeeling der galerij van schoone kunsten*, Amsterdam (also French edition). **1885**(1) *Kunstwerken van levende meesters bestemd voor de tentoonstelling te Antwerpen*, Arti et Amicitiae. **1885**(2) *Schilderijen, teekeningen, schetsen en etsen, vervaardigd door Jozef Israëls*, Panoramagebouw. **1886**(1) *L.M.* **1886**(2) *Teekeningen van levende meesters*, Arti et Amicitiae. **1886**(3) *Eenige schilderijen uit particuliere verzamelingen*, Arti et Amicitiae. **1888**(1) *L.M.* **1891**(1) *Kunstwerken door leden der. maatschappij*, Arti et Amicitiae. **1891**(2) *Kunstwerken door J.W. en A.G. Bilders*, Arti et Amicitiae (introduction by J. Gram). **1895**(1) *L.M.* **1895**(2) *Eenige schilderijen van Jozef Israëls unit particuliere verzamelingen*, Arti et Amicitiae. **1898**(1) *Schilderijen enz. vervaardigd door leden der maatschappij ter gelegenheid der inhuldiging van H.M. de Koningin*, Arti et Amicitiae. **1898**(2) *Schilderijen en aquarellen van Jacob Maris*, Arti et Amicitiae. **1899**(1) *L.M.* **1899**(2) *Eere-tentoonstelling Jacob Maris*, Arti et Amicitiae. **1899**(3) *Schilderijen en aquarellen door J.H. Weissenbruch*, Art dealer F. Buffa & Zn. **1900**(1) *Teekeningen en beeldhouwwerken vervaardigd door leden der maatschappij*, Art et Amicitiae. **1900**(2) *Eere-tentoonstelling Johannes Bosboom*, Arti et Amicitiae. **1904** *Keuze-tentoonstelling van aquarellen door Hollandsche meesters*, Stedelijk Museum. **1905** *P.J.C. Gabriël*, Arti et Amicitiae. **1906**(1) *Teekeningen en beeldhouwwerken vervaardigd door leden der maatschappij*, Arti et Amicitiae. **1906**(2) *Eere-tentoonstelling van kunstwerken door Hollandsche meesters, ter gelegenheid van de Rembrandt-herdenking*, Arti et Amicitiae. **1907**(1) *L.M.* **1907**(2) *W. Roelofs*, Art dealer B.L. Voskuyl (leaflet). **1909**(1) *Teekeningen en beeldhouwwerken vervaardigd door leden der maatschappij*, Arti et Amicitiae. **1909**(2) *Verzameling E.H. Crone*, Arti et Amicitiae (introduction by H.L. Berckenhoff). **1910**(1) *Retrospective tentoonstelling ter gelegenheid van het 70-jarig bestaan van de maatschappij*, Arti et Amicitiae. **1910**(2) *Schilderijen en teekeningen van P.J.C. Gabriël*, Larensche Kunsthandel (introduction by H. de Boer). **1911**(1) *Moderne Hollandsche en Fransche schilderijen en aquarellen ter inwijding der nieuwe kunstzalen*, Art dealer E.J. van Wisselingh & Co. **1911**(2) *Schilderijen van Willem Roelofs en Louis Artan*, Larensche Kunsthandel (introduction by H.F.W. Jeltes). **1912**(1) *Kunstwerken van J. Bosboom – J. Israëls – J. Maris – W. Maris – A. Mauve en enkele tijdgenooten uit de verzameling van A. Preyer, 's-Gravenhage*, Arti et Amicitiae (3 editions, of which 2 are illustrated). **1912**(2) *Stedelijke internationale tentoonstelling van kunstwerken van levende meesters*, Stedelijk Museum. **1917** *Schilderijen en teekeningen ter herdenking van den 100-jarigen geboortedag van Johannes Bosboom*, Larensche Kunsthandel (text by H.L. Berckenhoff). **1919–20** *Keuze-tentoonstelling van werken door leden (tijdvak 1888 tot heden). Ter herdenking van het 80-jarig bestaan der maatschappij*, Arti et Amicitiae.

1923(1) *1898 Regeringsjubileum 1923. Tentoonstelling van Nederlandsche beeldende kunsten*, Stedelijk Museum. **1923**(2) *Vereeniging 'Rembrandt'. Jubileum-tentoonstelling tot behoud en vermeerdering van kunstschatten in Nederland*, Rijksmuseum. **1924** *Vereeniging tot het vormen van eene openbare verzameling van hedendaagsche kunst te Amsterdam. Portretten van kunstenaars, wier werk in hare verzameling is vertegenwoordigd, ter gelegenheid van het vijftig-jarig bestaan der vereeniging*, Stedelijk Museum (introduction by H.K. Westendorp). **1929** *Nederlandsche portretkunst. Ter gelegenheid van het 90-jarig bestaan van de maatschappij*, Arti et Amicitiae. **1931**(1) *Bosboom*, Art dealer F. Buffa & Zn. **1931**(2) *Nederlandsche schilderkunst van omstreeks 1850 tot heden*, Art dealer Huinck & Scherjon. **1933**(1) *Eene verzameling schilderijen door Nederlandsche en Fransche meesters*, Art dealer Huinck & Scherjon. **1933**(2) *Johan Hendrik Weissenbruch 1824–1903*, Art dealer F. Buffa & Zn. **1934**(1) *Zestig-jarig bestaan der Vereeniging tot het vormen van eene openbare verzameling van hedendaagsche kunst. Tentoonstelling van aquarellen*, Stedelijk Museum. **1934**(2) *Voorjaars tentoonstelling van Hollandsche schilderijen en aquarellen der XIXe en XXe eeuw*, Art dealer E.J. van Wisselingh & Co. **1937**(1) *Nederlandsche- en Fransche kunst*, Art dealer Huinck & Scherjon. **1937**(2) *Hollandsche en Fransche schilderkunst der XIXe en XXe eeuw*, Art dealer E.J. van Wisselingh & Co. **1938**(1) *Nederlandsche- en Fransche kunst*, Art dealer Huinck & Scherjon. **1938**(2) *Nederlandsche schilderkunst. Meesterwerken uit de XIXe en XXe eeuw*, Art dealer E.J. van Wisselingh & Co. **1938–39**(1) *Kersttentoonstelling*, Art dealer Huinck & Scherjon. **1938–39**(2) *Gerard Bilders 1838–1865. Enkele voorgangers en tijdgenoten*, Museum Fodor (introduction by H.F.W. Jeltes). **1939**(1) *Nederlandsche- en Fransche kunst*, Art dealer Huinck & Scherjon. **1939**(2) *P.J.C. Gabriël*, Art dealer E.J. van Wisselingh & Co. **1946**(1) *Schilderijen en aquarellen door G.H. Breitner. Aquarellen door J. Bosboom*, Art dealer E.J. van Wisselingh & Co. **1946**(2) *5 Generaties. Tentoonstelling van schilderijen van 1800 tot heden*, Stedelijk Museum (no cat.; booklet with text by C. Werlemann). **1948**(1) *De verzameling van de Vereeniging tot het vormen eener openbare verzameling van hedendaagsche kunst te Amsterdam*, Stedelijk Museum. **1948**(2) *Vincent van Gogh en zijn Nederlandse tijdgenoten*, Stedelijk Museum (no cat.; booklet). **1957** *Oog in oog. Nederlandse zelfportretten van Vincent van Gogh tot heden*, Stedelijk Museum. **1957–58** *Breitner tussen de schilders van Amsterdam*. Stedelijk Museum (introduction by J.C. van der Waals). **1958** *Van Romantiek tot Amsterdamse School. Schilderijen uit de collectie B. de Geus van den Heuvel*, Stedelijk Museum. **1963** *150 Jaar Nederlandse kunst. Schilderijen, beelden, tekeningen, grafiek, 1813–1963*, Stedelijk Museum. **1963–64** *Hollandse kunstenaars in hun ontboezemingen. Drie perioden uit honderdvijftig jaar: 1813, 1888, 1963 (tentoonstelling ter gelegenheid van de nationale herdenking 1813–1963)*, Rijksmuseum (introduction by K.G. Boon). **1964–65** *Jubileum-tentoonstelling ter gelegenheid van het 125 jarig bestaan van de maatschappij Arti et Amicitiae*, Arti et Amicitiae. **1975–76** *De verzameling van H. van Leeuwen*, Rijksprentenkabinet, Rijksmuseum (text by L.C.J. Frerichs & P. Schatborn). **1979**(1) *Nederlandse schilderkunst 1815–1914. Dutch Painting from the Century of*

Van Gogh, Rijksmuseum Vincent van Gogh (leaflet; text by R. de Leeuw). **1979**(2) *Haagse School & impressionisten* [from the coll. of art dealer Ivo. Bouwman, The Hague], Arti et Amicitiae. **1980–81** *Vincent van Gogh in zijn Hollandse jaren. Kijk op stad en land door Van Gogh en zijn tijdgenoten 1870–1890*, Rijksmuseum Vincent van Gogh (text by G. Pollock).

ANTWERP **1894** *Wereldtentoonstelling der schoone kunsten te Antwerpen*, Koninklijke Maatschappij van Aanmoediging der Schoone Kunsten (also French edition). **1937** *Nederlandsche schilderijen uit het Gemeentemuseum van 's-Gravenhage 1850–1910*, Koninklijk Museum van Schoone Kunsten (introduction by G. Knuttel Wzn.). **1955** *Vincent van Gogh en zijn Hollandse tijdgenoten*, Zaal Comité voor Artistieke Werking (introduction by M.E. Tralbout). **1979** *De Haagse School. Aquarellen en tekeningen uit de collectie van het Haags Gemeentemuseum*, Koninklijk Museum voor Schoone Kunsten, Antwerp/Musée de l'État, Luxemburg (also French edition; text by M. Josephus Jitta & J. Sillevis).

ARNHEM **1936** *2de Tentoonstelling der Kröller-Müller-Stichting*, Gemeente Museum. **1954** *Schilders van de Veluwezoom*, Gemeentemuseum. **1974** *Een eigenaardig kunstig leven. Romantische schilderijen uit Nederland 1820–1860*, Arnhems Museum.

ATHENS **1953** *Ekthesis ollandoon zoo graphoon*.

BERLIN **1901** *Dritte Kunstausstellung der Berliner Secession*. **1979–80** *Max Liebermann in seiner Zeit*, Nationalgalerie Berlin Staatliche Museen Preussischer Kulturbesitz, Berlin/Haus der Kunst, Munich.

BOIS-LE-DUC **1977** *Aquarellen en tekeningen 1860–1940*, Art dealer Borzo. **1979** *Najaarstentoonstelling. Schilderijen en aquarellen*, Art dealer Borzo. **1980** *Nieuw*, Art dealer Borzo (no cat.; leaflet).

BONN **1972** *Die Haager Schule – Holländische Maler vor hundert Jahren*, Rheinisches Landesmuseum, Bonn/Kunsthalle, Hamburg (introduction by A. Wagner).

BREDA **1961** *Jan en Jan Hendrik Weissenbruch*, Cultureel Centrum De Beyerd (introduction by Th. van Velzen & [R.G.] de Boer). **1962** *Nederlandse aquarellen en gouaches van 1850 tot heden*, Cultureel Centrum De Beyerd.

BREMEN **1978** *Zurück zur Natur*, Kunsthalle.

BRUSSELS **1852** *Le Salon*, La Société des Beaux-Arts. **1863** *Exposition générale des beaux-arts*. **1932** *Honderd jaar Nederlandsche schilderkunst. Cent ans de peinture néerlandaise*, Koninklijk Museum voor Moderne Kunst.

CHICAGO **1893** *World's Columbian exposition. Part X. Department K, Fine Arts*.

DELFT **1952** *Internationale tentoonstelling. De Aquarel 1800–1950*, Museum Het Prinsenhof. **1955–56** *De Romantische School*, Museum Het Prinsenhof. **1958–59** *Johannes Bosboom (1817–1891)*, Museum Het Prinsenhof.

DORDRECHT **1904**(1) *Verzameling W.H. Bilderbeek*, Dordrechts Museum. **1904**(2) *Verzameling Hidde Nijland tentoongesteld ter gelegenheid van de opening van het* *nieuwe museum*, Dordrechts Museum. **1909–10** *Schilderijen, aquarellen en schetsen van J.H. Weissenbruch, welwillend afgestaan door den Heer Hidde Nijland*, Dordrechts Museum. **1916** *Schilderijen, aquarellen en teekeningen van Willem Roelofs (1822–1897)*, Kunstzaal, Voorstraat. **1951** *Ons element*, Dordrechts Museum. **1955** *Boom, bloem en plant. Nederlandse meesters uit vijf eeuwen*, Dordrechts Museum. **1957**(1) *Een keuze uit de Rijksverzameling Van Bilderbeek-Lamaison*, Dordrechts Museum. **1957**(2) *Mens en muziek*, Dordrechts Museum. **1966–67** *Nederlandse zelfportretten. Van Vincent van Gogh tot heden*, Dordrechts Museum, Dordrecht/Gemeentemuseum, Arnhem. **1973–74** *Rondom ruimte*, Dordrechts Museum. **1978** *Verzameling Van Bilderbeek*, Dordrechts Museum, (introduction by G.J. Schweitzer).

DUBLIN **1907** *Irish International Exhibition*.

DÜSSELDORF **1928** *Ausgewählte Kunstwerke aus der Sammlung der Frau H. Kröller-Müller, Den Haag*, Kunsthalle. **1950** *Holländische Impressionisten. Haagsche und Amsterdamsche Schule. Leihgaben aus holländischem Museumbesitz*, Kunstsammlungen der Stadt Düsseldorf (introduction by W. Doede).

EDINBURGH **1886**(1) *French and Dutch Loan Collection. International Exhibition*. **1886**(2) *First Annual Exhibition of Pictures* [from the coll. of E.J. van Wisselingh, The Hague], Mr Wilson's Fine Art Galleries. **1957** *Children in Three Centuries*, National Gallery of Scotland.

ENSCHEDE **1980** *Oost-Nederland model. Landschappen, stads- en dorpsgezichten, 17de–19de eeuw*. Rijksmuseum Twenthe.

FLORENCE **1981–82** *Verso l'astrattismo. Mondrian e la Scuola dell'Aia*, Instituto Universitario Olandese di Storia dell'Arte, Florence/Galleria d'Arte Moderna, Milan/Institut Néerlandais, Paris (text by J.Th. Sillevis & H. Henkels).

GLASGOW **1888** *International Exhibition*. **1901** *International Exhibition*. **1947** The Scottish Arts Council. **1967** *A Man of Influence: Alex Reid 1854–1928*, The Scottish Arts Council.

GRONINGEN **1961–62** *Herdenkingstentoonstelling Jozef Israëls 1824–1911*, Groninger Museum voor Stad en Lande, Groningen/Gemeente Museum, Arnhem (introduction by W.J. d[e] G[ruyter], bibliography by J. Bolten). **1969** *Verzameling R.J. Veendorp*, Groninger Museum voor Stad en Lande (introduction by R.J. Veendorp & J. de Gruyter).

HAARLEM **1981–82** *De kunst van het moederschap*, Frans Halsmuseum, De Hallen.

HEERLEN **1948** *Amsterdam eert Heerlen. Vijf eeuwen Amsterdamse kunst*, (introduction by H.J.).

KREFELD **1903** *Nederlandsche kunsttentoonstelling*, Keizer Wilhelm Museum.

LAREN **1957** *Meesters van de Haagse School en enige tijdgenoten*, Singer Museum (introduction by H.E. van Gelder). **1959–60** *Anton Mauve 1838–1888*, Singer Museum. **1960–61** *Jan en Jan Hendrik Weissenbruch. Schilderijen. Aquarellen. Grafiek*, Singer Museum (introduction by R.G. de Boer). **1964** *Schilderkunst uit La Belle Epoque*, Singer Museum. **1966** *Keuze uit de collectie B. de Geus van den Heuvel. Schilderijen, aquarellen, 18de–20ste eeuw, ter gelegenheid van zijn tachtigste verjaardag*, Singer Museum. **1969** *Het kind in de Noord-nederlandse kunst*, Singer Museum (introduction by G. Bomans).

LEIDEN **1953–54** *Tussen Romantiek en Haagse School*, Stedelijk Museum De Lakenhal (introduction by J.N. van Wessem).

LIÈGE **1961–62** *Aquarelles et gouaches hollandaises de 1850 à nos jours*, Musée des Beaux-Arts (introduction by Th. van Velzen).

LONDON **1862** *International Exhibition*, South Kensington. **1880** The Grosvenor Gallery. **1888** *A Collection of Pictures by James Maris. Together with a few Examples by his Brothers Matthew Maris & William Maris*, The Goupil Gallery (introduction by Ch. Destree). **1889** The Dowdeshill Gallery. **1890**(1) *Josef Israëls*, The Hannover Gallery. **1890**(2) *A Collection of Paintings, Drawings & Sketches by the Late Anton Mauve. Born 1838. Died 1888* [from the coll. of art dealer Boussod, Valadon & Co, The Hague], The Goupil Gallery. **1896**(1) *Winter Exhibition. A Loan Collection of Modern Pictures; Chiefly of the Barbizon and Dutch Schools*, The Grafton Galleries. **1896**(2) *Exposition Hollandaise. Special Exhibition of Pictures by the Leading Artists of Holland*, The Continental Gallery. **1897** *A Collection of Cabinet Works by Jozef Israëls*, The Goupil Gallery (introduction by E. Knuttel-Fabius). **1899** *Spring Exhibition*, The Goupil Gallery. **1903** *A Selection of Works by Early and Modern Painters of the Dutch School*, Art Gallery of the Corporation of London, Guildhall (text by A.G. Temple F.S.A.). **1904** *Dutch Exhibition*, Whitechapel Art Gallery. **1905**(1) *Winter Exhibition*, Arthur Tooth & Sons' Galleries. **1905**(2) *A Selection of Paintings and Drawings from the Collection of the Late James Staats Forbes*, The Grafton Galleries. **1909** *Selected Works by Jos. Israëls, Matthijs Maris, Léon Lhermitte, Henri Harpignies*, The French Gallery (introduction by F. Wedmore & P.G. Konody). **1910** *Selected Works by James Maris, Anton Mauve, H. Fantin Latour*, The French Gallery. **1911** *Selected Works by Johannes Bosboom and William Maris*, The French Gallery. **1912**(1) *Summer Exhibition*, Thomas McLean's Galleries. **1912**(2) *Pictures by Josef Israëls*, The French Gallery. **1924** *Modern Masters of the Burrell Collection*, The Tate Gallery. **1929**(1) *Dutch Art 1450–1900*, Royal Academy of Arts. Figs. in *Commemorative Catalogue of the Exhibition of Dutch Art Held in the Galleries of the Royal Academy, Burlington House, London, January–March 1929*, Oxford/London 1930 (introduction by C.J. Holmes). **1929**(2) *Johannes Bosboom, Josef Israëls, the Maris Brothers, Anton Mauve*, Barbizon House. **1931** The Tate Gallery. **1949** The Ben Uri Art Gallery.

LUXEMBURG **1948** *La peinture hollandaise. Les impressionistes*, Musée de l'État (introduction by A.M.W.J. Hammacher).

MAASTRICHT **1945–46** *Haagsche meesters Nederlandsche schilders* XIXe *eeuw*, Maastricht/Stadhuis, Heerlen/Eindhoven/Bois-le-Duc/Rijksmuseum Twenthe, Enschede/Groningen.

MANCHESTER **1980** *Mondriaan and The Hague School. Watercolours and Drawings from the Gemeentemuseum in The Hague*, Whitworth Art Gallery, University of Manchester, Manchester/Southampton Art Gallery Civic Centre, Southampton/Birmingham City Museum and Art Gallery, Birmingham/Norwich Castle Museum, Norwich.

MÖNCHEN-GLADBACH **1957** *Von Jongkind bis Van Gogh, Aquarelle und Zeichnungen*, Städtisches Museum (introduction by H.E. van Gelder).

MONTPELLIER **1952** *De Jonkind à Van Gogh, Dessins et aquarelles du Musée Municipal de la Haye*, Musée Fabre.

MONTREAL **1897** *Loan Exhibition*, Art Association of Montreal. **1898** *Loan Exhibition*, Art Association of Montreal. **1899** *Loan Exhibition*, Art Association of Montreal. **1900** *Loan Exhibition*, Art Association of Montreal. **1914** *Loan Exhibition*, Art Association of Montreal. **1962** *The Hague School*, The Montreal Museum of Fine Arts (no cat.).

MUNICH **1888** *Internationale Kunst Ausstellung*, Glaspalast.

NEW YORK **1892** *Exhibition by the American Fine Arts Society of the Pictures Contributed by Sweden, Norway, and Holland to the World's Columbian Exposition*, Fine Arts Building.

NIEUWKOOP **1982** *Nieuwkoop en Noorden in de schilderkunst 1875–1940*, Gemeentehuis (introduction by C. Kortenbach).

NIJMEGEN **1970** *Van Romantiek tot Toorop. Schilderijen uit het Jan Cunen-museum te Oss*, Gemeentemuseum.

PARIS **1861** *Salon*. **1872** *Salon*. **1873** *Salon*. **1878** *Exposition universelle internationale*, Champ-de-Mars. **1887** *Salon*. **1888**(1) *Salon*. **1882**(2) Galerie Goupil. **1889**(1) *Exposition universelle de 1889. Catalogue illustré des beaux-arts, 1789–1889*, Galerie des Beaux-Arts, Champ-de-Mars. **1889**(2) *Salon*. **1890** *Salon*. **1891**(1) *Salon*. **1891**(2) *Exposition de peinture des maîtres hollandais*, Pavillon de la Ville de Paris. **1921** *Exposition hollandaise. Tableaux, aquarelles et dessins anciens et modernes*, Tuileries (introduction by L. Bénédite). **1963** *L'Aquarelle néerlandaise au siècle dernier*, Institut Néerlandais.

PASSAU **1956** *Holländische Bilder um 1900*, Grosser Redoutensaal.

PITTSBURGH **1902–03** *A Loan Exhibition of Paintings*, The Carnegie Institute.

POTSDAM **1925** *50 Jahre holländischer Malerei 1875–1925* (introduction by H.E. van Gelder).

REGINA **1969–70** *Piet Mondriaan and the Hague School of Landscape Painting*, Norman Mackenzie Art Gallery, Regina/Edmonton Art Gallery, Edmonton/The Montreal Museum of Fine Arts, Montreal.

ROTTERDAM **1858** *L.M.* **1862** *L.M.* **1864** *L.M.* **1867** *L.M.* **1870** *L.M.* **1873** *L.M.* **1888** *L.M.* **1889** *Schilderijen, studies en teekeningen door W. Roelofs*, Kunstclub (leaflet). **1893** *Werken van de gebroeders Maris*, Rotterdamsche Kunstkring (introduction by P.C. de Moor). **1894**(1) *L.M.* **1894**(2) *Israëls-tentoonstelling*, Rotterdamsche Kunstkring (introduction by P. H[averkorn] v[an] R[ijsewijk]). **1895**(1) *Verzameling H.W. Mesdag*, Rotterdamsche Kunstkring. **1895**(2) *Mauve-tentoonstelling*, Rotterdamsche Kunstkring. **1906**(1) *L.M.* **1906**(2) *Aquarellen, teekeningen en schetsen van J.H. Weissenbruch, welwillend afgestaan door den Heer Hidde Nijland te Dordrecht*, Rotterdamsche Kunstkring. **1908–09** *Collectie schilderijen, aquarellen en teekeningen, toebehoorende aan den WelEdel Geboren Heer W.J. van Randwijk, te 's-Gravenhage*, Academie van Beeldende Kunsten en Technische Wetenschappen. **1954** *Collectie Pieter A. Scheen*, Rotterdamsche Kunstkring. **1955** *Collectie Pieter A. Scheen*, Rotterdamsche Kunstkring.

SEOUL **1979** *Dutch Landscape Painting of the Nineteenth Century*, Seoul Sejong Cultural Center Exhibition Hall (text by R. de Leeuw).

THE HAGUE **1853** *L.M.* **1857** *L.M.* **1863** *L.M.* **1865** *L.M.* **1866** *L.M.* **1875** *L.M.* **1878**(1) *L.M.* **1878**(2) *H.T.M.* **1882** *H.T.M.* **1884**(1) *L.M.* **1884**(2) *H.T.M.* **1886** *H.T.M.* **1887**(1) *L.M.* **1887**(2) *H.T.M.* **1891**(1) *H.T.M.* **1891**(2) *Bosboom*, Pulchri Studio. **1893**(1) *L.M.* **1893**(2) *H.T.M.* **1895**(1) *Schilderijen en aquarellen van Jozef Israëls*, Pulchri Studio. **1895**(2) *Schilderijen en teekeningen van Jacob Maris*, Pulchri Studio. **1895**(3) *Mauve-tentoonstelling*, Haagsche Kunstkring. **1899**(1) *Keuze-tentoonstelling van kunstwerken van Hollandsche meesters van de laatste 25 jaren ter gelegenheid van de vredes-conferentie te 's-Gravenhage*, Pulchri Studio. **1899**(2) *Eere-tentoonstelling Jacob Maris*, Pulchri Studio. **1900**(1) *H.T.M.* **1900**(2) [*untitled*] Diligentia. **1903**(1) *H.T.M.* **1903**(2) *Aquarellen, teekeningen, etsen, lithographieën en beeldhouwwerk door werkende leden*, Pulchri Studio. **1904**(1) *Werken van P.J.C. Gabriël*, Pulchri Studio (preface by H.W. Mesdag). **1904**(2) *Aquarellen en teekeningen door J.H. Weissenbruch. Eigendom van Mevrouw J. Slagmulder-van Gent, te Amsterdam*, Haagsche Kunstkring (introduction by C.L. Dake). **1905**(1) *H.T.M.* **1905**(2) *Schilderijen en teekeningen door Hollandsche meesters, waarbij een belangrijk deel der verzameling van wijlen J. Staats Forbes, Esq., verzameld door A. Preyer Kunsthandel*, Pulchri Studio. **1907**(1) *H.T.M.* **1907**(2) *Eere-tentoonstelling Willem Roelofs 1822–1897*, Pulchri Studio (introduction by F.A.E.L. Smissaert). **1908**(1) *H.T.M.* **1908**(2) *Schilderijen, enz., door leden van Pulchri Studio bijeengebracht om ten bate van het Weduwen- en Weezenfonds van het Genootschap te worden verkocht*, Pulchri Studio. **1909**(1) *H.T.M.* **1909**(2) *Schilderijen en aquarellen van Jozef Israëls, eigendom van Boussod, Valadon & Cie, en van zijn schilderij 'Als men and wordt' uit de verzameling Hijmans van Wadenoyen*. Art dealer Boussod, Valadon & Co (no cat.). **1911**(1) *H.T.M.* **1911**(2) *Kunstwerken. Moderne schilderijen en aquarellen* [from the coll. of art dealer A. Preyer, The Hague], Pulchri Studio. **1911**(3) *Schilderijen teekeningen van P.J.C. Gabriël*, Kunstzaal Kleykamp (introduction by H. de Boer). **1911–12** *Eeretentoonstelling Jozef Israëls*, Pulchri Studio. **1912**(1) *Kunstwerken. Moderne schilderijen en aquarellen* [from the coll. of art dealer A. Preyer, The Hague], Pulchri Studio. **1912**(2) *Werk van diverse moderne meesters*, Art dealer Esher Surrey. **1913**(1) *Werken van overleden meesters*, Pulchri Studio. **1913**(2) *Schilderijen van Jacob en Willem Maris uit de collectie van Mr A.L.C. Kleijn*, Gemeentemuseum (leaflet). **1917**(1) *Moderne schilderijen en aquarellen door Hollandsche meesters* [from the coll. of art dealer Th. Vlas, Amsterdam and art dealer J.H.W. Kever, Amsterdam], Pulchri Studio. **1917**(2) *Eere-tentoonstelling ter herdenking van Johannes Bosboom*, Pulchri Studio. **1923** *Haagsche schilder- en beeldhouwkunst der laatste 25 jaren (ter gelegenheid van de 25-jarige regeering van Hare Majesteit de Koningin)*, Pulchri Studio. **1924**(1) *Jozef Israëls tentoonstelling*, Gemeentemuseum voor Moderne Kunst (leaflet). **1924**(2) *Matthijs Maris*, Koninklijke Kunstzaal Kleykamp (introduction by A. Hallema). **1924**(3) *Eere-tentoonstelling H.J. Weissenbruch 1824 Juni 1924. Aquarellen, teekeningen en schetsen uit de verzameling Hidde Nijland*, Pulchri Studio (introduction by W. Martin). **1935–36** *Maris tentoonstelling*, Gemeentemuseum, Den Haag/Stedelijk Museum, Amsterdam (introduction by G. K[nuttel Wzn.]). **1938–39** *Herdenkingstentoonstelling Anton Mauve 1838–1889*, Gemeentemuseum (introduction by G. K[nuttel Wzn.]). **1939**(1) *Hollandsche en Fransche schilderkunst der* XIXe *en* XXe *eeuw. Keuze tentoonstelling* [from the coll. of art dealer E.J. van

Wisselingh & Co, Amsterdam], Pulchri Studio (leaflet). **1939**(2) *Matthijs Maris 1839 – 17 augustus – 1939*, Gemeentemuseum (introduction by H.E. van Gelder). **1945** *Den Haag eert de Nederlandsche schilders van de 19de eeuw. Een keuze van werken uit Nederlandsche openbare verzamelingen*, Pulchri Studio (introduction by [G.] Knuttel [Wzn.]). **1947** *Honderd jaar Pulchri Studio*, Gemeentemuseum (introduction by H.E. van Gelder). **1948** *Zeven eeuwen Den Haag*, Vereeniging 'Die Haghe', Gemeentemuseum. **1954**(1) *Collectie Pieter A. Scheen (catalogus x)*, Art dealer P.A. Scheen. **1954**(2) *Collectie Pieter A. Scheen (catalogus x1)*, Art dealer P.A. Scheen. **1955**(1) *Collectie Pieter A. Scheen (catalogus x11)*, Art dealer P.A. Scheen. **1955**(2) *Collectie Pieter A. Scheen (catalogus x111)*, Art dealer P.A. Scheen. **1963** *Haagsche School. Tekeningen, aquarellen*, Haags Gemeentemuseum (introduction by W.B.). **1964** *Schilderijen, verworven uit het bezit van Erven E. H. Crone met steun van de Vereeniging Rembrandt en de Vereeniging Haagsche Museumvrienden*, Haags Gemeentemuseum (typed list). **1965**(1) *Meesters van de Haagse School*, Haags Gemeentemuseum (introduction by J. de Gruyter). **1965**(2) *Collectie Pieter A. Scheen (catalogus x1x)*, Art dealer P.A. Scheen. **1967**(1) *Jubileumtentoonstelling Pulchri Studio 1847/1967*, Pulchri Studio (introduction by A.C. Esmeijer; leaflet and illustrated booklet). **1967**(2) *Aspecten van stad en land*, Art dealer. Nieuwenhuizen Segaar (leaflet). **1971**(1) *Herfst-collectie*, Galerie des Arts. **1971**(2) *Zomertentoonstelling Haagse School (catalogus x x1)*, Art dealer P.A. Scheen. **1972**(1) *Aspekten 125 jaar beeldende kunst Pulchri Studio*, Pulchri Studio (leaflet; no cat.). **1972**(2) *Juwelen van Romantiek en Haagse School*, Galerie des Arts. **1974**(1) *Romantiek en Haagse School*, Galerie des Arts. **1974**(2) *Zomertentoonstelling Romantische en Haagse School (catalogus x x111)*, Art dealer P.A. Scheen. **1974–75** *Matthijs Maris*, Haags Gemeentemuseum (introduction by A. Wagner). **1975**(1) *Zomer-*

tentoonstelling (catalogus x x1v), Art dealer P.A. Scheen. **1975**(2) *Voorjaarstentoonstelling*, Art dealer 'Les Beaux Arts'. **1976**(1) *Zomertentoonstelling. Romantische en Haagse School, (catalogus x x v)*, Art dealer P.A. Scheen. **1976**(2) *Hollandse en Franse meesters der 19e en 20e eeuw. Verkooptentoonstelling* [from the coll. of art dealer G.J. Scherpel, Bussum], Pulchri Studio (introduction by H. Redeker). **1978**(1) *Kunstenaren der idee. Symbolistische tendenzen in Nederland, c. 1880–1930*, Haags Gemeentemuseum. **1978**(2) *Zomerverkooptentoonstelling*, Art dealer 'Les Beaux Arts'. **1980**(1) *Hague School & Impressionists*, Art dealer Ivo Bouwman. **1980**(2) *Verkooptentoonstelling (catalogus x x v111)*, Art dealer P.A. Scheen. **1982**(1) *Koninklijke Academie 300 jaar. Haagse School in Pulchri*, Pulchri Studio. **1982**(2) *Voorjaarstentoonstelling Haagse School & impressionisten*, Art dealer Ivo Bouwman.

TILBURG **1950** *Collectie Pieter A. Scheen*. **1952** *Nederlandse impressionisten. Haagse- en Amsterdamse School*, Paleis-Raadhuis. **1955** *Collectie Pieter A. Scheen*, Kunstzaal Donders.

TOKYO **1979** *Dutch Painting from the Century of Van Gogh*, Odakyu Grand Gallery, Tokyo/Hokkaido Museum of Modern Art, Sapporo/The Hiroshima Prefectural Museum, Hiroshima/Aichi Prefectural Art Gallery, Nagoya (text by J. Sillevis, R. de Leeuw & J. Joosten).

TOLEDO **1912** *The Inaugural Exhibition. Part III: European Paintings. Part IV: A Memorial Exhibition of the Work of Josef Israëls*, The Toledo Museum of Art. **1937** The Toledo Museum of Art. **1966** *Drawings and Watercolors by Anton Mauve*, The Toledo Museum of Art (in *Museum News. The Toledo Museum of Art* N.S IX [1966], pp. 75–94; text by J.W. Keefe).

UTRECHT **1866** *Algemeene tentoonstelling van teekeningen van Levende Meesters*. **1896** *Keuzetentoonstelling van hedendaagsche Nederlandsche kunst*

bijeengebracht door de Vereeniging 'Voor de Kunst' te Utrecht ter gelegenheid van de lustrumfeesten der Utrechtsche Universiteit. **1924** *Oude en moderne schilderijen uit Utrechtsche verzamelingen*, Vereeniging 'Voor de Kunst' (leaflet). **1961** *Keuze uit tien jaar aanwinsten 1951–1961*, Centraal Museum. **1971–72** *Keuze uit 10 jaar àanwinsten 1961–1971*, Centraal Museum.

VANCOUVER **1958** *The Changing Landscape of Holland, an Exhibition of Watercolours and Drawings of the Netherlands from 1600 to 1900*, Fine Art Gallery University of British Columbia.

VENICE **1897** *Deuxième exposition internationale des beaux-arts de la ville de Venise*. **1910** *IX. Esposizione internationale d'arte della città di Venezia*.

VIENNA **1873** *Welt Ausstellung*, Prater. **1929** *Holländischer Kunst 1850–1929*, Künstlerhaus (introduction by H.E. van Gelder).

ZAGREB **1953** *Izbor dela iz nizozemskog slikarstva od 1850 do 1950 godine*, Zagreb/Belgrade.

ZEIST **1975** *17 Schilders in hun Haagsche tijd. 1870–1950*, Zeister Slot (text by A. Wagner).

Travelling Exhibitions

GERMANY **1955** *Holländische Impressionisten. Meister der Haager und der Amsterdamer Schule* (leaflet; Bochum, Mönchen-Gladbach, Munich, a.o.).

GREAT BRITAIN **1958** *Dutch Paintings. The Hague School and Amsterdam Impressionists* (introduction by H.L.C. Jaffé; London, York, a.o.).

ISRAEL **1954** *Dutch Painting 1850–1950* (introduction by H.L.C. Jaffé).

General Bibliography

The Nineteenth Century

J. Gram, *Onze schilders in Pulchri Studio*, Rotterdam [1880].

C. Vosmaer, *Onze hedendaagsche schilders*, The Hague/Amsterdam 1881–85.

Ph. Zilcken, *Peintres hollandais modernes*, Amsterdam 1893.

Ph. Zilcken, *Moderne Hollandsche etsers*, Amsterdam [1896].

M. Rooses (ed.), *Het Schildersboek. Nederlandsche schilders der negentiende eeuw in monographieën door tijdgenooten*, 4 vols., Amsterdam 1898–1900.

J. Veth, *Gedenkboek der Hollandsche schilderkunst uit het tijdperk van 1860–1890*, Amsterdam 1898.

G.H. Marius, *De Hollandsche schilderkunst in de negentiende eeuw*, The Hague 1903 (second edition 1920; German edition 1906; English edition 1908, 1973).

J. Gram, *Onze schilders in Pulchri Studio (1880–1904)*, Leiden [1904].

J. Gram, 'De Haagsche schilderkunst in de XIXe eeuw', *Die Haghe. Bijdragen en Mededeelingen* (1905), pp. 50–90.

J. Veth, *Hollandsche teekenaars van dezen tijd*, Amsterdam 1905.

G.H. Marius, *Die Holländische Malerei im neunzehnten Jahrhunderts*, Berlin 1906.

E.B. Greenshields, *Landscape Painting and Modern Dutch Artists*, New York [1906].

F.M. Lurasco, *Onze moderne meesters*, Amsterdam 1907.

J. Meier-Graefe, *The Development of Modern Art*, New York 1908.

G.H. Marius, *Dutch Painting in the Nineteenth Century*, London 1908.

M. Osborn, 'Neuere holländische Malerei', *Neue Kunst* (Dec. 1908), pp. 3.

J. Veth, *Portretstudies en silhouetten*, Amsterdam [1908] (second edition 1914).

A. Plasschaert, XIXde *Eeuwsche Hollandsche schilderkunst*, Amsterdam [1909].

L. Bénédite, *De schilderkunst der* XIX*de eeuw in Frankrijk, Engeland, America, Nederland . . .* Amsterdam 1910 (Dutch adaptation by G.H. Marius).

A.M. Hammacher, *Amsterdamsche impressionisten en hun kring*, Amsterdam 1911 (second edition 1941)

A. Plasschaert, *Beschouwingen*, 5 vols., Middelburg 1917–25.

A. Plasschaert, *Korte geschiedenis der Hollandsche schilderkunst van af de Haagsche School tot op den tegenwoordigen tijd*, Amsterdam 1923.

H. Kröller-Müller, *Beschouwingen over problemen in de ontwikkeling der moderne schilderkunst*, Maastricht 1925 (German edition 1927).

G. Brom, *Hollandse schilders en schrijvers van de vorige eeuw*, Rotterdam 1927 (revised edition 1959).

H. Kröller-Müller, *Die Entwicklung der modernen Malerei. Ein Wegweiser für Laien*, Leipzig [1927].

G. Knuttel Wzn., *De Nederlandsche schilderkunst van Van Eyck tot Van Gogh*, Amsterdam 1938 (second edition 1950).

G. Colmjon, *De rennaissance der cultuur in Nederland in het laatste kwart der negentiende eeuw*, Arnhem 1941.

J. Wessenlink, *Schilders van den Veluwezoom*, Amsterdam 1943.

P.A. Scheen, *Honderd jaren Nederlandsche schilder- en teekenkunst. De Romantiek met voor- en natijd (1750–1850)*, The Hague 1946.

J. Knoef, *Van Romantiek tot Realisme. Een bundel kunsthistorische opstellen*, The Hague 1947.

H.E. van Gelder, *Honderd jaar Haagse schilderkunst in Pulchri Studio*, Amsterdam 1947.

J. Knoef, *Een eeuw Nederlandse schilderkunst*, Amsterdam 1948.

C. Veth, *De Nederlandse schilderkunst in vogelvlucht*, Rotterdam 1948 (third edition 1969).

B. Polak, *Het fin-de-siècle in de Nederlandse schilderkunst*, The Hague 1955.

G. Brom, *Schilderkunst en litteratuur in de 19e eeuw*, Utrecht/Antwerp [1959].

A.B. Loosjes-Terpstra, *Moderne kunst in Nederland 1900–1914*, Utrecht 1959 (Utrechtse Kunsthistorische Studiën, vol. 3).

H. Gerson, *De Nederlandse schilderkunst* III: *Voor en na Van Gogh*, Amsterdam 1961 (De Schoonheid van ons Land, vol. 17).

H. Gerson, *Drie eeuwen Nederlandse schilderkunst*, vol. 3, Amsterdam 1962.

W.A.L. Beeren, *Beeldverhaal, een weg door de moderne Kunst*, Amsterdam 1962.

R. Zeitler, *Die Kunst des 19. Jahrhunderts*, Berlin 1966 (Propyläen Kunstgeschichte, vol. 3).

P.A. Scheen, *Lexicon Nederlandse beeldende kunstenaars 1750–1950*, 2 vols., The Hague 1969–70.

[G.H.] Marius (ed. G. Norman), *Duch Painters of the 19th Century*, [Woodbridge, Suffolk 1973].

Exh. cat. '*Bekende tydgenoten*'. *Schrijvers en schilders geportretteerd door Jan Veth (1864–1925)*, Kunsthistorisch Instituut der Universiteit van Amsterdam, Amsterdam 1975.

R. Rosenblum, *Modern Painting and the Romantic Tradition*, London 1975.

C.H.A. Broos a.o. (ed.), *19de Eeuwsche Nederlandse schilderkunst. Een zestal studies*, Haarlem 1977 (Nederlands Kunsthistorisch Jaarboek 1976, vol. 27).

R.H. Fuchs, 'Subject and Style. The Eighteenth and Nineteenth Centuries', in *Dutch Painting*, London 1978, pp. 143–74.

P.A. Scheen, *Lexicon Nederlandse beeldende kunstenaars 1750–1880*, The Hague 1981.

V. Hefting, *Schilders in Oosterbeek 1840–1870*, Zutphen/Arnhem 1981 (Uitgaven van de Stichting De Gelderse Bloem, no. 30).

The Hague School

P.A.M. Boele van Hensbroek, *De Haagsche School in het Mesdag-Museum*, Amsterdam [1910].

M. Eisler, *Die neuholländische Kunst (Die Haager Schule)*, Munich 1911.

E.J. van Wisselingh & Co, *Half a Century of Picture Dealing, an Illustrated Record, with a Note on the Connection Between the Barbizon and The Hague Schools by Jan Veth*, Amsterdam 1923.

G. Brom, 'De Haagse School', in H.E. van Gelder (ed.), *Kunstgeschiedenis der Nederlanden*, Utrecht 1937 (second edition 1946, third edition 1954–56; fourth edition 1963–66).

H. Luns, 'De Haagse School', in *Holland schildert*, Amsterdam [1941], pp. 239–58.

G. Colmjon & P.A. Scheen, *De Haagse School. De vernieuwing van onze schilderkunst sinds het midden der negentiende eeuw*, Rijswijk 1950 (English edition 1951).

G. Colmjon & P.A. Scheen, *The Hague School. The Renewal of Dutch Painting Since the Middle of the Nineteenth Century*, Rijswijk 1951.

W.A.L. Beeren, 'De Haagse School', *Wikor* IV (1956),

no. 5, pp. 184–88.
Ch. Carter, 'Where Stands The Hague School Now?', *Apollo* LXXI (June 1960), pp. 173–76; LXXII (July 1960), pp. 7–10.
A.J. Petersen, 'Haagse School en Amsterdams impressionisme', in exh. cat. Amsterdam 1963.
Exh. cat. *Haagsche School. Tekeningen, aquarellen,*

Haags Gemeentemuseum, The Hague 1963 (introduction by W.B.).
Exh. cat. *Meesters van de Haagse School,* Haags Gemeentemuseum, The Hague 1965 (introduction by J. de Gruyter).
J. de Gruyter, *De Haagse School,* 2 vols., [Rotterdam 1968–69].

E. van Schendel, 'De Haagse School', in cat. Museum Mesdag 1975, pp. 10–11.
'De schilders van de Haagse School en hun ateliers', in: *Het atelier van de kunstenaar. Van Haagse School tot Van der Heyden,* The Hague 1982, pp. 10–14.
Exh. cat. *Koninklijke Academie 300 jaar. Haagse School in Pulchri,* Pulchri Studio, The Hague 1982.

The Artists

D.A.C. ARTZ

R. Heath, 'Adolphe Artz', *The Magazine of Art* (1896–97), pp. 80–84.
P.A. Haaxman Jr., 'David Adolphe Constant Artz', in M. Rooses (ed.), *Het Schildersboek,* vol. 3, Amsterdam 1899, pp. 137–54.

A.G. BILDERS

J. Kneppelhout (ed.), *A.G. Bilders. Brieven en dagboek. Geb. 9 Dec. 1838, overl. 8 Maart 1865,* 2 vols., Leiden 1868–76.
A.G. Bilders, *Vrolijk versterven. Een keuze uit zijn dagboek en brieven door Wim Zaal,* Amsterdam 1974.
H.F.W. Jeltes, *Gerard Bilders. Een schildersleven in het midden der 19de eeuw,* The Hague 1947.
Exh. cat. *Gerard Bilders, 1838–1865. Enkele voorgangers en tijdgenoten,* Museum Fodor, Amsterdam 1938–39.

B.J. BLOMMERS

A.G.C. van Duyl, 'B.J. Blommers', in M. Rooses (ed.), *Het Schildersboek,* vol. 2, Amsterdam 1898, pp. 158–75.
Th. de Veer, 'Van een schildersleven', *E.G.M.* XVI (1906), vol. XXXII, pp.147–63.
D.A.S. Cannegieter, 'Blommers een schilder uit de Haagse School', *Antiek* VII (1972–73), pp. 446–61.

J. BOSBOOM

Een en ander betrekkelijk mijne loopbaan also schilder, beschreven door Johannes Bosboom. Herdrukt naar de oorspronkelijke uitgave van 1891. Toegelicht door A. Glavimans, Rotterdam/Antwerp 1946.
H.F.W. Jeltes, *Uit het leven van een kunstenaarspaar. Brieven van Johannes Bosboom,* Amsterdam 1910.
G.H. Marius & W. Martin, *Johannes Bosboom,* The Hague 1917.
G.A. Evers, 'Johannes Bosboom, 1817–1917. Geschriften over den schilder en zijn werk', *Bibliotheekleven* II (1917), pp. 46–51, 146–48.
H.E. van Gelder, 'Brieven van en aan Johannes Bosboom', *O.H.* XLI (1913–14), pp. 37–47, 92–96, 184–92, 231–40.
M.F. Hennus, *Johannes Bosboom,* Amsterdam [1940] (Paletserie).
Cat. *Eere-tentoonstelling ter herdenking van Johannes Bosboom,* Pulchri Studio, The Hague 1917.
Exh. cat. *Johannes Bosboom (1817–1891),* Museum Het Prinsenhof, Delft 1958–59.

P.J.C. GABRIËL

L. de Haes, 'P.J.C. Gabriël', in M. Rooses (ed.), *Het Schildersboek,* vol. 1, Amsterdam 1898, pp. 212–36.
G. Riat, 'Artistes contemporaraines. Robert Mols. – P.J.C. Gabriël', *G.B.A.,* 3e pér XXX (1903), pp. 427–28, XXXI (1904), pp. 158–66.
H.E. van Gelder, 'Brieven uit P.J.C. Gabriël's Brusselschen tijd', *O.H.* XLII (1925), pp. 178–80.
H.F.W. Jeltes, 'Brieven van Gabriël', *O.H.* XLIII (1926), pp. 117–27.
Exh. cat. *Werken van P.J.C. Gabriël,* Pulchri Studio, The Hague 1904 (preface by H.W. Mesdag).
Exh. cat. *Schilderijen en teekeningen van P.J.C. Gabriël,* Larensche Kunsthandel, Amsterdam 1911 (introduction by H. de Boer).

J. ISRAËLS

J. Israëls, *Spanje, een reisverhaal,* The Hague 1899.
J. de Meester, 'Jozef Israëls', in M. Rooses (ed.), *Het Schildersboek,* vol. 1, Amsterdam 1898, pp. 82–99.
M. Liebermann, *Jozef Israëls. Kritische Studie. Mit einer Radierung und dreizehn zum Teil ganzseitigen Abbildungen,* Berlin 1901.
W. Steenhoff, 'Jozef Israëls', *Onze Kunst* III (1904), vol. I, pp. 29–51.
H.J. Hubert, *De etsen van Jozef Israëls. Een catalogus,* Amsterdam 1909.
C.L. Dake, *Jozef Israëls,* Amsterdam [1911].
J.E. Pythian, *Jozef Israëls,* London 1912.
M. Eisler, *Josef Israëls,* London 1924 (Special Spring Number of *The Studio*).
H.E. van Gelder, *Jozef Israëls,* Amsterdam [1947] (Paletserie).
Exh. cat. *Schilderijen, teekeningen, schetsen en etsen, vervaardigd door Jozef Israëls,* Panoramagebouw, Amsterdam 1885.
Cat. *Eeretentoonstelling Jozef Israëls,* Pulchri Studio, The Hague 1911–12.
Exh. cat. *Pictures by Josef Israëls,* The French Gallery, London 1912.
Cat. *The Inaugural Exhibition – Part IV: A Memorial Exhibition of the Work of Jozef Israëls,* The Toledo Museum of Art, Toledo (Ohio) 1912.
Cat. *Herdenkingstentoonstelling Jozef Israëls 1824–1911,* Groninger Museum voor Stad en Lande, Groningen/ Gemeente Museum, Arnhem 1961–62 (introduction by W.J. d[e] G[ruyter], bibliography by J. Bolten).

THE MARIS BROTHERS

Ph. Zilcken, *Les Maris: Jacob-Matthijs-Willem,* Amsterdam 1896.
D. Croal Thomson, *The Brothers Maris (James-Matthew-William),* London/Paris 1907 (Special Summer Number of *The Studio*).
M.H.W.E. Maris, *De geschiedenis van een schildersgeslacht,* Amsterdam 1943.
Cat *Maris tentoonstelling,* Gemeentemuseum. The Hague/Stedelijk Museum, Amsterdam 1935–36.

J. MARIS

G.H. Marius, 'Jacob Maris', in M. Rooses (ed.), *Het Schildersboek,* vol. 2, Amsterdam 1898, pp. 2–16.
Th. de Bock, *Jacob Maris. Met 90 photogravures naar zijne werken en zijn portret naar M. van der Maaten,* Amsterdam 1902.
Cat. *Eere-tentoonstelling Jacob Maris,* Arti et Amicitiae, Amsterdam 1899.
Exh. cat. *Selected Works by James Maris, Anton Mauve, H. Fantin Latour,* The French Gallery, London 1910.

M. MARIS

G.H. Marius, 'Matthijs Maris', in M. Rooses [ed.], *Het Schildersboek,* vol. 4, Amsterdam 1900, pp. 2–21.
P. Haverkorn van Rijsewijk, 'Matthijs Maris te Wolfhezen en Lausanne', *Onze Kunst* XI (1912), vol. XXII, pp. 48–59.
D. Croal Thomson, E.D. Fridlander, F. Lessore & M.E. Sadler, *Matthew Maris. An Illustrated Souvenir,* London 1918.
P. Haverkorn van Rijsewijk, 'Matthijs Maris', *Onze Kunst* XVI (1918), vol. XXXIII, pp. 29–43, 85–90, 122–38, vol. XXXIV, pp. 17–27; XVII (1919), vol. XXXV, pp.

33–44, 117–30, XXXVI, pp. 92–102.
W. Moll, 'Brieven van Thijs Maris', *M.D.K.W.* 1 (1919–25), pp. 143–48.
H.E. van Gelder, 'Matthijs Maris-documenten', *O.H.* XLIV (1927), pp. 35–43, 103–11.
W. Arondéus, *Matthijs Maris. De tragiek van den droom,* Amsterdam [1939].
H.E. van Gelder, *Matthijs Maris,* Amsterdam [1939] (Paletserie).
J.F. Heijbroek, 'Matthijs Maris in Parijs. 1869–1877', *O.H.* LXXXIX (1975), pp. 266–89.
H.E.M. Braakhuis & J. van der Vliet, 'Patterns in the Life and Work of Matthijs Maris', *Simiolus* X (1978–79), pp. 142–81.
Cat. *Memorial Exhibition. A Collection of Works by Matthew Maris,* The French Gallery, London 1917 (introduction by Sir C. Phillips).
Exh. cat. *Matthijs Maris 1839 – 17 Augustus – 1939,* Gemeentemuseum, The Hague 1939.
Exh. cat. *Matthijs Maris,* Haags Gemeentemuseum, The Hague 1974–75 (introduction by A. Wagner).

W. MARIS

C.H. Tiepen (ed.), *Willem Maris. Herinneringen,* The Hague 1910.
G.H. Marius, 'Willem Maris', in M. Rooses (ed.), *Het Schildersboek,* vol. 2, Amsterdam 1898, pp. 100–13.
H. de Boer, *Willem Maris,* The Hague 1905.

A. MAUVE

H.L. Berckenoff, *Anton Mauve. Etsen door Ph. Zilcken. Met een beschrijvenden catalogus van door den meester vervaardigde niet uitgegeven etsen,* Amsterdam 1890.
H.P. Baard, *Anton Mauve,* Amsterdam [1947] (Paletserie).
E.P. Engel, *Anton Mauve (1838–1888). Bronnenverkenning en analyse van zijn oeuvre,* Utrecht 1967.
Cat. *Herdenkingstentoonstelling Anton Mauve 1838–1888,* Gemeentemuseum, The Hague 1938–39 (introduction by G. Kn[uttel Wzn.]).
Exh. cat. *Anton Mauve 1838–1888,* Singer Museum, Laren 1959–60.
Exh. cat. *Drawings and Watercolors by Anton Mauve,* The Toledo Museum of Art, Toledo (Ohio) 1966 (in *Museum News. The Toledo Museum of Art* N.S. IX [1966], pp. 75–94; text by J.W. Keefe).

H.W. MESDAG

Ph. Zilcken, *H.W. Mesdag, de schilder van de Noordzee. Etsen naar schilderijen en begeleidende tekst,* Leiden 1896.
A.C. Croiset van der Kop, 'Hendrik Willem Mesdag', in M. Rooses (ed.), *Het Schildersboek,* vol. 2, Amsterdam 1898, pp. 34–58.
P.H. Hefting, 'H.W. Mesdag (1831–1915). Panorama Mesdag', *O.K.* XI (1967), no. 25.
J.J. Th. Sillevis, 'Een schilderij zonder grenzen', *O.K.* XXIV (Oct./Nov. 1980).
E.J. Fruitema & P.A. Zoetmulder, *Het Panorama fenomeen,* The Hague 1981, pp. 101–11.
J. Poort, *Hendrik Willem Mesdag, 'artiste peintre à la Haye',* The Hague 1981.
S. de Bodt, 'Hendrik Willem Mesdag en Brussel', *O.H.* XCV (1981), pp. 59–87.
Exh. cat. *Schilderijen van H.W. Mesdag en Mevr. Mesdag-geb. Van Houten,* Pulchri Studio, The Hague 1889.

A. NEUHUYS

J. van Rennes, 'Albert Neuhuys', in M. Rooses (ed.), *Het Schildersboek*, vol. 2, Amsterdam 1898, pp. 18–32.

W. Martin, *Albert Neuhuys. Zijn leven en zijn kunst*, Amsterdam 1915.

Cat. *Eere-tentoonstelling Albert Neuhuys*, Arti et Amicitiae, Amsterdam 1914 (introduction by E. K[arsen]).

Exh. cat. *Albert Neuhuys*, Museum Boymans-van Beuningen, Rotterdam 1961 (introduction by J.C. E[bbinge] Wubben).

W. ROELOFS

H. Smissaert, 'Willem Roelofs', in M. Rooses (ed.), *Het Schildersboek*, vol. 1, Amsterdam 1898, pp. 62–80.

F. Rutter, 'A Pioneer Painter of Holland: Willem Roelofs', *The Studio* XLII (1908), pp. 177–84.

H.P. Bremmer, *Willem Roelofs. 100 Lichtdrukken naar zijn werken vertegenwoordigd op de eeretentoonstelling in 'Pulchri Studio', October 1907*, Amsterdam 1909.

H.F.W. Jeltes, *Willem Roelofs. Bizonderheden betreffende zijn leven en werk. Met brieven en andere bijlagen*, Amsterdam 1911.

H.F.W. Jeltes, 'Brieven van Willem Roelofs aan Mr P. VerLoren van Themaat', *O.H.* XLII (1925), pp. 86–96, 131–40.

Cat. *Eere-tentoonstelling Willem Roelofs 1822–1897*, Pulchri Studio, The Hague 1907 (introduction by F.A.E.L. Smissaert).

J.H. WEISSENBRUCH

F.A.E.L. Smissaert, 'Jan Hendrik Weissenbruch', in M. Rooses (ed.), *Het Schildersboek*, vol. 1, Amsterdam 1898, pp. 122–38.

E.B. Greenshields, *The Subjective View of Landscape Painting. With Special Reference to J.H. Weissenbruch and Illustrations from Works of his in Canada*, Montreal 1904.

H. de Boer, 'Weissenbruch als aquarellist', *E.G.M.* XXXIV (1924), vol. LXVIII, pp. 66–70.

H.E. van Gelder, *J.H. Weissenbruch*, Amsterdam [1940] (Paletserie).

Exh. cat. *Schilderijen en aquarellen door J.H. Weissenbruch*, Art dealer Frans Buffa & Zn., Amsterdam 1899 (preceded by an interview with the painter).

Exh. cat. *Jan en Jan Hendrik Weissenbruch. Schilderijen aquarellen grafiek*, Singer Museum, Laren 1960–61 (introduction by R.G. de Boer).

Index of Persons

Royal Academy Trust

Friends of the Royal Academy

PATRON H.R.H. The Duke of Edinburgh, KG, KT

The Friends of the Royal Academy receive the following privileges
FRIENDS £15.50 annually
FRIENDS (Concessionary) £12.50 annually for full-time Museum Staff
and Teachers
£10.00 annually for Pensioners and Young
Friends under the age of 25 years

Gain free and immediate admission to all Royal Academy
Exhibitions with a guest or husband/wife and children under 16.
Obtain catalogues at a reduced price.
Enjoy the privacy of the Friends' Room in Burlington House.
Receive Private View invitations to various exhibitions including
the Summer Exhibition.
Have access to the Library and Archives.
Benefit from other special arrangements, including lectures, concerts
and tours.

COUNTRY FRIENDS £10.00 annually for Friends living more than 75
miles from London.
Gain free and immediate admission to Royal Academy Exhibitions

on 6 occasions with a guest or husband/wife and children under 16.
Receive all the other privileges offered to Friends.

ARTIST SUBSCRIBERS £25.00 annually
Receive all the privileges offered to Friends.
Receive free submission forms for the Summer Exhibition.
Obtain art materials at a reduced price.

SPONSORS £500 (corporate), £150 (individual) annually
Receive all the privileges offered to Friends.
Enjoy the particular privileges of reserving the Royal Academy's
Private Rooms when appropriate and similarly of arranging evening
viewings of certain exhibitions.
Receive acknowledgement through the inclusion of the Sponsor's
name on official documents.

BENEFACTORS £5,000 or more
An involvement with the Royal Academy which will be honoured
in every way.

*Further information and Deed of Covenant forms are available from
The Friends of the Royal Academy, Royal Academy of Arts, Piccadilly,
London W1D 0DS*

Benefactors and Sponsors

BENEFACTORS
Mrs Hilda Benham
Lady Brinton
Mr and Mrs Nigel Broackes
Keith Bromley, Esq.
The John S. Cohen Foundation
The Colby Trust
Michael E. Flintoff, Esq.
The Lady Gibson
Jack Goldhill, Esq.
Mrs Mary Graves
D.J. Hoare, Esq.
Sir Antony Hornby
George Howard, Esq.
Irene and Hyman Kreitman
The Landmark Trust
Roland Lay, Esq.
The Trustees of the Leach Fourteenth Trust
Hugh Leggatt, Esq.
Mr and Mrs M.S. Lipworth
Sir Jack Lyons, CBE
The Manor Charitable Trustees
Lieutenant-Colonel L.S. Michael, OBE
Jan Mitchell, Esq.
The Lord Moyne
Mrs Sylvia Mulcahy
G.R. Nicholas, Esq.
Lieutenant-Colonel Vincent Paravicini
Mrs Vincent Paravicini
Richard Park, Esq.
Phillips Fine Art Auctioneers

Mrs Denise Rapp
Mrs Adrianne Reed
Mrs Basil Samuel
Eric Sharp, Esq., CBE
The Revd. Prebendary E.F. Shotter
Dr Francis Singer
Lady Daphne Straight
Mrs Pamela Synge
Harry Teacher, Esq.
Henry Vyner Charitable Trust
Charles Wollaston, Esq.

CORPORATE SPONSORS
Barclays Bank International Limited
Bourne Leisure Group Limited
The British Petroleum Company Limited
Christie Manson and Woods Limited
Citibank
Consolidated Safeguards Limited
Courage Limited
Davidson Pearce Limited
Delta Group p.l.c.
Esso Petroleum Company Limited
Ford Motor Company Limited
The Granada Group
Arthur Guinness Son and Company Limited
Guinness Peat Group
House of Fraser Limited
Alexander Howden Underwriting Limited
IBM United Kingdom Limited
Imperial Chemical Industries PLC
Investment Company of North Atlantic
Johnson Wax Limited

Lex Service Group Limited
Marks and Spencer p.l.c.
Mars Limited
The Worshipful Company of Mercers
Merrett Syndicates Limited
Midland Bank Limited
The Nestle Charitable Trust
Ocean Transport and Trading Limited
(P.H. Holt Trust)
Ove Arup Partnership
Philips Electronic Associated Industries
Limited
The Rio Tinto–Zinc Corporation PLC
Rowe and Pitman
The Royal Bank of Scotland Limited
J. Henry Schroder Wagg and Company
Limited
The Seascope Group
Shell UK Limited
Thames Television Limited
J. Walter Thompson Company Limited
Ultramar PLC
United Biscuits (U.K.) Limited

INDIVIDUAL SPONSORS
The A.B. Charitable Trust
Abdullah Een Saad Al-Saud
Mrs John W. Anderson II
Ian Fife Campbell Anstruther, Esq.
Mrs Ann Appelbe
Dwight W. Arundale, Esq.
Edgar Astaire, Esq.
The Rt. Hon. Lord Astor of Hever

The Rt. Hon. Lady Astor of Hever
Miss Margaret Louise Band
A. Chester Beatty, Esq.
Mrs E.D. Blythe
Godfrey Bonsack, Esq.
Peter Bowring, Esq.
Mrs Susan Bradman
Cornelis Broere, Esq.
Jeremy Brown, Esq.
Simon Cawkwell, Esq.
W.J. Chapman, Esq.
Major A.J. Chrystal
Alec Clifton-Taylor, Esq.
Henry M. Cohen, Esq.
Mrs Elizabeth Corob
Mrs Yvonne Datnow
Raymond de Prudhoe, Esq.
Raphael Djanogly, Esq. JP
Thomas B. Dwyer, Esq.
Mrs Gilbert Edgar
Brian E. Eldridge, Esq.
Aidan Ellis, Esq.
Eric Ford, Esq.
Victor Gauntlett, Esq.
Lady Gibberd
Peter George Goulandris, Esq.

J.A. Hadjipateras, Esq.
Mrs Penelope Heseltine
H.J. Holmes, Esq.
Geoffrey J.E. Howard, Esq.
Mrs Patricia D. Howard
Roger Hughes, Esq.
Mrs Manya Igel
J.P. Jacobs, Esq.
Mrs Christopher James
Alan Jeavons, Esq.
Irwin Joffe, Esq.
S.D.M. Kahan, Esq.
David J. Kingston, Esq.
Peter W. Kininmonth, Esq.
Owen Luder, Esq.
A. Lyall Lush, Esq.
Mrs Graham Lyons
Jeremy Maas, Esq.
Ciaran MacGonigal, Esq.
Dr Abraham Marcus
Peter Ian McMean, Esq.
Princess Helena Moutafian, MBE
David A. Newton, Esq.
Raymond A. Parkin, Esq.
Mrs M.C.S. Philip
Dr L. Polonsky

Cyril Ray, Esq.
Mrs Margaret Reeves
The Rt. Hon. Lord Rootes
The Hon. Sir Steven Runciman
The Master, The Worshipful Company of
    Saddlers
Sir Robert Sainsbury
R.J. Simia, Esq.
Christina Smith
Steven H. Smith, Esq.
Thomas Stainton, Esq.
Cyril Q. Stringer, Esq.
Mrs A. Susman
Mrs G.M. Susman
The Hon. Mrs Quentin Wallop
Sidney S. Wayne, Esq.
Frank S. Wenstrom, Esq.
David Whitehead, Esq.
David Wolfers, Esq. M.C.
Brian Gordon Wolfson, Esq.
Lawrence Wood, Esq.

*There are also anonymous Benefactors and
Sponsors*